Laboratory Planning

for Chemistry and Chemical Engineering

The amenity of pleasant surroundings can be achieved at little additional cost when the functional structure of the cooling pond is modified.

Laboratory

Planning

for Chemistry

and Chemical

Engineering

EDITED BY

Harry F. Lewis, Ph.D.

A project of the Committee on Design, Construction and Equipment of Laboratories, Division of Chemistry and Chemical Technology, National Academy of Sciences—National Research Council.

Reinhold Publishing Corporation

NEW YORK

Chapman & Hall, Ltd.

LONDON

DESIGNED BY DAVID W. DE ARMAND

PHOTO COMPOSITION BY GRAPHIC SERVICES, INC.

PRINTED BY THE GUINN CO.

BOUND BY VAN REES BINDERY

20.00

Preface

Laboratory Planning for Chemistry and Chemical Engineering as the name indicates has been designed as a source of information for those who are responsible for planning new laboratories broadly intended for use by chemists and chemical engineers. The term "broadly" implies that such uses may involve not only the direct application of these disciplines in industry, government and teaching but also such applications as are on the borderline between two or more disciplines.

While the new volume is patterned somewhat after Laboratory Design, published by Reinhold Publishing Corporation in 1951, it is not just a new edition. Rather it has been completely reorganized and rewritten by a different group of authors and is slanted toward problems faced by laboratory planners.

Like Laboratory Design, Laboratory Planning for Chemistry and Chemical Engineering was sponsored by the Division of Chemistry and Chemical Technology of the National Research Council. It represents, in fact, a report from the Committee on the Design, Construction and Equipment of Laboratories to the National Research Council Division.

In view of the many new materials of construction which have appeared in the last decade, the changing patterns of research and technology and the evidences of new approaches to the teaching of chemistry, various authors have emphasized the principles of planning, leaving it to the readers to fit the applications to their own particular situations. As might be expected, there is not always complete unanimity; no attempt has been made to achieve this. Generally such differences of opinion cover minor points.

The book has been organized in seven sections. The first deals with the technique of organizing for planning and construction. The second takes up general considerations such as the factors to be considered in selecting the site, various types of construction materials and the means for insuring balanced circulation within the new structure.

This is followed in the third section by an extensive discussion of the various types of services required in the laboratory building and within the individual laboratory and the principles involved in the selection of the laboratory furniture.

Occupational health and safety are not always given their proper emphasis in laboratory planning. For this reason, the entire fourth section has been assigned to this subject. The building should be planned with these in mind; they should not be put in as an afterthought.

The fifth section is concerned with what might be called planning synthesis. This includes a chapter on the facilities which are required for the scientific and technical functions, another on the non-technical or common denominator facilities and a third with the integration of these in specific applications of current importance.

The planning of laboratories for academic purposes is discussed in the sixth section. The first three chapters in the section refer particularly to planning a chemistry building for university or college, a science building for a small college and a chemical engineering building. These are followed by a chapter which describes teaching laboratories for various branches of chemistry such as general chemistry, organic chemistry, quantitative analysis, instrumental analysis, inorganic synthesis and physical chemistry. The final chapter tells how lecture halls were constructed in one university.

The closing section of the book gives descriptions of industrial, government and academic laboratory buildings built since 1950. These have been selected partly because of the varieties of design and construction, partly because of the function they serve.

The appendix provides a listing of new buildings built since 1950 where work of a chemical or chemical engineering nature is carried out. The list is as complete as it has been possible to make it—the majority of the references were from the pages of CHEMICAL AND ENGINEERING NEWS. The major share of the work involved in gathering the information was done by three members of the staff of the American Chemical Society: Robert F. Gould, Robert E. Henze and Robert L. Silber. Their contributions are acknowledged with appreciation and thanks by the Editor. A general bibliography of references relating to the design and construction of science laboratories is included in the appendix. The majority of these have been published in the last five years.

The Chairman of the Committee who has also been serving as Editor wishes to express his thanks to the committee members and the many contributors who have given willingly of their time and without recompense other than the satisfaction which comes from helping to fill a need. He feels a real debt to The Institute of Paper Chemistry which has provided him with time, a place to work and much competent staff service in the area of photography, duplication, drafting and proofreading. He has been fortunate in having the services of a single secretary, Marilyn Vandenberg Kuehl, from the beginning of the project. To these and to his many friends who have given him encouragement, he owes much.

These acknowledgements would be incomplete without referring to the many architects, chemistry teachers, research directors, public relations officers and laboratory furniture manufacturers who have provided photographs and information.

Harry F. Lewis, *Editor*

Committee on Design, Construction and Equipment of Laboratories:

Robert F. Conklin
General Electric Company

R. C. Ernst
University of Louisville

Charles Haines
Voorhees, Walker, Smith, Smith and Haines

Clifford C. Japs
Minnesota Mining and Manufacturing Company

Harry F. Lewis, Chairman
The Institute of Paper Chemistry

W. A. Manuel
Ohio Wesleyan University

M. G. Mellon
Purdue University

Frank Ring, Jr.
Oak Ridge National Laboratories

M. A. Shapiro
University of Pittsburgh

Introduction

The implications of the title of this volume might indicate an over-simplification of the problem. While the anticipated audience is the prospective owner or occupant of a laboratory, the book is also directed to the attention of the architect and the builder. It has for its objective the development of an aid to all of the skills that must be coordinated to achieve an effective example of the most complicated contemporary building type. In order to accomplish this, time and money can be saved in varying amounts, if each of the multiplicity of principal contributors understands his own responsibility as well as the functions and responsibilities of the others. Comprehension, however, is insufficient; there also must be recognition of the capabilities of the other members of the group, so that their responsibilities and skills, in their own fields, are not impinged upon by any of the other participants.

CHARLES HAINES

Voorhees, Walker, Smith, Smith & Haines
New York, New York

Contributors

Bender, Paul, Professor of Chemistry, University of Wisconsin, Madison, Wisconsin. F.14.6.

Bradbury E. J., Project Leader, Battelle Memorial Institute, Columbus, Ohio. E.10.5.

Conklin, R. F., Advanced Manufacturing Engineering, Cathode Ray Tube Department, General Electric Company, Syracuse, New York. E.9.

deWahl, R. C., Project Manager, Ellerbe & Company, St. Paul, Minnesota. B.

Division of Research Services, National Institutes of Health, Bethesda, Maryland. E.10.4.

Dunkelberger, T. H., Professor of Chemistry and Administrative Officer, University of Pittsburgh, Pittsburgh, Pennsylvania. F.14.1.

Fawcett, Howard H., Consulting Engineer—Safety, General Electric Company, Schenectady, New York. D.7.

Fuller, A. B., Engineer, Oak Ridge National Laboratory, Oak Ridge, Tennessee. E.10.2c.

Gaddis, Gene, Senior Product Application Engineer, Minneapolis-Honeywell Regulator Company, Minneapolis, Minnesota. E.10.6.

Glen, H. M., Supervising Engineer, Oak Ridge National Laboratory, Oak Ridge, Tennessee. E.10.2b.

Haines, Charles, Architect, Voorhees, Walker, Smith, Smith and Haines, New York, New York. Introduction and A.

Jaeger, Blaine F., formerly Project Engineer, Minnesota Mining and Manufacturing Company, St. Paul, Minnesota. E.10.1.

Japs, Clifford C., Manager, Central Research Pilot Plant, Minnesota Mining and Manufacturing Company, St. Paul, Minnesota. E.10.1.

Koffolt, Joseph H., Chairman, Chemical Engineering Department, The Ohio State University, Columbus 10, Ohio. F.13.

Larsen, Edwin M., Professor of Chemistry, University of Wisconsin, Madison, Wisconsin. F.14.5.

Lewis, Harry F., Dean Emeritus, The Institute of Paper Chemistry, Appleton, Wisconsin. F.12 and G.

Mellon, M. G., Professor of Analytical Chemistry, Purdue University, Lafayette, Indiana. F.11.

Merritt, Lynne L., Jr., Professor of Chemistry, Indiana University, Bloomington, Indiana. F.14.3 and F.14.4.

Ring, Frank, Jr., Retired, formerly Superintendent of Design, Oak Ridge National Laboratory, Oak Ridge, Tennessee. E.10.2d.

Robertson, G. Ross, Professor of Chemistry, University of California at Los Angeles, Los Angeles, California. F.14.2 and F.14.7.

Schaap, Ward B., Professor of Chemistry, Indiana University, Bloomington, Indiana. F.14.3 and F.14.4.

Snow, Donald L., Chief, Laboratory Design Documentation Project, National Institutes of Health, Bethesda, Maryland. D.7 and E.10.3.

Solomon, M. M., formerly of Silicone Products Department, General Electric Company, Waterford, New York, presently Consulting Liason Scientist, Missile and Space Vehicle Department, Space Sciences Laboratory, Valley Forge Space Technology Center, King of Prussia, Pennsylvania. C.6 and E.8.

Syska & Hennessy, Engineers, New York, New York. C.5.1-5.

Syverson, Aldrich, Professor of Chemical Engineering, The Ohio State University, Columbus, Ohio. F.13.

Thailer, Henry J., The Public Health Research Institute of the City of New York, Inc., New York, New York. Formerly of National Institutes of Health. E.10.3.

Walker, H. K., Supervising Engineer, Oak Ridge National Laboratory, Oak Ridge, Tennessee. E.10.2e.

Ward, Donald R., Engineer, Oak Ridge National Laboratory, Oak Ridge, Tennessee. E.10.2a.

Contents

SECTION A

Organization for Planning and Construction

CHAPTER I

The Technique
of Organizing
for Planning
and Construction

CHARLES HAINES

Voorhees Walker Smith Smith & Haines
New York, New York

THE OWNER'S ORGANIZATION

The need for a laboratory building has arisen, and management has made certain policy decisions with respect to its cost and the method of finance. This policy decision usually takes one of three forms: (1) the Board may say, "We believe this building is worth only X dollars to the organization; therefore we shall develop the requirements and design the most suitable building within the stated cost limitations"; (2) the decision may be an approval of needs with a directive to find out the cost of a satisfactory facility meeting those needs; (3) more frequently, however, management, after a superficial study of the needs approves an inadequate budget. In addition, the responsibility for executing this decision is probably given by management to some other person who promptly discharges it by delegating the assignment to a committee.

Under modern management practices, this committee is usually limited to three. While the following are criteria for membership, it is surprising how frequently these criteria are ignored in making the appointments.

(1) Each member must have sufficient standing in the organization to command the respect of the other members and those from whom information will be gathered.

(2) One member should represent the agency which will finally operate the building.

(3) Another member should represent the scientific group or groups who will occupy the laboratories.

(4) A third member, quite possibly the Chairman, should be selected for his ability to represent the broader view of management in regard to questions of suitability, economy, esthetics, and amenities.

(5) All members must be relieved of any other duties which might interfere with their giving the time and energy necessary to the work of the committee.

Not only their responsibilities, but also their authority must be fully defined by management.

A great many vital questions now arise. How and when shall an architect be selected? How should the site be selected? Should other similar organizations be visited? How may the requirements be more accurately defined? What should the building look like? What do laboratories cost? Is air conditioning necessary? In short, what is the proper procedure?

At this stage, selection of the architect is of prime importance in helping the committee to:

(1) develop the requirements,

(2) select the site, and

(3) determine the quality and character of the building.

SELECTION OF THE ARCHITECT

Selecting the architect at this point will save considerable time. While it may be argued that the three foregoing considerations are clearly the responsibility of the committee, or even that the final decision lies with someone of higher authority, nevertheless the advice and counsel of a professional can prevent hasty action. Sound conclusions are best reached after full exploration of the alternatives. Although it is too soon to select the builder, by this time the project will have become common knowledge, and the committee will be beset by an avalanche of builders' representatives. Many will be extremely well sponsored, and each will present long and apparently valid reasons for his immediate employment. If the architect has been selected, much of this time-consuming work can be referred to him. (Courtesy demands that these prospective builders be interviewed.) In further support of the argument for early selection of the architect, those companies and institutions that have had previous experience with complicated construction projects tend to employ their architects sooner in succeeding programs.

A survey of research organizations and institutions which have most recently done similar buildings is an excellent means of compiling a list of architects from which to choose. The following are some of the questions which should be included in a letter to such an organization:

(1) What was the architect's name and address?

(2) What were the names of the partner-in-charge and his principal assistants?

(3) What was the size of your project in gross area?

(4) What was the scope of the architect's services?

(5) Did he perform all his services with his own employees, or did he engage engineering consultants?

(6) How did his estimate of construction cost compare with the actual cost?

(7) Did you find that his employees worked harmoniously with your assistants, who were authorized to approve the engineering aspects of your project?

(8) Were the construction documents completed in accordance with the agreed schedule?

(9) Considering the complexity of the project, were the size and number of "extras" to the contract unusual?

(10) Would you employ this architect again for a similar project?

The names received from the above survey, together with prominent local architects and those who may have been recommended by management or persons on the committee, will provide a fairly definitive list. In making the final selection, the data which should be weighed include:

(1) willingness and availability to undertake the commission;

(2) experience in laboratory design;

(3) recommendations of former clients;

(4) qualifications of the key personnel to be assigned to the project;

(5) qualifications of the engineering consultants if the architect does not perform such services;

(6) methods for and degree of success in keeping within the construction budget.

Analysis of these data will reduce the list to a reasonable number of architects, whose offices should then be visited. Prior to the meeting, each architect should be required to state his interest in the project and list his personnel, giving the experience of those who will actually create the design. If the architect intends to rely on engineering consultants, he should list the firms he intends to employ, and he should provide from each of these consultants the information that was requested of him. Each architect interviewed should be encouraged to elaborate fully on his own design technique.

After these interviews, the number of candidates for selection will have been reduced to two or three. It is then desirable for each architect to take the committee on a tour of one of his buildings which he considers most similar to the project at hand.

A proposal is then requested from the architect selected. If the terms of the proposal are satisfactory, he should be employed. The fees for design services cannot be put on a competitive basis. The difference in fees for architectural services may seem at first to be significant; however, in terms of the total cost of the project, it shrinks to insignificance. The scope of the services and the skill with which the services are performed may save many times the additional fee in terms of economy of construction, reduction of extras to the construction contract, and excellence of design.

There may be instances in which it is desirable to employ an architect who may not be experienced in the field of laboratory design. In this case the architect should be requested to collaborate with a consultant who is selected in the manner outlined above, but who is actually retained by the architect. Such a procedure is not uncommon, and has resulted in well designed buildings. There is a distinct advantage in having the architect make the arrangements for his associate firm, as long as he retains full responsibility.

In the above discussion no consideration is given to the so-called design-construction package. The salesmen representing builders' organizations will undoubtedly have been in contact with members of the committee. Briefly, the system entails buying from a building construction corporation for a negotiated lump sum the design and construction of a completed building. This system has gained favor for warehouses and factory structures for which the basic design has been predetermined and accurately described, but it is not adequate for complicated laboratory buildings. Since the basic ingredient of a lump sum agreement is accurate description, the project must be designed prior to the execution of the contract. Two major flaws arise from the hasty design procedures so necessitated. The first will produce a poor esthetic concept; the second will invite insufficient study of the owner's plan requirements, with the result that changes become necessary as the construction drawings are being prepared. If these modifications are accepted, the sole advantage of the contract, i.e., the lump sum cost feature, disappears, as does control of the construction budget. If the desired changes are not made, an expensive structure is built with made-to-order features which promote early obsolescence. The package deal also prevents competitive bidding on construction.

Once the architect has been selected, all skills may be brought to bear on the solution of the design, and the series of problems previously mentioned, as well as those following, may be attacked simultaneously.

DEVELOPMENT OF THE PROGRAM

The architect, from his experience, should assist the committee in preparing the program of requirements. The requirements can be reduced to those items essential to the development of preliminary drawings. The following questionnaire is quite complete in regard to requirements for planning the site and building for an industrial research project. With minor modifications, it can be adapted to the design of teaching laboratories.

Before submitting the questionnaire to the owner, there should be one or more conferences in which the generalities of laboratory planning are discussed. Except for a few highly specialized organizations, most of the space requirements can be divided into categories of repetitive and special space. The term "special laboratory" is applied to any space whose mechanical, structural or dimensional characteristics are such that to include them in standard or repetitive space would add substantial cost in these respects to all other standard spaces, or would seriously inhibit the functioning of the work to be done in such space. Modular or repetitive space has come to be accepted as permitting maximum capabilities of future rearrangement. Hence, the more laboratories an owner can assign to this category the better the opportunity for retarding obsolescence.

While there is an obvious advantage to minimizing the number of types of repetitive space, it is seldom possible to assign office, laboratory and pilot plant requirements to a single unit having the same mechanical, structural, electrical and dimensional characteristics. It is therefore perfectly reasonable to expect that a single building may have as many as three quite different modular requirements. In order to assist in these early determinations the architect should have added to his knowledge of general laboratory concepts, knowledge of the specific project in hand by a thorough survey of the owner's existing facilities that are intended to be relocated. The owner's organization chart and manner in which the working laboratory is supervised must be understood. The size and make-up of the typical laboratory team should be stated. It is then that the questionnaire may be submitted and the architect can work with the owner's staff in completing the form.

For the purposes of this questionnaire the repetitive module is described as having three dimensions, specific floor loading, air conditioning, illumination, (both natural and artificial), and a means of supplying to it, required mechanical and electrical services. Such modules are the smallest single units of space occupied as a single laboratory, office or pilot plant, or one or more of such units may be combined to form the smallest working area to which adjacent modules are added by increments to produce varying sizes of spaces.

Design Questionnaire for Space Requirements

(A) Laboratories
  (1) Module
    (a) Width of working aisle _____ feet _____ inches.
    (b) Desirable maximum continuous length of work surface _____ feet.
    (c) Height of tallest common laboratory apparatus _____ feet _____ inches.
    (d) Desirable hood location within the laboratory, near door _____ ; near window _____ ; other _____ .
    (e) Linear feet of hood per module _____ feet.
    (f) Number of sinks per module; one _____ ; one for each laboratory _____ .
    (g) Minimum door width _____ feet _____ inches.
    (h) Number of office type desks for laboratory workers per module _____ .
    (i) Number of kneehole spaces per module _____ .
    (j) Length of desk _____ feet; _____ inches.

    (k) Number of filing cabinet drawers _____ .
    (l) Linear feet of shelf space in closed storage cabinets per module _____ feet.
    (m) Coat and laboratory apron closets _____ .
  (2) Safety
    (a) Secondary egress from the laboratory _____ .
    (b) Safety showers at entrance to each laboratory _____ . (If in corridor, give separation) _____ feet.
    (c) Eye wash fountain in each laboratory _____ .
    (d) Safety blanket storage in each laboratory _____ .
    (e) Hand fire extinguisher at entrance to each laboratory _____ .
    (f) Closet for other safety devices on each floor _____ . List items to be included _____ _____ .
  (3) Services
    (a) Centrally generated and generally distributed services:
      (1) Piped services. Cold water _____ ; 40° chilled water _____ ; hot water _____ ; distilled water _____ ; gas _____ ; high pressure air _____ psi; low pressure air _____ psi; vacuum _____ ; steam _____ psi; hydrogen _____ ; nitrogen _____ ; oxygen _____ ; laboratory wastes _____ ; clear water drains _____ ; other _____ .
      (2) Electrical power, 120/208 single phase and/or 3 phase, 4 wire a.c. _____ volt-amperes per square foot; 480 volts three phase a.c. _____ volt-amperes per square foot; regulated a.c. _____ volt-amperes per square foot; 400 cycles a.c. _____ volt-amperes per square foot; direct current _____ volts; _____ volt-amperes per square foot; ground _____ ; other _____ _____ .
      (3) Hood exhaust. Area of hood opening per module _____ square feet; hood face velocity _____ feet per minute; maximum square feet of hood opening in any one module or laboratory _____ square feet.
    (b) The Special Services
      (1) Special gases _____ ; _____ ; _____ .
      (2) Electrical low voltage _____ ; other _____ .
      (3) Special air conditioning. Assuming that the entire building will be air conditioned for comfort, laboratory space requiring special conditions of humidity and temperatures:
        Number of Modules   Temperature Range
        Humidity Range   Internal heat gain in Btu

(B) Offices
  (1) Module
    (a) Laboratory leader. One person occupancy

_____ ; two person occupancy _____ ; furniture required per person _____ .

- (b) Group leader. One person occupancy _____ ; two person occupancy _____ ; furniture required per person _____ .
- (c) Staff and administrative personnel. One person occupancy _____ ; two person occupancy _____ ; group occupancy _____ square feet per person _____ in group office occupancy.
- (d) Executive personnel. Size _____ feet by _____ feet; adjacent secretarial space _____ ; connecting lavatory _____ .

(C) Pilot Plant
- (1) Module
  - (a) Width _____ feet.
  - (b) Height _____ feet.
  - (c) Depth _____ feet.
  - (d) Piped services.
  - (e) Electrical services.
  - (f) Ventilation. Average exhaust air per module _____ cubic feet per minute; maximum exhaust air per module _____ cubic feet per minute.

(D) Library _____ (if required, develop needs by conference).

(E) Cafeteria _____ (if required, develop needs by conference).

(F) Conference Rooms
- (1) Maximum number of people _____ .
- (2) Fixed seats _____ ; movable seats _____ .
- (3) Blackboards _____ linear feet.

- (4) Projection facilities _____ .
- (5) Laboratory demonstration facilities _____ .

(G) Shops
- (1) Type and area of each.

(H) Locker Rooms
- (1) Lockers. Size _____ .
- (2) Shower facilities _____ .

(I) Auxiliary Space
- (1) Lockers. Size of locker _____ .
- (2) Laboratory supply storage. Linear feet of shelf _____ .
- (3) Gases under pressure _____ ; number of types _____ ; number of drums _____ .
- (4) Solvent storage. Linear feet of shelf _____ ; number of drums _____ .
- (5) Dangerous chemicals. Linear feet of shelf _____ .
- (6) General and office supplies. Linear feet of shelf _____ .
- (7) Photographic and reproduction space area _____ .
- (8) Janitors' and guards' locker rooms _____ .

(J) Number of Employees

	Men	Women
(1) Total personnel	_____	_____
(2) Office personnel (Include those in categories (3), (4) and (5) who are located in offices in addition to having desk space elsewhere)	_____	_____
(3) Laboratory personnel	_____	_____
(4) Shop personnel	_____	_____
(5) Pilot plant personnel	_____	_____
(6) Locker rooms	_____	_____
(7) Janitors, guards and maintenance	_____	_____

(K) Space Quantities

Number of Modules

	Laboratories, Large	Laboratories, Small	Pilot	Offices	Square Feet Laboratories Special
(1) Laboratories					
(a) Standard	_____	_____	_____	_____	_____
(b) Special	_____	_____	_____	_____	_____
(2) Offices					
(a) Scientist	_____	_____	_____	_____	_____
(b) Group leaders	_____	_____	_____	_____	_____
(c) Assistants staff	_____	_____	_____	_____	_____
(d) Executive	_____	_____	_____	_____	_____
(e) Secretarial	_____	_____	_____	_____	_____
(f) Small conference rooms	_____	_____	_____	_____	_____

From these data and conferences with the owner, the size of the repetitive modules can be determined quickly, and the planning can proceed as described in later sections of this volume.

SELECTION OF THE SITE

Site selection, in the case of educational institutions, usually does not constitute a problem if

Figure 1.1 An illustration of the necessity for sufficient usable land for parking and the peripheral protection to insure one's own environment against encroachment of neighbors.

the over-all master plan has been the basis of determination. The question does not arise in the case of industrial research organizations where the building program is intended to be part of an existing plant or research facility. However, the care with which the site for a new laboratory is chosen will have much to do with the ultimate success of the venture. The committee, working with the architect, should establish the criteria of the desirability of each site under consideration.

The importance of selecting a site with sufficient usable land for expansion cannot be overstressed. Acquiring adjacent property at a future date may be prohibitively expensive or even impossible. Research organizations tend to grow at unbelievable rates. This simple fact has resulted in the relocation of a number of large organizations which had made heavy investments in inadequate sites. The technique of site selection is covered in a later chapter.

DETERMINATION OF THE QUALITY AND CHARACTER OF THE DESIGN

After the initial discussions, and before the program of requirements has been fully defined, visits should be made to other recently constructed facilities of a similar nature. These trips should not be restricted to those buildings designed by the architect; rather, a survey should be made with a view toward disclosing the major alternatives in regard to the following:

(1) planning arrangement;

(2) types and size of modules;

(3) means of handling conveniences (stock rooms, storage, central dishwashing, distribution of mechanical and electrical services, library, large lecture room or auditorium);

(4) amenities;

(5) area per person of usable space by categories;

(6) avoidable errors in design and construction;

(7) architectural character;

(8) materials of construction.

It is just as necessary to consider the long-range growth of the teaching laboratory as of the industrial research organization. Two types of growth should be given consideration: that which is immediately foreseeable, and that which is beyond definition. The immediate growth pattern may consist merely of those needs which the construction budget cannot encompass, or the growth required to house research programs contemplated in the near future, say within five years. The long-range growth pattern necessitates a certain amount of soul searching on the part of management. Since it can only be approximated, it should not be limited by a specific design. The site plan, however, should indicate the growth of particular types of space. Also to be considered is management's conception of the maximum program or number of personnel to be situated in one location. Many large organizations intentionally develop several centers at which research is undertaken simultaneously. The optimum number of people assigned to a given location will vary according to the opinions of the company executives; it will also be affected by the endeavors of other companies competing in the same field.

Since the rate of growth is frequently such that a building planned on existing needs becomes crowded on the date of completion, attention should be directed to this factor when determining the size of the project. Design, construction, and occupancy may take from two and a half to three years. Courtesy dictates that management not be asked to contribute funds for expansion until the building has been lived in at least long enough for its deficiencies to be explored. When a request for further facilities is made, it will again be several years before the addition can be occupied. Therefore, initial planning should take into account the growth of the organization for five years.

The successful planning and design of a new building is aided materially by excellent team work by the owner and architect. One of the ways in which this team work will manifest itself is the lessening of the effects of early obsolescence. The useful lives of buildings are more frequently shortened because they become obsolete, rather than from inadequacy of materials or construction. With the advent of new equipment, techniques and avenues of endeavor, the laboratory building has been particularly subject to this type of deterioration. It should also be remembered that obsolescence begins when the design is frozen. Therefore, the owner should not shirk the responsibilities of close cooperation with his architect during the early planning and design phases of the project, or unduly expedite these phases because of a desire to start construction. While it is perfectly true that no one can foresee the specialized needs of housing future designs of equipment and laboratory techniques, one can at least try to avoid built-in road blocks for these future avenues. In its desire to provide a highly specialized arrangement to suit a particular organization chart and specialized laboratory procedures, management may overlook the fact that in a few years the organization chart will have changed, together with the techniques that suggested such a special arrangement. Such an oversight may well accelerate obsolescence.

COST CONTROL

The matter of cost control is of extreme importance. Regardless of the quality of materials, it is the desire of every owner not only to obtain the most for his money but to have a clear concept of final cost before major commitments have been made. The following method has been used successfully in many large projects:

(1) An order-of-magnitude cost estimate should be prepared immediately after the requirements have been established and the preliminary sketches have proceeded to the point of an acceptable general plan, determination of architectural character, and sufficient outline specifications to define the quality of construction. Such an estimate should carry a 10% contingency allowance to cover inaccuracies in the technique of estimating this early, undeveloped state of the design. This preliminary, order-of-magnitude cost estimate should be based on the square-foot method and adjusted to the locale, time, and type of construction.

(2) If found necessary, the design should be adjusted by quantity and/or quality so that it comes within the proper economic range.

(3) The design should be decided on, all architectural and engineering determinations should be made, and drawings should be done in sufficient detail to permit a thorough estimate by trades. During this stage, the architect is called upon to coordinate all the engineering and architectural skills to enable the owner to make decisions with respect to everything except design details. As the design is developed, neither the owner nor the architect should materially change the preliminary design either in scope or quality unless it is recognized that the construction cost will be affected.

(4) A second construction cost estimate should be prepared from these completed fundamental design drawings. This estimate should be made up from an actual take-off of labor and materials. Its accuracy should be within 5 per cent of the lowest lump sum construction proposal obtained when actual bids are received on the finished working drawings and specifications.

(5) Minor adjustments in the fundamental design should be made as required by the estimate. The working drawings should not be started until the owner is prepared to approve the fundamental design without changes. Changes made after approval of the fundamental design have the following consequences:

(a) increased cost of design;

(b) longer working-drawing period;

(c) increase in the probability of discrepancies in drawings resulting in construction "extras" on the part of the contractor.

(6) The working drawings should be prepared with a few alternative proposals which will enable the owner to engage the builder promptly upon the receipt of bids. Such alternative proposals should be detailed with sufficient care so that any or all can be accepted and incorporated in the contract without further change. By means of this device, deviations between the fundamental design estimate and the low bidder's proposal may be corrected. Such deviations may be expected to result from unforeseen inflationary or market conditions arising between the time the fundamental design estimate was prepared and the firm proposals were received.

(7) The lump sum bidders should be prequalified. While the owner should reserve the right to reject any bid, let it clearly be understood that the low bidder will receive the contract award. Avoid having more than five or six bidders. Be assured of each bidder's interest before issuing the invitation. Attempt to make the bid list contain only those bidders who are comparable in quality of work and the size of their organizations.

(8) *Do not make changes in the design after the contract has been awarded.*

There are a number of satisfactory independent estimating organizations throughout the country. If the owner feels that the architect cannot provide satisfactory estimating service through his own staff or a builder's staff, he should request the architect to employ such an independent organization to provide the order-of-magnitude cost and the detailed fundamental design estimate. Any money spent in making a complete estimate after the working drawings have been started is wasted. This does not mean, however, that if there are modifications in the design they should not be evaluated in regard to the effect on construction cost. Estimates prepared after the working drawings are completed can never be as accurate as those prepared by the serious bidder, and they will take the same length of time.

THE CONSTRUCTION CONTRACT

The owner has a number of choices in the selection of the type of contract for building construction. All have their uses; preference varies from one part of the country to another, and this factor should be considered. The common forms are listed below:

(1) cost plus a percentage fee
(2) cost plus a fixed fee
(3) upset price with shared savings
(4) segregated lump sum
(5) lump sum.

If the builder is to be employed on the basis of cost plus a fee, he should be signed up shortly after the architect is engaged. The fee may be either a lump sum or a percentage of the cost. The cost is the sum of all labor, materials, and amounts paid to subcontractors in construction of the project. The advantages of such a contractual arrangement are:

(1) The builder is available to prepare estimates of construction cost during the development of design.

(2) The builder can provide cost advice in the selection of materials and construction methods to assist the committee and the architect in obtaining the most economical structure to suit the needs of the project.

(3) Construction can start and the project can be completed earlier.

(4) Better subcontractors will be employed.

(5) The builder is put in the position of a professional construction manager and should provide better control of the subcontractors.

There are disadvantages to the cost-plus contract which will frequently tend to offset some of the advantages:

(1) The cost is usually higher.

(2) The construction period is usually longer.

(3) The owner must either furnish an auditing staff or pay the architect to perform such service.

The advantages stated above do not materialize in some cases because:

(1) More know-how and experience is required on the part of the owner and the architect to carry out this type of construction contract successfully.

(2) The architect should be fully capable of preparing satisfactory estimates of construction cost. An architect's estimates are frequently better than a builder's, since the early estimates are made from preliminary plans and outline specifications. The builder has a tendency to estimate only what he sees, and therefore often gives too low an estimate; on the other hand, he may be overly cautious and give too high a preliminary estimate.

(3) It is the architect's responsibility to give advice regarding the economy and suitability of materials and construction methods.

(4) Starting construction of laboratory buildings prematurely frequently brings about extras because of incomplete design information. The urgency to begin is frequently overemphasized, since land cost is usually low and the foundation construction uncomplicated.

(5) There is a tendency on the part of the owner to believe that changes are less costly when this form of construction contract is used. As a consequence, the owner sometimes feels that it is not necessary to come to a decision as promptly as he should. It must be remembered that changes during a construction period are always costly. The confusion arising out of modifying the drawings and changing directives to the subcontractors delays completion of the building.

The employment of the builder on a cost plus a fixed fee basis is similar in all respects to the percentage fee cost plus type of contract, except that a percentage fee enables the builder to increase his profit if the cost of the project increases. In nearly all laboratory projects the scope of the work can be sufficiently defined for the builder to accept a lump sum fee.

A third type of cost plus contract is known as the upset price; it usually includes a clause stating that if the final cost is under the guaranteed upset total, the builder will receive a proportion of the savings so effected. The guaranteed maximum price is determined by estimating the sum of the work on each construction trade, to which is added an allowance for the general conditions, miscellaneous work, overhead, and profit. Negotiations with the builder concerning this type of contract may occur any time after the complete preliminary drawings and outline specifications have been prepared. In this instance, the fee is usually a lump sum and the guaranteed total is a liberal allowance for the work shown. The theory favoring this type of contract stems from the apparent generosity of the contractor in giving up part of his profit. Actually, the owner is entitled to all such savings, inasmuch as a liberal fee has already been negotiated. Furthermore, the system for deriving the guaranteed maximum price will tend to make the construction cost higher than necessary.

Segregated lump sum contracts involve securing competitive lump sum proposals from each of the principal subtrades, i.e., plumbing, heating, electrical, laboratory equipment, and general work. This device forces the owner to establish and pay for an organization to manage, schedule, and coordinate the various contractors. Theoretically, the general contractor's profit is saved. However, each sub-bidder recognizes that since there is no experienced over-all direction, the construction time will be greatly increased; therefore, he must increase his allowance for overhead for this longer period. As a consequence, the effort to reduce the cost of construction by attempting to save the cost of management results in longer construction schedules and greater costs.

Finally, the most commonly used and advantageous system is the lump sum contract, obtained through competitive bidding, in which the contract is awarded to the lowest qualified bidder. This is the system generally used by the largest owner of buildings in the country, the American Telephone and Telegraph Company. The advantages are:

(1) lower construction costs
(2) faster construction schedules
(3) minimum cost for architectural supervision
(4) minimum cost for management by the owner
(5) better cost control.

Desire to start construction is great on the part of owners once the decision is made to have a new building. They are therefore easy prey for the noncompetitive builder who convinces them that a fee type of construction contract, rather than the competitive lump sum, will produce the building faster by enabling "ground breaking" to proceed while the design is being completed. Since World War II no other form of construction

contract has proved more economical or has taken less time, from authorization of design to completion of building, than the lump sum competitive type.

CONSTRUCTING THE BUILDING

During the construction of the building, the owner, the architect, and the builder have the following responsibilities:

Owner:

(1) Expedite payments of contractors' bills.
(2) Avoid changes in the contract. Changes are so upsetting to schedules and procedures that the costs are necessarily high for the contractor. It is frequently less expensive to complete the contract as designed and make the contemplated changes immediately after moving in, than to make it during the construction period.
(3) Avoid giving directions to the builder, except through the architect.
(4) Make prompt decisions with respect to submission of samples, colors, and finishes.
(5) Leave the review of shop drawings entirely to the architect.

Architect:

(1) Require the contractor to submit promptly schedules of construction, payments, shop drawings and samples.
(2) Before the start of construction, clearly define the procedure for handling changes so that they may be made quickly and at a minimum cost.
(3) Avoid recommending changes in design.
(4) Process and certify builder's payments promptly.
(5) Provide sufficient inspection personnel to anticipate problems in coordination before they arise.
(6) Make shop inspections to avoid rejections in the field of prefabricated finished materials.
(7) Draw fair and complete lists of items to be done at the time of the final inspection. Gain the owner's agreement that such a list is complete.
(8) Secure various certificates of inspection in addition to assurance that bills have been paid before certification of final payment.

Builder:

(1) Provide schedules and data requested by the architect.

(2) Accept directions from the architect and the owner.

(3) Provide estimates for change orders expeditiously.

(4) Anticipate coordination problems in order to give sufficient time for a sound decision.

If the owner has observed care in the selection of the architect and the builder, and persists in his decision not to modify the construction documents, the building will proceed with a minimum of difficulty.

Organizations that are required by law to permit any builder to submit a proposal for construction must demand a bond guaranteeing the completion of the project. Such a bond adds approximately from three-quarters to one per cent to the construction cost. It should be remembered, however, that the ability of the bidder to furnish a bond does not do anything but attest to the fact that some bonding organization believes the bidder to be sufficiently strong financially to be able to carry out the contract. In the event of his financial failure, the bonding company moves in and completes the contract to the best of its ability. The usual result is a very extended construction period, poor craftsmanship, and other unforeseen difficulties. If the owner and the architect prequalify the bidders (one of the important qualifications being financial stability), and care is used in the approval of progress payments, the added cost of the completion bond can be saved.

Finally, there can be no substitute for skill and professional responsibility on the part of the owner, the architect, and the builder.

General

Considerations

CHAPTER II

Selection

of the Site

R. C. deWAHL

Ellerbe & Company
St. Paul, Minnesota

Once the decision to proceed with a laboratory development has been made and the program defined, a site must be selected. The following considerations are based on the need for a new site rather than for expansion of existing facilities; however, those factors which dictate the selection of a particular site are also pertinent when the advisability of expanding an existing facility or locating a new science building on a college campus is under consideration.

SIZE AND PHYSICAL LOCATION

It is important that any site selected be large enough to meet all present and foreseeable needs. It should be readily accessible to both public and private transportation. If the site is to be visited frequently by out-of-towners, proximity to air and rail transportation as well as to hotel or motel accommodations is necessary.

Certain basic needs of the laboratory occupants cannot be overlooked. Eating, banking, and some types of retail facilities must be within easy reach of their place of employment, or it will be necessary for the employer to establish them on the site.

Wherever possible, it is generally more economical to develop a site where basic utilities, such as storm and sanitary sewers, water and gas, are available from an established community. Ample electric power can normally be obtained in any reasonable location without undue penalty. The remote suburban location is frequently attractive because of lower land costs and an apparent tax advantage. Establishment of any large operation in these areas, however, tends to increase the need for housing, schools, and the gamut of municipal services to such an extent that tax advantages may become liabilities.

Currently the competition for all types of technically trained personnel makes it necessary to provide them with better-than-average working conditions, both to attract them initially and to assure their maximum effectiveness. Campus-type laboratory developments with slightly rolling contours, ample space between buildings to allow for generous grassed areas and landscaping all contribute to the success of the project. From an ideal standpoint it would be desirable for a research site to be bordered by undeveloped ground, parks or reserves, but this is seldom possible. A bordering area of carefully developed housing would be somewhat less desirable, and a heavily developed industrial area would be the least desirable. If, in the final analysis, it becomes necessary to locate the site adjacent to an undesirable environment, the acquisition of sufficient ground for a generous buffer area with grass and landscaping to separate the laboratory structures from the adjoining property can be a considerable compensation.

SOIL CONDITIONS

Soil conditions will also affect the final selection of any building site. Consideration of the bearing value of the soil and a preliminary study of the foundation structure are quite imperative. Actually there is no such thing as a perfect site from a foundation designer's approach. All sites have peculiarities owing to the particular location, and these must be taken into account in each case.

The ideal situation is one where buildings can be located on relatively high ground so that advantage can be taken of natural drainage. Some of the things to be aware of when judging a site for a foundation are topography, drainage, subsoil conditions, access for construction materials, and snow removal. Site selection for a laboratory building, from the foundation viewpoint, will fall into practically the same category as the foundation for any structure; loads for certain laboratories may be significantly heavier than those for other structures. Some commercial laboratories have exceedingly heavy work loads, and the number of stories permissible without excess foundation cost can be determined by thorough soil and foundation studies.

A site which may not have good foundation characteristics should not be ruled out for that reason alone; an analysis should be made of the extra costs for foundation work compared with other factors. Quite frequently, the geographic location is sufficiently desirable to counterbalance the extra work involved in overcoming the handicap of the foundation conditions.

Some of the things that determine or are indicative of soil conditions are as follows:

(1) general characteristics of the soil in the area

(2) out-cropping rock

(3) deep surface layers of organic matter

(4) pools of water

(5) boggy or spongy areas

(6) high grass of the wide-bladed variety (usually indicates soft areas in the presence of high water table).

Water is the builder's natural enemy. The presence of water affects the soil-bearing capacity of different soil types in different ways. For instance, high water table in sand generally will not affect the bearing capacity, whereas in clays it can be very detrimental. The clay soils in a dry condition that are above the water table can also be hazardous if the clay has a low liquid limit, since a small additional amount of water will turn the soil into a suspension with a complete loss of bearing strength.

In the absence of exploratory borings, much information can be obtained by making inquiries in the municipality where the site is located. Public utility companies, city water and local highway departments usually have complete records of the soil conditions encountered when their works were installed.

Although sites are definitely individual, a record of the terrain within a reasonable distance of the site in question can sometimes be very helpful, indicating the conditions which may be encountered.

Sites which require large amounts of fill usually entail more development expense than those which require extensive cutting and grading. Most engineers and contractors will concede that 10 to 12 feet of fill can be installed and compacted for the cost of a self-supporting structural slab. These figures are of course contingent on the availability and type of fill.

Conditions that require piling increase the cost of the structure by the amount of the piling cost. The structure supported, for example, by cast-in-place piling will cost approximately $2.75 per ton based on 50-ton capacity piles, and for general estimating purposes alternate spread footing foundations would add a cost of equal magnitude.

Exploratory borings strategically located on the site usually supply enough information to complete a site-selection study; they should be followed by design borings on any selected site after the ground area of the building is determined. Design borings differ from exploratory borings by being more thorough in both field and laboratory work. Laboratory work in design borings is completed for a thorough analysis, whereas in exploratory borings various checks are made on the material, plotted on a curve, and the areas between the points on the curve approximated. Thus, a saving in money and time is realized. If the site would prove to be unsuitable, approximations would certainly suffice in lieu of an expensive, thorough soil analysis.

Soils that have large areas of peat should be viewed with caution, but not necessarily disregarded until complete studies are made, since sometimes the peat can be removed and replaced with fill while keeping the cost within reason. This applies more to structures that cover a substantial percentage of the site area than to industrial laboratories where the ground areas are extensive in relation to the areas occupied by the structures. Peat must be removed not only from the area of the building but also from any roads, parking lots and auxiliary facilities. Where these areas are great, the removal of peat, if it is very deep, will render the site completely unsuitable from a cost standpoint.

High water tables sometimes render a site unsuitable if a basement structure is required. A 10-foot head of water will produce about 600 pounds per square foot uplift on a structural slab. Essentially, this requires the design of the floor slab in reverse to carry that load per square foot. This becomes quite expensive in view of the membrane waterproofing required to seal the building from the intrusion of water. It usually costs the owner less to install a permanent pumping system and design for normal earth pressures, using either a drainage system or sewer out-fall where the sub-surface water can be wasted. If these drainage systems are not available within reasonable distance of the site, then the building must be constructed above the water table with foundations extending down to good bearing soil. These conditions all add to the cost of the structure, which can be determined only after exploratory borings are made and analyzed and foundation types assumed for the purpose of estimating.

A site consisting chiefly of rock can also be found underlying shallow depths of top soil. In this case, although the problem of foundation design is a simple one, the site may prove extremely expensive. Installation of underground utilities becomes a major operation, and the development of roadways may offer similar difficulties. Furthermore, the cost of the amenities, i.e., trees, shrubs, lawn and variations in grading, may be almost prohibitive.

ROADS

Good, hard-surfaced, "all-weather" roads must be laid on the laboratory site, construction materials being dictated by the volume of traffic generated and the geographical location. In some instances roads are designed not only to handle vehicular traffic but to carry storm-water drainage by means of adequate curbing to suitable pick-up points. In northern climates, where snow removal is a problem, it is generally desirable to have well-crowned roads without any sharp breaks such as curbing to impede plowing operations.

If the proposed project is a large one, first consideration should be given to the development of main arteries which will handle the bulk of traffic to and from principal parking areas during the two periods bearing maximum traffic. Two peak periods will occur: one in the morning at the start of normal working hours and the other at night at their close. Since morning peaks tend to extend over a longer period than the evening peaks, the latter will provide the criteria for design. Generally, roadways should be designed to permit complete clearing of the site in a maximum of 30 minutes.

Care will have to be exercised in planning the main arteries to ensure that traffic is directed to off-site roadways which are capable of handling it. Cooperation of state and municipal authorities in the early stages of planning will be helpful in developing a well-integrated system of traffic control.

Other on-site roads of a secondary nature will frequently be required to handle truck and other in-plant traffic.

UTILITIES

Planning utilities for the research site is as important a project as planning a building unit. Certain basic decisions must be made in their design which it may never be possible to change; therefore adequate time must be spent in the planning stage to assure the best possible investment of the rather sizable funds required for these utilities.

After a land use plan has been developed showing maximum building possibilities, including the location of roads and parking lots, the engineer is ready to begin a serious study of utility development. In all probability, the immediate building construction is limited to one to three units. Each utility which is planned to serve these must fit into the larger development required as other units are authorized. Thus, the first few buildings erected on a new site will be penalized in utility costs because they must bear some extra costs in utility development, but these are good investments in terms of long-range planning.

In principle, planning of the utilities follows a definite pattern. First it is necessary to study the requirements for each building; these are then combined to provide a picture of over-all needs. Considerable imagination is required to do this because many units may be little more than a block on a site plan. Past experience with similar developments and the best judgment available may well be the basis for establishing these requirements. It is important to remember that the over-all design is going to be executed in a series of construction projects; hence the basic planning will be subjected to continual review as each unit is authorized. Adjustments should be made in estimates as more definite design criteria become available.

When preliminary requirements have been established, it is necessary to develop a master layout which will become the guide to the final design of each utility as it becomes needed in a given area. Generally, it is economically advisable to plan each branch or segment of a given utility for full ultimate size so that any given ground area is disturbed but once for any utility. One exception to this rule is the installation of power or communication feeders where conduit requirements can be met in a given area and cable added as load requirements build up.

Today, it is customary practice to locate all utility distribution systems on a given site below grade. In most instances, each utility is a separate unit in its own trench or covering. Occasionally, however, a number of utilities may be installed in a common tunnel which serves as access for maintenance or can be combined with tunnels providing personnel communications between buildings. Tunnel developments represent a premium construction and seldom can be justified on the basis of serving utilities only, unless unusual soil conditions are detrimental to more conventional direct burial methods.

If the site to be developed will ultimately be of substantial size, it follows that the utility requirements will also be large. In these instances, it is desirable to set aside a centrally located area, probably along one border of the site, adequate in size to house steam-generating facilities, cooling towers and power terminal structures as well as the central maintenance headquarters, shops and warehouses which support the complex. Aside from considerations of appearance, such a grouping brings together the various types of operating personnel in a most efficient manner.

Every research building unit requires heat and all industrial research laboratories are air conditioned. Unfortunately air-conditioning of college and university science buildings has been considered a luxury rather than a necessity. Consequently, in many recent academic buildings air-conditioning has either been left out entirely or concentrated in offices, library rooms, an auditorium or in a few research laboratories requiring conditioned air. The trend toward more effective use of college facilities, particularly during the summer months, will inevitably lead to a restudy of the importance of air-conditioned academic buildings.

The merits of central versus individual heating and cooling installations in separate building units should be given careful study. Obviously, the addition of a new science unit to a well-established college campus presents an entirely different problem from the first building project in a completely new facility. More economical performance of larger heating and cooling equipment, possible savings in operating personnel, lower unit costs of construction, and the possibility of taking advantage of diversity factors in the determination of total requirements are all in favor of the central utility development.

It is impossible to justify the cost of the central plant concept on the basis of a single building unit, but the long-range aspect of the project may well dictate a central plant to serve the first building unit on a new site. Unless the decision to develop a central utilities plant is made before many individual installations are created, the possible economies for the ultimate development will be lost.

RELATIONS TO OTHER BUILDINGS AND SERVICES

There are no rules that apply broadly to the selection of a building site. For example, a factor which may be of prime importance to an industrial development may have little or no value in the location of an academic building. Some of the factors which should be weighed in selecting a site are discussed below.

Relative Importance of Building

Some building units will assume a greater importance than others on the over-all site; for instance, a building that might also contain principal administrative offices or generate more traffic with the general public should occupy a position of greater prominence than one limited primarily to the use of the occupants.

Common Functions

Frequently, it is desirable to apportion certain service functions, such as libraries, cafeterias and supply rooms, between two or more building units. When the volume of traffic generated by these common services is substantial, it is important to have the buildings reasonably close together. Proximity is not quite as important with other shared services which are less frequently used.

Type of Activity

The use of a laboratory building to some degree controls its location. Pilot plant operations with need for dock and trucking facilities and perhaps unusually heavy utility requirements should occupy a position of less prominence. The costs of operation of the pilot plant from a utility standpoint might well be the determining factor in its location. Basic research laboratory buildings, which conversely are not tied down as rigidly by costs of utilities services, tend to be clean, attractive units adaptable to nearly any location. They can be designed to fit almost any style of architecture found in adjacent buildings.

Special Topographical Requirements

Occasionally, a laboratory activity is best served by a multi-story development with need for dock facilities at more than one level. In these instances, an area where a natural slope can be inexpensively adapted is frequently desirable.

Minimum Separation—Expansion

Each building site should be sufficiently removed from an adjacent building to permit adequate space for a reasonable amount of grassed area, landscaping and roadways between the units. Even more important is the possible future need for expansion of the building unit under consideration and of that to which it is adjacent. If there is a question of adequacy of separation between building units, increasing the area is the best insurance of future satisfaction.

General Considerations

In our present economy, the factors of growth have produced substantial building activity in areas where static conditions have been common for many years. Recent developments of a commercial or industrial nature are being expanded almost continuously, with every indication that this is a new trend rather than a temporary situation. In these cases, particularly, there is merit in planning the building expansion program so that new construction will complete a specific portion of the over-all site; otherwise, the entire development will be in a continuous state of disruption. The construction of roads, parking facilities and utilities by this "stage" type of planning is economically sound.

PARKING

On a site where the greatest concentration of occupants is in the professional or semi-professional category, private automobiles will provide the major volume of transportation. This group of employees generally prefers flexibility in their arrival and departure time and consequently, it is necessary to provide parking facilities within a range of 0.67 to 0.9 space per person.

Parking areas should be established reasonably close to the buildings served; they should be surfaced for lighter duty than roadways, but should be dust- and dirt-free. For maximum efficient ground usage, parking positions should be defined by painted guide lines and wood or precast concrete wheel stops to control the effective space occupied by each vehicle. Such wheel stops have an advantage over permanent curbing in that repairs necessitated by such activities as snow-plowing are more easily made. Moreover, modifications in parking practices are easier to carry out than with permanent-type curbing. Particular attention should be given to careful grading of parking areas to assure run-off of rain water.

A more pleasing site can be developed if parking areas are kept to a size proportionate to adjacent structures and landscaped areas. No set formula can be established, but a study of balance in these areas will yield parking areas which can be landscaped and made attractive.

FUTURE EXPANSION

Over-all site selection is not likely to become a problem when laboratory facilities are to be added to educational institutions or industrial research organizations planning expansion of exist-ing facilities. Although this general statement is a valid one in the case of educational planning, the specific location of a new science building on a long-established college campus presents many problems of which the various features must be carefully studied. A word of caution must also be injected regarding industrial organizations.

No business is so well established today that it can afford to be without a research program of some kind. The result of such policy would prove fatal to the financial well-being of the organization. Growth can be maintained by development of new products, by improvement in efficiency of present processes through quality control and reduction in manufacturing costs, and by a program of long-term basic research. These call for well-trained research personnel together with modern research facilities in which to work.

Obviously, economic factors ultimately have a large bearing on the location of any new research facility. Before the final decision is made to locate such a unit on or adjacent to the site of existing facilities, it is extremely important that the advantages and disadvantages be analyzed carefully. If, at the time a new facility is under consideration, it becomes apparent that the available site will not accommodate foreseeable requirements or will require heavy future expenditures or compromises, the possibility of another site must be examined. Experience in industry has proved that the boundaries of research are indeed limitless; it is said that the research plant has yet to be built which in time did not continue to grow beyond any predictions made for its ultimate size or complexity. Therefore, it requires careful planning, bold concepts and strong convictions to assure adequate and satisfactory space to meet the future research needs of the organization in terms of site and location of building units and services. Time spent on site planning is well worth while.

CHAPTER III

Materials

of Construction

R. C. deWAHL

Ellerbe & Company
St. Paul, Minnesota

Usually, there are only two absolute limiting factors to the selection of materials of construction for any building project. The first of these is the purpose for which the building is to be used, and the second is the necessity for adherence to local, state and national codes. Within these limits, a broad range of materials and techniques are available to the designer. For the purposes of this volume, it is assumed that all laboratory operations except the most temporary in nature will require fireproof construction, thus eliminating the use of wood as a basic construction material.

RELATIVE COSTS

The only reliable way to compare relative costs of building construction is to analyze a particular project with local unit material costs and labor conditions in mind. Geographic location frequently permits use of a relatively inexpensive material in one area which may be completely unsatisfactory in another, because of great variations in temperature, salt conditions and a host of other deleterious conditions in different parts of the country.

Moreover, cost must be weighed not only in terms of the original cost of materials in plan but also in terms of maintenance over the normal life span of the building unit. Often, a time schedule which must be met in the completion of a laboratory building will affect costs because of seasonal construction problems thereby imposed.

In the following discussion of various elements of building construction, only general statements will be made concerning cost categories. Each designer will want to make an independent and exact cost analysis of those particular materials which satisfy the requirements of the project under consideration.

BUILDING FRAMING SYSTEMS

Except for the small laboratory unit that might be developed with load-bearing masonry walls, each building unit must have a steel or concrete framework or structural system. In many cases, the choice must be made on the basis of factors other than cost, since cost alone may well be substantially the same in both systems.

Steel framing is usually the simpler material with which to work because of smaller dimension required for equal strength. Steel layouts may also be modified more easily to accommodate unusual clearance problems for piping and ductwork.

On the other hand, if construction speed is required, it is frequently possible to get a job under way more rapidly with a concrete design. The possibility of a combination of steel and reinforced concrete design should not be overlooked. Often, space below grade can be built in concrete and by the time the structure has reached grade level, steel delivery can be obtained for the balance.

EXTERIOR WALLS

The various materials available for exterior wall construction are many. In the order of relative cost, the broad categories are:

Lowest cost: Cement—asbestos
Masonry—concrete block
Sandwich wall
Masonry—brick with block, tile or brick back-up
Some native stones—masonry back-up
Curtain wall
Highest cost: Stone—masonry back-up

Cement—Asbestos

This class of product is most applicable to the pilot plant type of laboratory where low first cost is important, where an extremely corrosive atmosphere will be present, or in those instances where the construction is considered to be semipermanent. It is also useful for the enclosure of special building appendages such as penthouses.

Masonry—Concrete Block

Probably the least expensive permanent exterior wall material is concrete or lightweight aggregate building block. The lightweight block requires some type of sealer to make it resistant to rain, and both types can be relatively attractive when care is used in the laying process. Paint can provide an adequate interior surface.

Sandwich Wall

A good many combinations of sandwich wall panels are available, ranging from baked enamel on steel to stainless steel for exterior as well as interior surfaces. A similar variety of insulating materials may be obtained to suit nearly every requirement.

Sandwich wall material is generally accepted for the pilot plant rather than for the basic type of research laboratory. Its cost can vary widely, depending on the choice of combinations. A distinct advantage of this construction is the ease with which large wall sections can be opened and reclosed when substitution or replacement of large equipment units is necessary.

Masonry—Brick with Block, Clay Tile, or Brick Back-Up

Brick, the most common of the permanent types of construction, is ageless. Its varieties are almost unlimited, and the cost of maintenance exceptionally modest if the structure is properly erected. For a complete masonry wall, brick may be backed up with concrete or lightweight block, clay tile or other grades of brick. Block back-up and even brick, if carefully laid up, can be used as the finished interior wall. Structural clay tile is usually unsatisfactory as a finish wall material, but a salt or ceramic glaze tile will produce an excellent surface for interior finish, particularly in laboratory areas where there is a problem of cleanliness.

Native Stone

Occasionally, the geographical location of a laboratory project will permit the use of stone as an exterior construction material at a relatively modest cost. Furthermore, a dense grade of stone produces a building of lasting quality.

Curtain Walls

Curtain wall construction, which can best be defined as a relatively light skin covering applied to a basic building frame, can be developed in innumerable forms. The materials making up the skin are generally a framework of steel or aluminum containing the skin elements of varying degrees of transparency.

A certain proportion of each exterior wall normally is glazed to provide natural light and permit the occupants to enjoy the view. There has been a trend toward extremely large proportions of glass in curtain wall construction, but the planner would be well advised to consider the economic as well as aesthetic aspects when determining the amount to be used, and to balance the difference in cost of heating, air conditioning, ventilation, and sun control against the benefits of the glazed area.

For translucent portions of curtain wall, plastics of both homogeneous and reinforced varieties are available in large numbers. Although satisfactory results have been shown in accelerated life tests, most of these materials are new to the building field; consequently, they should probably be used in only limited proportions until their satisfactory qualities are demonstrated.

Opaque materials are again almost limitless for curtain wall construction. Some are:

"Transite"
Enameled or porcelainized steel
Aluminum in natural or color-processed
    finishes
Metal clad plywood or fiber panels
Glass
Precast mosaic
Cut stone

This wide variety permits choices of color, texture and a very considerable range of cost.

Depending on climate, portions of the curtain wall other than glazed areas require insulation to provide an adequate barrier to heat and cold. This introduces the need for a separate interior wall material which again can be as varied as that selected for the exterior.

Curtain wall construction, because of its complexity, offers some very real problems in achieving completely weather-tight construction. There are adequate sealants on the market, but each design should be carefully tested in full scale mock-up form before being approved for construction. An extremely thorough inspection should be carried on during construction.

Stone Exterior—Masonry Back-Up

The use of stone for exterior laboratory building surfaces is rapidly being limited to feature areas such as entryways, trim, etc., because of the cost. It is generally a premium construction material and although completely satisfactory, is frequently beyond the budget available.

A special type of exterior, the window wall, made up primarily of a combination of fixed and operating metal sash within a similar metal framework, has its place in laboratory design. This form of construction is used where large areas must be provided for possible explosion relief around potentially hazardous operations. Where a window wall is used to meet explosion hazard requirements, it should be oriented to minimize sun load and built toward open areas rather than toward closely spaced adjacent structures.

WINDOWS

Almost anything the designer may want in the window field is available as stock material. Budget permitting, metal frames tend to be preferred because of low maintenance costs; aluminum eliminates the need for periodic painting. Climatic conditions will determine the choice of glazing, and orientation of the particular building may dictate examination of some of the tinted, heat-resistant glass products.

DOORS AND FRAMES

As in windows, the trend appears to be in the direction of the metal products for doors and frames. Aluminum for primary entrances is preferable to minimize maintenance. Labor savings in installation and finishing costs will in most instances permit the use of hollow metal doors and frames throughout a laboratory building. Wooden doors may be chosen in certain areas where a better grade of finishing is required.

ROOF CONSTRUCTION

Beyond the requirements demanded by codes or underwriters, no special precautions apply to laboratory construction as such. However, if roof surfaces are to be used as work areas, as for weathering test installations, meteorological stations, and portable telescopes, or if mechanical equipment is located on the roof, these must be given special consideration in the planning.

INTERIOR WALLS

The choice of construction materials for certain walls within the laboratory building will be more or less fixed by building codes. Enclosures around stairways, elevators, piping and ventilating shafts or other clear openings extending beyond one story in height must generally have a fire-resistant rating which will automatically require some form of masonry construction.

For other interior partitions subdividing the floor space, there is again available to the designer a rather wide range of construction materials, the ultimate choice of which is dependent on a number of factors. First, consideration must be given to the permanence of the area created. A classroom area in an academic building will generally remain static in size for the life of the building, whereas a laboratory in an industrial or commercial building may be altered with relative frequency to accommodate current research programs. Secondly, the purpose for which a given space is to be used may have a vital bearing on the choice of construction materials for partitions.

Special attention must be given in controlled temperature and humidity areas to vapor barriers of better than average quality. See Chapter 10, Part 6. A laboratory with unusual requirements for cleanliness or one which handles dusty or dirty operations will also require special planning.

The occupancy of a partitioned area influences the finishing materials used on partition wall surfaces. Areas accommodating large groups or those subject to heavy traffic are more susceptible to high maintenance costs unless durable wall finishes are selected.

Very little in the way of wood products finds its way into laboratory building partitions except in offices, conference rooms and similar areas where there is relatively no fire hazard. Here, wood stud partitions with dry wall, plaster or paneling represent the standard construction methods in increasing order of cost.

For more or less permanent partition wall construction, a concrete block wall is the simplest and least costly approach, either unpainted or treated with a paint finish. Next are the clear or color-glazed structural tiles having excellent characteristics as far as maintenance is concerned (washable and durable), but with very poor acoustic properties. Following in the order of cost is the old stand-by partition—tile with plaster coating, producing a smooth durable surface subject to a variety of finishing methods.

The most expensive partition from the standpoint of first cost is the prefabricated partition of metal or a number of inorganic materials. These are usually recommended in areas where partition alterations are likely to occur, because of their unit-type construction and adaptability to re-use without waste. Although the re-usability factor is undeniable, the designer would be well advised to analyze the extent and frequency of probable alterations and their relation to the total quantity of partitioning of this type being considered. Unless the possible alterations represent a fairly large percentage of the total of such partitions installed and within a relatively short time cycle, the cost of removing and re-erecting masonry partitions might still be desirable from an economic standpoint. It would only be fair to point out that when making an analysis of prefabricated partition material, the cleanliness factor involved in partition rearrangements is strongly in favor of the prefabricated product. On the other hand, it should also be pointed out that if many attachments, such as reagent shelf supports, pipe hangers and the like, are applied to prefabricated panels, the value of their re-use is frequently reduced.

No attempt will be made in this chapter to cover specific approaches to the special problems of insulating properties, unusual humidity conditions, electrostatic shielding or the many other special requirements that can arise in laboratory design. Once the existence of a special problem is recognized, the solution is often available through consultation with experts in the particular field or with manufacturers of products adaptable to the specific situation.

Wall Finishes

Prior to the forties, the subject of wall finishes was a relatively simple one. The average designer generally thought in terms of plastered walls and lead and oil paints as the standard solution to most wall-finishing problems, although lead paint even then was a poor choice for a laboratory wall finish. The post-war period, with its need for careful analysis of building costs at a time when all costs were spiralling, has seen keen competition bring out many new products which have opened new vistas for the designer.

Paint products as they have been known over the years are fully as good as, and in most instances, even better than ever before. Some of the economic aspects, however, have changed materially; this is particularly true of labor costs, which make many of the older products too expensive to use. In spite of higher material costs, the designer must give careful consideration to some of the more recent developments in alkyd resins, patented multicolored wall preparations and plastics, and then carefully weigh the first cost against maintenance expenditures before making his final determination of wall finish material. Some of the most expensive materials in terms of first cost will frequently justify their use in a very few years.

FLOOR FINISHES

Although we might describe this subject as "floor coverings," the term of "floor finishes" has been chosen in order not to eliminate serious consideration of a superior natural floor. Today, we assume that all floors are basically concrete, either in the form of topping over a steel cellular floor or as solid concrete slabs. Concrete in itself can be made as dense, dust-free, and durable as required. It does have the disadvantages of being difficult to maintain, tiring to stand on for prolonged periods of time, and aesthetically lacking. What one might do to improve these characteristics depends entirely on the use to which any specific area is put.

For facilities of the pilot plant type, when heavy loads are likely and where relatively few workers are involved, a hard concrete floor, resistant to chemicals, will probably be the most satisfactory solution. The particular hardening agent used will be indicated by an analysis of the materials to be handled in the area. In some very special instances, chemicals which are injurious to

concrete and any treatment to which it might be subjected will be in use and subject to spillage on the concrete floor. There are a number of special brick and tile products, together with suitable mortars, that may be applied over the concrete which will withstand under the severe service imposed. The resistance of the specific combination of products to special conditions must be established before use by careful investigation and by consultation with the manufacturers of the materials.

In the field of floor coverings, asphalt tile is the least expensive material generally used in laboratory construction. However, it is unsatisfactory in contact with many oils and chemicals, has a low resistance to abrasion, and can be damaged by concentrated loading as from supports for heavy furniture and equipment. Used within its limitations and with adequate maintenance, it is a very serviceable product.

The more recent vinyl-asbestos tile is next step upward in cost. Colors are somewhat brighter, the areas of satisfactory use are broader, and general resistance to abrasion is higher. It will qualify for use in the limited budget project.

The well-known linoleum is available in tile as well as sheet form and is finding wide acceptance. In tile form, it can be manufactured with a high degree of surface temper and will give adequate service when properly maintained. Colors are quite attractive and are available in a wide range. The use of sheet linoleum is quite uncommon in commercial and industrial buildings today, principally because it cannot be repaired as simply as a flooring in tile form. Any damaged tiles, whether asphalt, vinyl-asbestos or linoleum, are easily and quickly replaced by any reasonably adept maintenance man.

The most expensive class of floor-covering material from the standpoint of first cost includes two products, vinyl tile and rubber tile. Among the best looking of the various floor-covering materials, both are more comfortable to stand on for long periods of time and are highly resistant to abrasion. Either can take much heavier furniture loadings than most other products in this field and tend to stand up better with something less than adequate maintenance. Even these materials, however, may be unsatisfactory under certain laboratory conditions and a compromise may be necessary on the part of the designer.

Until a relatively few years ago, only asphalt tile was recommended for installation on basement floors and slab on grade concrete floors. Today, manufacturers of all the types of floor covering have special adhesives available which permit a guaranteed installation, but the adhesives tend to increase the installed cost somewhat.

At this writing, a number of new floor covering products which apparently have even better properties than the ones described are being readied for market; consequently, the planner should be alerted to examine them as they become available.

CEILING—SOUND INSULATION

Suspended ceilings are being installed widely in academic laboratory buildings. In such buildings occupancy is generally high, with the attendant requirement for sound control both within and between adjacent rooms; furthermore, the building layout is unlikely to be altered to any great extent during the useful life of the structure. In this situation, partition walls should be generally carried through the suspended ceiling to the floor above, particularly where classrooms, library, and offices are involved.

On the other hand, commercial and industrial laboratories frequently have suspended ceilings in public areas such as lobbies, corridors, toilet and locker rooms, cafeterias, private offices and conference rooms, but not in the laboratory areas themselves. Ceiling areas of most laboratories contain many mechanical and electrical piping lines as well as ductwork, all of which are subject to modification to keep pace with the ever-changing patterns of research. If these services are carefully laid out and coordinated with an eye toward symmetry and orderliness, they can be functionally attractive rather than so ugly that they require concealment.

Most divisions of laboratory space, except for the academic facilities, will be occupied by one or at most a very few specialists and technicians generally performing work which is not noisy in nature. Under these conditions, partition walls extended to the underside of the next floor or

roof construction will provide adequate sound control between laboratory areas. Installation of suspended ceilings in these areas is looked upon as a nicety that is being foregone as construction costs continue to rise.

It is extremely difficult to establish a definite cost relationship between various ceiling construction methods because several elements enter into each scheme; moreover, each element in itself can range over quite an area of cost. Instead, the following discussion will outline the points to be considered in analyzing the problem of ceiling construction.

For all-around durability and ease of maintenance, the standard plaster ceiling cannot be challenged. It will take plenty of abuse and can be washed or painted with no special precautions. An exception to this might be in large student laboratories where acid fumes may be present. Access to facilities in the ceiling space must be obtained by suitable panels planned at the time of construction. Plaster has no value as a sound attenuator but will tend to contain sound within the area enclosed. The construction procedure requires use of large quantities of water which in some instances might introduce some problems on an extremely tight construction schedule. Any number of insulating materials may be applied to a plaster ceiling surface for effective control of sound within the enclosed area.

Under certain conditions, acoustic plaster will do a good job for both enclosing and sound purposes. The finished surface tends to be soft, however, and cannot be mistreated. When acoustic plaster becomes unsightly, it can be painted, preferably with a water-base paint, using great care that the voids are not unduly filled with the new coating. Each successive application tends to lessen the acoustic value of the material.

If laboratory spaces are built with solid partition walls extending to the floor or roof construction above, a suspended ceiling consisting of insulating material only will provide good overall sound control. The suspension system can be any one of a number of patented units providing concealed or exposed suspension devices. The principal advantage of such a ceiling system is the ability to remove tile sections readily for access to or remodeling of facilities enclosed within the furred ceiling space; furthermore, upon completion of the work, the ceiling can be restored to its original condition without expensive waste of construction materials.

Sometimes partition walls are carried only to the height of a suspended ceiling and when this is done, acoustic ceiling material other than plaster is inadequate to control or limit transmission of sound from one partitioned area to the next. In such cases, it is necessary to provide additional mass in the ceiling construction which can be done by suspending a backer board ceiling on which acoustic materials are then applied. This will sacrifice the aspect of ease of service to the furred ceiling area.

Generalizing, there are certain advantages to each of the manufactured acoustic materials:

(1) Plastic film-faced tile: easily cleaned; absorbs little dust.

(2) Metal pan and blanket: easily cleaned; absorbs no dust; obtainable in several metals; rich in appearance.

(3) Perforated tile (vegetable, wood fiber or mineral): good acoustic properties; easily installed and painted with roller.

(4) Fissured tile (vegetable, wood fiber or mineral): good acoustic properties; easily installed; requires greatest care in painting not to lessen reduction of acoustic properties.

ILLUMINATION

For the purposes of this chapter, the broad subject of illumination in the laboratory will be discussed generally. An exacting science, it should be entrusted to a competent engineer who has available a wealth of information on the subject.

Except where there are very special requirements of color or where there is need to operate where hazards of explosion or other unusual conditions exist, the laboratory building will no doubt use fluorescent lighting for economic reasons. Available from many sources and in as many combinations and qualities as an owner may wish, fluorescent equipment is undergoing continual change, thereby necessitating evaluation of the products available at the time of construction of each building.

Care should be given to the establishment of a modular lighting pattern to the greatest extent possible. Setting such a modular pattern and holding to it as rigidly as possible makes for fewer lighting alterations as laboratory arrangements are changed.

If the budget will permit, recommended standards of illumination levels as established by the Illuminating Engineering Society should be used as minimum requirements. By so doing, the planner is in effect building some degree of forward planning into his layout. The trend is toward higher levels of illumination and any compromise at this point might be considered as pre-aging the job before it starts.

A good lighting job does not necessarily call for a maximum of investment in lighting fixtures. Frequently, an industrial fixture can serve as well as the more costly unit designed for aesthetic appeal as well as performance. After determining what you want to accomplish and looking at all the equipment capable of performing the job, balance appearance against cost.

Just as important as the first cost of lighting fixtures is the cost of maintaining them. Over the life of a laboratory building, more hours will be spent on the maintenance of lighting equipment than on any other building service. Lamps must be replaced periodically, lenses and fixture bodies cleaned, and ballasts replaced when necessary. Maintenance labor is expensive; therefore, the seemingly minor features of ballast accessibility, ease of lamp removal, etc., are points to examine very critically.

CHAPTER IV

Circulation

R. C. deWAHL

Ellerbe & Company
St. Paul, Minnesota

The minimum requirements for the number of stairways as well as their size and general location are determined by local building codes. Usually, stairs that meet the code requirements are sufficient for circulation purposes. Most laboratories involve a certain degree of fire hazard. For this reason, all stairways should be in fire-resisting enclosures, whether or not this is required by the building code. Also, the stairs should be arranged so that there will be at least two safe exits from any point in case of fire. The materials for the stairways will be dictated by compromise between economy and appearance, providing that code requirements are met.

Elevators should be of the automatic, push-button, self-service type. The extra cost is very quickly offset by elimination of elevator operators. The principal elevator manufacturers have excellent methods for calculating the size, speed, and number of elevators required for any installation and will provide planners with formulas for making preliminary elevator requirement surveys.

Considerations of economy will usually dictate that supplies and other freight will be carried by the passenger elevators whenever this does not interfere with peak passenger loading. If the bulk, weight or other characteristics of material to be handled prohibit the use of the passenger elevators, a separate freight elevator will be required.

The pattern of corridors will naturally be determined by the disposition of other elements of the building. The corridor pattern should be simple and direct, and should be as short as possible when connecting points between which there is frequent communication. Consideration must be given in the planning to the possibility of moving heavy or bulky items of material or equipment as well as to pedestrian traffic.

Sometimes it is desirable to provide service corridors separate from the traffic corridors. These may be used to house pipe and ducts for mechanical services. This is especially desirable if the nature of the work done in the laboratories is such that frequent changes in plumbing, electrical or ventilation supplies to the laboratories must be made.

The walls and floors of corridors are usually subject to more abuse than any other part of a building since they are damaged by hand-trucks and soiled by people. Thus, the wall surfaces should be more durable than plaster and paint. Glazed structural clay tile is satisfactory, and also there are other wall coverings such as sheet vinyl. Rubber tile or vinyl tile make satisfactory floor covering. Acoustic ceilings in the corridors will help to reduce the noise level in the adjoining laboratories.

Circulation in a laboratory should so far as possible be limited to the people who are working there. The circulation pattern is determined by the equipment layout. It should be such that the people who are working are not disturbed by the necessary traffic. One way to accomplish this in large industrial laboratories is to arrange one or more traffic lanes and place the work counters in a series of horseshoe units which open into the traffic lane.

What has been said above about the restriction of circulation within the laboratory to people working in the laboratory is fully as important in academic as in industrial laboratories. Teaching laboratories should never be used to handle general traffic.

Specific

Considerations

CHAPTER V

Services

SYSKA & HENNESSY, INC.

New York, New York

PART 1: PLUMBING

GENERAL

The mechanical services required for laboratory buildings are most complicated. The keynote of their design is flexibility. Since both the nature of the experiments and the particular services required are subject to change from time to time, it follows that changes may have to be made in the arrangements within the various laboratory rooms. In order to carry out such changes, not only at a minimum cost but with the least interference with services in other laboratories, the system supplying the various services must be very carefully planned. It is particularly important that the design permit change without interference with services in other laboratories, for some experiments require months and even years to complete and disruption of services might involve the repetition of a great deal of work. Money spent in careful planning can mean the saving of both time and money in the long run. This is particularly true in laboratories for industrial research. For somewhat different reasons careful planning of service systems is also important in teaching laboratories.

In order to achieve the desired flexibility, it is necessary to consider the type of building and the arrangement of the laboratories within the building. Buildings of one or two stories usually lend themselves to a horizontal distribution of services in the ceiling of the lower floor, with valved branch connections in each bay; however, in multi-story buildings, it is more economical to run risers and stacks in each bay to serve the laboratories of that bay with valved connections on every floor.

Final decisions as to just how piping shall run from mains or risers to the equipment must be reached after the type of equipment and room arrangement are known. For example, if island benches are to be provided, piping must come from the ceiling below to avoid being dropped in the middle of the room; however, if only wall or peninsular benches are to be used, piping may be fed from the ceiling to the bench. This has the advantage of placing the valve which controls the branches to a laboratory within the laboratory space solely under the jurisdiction of the operator of that laboratory. To avoid the possibility of a change or accident in one laboratory discontinuing services to neighboring ones, no branch valve should control more than one laboratory. Serious consideration should be given to providing in duplex all key equipment subject to breakdown or requiring servicing to avoid any possibility of interruption of service.

The engineer designing the services for a laboratory must confer with the technicians in charge and carefully review their requirements for the various types of services and the different characteristics of a particular service, so that the proper systems can be supplied to satisfy all present and probable future needs. This stage of the design requires painstaking checking between the engineer and the technicians so that the latter will be provided with the necessary services. If this is not done carefully, services may be found to be inadequate at the time the building is occupied.

In research laboratories, provision is usually made for a great number of various outlets in each room. This does not mean that the load will be as heavy as indicated by the number of outlets. In most cases, extra outlets are provided so that separate hook-ups of equipment can be available in each location and can be operated at different times without having to disconnect one to connect another. Since this is a matter of convenience rather than necessity, it should be considered in sizing the supply pipes for these outlets. It should have a weighted effect on the use factors considered in the sizing of mains, risers, and branches for the various systems serving the laboratories and on the equipment supplying them.

It should also be noted that use factors will be far higher in academic laboratories than in research laboratories, since many students perform the same experiment simultaneously as compared with the occasional and varied experiments carried out in a research laboratory.

Exposed service piping should be run in a neat and orderly manner so as to present an attractive appearance without hampering accessibility for maintenance and repair. Where service piping is concealed, easy and adequate access to it must be provided to allow for maintenance, repair and future changes.

Services required for a modern laboratory may well include many of the following:
(1) Drainage systems
(2) Water supply systems
(3) Gas system
(4) Compressed air system
(5) Vacuum air system
(6) Special gas systems
(7) Fire protection systems
(8) Disposal and/or treatment systems

DRAINAGE SYSTEMS

The drainage systems required include those for storm water, sanitation and waste water. Obviously, rainwater must be piped to yard sewers. Rain falling on the building is usually handled by roof drains and inside leaders which run down in convenient shafts to a horizontal main drain located on the basement ceiling and running out through the wall, where it joins the site storm water sewers. These in turn empty into main storm sewers, adjacent watercourses, or dry well. Sizing must be in accordance with local code requirements, or where no code exists, the "National Plumbing Code" ASA, A40.8, is highly recommended.

Sanitary drainage systems for the toilet and kitchen facilities must be properly designed and piped either to an existing sewer or to a sewage treatment plant on the property. Sanitary drainage and vent systems for toilet and kitchen equipment are usually planned in accordance with local code requirements or in the absence of such code the "National Plumbing Code," ASA, A40.8.

The question of provision of floor drains to allow for possible laboratory accidents, emergency showers or sprinkler discharges is one that requires careful study. Such drains, if installed, should be connected to the sanitary or waste water drainage systems of the building. Traps must be provided to prevent the escape of gases and fumes into the building. Unfortunately the seals in such traps are frequently not maintained (due in part to poor maintenance and in part to the infrequent occurrence of accidents of the above kind) and so toxic or explosive gases or unpleasant odors may penetrate throughout the building. Under these conditions, drains are more of a hazard than a help. In addition, there are those who believe that floor drains lead to unauthorized use of emergency showers. For these reasons, the installation of floor drains in laboratories is the exception rather than rule. When they are installed, they should be restricted to areas that receive sufficient water in normal use to maintain the seal.

The chief problem in waste disposal involves special wastes which may be different in every laboratory. These include wastes containing chemicals, radioactive materials, and suspended solids, all of which must be treated in special ways before they can be readily disposed of. This problem exists because these wastes may contain many toxic products capable of contaminating adjacent ground or watercourses. After they have been studied carefully for content and concentration, they must be divided into separate systems, since each has different characteristics requiring special treatment. Similarly, to avoid dilution of such wastes in treatment plants, a special system for clean water wastes should be provided, unless dilution is part of the required treatment. This latter system takes cooling water, aspirator wastes, and other uncontaminated water; frequently this system can be run directly into the storm water system or into the sanitary system.

Generally, laboratory wastes containing dissolved chemicals and those containing suspended solid materials should be separated, since their treatment is quite different. Radioactive wastes should be kept apart and provided with monitoring devices to keep track of the degree of radioactivity at all times.

It is imperative that all laboratory waste outlets be trapped even if they are not connected to the sanitary system, since the absence of traps will allow the passage of odors, fumes or toxic gases from the outlets in one laboratory into the adjoining laboratory. Traps must be either protected by vents or be the antisyphon type in order to ensure maintenance of their seals at all times. Antisyphon traps, which have the advantage of eliminating the vent piping that often introduces a space and height problem for some laboratory

equipment, can be used only in communities where they are not prohibited by code. Since their trap seal is not as well maintained as in conventional "P" or "running" traps with vents, their use should generally be restricted to locations where conventional venting is impractical.

Sinks are usually provided with 2-in. outlets and a weight of two fixture units; unfortunately in some school laboratories 1½-in. outlets, used on sinks serving several students, fail to provide adequate drainage. Cup drains are provided with 1½-in outlets and a weight of one fixture unit. Sizing of branches, stacks, and house drains is usually done by the code tables for sanitary drainage using the fixture unit weight allowances mentioned above.

The type of waste to be anticipated from a given laboratory or series of laboratories has a direct bearing on the kind of piping required for the drainage system. If very little acid or other corrosive material is likely to enter the drain, regular cast-iron hub and spigot piping will serve adequately at a minimum cost. Conversely, cast-iron piping for concealed waste connections is not recommended for acid wastes; moreover, it should be avoided in cases where laboratories may be idle for long periods, as in schools, because corrosion is usually more severe under these conditions. Where highly concentrated acids and other corrosive materials are expected to occur, special acid-resistant piping must be provided. This is especially true in school laboratories since a student cannot be expected to exercise the same care in disposing of corrosive materials as experienced technicians in research laboratories. Therefore, it is unwise to use anything but acid-resistant piping in such cases, for example, high-silicon iron, lead, chemical stoneware, glass, or plastic.

The use of lead for laboratory wastes should be confined to traps and to branch connections between outlets on laboratory furniture. Lead pipe used for domestic plumbing is unsatisfactory for chemical work because it contains a small percentage of zinc. Chemical lead should be 99.98 per cent pure to withstand the action of strong hot sulfuric acid up to about 312°C (608°F). Joints should either be wiped or burned; if wiped, the solder must be of satisfactory quality.

High-silicon iron piping ("Duriron" and "Corrosiron") is widely used for the disposal of corrosive wastes from laboratories, but its brittleness requires that care be exercised when installing and making joints to prevent damage to the pipe. At least two rings of pure asbestos rope packing, impregnated with graphite or mastic, should be placed at the bottom of the hub and packed tight. The remaining space is filled with molten lead at a moderate temperature.

"Pyrex" glass pipe is also used in some laboratories for waste lines. Its important characteristics are its very low thermal expansion and excellent chemical resistance. It is made in diameters of 1½-in. to 6-in. and in lengths of 5 and 10 ft. The ends of the glass are beaded to permit its use in a compression joint. The coupling consists of a stainless steel band surrounding an acrylonitrile rubber sleeve with a liner of "Teflon" 100X. The beaded ends of the glass are stabbed into both sides of the coupling, and the stainless steel band is tightened by means of a stainless steel bolt and nut. Only "Teflon" 100X and glass are in contact with the fluid being conveyed. A complete line of fittings and traps is available.

Although chemical stoneware is an excellent material for concealed waste stacks and horizontal runs, it is somewhat bulky and brittle for local exposed locations. The bell-and-spigot joints are made by tamping asbestos rope wicking, preferably impregnated with suitable graphite or mastic, tightly into the pipe socket and then pouring a melted, acid-proof caulking compound flush with the top of the hub.

Available today are numerous plastic pipe materials which have good corrosion resistance to the various chemicals occurring in laboratory wastes. However, as these substances do not have equal degree of resistance to the same chemicals, they should be carefully investigated in order to ensure optimum resistance in each case. Jointing of this piping may be done either by threading or welding.

Traps should always be of acid-resistant materials, even though the piping may not be, since waste waters often lie in them for a long period. As a result, corrosion is often greater in traps than in the piping itself. Traps are often made of chemical lead, but may be of the same acid-resistant material as the piping.

WATER-SUPPLY SYSTEMS

Water-supply systems include cold, hot, chilled, and distilled, and/or demineralized water systems. Special care should be taken to ensure adequate and constant pressure of water to all parts of the building, as some specialized laboratory equipment may require more than minimum pressures. This would have to be considered by the engineer in his conferences with the laboratory technicians.

Where there is adequate water in the street main to supply the needs of the building, no serious problems are involved; however, where there is inadequate pressure, steps must be taken to increase it, either by a gravity tank on the roof of the building or on a tower, or by a hydropneumatic pressure tank in the basement. The former is a cheaper, simpler system with less maintenance and a more constant pressure. To obtain constant pressure in the building, a hydropneumatic pressure tank must be kept at a higher pressure than normally required, with a pressure-regulating valve on the outlet. Stabilized pressure is very important in a laboratory, as certain experiments are set up for a given rate of water flow; if the pressure changes materially during the course of an experiment, the water flow will change correspondingly and thus upset the requirements of the experiment.

Frequently, laboratories are built in areas lacking a street water main; consequently, a system of water supply must be developed, which may come from deep wells or adjacent watercourses. In either case, adequate on-site storage must be provided to meet the laboratory's needs during periods of water shortage or breakdowns in the supply systems.

Hot water is usually generated in copper-lined steel storage heaters, and circulated to all parts of the building so that it will be readily available with little loss of time or water.

A chilled water system may be solely for the purposes of providing cold drinking water at drinking fountains, or it may be required for special experiments. These requirements may be served by one system, or by separate systems for drinking and for special purposes. The water is circulated so that it will be readily available at the required temperature without the delay involved in emptying dead leg lines.

The owner's need for distilled or demineralized water requires detailed study of his requirements. Since demineralized water is far cheaper to produce than distilled water, it should be used whenever possible, as a substantial saving is involved. Occasionally, certain experiments require that water be both distilled and demineralized. Distilled water is biologically pure, but is not necessarily free from certain chemicals carried over in the distillation process. Conversely, demineralized water is free from chemicals, though not biologically pure. Hence, there is a need for double treatment if both biological and chemical purity are required.

In the case of distilled water, a steam or electric still is provided in the penthouse with a storage tank beside it from which water runs by gravity to dispensing stations. It is desirable to locate these dispensing stations at strategic locations in the corridors rather than on the laboratory benches. Since this water is expensive, its use should be held to a minimum; therefore if it is not readily available in the laboratories, and must be secured from spot locations, the occupants will be more careful in its use. For similar reasons, self-closing faucets should always be used for distilled water dispensing stations. As the ion-exchange units required for demineralized water produce their effluent under pressure, they can be located in the basement, whence the water will be delivered to the dispensing stations.

For the protection of the laboratory technicians, emergency deluge showers should be strategically located in corridors or in each laboratory (depending on the type of work being performed) to wash off chemicals after an accident or to extinguish a flash fire on the clothing. Eye fountains are often provided for irrigating the eyes after accidental contact with chemicals.

Underground water piping 3-in. and larger is usually coated cast-iron bell-and-spigot pipe, sometimes cement-lined, where water conditions or purity of the water require it, with caulked lead or mechanically bolted joints. In sizes of 2-in. and smaller, and for inside cold and hot water, piping materials depend greatly on the chemical content of the water available. Based on analysis of the water, selection can be made between copper tubing, brass pipe, galvanized steel, galvanized wrought iron pipe, or suitable combinations thereof; threaded or flanged joints are used on steel, wrought iron, and brass pipe; silver-brazed or soldered joints are required on brass pipe and copper tubing.

Piping for distilled or demineralized water systems may be chosen from block tin, tin-lined ($\frac{1}{16}$-in. thick) brass, aluminum, stainless steel, or plastic depending on the quality of the water required and on available funds. Since block tin (the best pipe), is very expensive, a compromise is usually made for one of the other materials. Joints in the piping must be carefully planned so that no foreign contaminating substances get into the piping during construction or come into contact with the water during use. Joints in block tin tubing are usually of the flared or compression type, which present no special problem provided the materials are properly cleaned. Threaded joints for tin-lined brass, aluminum, stainless steel, and sometimes plastic pipe should be made with a special inert pipe thread compound similar to "Teflon," or "Alcoa" thread lubricant, pure white shellac, or other special compound. Joints in plastic pipe may also be made by welding, which presents no special contamination problems.

GAS SYSTEM

Although many of the new industrial laboratories are currently designed for electricity in place of gas, the latter is still widely used, and it must be considered in the design of a laboratory. It may be available from street mains, but where it is not, bottled gas installations must be provided. In the case of a large laboratory building, an underground or an on-site storage tank for liquefied petroleum gas may be used instead of individual bottles, since truck-load is more economical than bottle delivery. As the Btu content of manufactured gas, natural gas, and liquefied petroleum gas varies greatly, the sizing of the piping system will differ.

Use factors on the gas system depend to some extent on the type of outlets; duplex outlets result in lower use factors than single outlets. Since many of the outlets are provided for convenience rather than for simultaneous service, use factors must start with 100 per cent, but by the time the mains serving the building are reached, they will have dropped to from 25 to 30 per cent.

Gas systems are usually piped in black steel with standard-weight, malleable iron-threaded fittings inside the building. The outside service, if not provided by the gas company, is usually run in black steel "Mill-Wrap" pipe with welded joints and/or "Dresser" connections.

COMPRESSED AIR SYSTEMS

As the pressure required for compressed air seems to vary widely with different laboratories, this detail must be carefully established at the outset. If more than one pressure is required within a building, study must be given to determine whether independent high and low pressure systems are to be provided with separate compressors, or whether a system for the higher pressure should be installed with pressure-reducing valves to provide the lower pressures.

The quality of compressed air required in a laboratory is usually very high, and special attention must be given to producing and maintaining clean air until it reaches the outlet. Oil, water, and dirt are undesirable ingredients in compressed air, and every effort must be made to eliminate them before the air is delivered to the laboratory outlet. If low-pressure air (under 50 psi) is required, a compressor similar to those of Nash Engineering Company—a rotary type using a water seal and no oil—proves to be the best. It eliminates any addition of oil which later must be removed from the system. Where higher pressures are required, large horizontal water-cooled compressors are generally used. While standard compressors have oil lubrication in the cylinders, it is possible to obtain some made with carbon rings without oil; however, they have the disadvantage of shedding carbon dust into the compressed air.

Since compression heats air, which then tends to hold more moisture, the water must be removed by an aftercooler and/or separators and later stored in an automatically drained tank. On the tank's outlet is placed a pressure-regulating valve to feed constant pressure to the system while still allowing the air compressors their individual cycle operation. Absorption filters are customarily placed between the storage tank and the inlet side of the pressure-regulating valve to prevent moisture from getting into the final piping system. In this position, the variance in pressure loss through the filter does not affect the uniformity of pressure on the system.

If the quality of air is of no concern, black steel pipe with threaded, malleable iron or welded fittings may be used; however, the majority of laboratories use either galvanized steel pipes with threaded, malleable-iron fittings, or solder-joint copper tubing.

As most compressed air is used for intermittent periods, it is possible to take rather low use factors on the whole system. Again, in any local area, a high use factor must be started with and tapered down to the neighborhood of 10 to 15 per cent at the compressors. It is usually customary to allow one cfm free air per outlet.

VACUUM SYSTEMS

Many chemical processes can be accelerated by submitting their systems to vacuum. In academic laboratories students commonly use aspirators to accelerate filtration of precipitates and to lower boiling point in distillations. Water pressures are subject to pressure variations and these induce variations in the pressures obtained by the aspirator. Because of this, and the fact that aspirators represent a dangerous cross connection which may lead to the pollution of domestic water supplies by highly toxic substances (hence their use is banned in many cities), vacuum pumps of the rotary type such as the Nash pump are used to provide a central source of vacuum for piping to the different laboratories. In this a receiver or trap is placed in the vacuum line before the pump to prevent scale and liquids from getting into the pump. In the case of radioactive laboratories, filters are placed in the system before the vacuum tank to prevent radioactive material from getting into the pump and out into the atmosphere. It is also important to run the discharges of vacuum pumps out above the roof, since these often contain odors and gases from the laboratory.

The minimum piping that can be used—since liquids are often drawn into the vacuum system—is galvanized steel with galvanized, malleable iron-threaded fittings but with a strong preference for solder-joint, copper tubing.

Since the use of vacuum is likely to be more constant than that of compressed air, use factors usually drop from 100 per cent in a local area to 20–25 per cent at the pump. Usually it is customary to allow 1 cfm per outlet.

VALVES

Unless used as operating valves or for special throttling purposes, all control valves should be gate valves. Generally, on water systems, they may be of the solid wedge type, but on compressed and vacuum air systems, they should be of the split-wedge type since these seat tighter after wear and better maintain the air pressures. All underground valves should be of the split-wedge type because they hold better when distorted by strain on the valve due to settling pipes; all gate valves should be of the rising stem type so that their open or closed position can be determined at a glance. Small valves are usually all bronze; larger valves are flanged iron body and bronze-mounted. Globe valves are generally used as operating valves; however, in some cases, plug or ball valves, especially in the larger sizes, are more desirable as throttling valves. On water systems, swing-type check valves are generally used except in cases where high static back pressures are encountered, in which case spring-loaded, quiet-type valves are necessary. On compressed-air systems, spring-loaded valves are generally used as they are tighter to air pressure; on vacuum air systems, swing-type valves are used due to the possibility of muck coming through the piping, thus jamming the valves. On gas systems, plug-type valves are commonly used, of which the dry-plug type is used in small sizes, and the lubricated-plug type in larger sizes.

INSULATION

Insulation is always necessary in cold and hot water, chilled water, and drainage piping subject to sweating.

Cold water piping is usually insulated with wool felt 1-in. thick on mains and risers and ½-in. thick on local branches, or with ¾- and ½-in. fiber glass with vapor-sealed outer jacket.

Hot-water and hot water-circulating piping is usually insulated with 1-in. thick 85 per cent magnesia or ¾-in. thick fiber glass on mains and risers, with a thinner layer of fiber glass or a ½-in. thick air cell on local branches.

Chilled water piping is usually insulated with some form of cork insulation or fiber glass with a proper vapor-sealed jacket.

Drainage pipe subject to sweating, e.g., pipes between roof drains and leaders, exposed horizontal storm water drainage piping, drainage piping carrying chilled drinking water between fixture and stack or house drain, and general drainage pipes in a hot, moist room are insulated in the same manner as cold water mains or with hair felt or fiber glass wrapping.

Piping subject to freezing is similarly insulated with the required number of layers of either hair felt, fiber glass, or foam glass.

Generally it is unnecessary to insulate distilled water piping, since the temperature of the water is usually close to room temperature.

Hot-water heaters and storage tanks are insulated with 85 per cent magnesia block, fiber glass block or blanket.

SPECIAL PIPING SYSTEMS

Special piping systems for oxygen, hydrogen, nitrogen, etc., are sometimes required in laboratories; however, their use is usually so limited that a small, local cylinder is sufficient for practical use. However, there are times when an extensive central piping system may be required for one or more of these or other special gases. It is essential that these be treated separately and studied carefully, since the treatment of each varies.

Although nitrogen is harmless, both oxygen and hydrogen are potentially dangerous; consequently, special precautions must be taken to prevent a serious disaster after they are in use. In working with all these gases, the rules of the National Board of Fire Underwriters must be closely followed. These gases are usually provided from banks of high-pressure cylinders located in a convenient and safe place from which gas is piped through reducing valves to desired locations. All piping and equipment used in an oxygen system must be carefully disassembled and washed to remove all grease and oil before it is installed in the building system.

FIRE PROTECTION

Fire hazards are usually numerous in research laboratories and hence deserve very special consideration. If the building is on a city street, no site provisions for fire protection need be considered, but if it is in a rural area, a yard fire main with adequate fire hydrants fed from an adequate source of water must be provided around the building in addition to protection inside. A typical adequate source of supply may be a city main, an overhead storage tank, or a fire pump.

For inside protection, if the building is of sufficient size to warrant it, fire standpipe systems should be provided which may be of two types, depending on code or Underwriters' requirements: (1) a system with racks of 1½-in. hose for use by building occupants or (2) a system with 2½-in. hose valves for use by the fire department or occupant.

Special hazard areas of the building should be provided with automatic sprinkler systems. Where a building is provided with a complete sprinkler system, the racks of 1½-in. hose may be fed from this system instead of providing a separate system. Often where there is no provision for sprinklers in laboratories, automatic fire detection systems using rate-of-rise detection equipment are provided to sound an alarm if necessary. All sprinkler and automatic fire-detection systems should be connected to a central alarm panel.

If located within the building, special central chemical and solvent storage rooms are very often protected with an automatic, room-flooding carbon dioxide extinguishing system; this turns off all ventilating apparatus and closes all doors, windows and dampers and completely fills the room with carbon dioxide to smother the fire.

Finally, a sufficient number of appropriate fire extinguishers should be installed throughout the building; these should be of the type designed for the specific areas, e.g., the cartridge-operated, water type for office areas and the carbon dioxide type for laboratories, kitchens, and machine shops.

TREATMENT AND/OR DISPOSAL PLANTS

If no sanitary sewer is available to the laboratory, a sewage disposal or treatment plant must be provided in accordance with local or state codes. Both the size of the plant and the nature of the terrain will affect the design. In a small installation, it may be merely a septic tank with a tile field or leaching cesspool; however, if the ground is unreceptive to water, the septic tank may be followed by a sand filter and post-chlorination, the effluent leading into an adjacent watercourse. A large installation will necessitate a complete treatment plant for the sewage before disposal.

Laboratory waste water treatment plants are more varied and less standardized than sewage disposal plants since they must be carefully designed for the specific constituents found. As previously mentioned, it will be necessary to separate wastes into individual systems to give each the specialized treatment required which may be primarily mechanical, e.g., removal of solids, or entirely chemical, i.e., neutralizing or decomposing the chemical ingredients.

It is not possible to describe these plants in any detail, since each is designed to meet a given set of conditions. The particular system developed is the result of an extensive study leading to the most economical and complete treatment of the wastes from the research buildings. In this connection, local and state authorities should be consulted; in some areas, interstate groups have been set up to guard the purity of our waterways and watershed; therefore, schemes for laboratory waste-water-treatment plants should be carefully reviewed with these various agencies before progressing into the final details of the plant's design.

PART 2: STEAM

In laboratories steam service is necessary for heating, ventilating and air-conditioning systems, for the production of hot water and distilled water and finally as a bench service.

Steam is either provided by a boiler plant in the laboratory building or is piped in, if located elsewhere. The condensate may be returned to the boiler or wasted through the building's drainage system. Such wastage should be restricted to buildings served from district heating systems where no provision is made for return of the condensate.

Available steam pressure should be somewhat higher than that required for normal heating service. Usually, the requirements of a heating system are not above 15 psi. Steam pressure for domestic hot water heaters can be anywhere between 10 and 80 psi depending upon the pressure available, whereas general laboratory steam service should be between 40 and 60 psi. This is sufficient to serve the majority of laboratory requirements as stills, hot plates, sterilizers, glassware washing and heat-transfer apparatus. The usual bench steam service should be kept within these limits and separate service should be provided for higher pressures if these are needed. If the pressure required is above that available, it is possible to install a small, self-contained boiler to meet the needs.

Steam distribution in the building is achieved by risers and mains which convey steam at high pressure to stations where it is reduced according to requirements. The arrangement of each building will dictate the most desirable locations for such steam pressure-reducing stations. The heating, ventilating and air-conditioning steam requirements should be provided from separate reducing stations due to their relatively low pressure requirements.

Depending on the location of domestic hot-water heating apparatus, steam distribution for this purpose can be achieved by a separate pressure-reducing station from low-pressure steam mains serving the heating system or from the laboratory steam service at between 40 and 60 psi.

Reduced-pressure steam is provided by pressure-reducing valves regulated from the low-pressure side of the valve, which may be either the self-contained or external pilot type. With regard to the self-contained valve, the reduced pressure is opposed to a spring-loaded piston or diaphragm which positions the valve seat to maintain constant reduced steam pressure. However, the external pilot type may be steam- or air-actuated. The former valves work on the principle of a balance of forces between the high and reduced pressure side of the valve. Pneumatically operated reducing valves incorporate a pressure-sensing device at the valve's reduced pressure side to modulate a pneumatic valve operator which positions the valve according to the controller's fluctuations in pressure. Reducing valves of the external pressure, pilot type are the most accurate and will maintain reduced pressures within 1 psi of the valve setting.

Reducing valves should be single-seated, and suitable for complete stoppage when there is no steam demand. Since reducing valves become noisy when operating at capacities below 20 per cent of their rating, it is desirable to install two valves in parallel at main pressure-reducing stations—one for heavy loads up to 100 per cent and the other for reduced loads below 30 per cent.

If steam for laboratory use comes from a heating plant which is not normally operated during the summer months, an auxiliary steam boiler may prove to be an economical means of providing steam at such times. If possible, the boiler should be fully automatic. Portable boilers are available if needed.

Arrangements for conveying steam to individual laboratories will depend upon the numbers of positions at which it is required. In the modular type it is normal to provide steam to the same extent as laboratory gases, compressed air, vacuum and domestic hot and cold water thus allowing for flexibility of usage.

Coordinated with other laboratory service piping, concealment of steam and condensate piping will depend upon requirements for individual buildings; however, when it is concealed, adequate access to valves, strainers, steam traps and piping is a necessity.

There are two methods of running laboratory service piping: the horizontal distribution system and the vertical system. The former consists of horizontal steam mains at the ceiling of each floor where the required number of branch connections are provided for each laboratory. The latter consists of a horizontal steam main at the lowest, highest or intermediate floor levels from which individual risers are taken up or down to laboratories or groups of laboratories at corresponding locations on the floors directly above or below.

The selection of a particular distribution system will depend upon the building design and the requirements of other laboratory services. The vertical system is best suited to the modular type of laboratory in which partitions are located in the same positions at each floor, and the furniture and equipment are installed adjacent to walls or partitions; the horizontal system is better suited to nonmodular laboratory buildings where the arrangement of rooms and equipment on each floor is unrelated to that on other floors.

Steam connections for laboratory equipment may be made by means of downfeed connections from branch piping at the ceiling to equipment on the same floor, or upfeed connections from branch piping at the ceiling below to equipment on the floor above. With a vertical distribution system a third arrangement is possible whereby connections from the risers to the laboratory equipment are made by means of horizontal runouts along the wall behind the laboratory benches. This arrangement may also be used for peninsula benches. Island benches must, of necessity, be served by either upfeed or downfeed connections.

At strategic points of major distribution systems, connections between risers and steam mains and all final connections to laboratory equipment, valves should be provided. In cases where valved and capped outlets are required for future connections to equipment, the route of the future steam and condensate piping should be established when the initial design is prepared.

Condensate and steam should flow in the same direction in the steam piping, and horizontal pipes should be pitched 1-in. in 40 ft downward in the direction of flow. Condensate removal is by steam traps which are normally of the bucket type. From the steam traps the condensate flows by gravity through pipes pitched not less than 1-in. in 40 ft downward in the effluent direction to a flash tank, where the pressure of the condensate is reduced and flash steam vented to the low-pressure steam system or atmosphere. Low-pressure condensate from the flash tank is discharged to the general condensate return system by means of a float and thermostatic type steam trap.

Where reduced steam pressure is required for a particular piece of laboratory equipment, a self-contained reducing valve may be used. In this case, the reducing valve should be located as near as possible to the equipment and a pressure gage within sight of the operator provided to indicate the reduced steam pressure. When steam flow is controlled to regulate heat transfer through the equipment, it is essential that the control valve and its devices be of a suitable type in accordance with the manufacturer's recommendation. All reducing valves, steam traps and control valves should be protected by pipe-line strainers. Manual by-passes generally should be provided around reducing and control valves.

Laboratory steam piping is normally schedule 40 black steel with standard fittings, whereas condensate return piping may be schedule 40 black steel, wrought iron or possibly red brass. For the steam-distribution system, general-purpose shut-off valves for steam and condensate service should be 125# class gate pattern. To save space use the nonrising type of gate valve, but where extremely tight space conditions are encountered, use straight or angle-patterned globe valves.

Sizing the steam piping for a laboratory system is complicated by the fact that only a proportion of the steam outlets will be in use at any time.

It is undesirable to run steam pipes or individual laboratory connections less than ¾-in. It is assumed that the pipe will be reamed after cutting. A ¾-in. connection will handle up to 30 pounds of steam per hour, which is adequate for most laboratory equipment requirements. In sizing the steam pipes, a progressive diversity from the most remote outlet back to the steam source is used to determine the quantity of steam required in sizing the pipe at any part of the distribution system. For example, if 100 outlets are served by a reducing valve it would be sized for 50 outlets or 1,500 pounds of steam per hour if an over-all diversity of 50 per cent were used. Assignment of diversity factors will vary depending upon the nature of each project.

PART 3: VENTILATION

Laboratories are spaces devoted to experimental work in any of the sciences. At their simplest, such as in the science department of an average high school or in a very small college, they will be few in number and will normally be located in a building principally devoted to other purposes. At the other end of the scale is the highly complex industrial or educational research center, in which the laboratories are housed in special buildings or groups of buildings. While ventilation must be provided for laboratories falling under the first category, it is in this latter category that specialized consideration of ventilation systems has to be undertaken.

In addition to maintaining a comfortable temperature within the laboratory, the ventilation system must provide for the removal at their source of air contaminants which are toxic, explosive, radioactive, excessively malodorous or hazardous in some other manner. In addition, sufficient ventilation must be provided to dilute unpleasant odors which are too difficult or expensive to remove completely at their point of origin.

VENTILATION REQUIREMENTS

In any study of ventilation requirements, the quantity of air required to control the temperature rise in the laboratory should be determined separately from that required for exhaust. Design of the ventilation system will depend on which requires the greater quantity of air.

External heat gains are readily figured. They depend upon the type of structure, its geographic location, solar orientation, shading by external structures and the temperature to be maintained within the laboratory. Generally, the greatest source of external heat gain will come from solar heat transmitted through windows.

Internal heat gains are more difficult to estimate accurately; generally the estimate is made by the joint efforts of ventilation specialist and the scientist responsible for planning or operating the laboratory or group of laboratories. To establish the internal heat gain of a laboratory, list all pieces of heat-producing equipment with their rated energy input; then, item by item, estimate how much of the energy input is released to the space. For instance, a well insulated laboratory oven or furnace is thermostatically controlled and will only develop its maximum energy input for short periods of time. Equipment that is water-jacketed or is contained within an exhaust hood will yield only a small fraction of its energy input to the laboratory as an internal heat gain.

The variety of laboratory work results in infrequent concurrent operations of all heat-producing equipment; therefore, it is necessary to assign some factor of diversity for its usage.

An analysis of this type makes it possible to assign a value to the heat gain from laboratory equipment. For the most part, in an average research laboratory (240 sq ft in area) this equipment gain is rarely estimated at less than half a kilowatt (1706 Btu/hr) or more than two kilowatts (6826 Btu/hr). An average figure would be one kilowatt (3413 Btu/hr).

The heat gain from electric lights and people must be added to this equipment heat gain. It is correct to assume that lighting will be used whenever the laboratory is occupied.

When a group of laboratories is under consideration a uniform value may be assigned to laboratory equipment heat gain for similar laboratories based upon detailed surveys of typical laboratories. Laboratories containing unusual equipment, however, must be evaluated separately and in detail.

Laboratory exhaust requirements are established from a survey of all fume exhaust hoods, canopy hoods, glove boxes, dust-collecting hoods and any required special exhaust systems.

When a large research facility is under consideration, the exhaust requirements of the various laboratories may be established from surveys made on other projects by applying the results of these to groups of similar laboratories in the new project.

LABORATORY EXHAUST EQUIPMENT

In the usual research laboratories, sometimes called "bench scale," the most frequently encountered exhaust equipment will be the fume hood, which should be of standard design. It should remove light or heavy gases equally well and be so planned as to eliminate high-velocity air currents that may disturb a Bunsen burner flame. In order to maintain air balance, the quantity of air removed by an exhaust hood should be approximately the same for all working positions of the sash. This is done by proportionate by-passing of air into the fume hood as the sash is opened or closed.

Air quantities, expressed in cubic ft of air per minute per sq ft of hood face area, required for fume hood exhaust should be based upon the hood manufacturer's recommendations for the specific operation. Usually, the hood is considered as being fully open, and air quantities vary between 50 and 125 cfm per sq ft. For a standard fume hood having a full sash opening of 12½ sq ft, the total exhaust per hood would be between 625 and 1560 cfm.

For experiments involving gross hazards as encountered in radiochemistry, bacteriology or virology, totally enclosed glove boxes having completely filtrated exhaust air are used. Manufacturers' recommendations should be sought to establish the normally small exhaust requirements, e.g., a table-mounted glove box 3 ft 0-in. x 2 ft 0-in. x 20-in. requires 80 cfm of exhaust air.

In cases where sources of major contamination by fumes, dust, gases or excessively hot processes require separate exhaust, and totally enclosed fume hoods are not feasible, canopy hoods which are frequently used to provide suitable control of local conditions, should be located as close as possible to and overlap all sides of the source of the contaminant; the quantity of air required will increase proportionately to the square of the distance from the contaminant source. The hood overlap should be 25 per cent of the vertical height between the contaminant and the hood.

The ventilation specialist normally determines canopy hood exhaust requirements on the basis of empirical formulae. Factors determining the total exhaust quantity are the height of the hood above the contaminant source, the perimeter, the total size of the hood as well as the control velocity of required air expressed in feet per minute per linear ft of hood perimeter. Control velocities vary between 40 and 100 fpm.

In order to minimize spillage of gases and vapors around the hood's perimeter, a baffle is frequently installed to increase the peripheral control velocity. A variant of this method is to utilize an inner and outer hood with a slotted opening usually 2-in. wide around the perimeter between the hoods.

For canopy hoods in excess of 4 ft 0-in. long it is necessary to make more than one exhaust connection. In cases where these are required for heat removal, it is desirable to locate the exhaust duct connection at the top of the hood to take advantage of natural stack effect.

When local exhaust is required for the removal of gases heavier than air or an overhead hood is impracticable due to interference with handling operations, necessary exhaust can be achieved by means of slots around the perimeter and directly above the contaminated source. The total air quantity to be exhausted for a particular installation will depend upon the area to be exhausted and the design, and control velocity through the peripheral slot. Many variations of this type of exhaust arrangement exist.

VENTILATION SUPPLY SYSTEMS

Ventilation systems for laboratories often include air conditioning. Those which do not are designed to restrict the temperature rise to a maximum level dependent upon the outdoor temperature. In the northeastern United States where the maximum outdoor temperature is 95°F, 10°F is the most frequently used design basis for internal temperature rise. Although this involves a maximum inside temperature of 105°F, which is beyond the range of human comfort, it must be remembered that the maximum outdoor temperature is of short duration; moreover, it is expected that laboratory personnel will minimize the use of heat-producing equipment during periods of intense heat. Decreases in outdoor temperature from the maximum design point cause correspondingly lower indoor temperatures. Air should not be introduced into the laboratory at temperatures much below 60°F.

With the greater cooling potential of outside air at lower temperatures and the heat lost by transmission from the laboratory to the outside air, it is possible to maintain desirable inside temperatures, with quantities of outside air diminished to the point at which an air-conditioning system is normally designed. If a ventilation system in being planned for future conversion to air-conditioning, the change can be facilitated by arranging the supply ventilation so that it can be operated at either peak or minimum air quantities. This results in lower operating costs, since when heating is required, the supply air quantity is merely sufficient to meet the exhaust requirements or to absorb the internal heat gains with air at approximately 60°F or above.

Ventilation systems which incorporate air-conditioning utilize mechanical or natural means of air cooling to reduce the temperature and humidity of the air to a predetermined level. In such a design, it is normal to establish exhaust requirements and subsequently to fix the temperature so that the supplied air will balance the exhaust requirements. The minimum temperature should not be appreciably below 60°F. If it is necessary to supply more air than has to be exhausted from hoods and equipment, it is possible to recirculate the excess air, providing that there are no odor transmittal problems and that enough outdoor air is introduced to dilute existing odors to an acceptable level.

Frequently, individual laboratories equipped with fume hoods require more air for the hood than necessary to meet the cooling load requirements; moreover, since fume hoods are not installed in all laboratories, the total supply and exhaust for a group of them will be in balance. In this case, it may be possible, depending on the usage of the laboratories without hoods, to allow supply air to be transferred from laboratories with a net surplus to those with a net deficiency through transfer grills via the corridors on a single floor, or mechanically by means of a transfer fan between floors.

A second means of supplying net deficiencies between necessary air supply to meet a cooling load and air required for equipment exhaust is to supply make-up air at a fixed temperature via the corridors through transfer grills to laboratories requiring it, provided they permit the installation of grills. Controls for air-conditioning require special consideration.

Because of the variability of the cooling loads the most desirable system is to have a separate thermostat in each laboratory. Individual rather than zone control is merited because internal heat gains are 100 per cent variable. Means of achieving individual control depend upon the air-conditioning system selected, of which the most widely used are the all-air and the air reheat type.

In the former type, known as the "Dual Duct" System, the air is supplied through central systems wherein it is filtered and, depending upon outdoor temperature, heated or cooled to a fixed state. Then, it is passed through a fan to two separate branches, one containing a heating coil and the other frequently containing a cooling coil. Called respectively the hot deck and the cold deck, they supply air to mixing boxes adjacent to or within the laboratory they serve. Regulation by the laboratory thermostat controls the proportions of air supplied through the mixing box to maintain required conditions. Psychrometric analysis will determine whether operating economies can be effected by introducing a booster cooling coil into the cold deck. If the required supply air temperature at peak cooling load is appreciably below the theoretical apparatus dew point, use one cooling coil to reduce the entire air supply to the theoretical dew point and a second cooling coil to reduce the air to the selected dew point. This does effect operating economies because only the air passing through the cold deck receives a superimposed cooling load.

The latter type supplies air from a central system similar to the all-air system except that the total cooling load is achieved by means of a single cooling coil; conversely, reheat coils are added to the individual branch connection to laboratories and are controlled by individual thermostats to permit the addition of reheat air whenever heat falls below the maximum design point. Ordinarily reheat is achieved by means of steam or hot water, or occasionally by electricity. A variant of this system involves the installation of cooling coils and reheat coils in branch ducts to laboratories having greater than normal heat gains from equipment.

Sometimes it is desirable to use two systems of air conditioning, such as when a perimeter induction system is used from the skin of a building to counteract the external heat gains or losses and an interior system of all air or air reheat type is used to counteract all or part of the internal heat gains. This should be considered when the laboratory extends to some depth from the outside wall to the corridor and where overhead air distribution is not feasible.

Vitally important to the successful operation of ventilation systems are the selection of air outlets, their position, appearance and performance. Air supplied per unit of space volume is frequently higher than in average air conditioning, and the difference in temperature between the room and the supply air at maximum cooling load often limits the choice of air outlets. Draft-free distribution of air is essential to avoid disturbing the performance of fume and canopy hoods. Supply outlets should be arranged so that the air does not short-circuit into the exhaust hood or outlets if the desired cooling effect is to be achieved.

VENTILATION EXHAUST SYSTEMS

Laboratory exhaust systems for either equipment or general exhaust may be either of the central type in which groups of exhaust outlets, fume or canopy hoods and glove boxes are served by one fan or of the unitary type in which each item of equipment is served by a separate exhaust fan.

Only occasionally will exhaust hoods be installed in every laboratory in a research facility; in the interest of flexibility, however, provision should be made for their installation in each laboratory. In order to do this, the exhaust ducts from each laboratory must be sized for both current needs and future increases. If the central system is to be used, the main ducts must be sized in line with the difference between the number of laboratories with and without hoods so that the duct size at the exhaust fan will be correct for the total air volume being handled.

Unitary systems should allow for the installation of an exhaust hood and the required fan in any laboratory, and machine room space be allocated accordingly. Frequently it is necessary to use a supplementary general exhaust or recirculation system to serve laboratories which are without fume hoods. Exhaust hoods may be connected to this system from time to time; the air inlet dampers are necessary in order to vary the capacity of the central exhaust or recirculation fan in line with the number of hoods used.

Features to illustrate the advantages of the unitary exhaust system are: individual control for each hood; ability to operate individual hoods out of normal working hours, improved service resulting from separate fans, and the opportunity to use a variety of construction materials to suit specific use requirements.

SPECIAL LABORATORIES

The ventilation of conventional laboratories has been described above. However, the planner is often called upon to provide special ventilation systems for laboratories having unique functions.

In one group, controlled atmospheric conditions must be provided. Cases in point are:

Spectrographic and Microscopic Laboratories

These require relative humidities between 35 and 50 per cent at a temperature of 76°F. They should also have air filtration efficiencies of at least 90 per cent based upon the U. S. Bureau of Standards discoloration test.

To avoid using large central systems where they are otherwise unnecessary, separate self-contained refrigeration and air-handling equipment are indicated. Double or triple sheet glass with air spaces is required to avoid moisture condensation on windows during cold weather.

Fine Tolerance Measuring Laboratories

Since these will require constant temperatures and frequently constant humidities as well, separate air-conditioning systems, equipped with automatic controls, are used.

Animal Laboratories

Animal laboratories require 100 per cent exhaust systems, separate and so designed as to eliminate the possibility of odor transfer into other parts of the building. These must operate continuously; to ensure this, emergency power must be available.

Environmental Study Laboratories

Laboratories of this type must have extensively flexible air-conditioning systems depending upon the studies to be undertaken; therefore, they require separate supply and exhaust systems. A second class of laboratories involving special ventilation design are those providing special hazards by possible air-borne transmission of contaminants. Cases in point here are:

Radiochemistry Laboratories

Here the exhaust air must be filtered and safe means for the disposal of radioactive filter media devised. Usually the filters are located in the contaminated space and baffles are provided in the supply system to prevent radiant transfer of contaminants.

Bacteriological Laboratories

In research laboratories where communicable diseases are being studied, the exhaust air from all contaminated sources must be sterilized by heat or the organisms removed by filtration.

Since the foregoing laboratories require special ventilation equipment, their location should not be subject to change. To facilitate these special ventilation requirements, every attempt should be made to locate the special laboratories adjacent to the mechanical spaces serving them.

MATERIALS OF CONSTRUCTION

Supply ventilation systems rarely require special construction materials, e.g., ducts are ordinarily made of galvanized sheet steel, the gage of the metal being selected on the basis of duct size and velocity of air in the duct. Conversely, exhaust systems require special consideration, since hood exhaust gases tend to be corrosive; therefore, materials used for conveying hood exhaust should be inactive or embody an inert coating; asbestos cement ducts are frequently used since they are inert to most chemicals. Some success has been achieved with sheet steel ducts coated with an asphaltic compound during the galvanizing process. The resulting chemically inert ducts have an advantage, as they can be fabricated in the same manner and by using the same tools as ordinary galvanized steel ducts. Other materials used for conveying hood exhaust are black iron coated with inert paint, aluminum, and stainless steel. Ordinarily stainless steel is too expensive to use except in special cases such as the exhaust ducts from hoods in radiochemical laboratories or from hoods used for experiments with perchloric acid.

Certain alloys have been found very satisfactory for fans handling hood exhaust, e.g., stainless steel, the most commonly used metal for corrosion-resistant impellers, is satisfactory for exhausting the fumes of many acids.

Special coatings on fan housings and impellers include cadmium plating and hot galvanizing, either of which is used in conjunction with zinc chromate paint with which they form a chemical bond. Another method of coating fan housings and impellers is with nonporous and chemically resistant vulcanized rubber.

ECONOMIC CONSIDERATIONS

Although the desirability of air-conditioning cannot be questioned, the choice between the alternative methods of ventilating laboratories will inevitably be based upon economic considerations of original and operating costs.

Proximity to an adequate source of cold water from wells can reduce considerably the cost of installing and operating an air-conditioning system. Since cooling and heating of outdoor air is the largest single item of installation and operating cost for the average laboratory ventilation system, climate data for alternative locations should be studied. External heat gains can be reduced by careful orientation of the building and by sun-shielding devices (louvers) at windows.

Internal heat gains should be minimized by the insulation and shielding of heat-producing sources either by enclosing them in fume hoods or providing canopy hood exhausts. Care should be used to determine the minimum quantities of air to be exhausted for satisfactory operation.

When a ventilation system lacking air-conditioning is to be installed, future conversion to an air-conditioning system should be borne in mind and all space and arrangement provisions made at the time of the initial installation.

PART 4: REFRIGERATION

Laboratory refrigeration systems are needed for air-conditioning, cold storage rooms, cold work rooms, low-temperature testing rooms, and process cooling for experimental work.

It is desirable to establish a separate refrigeration system consisting of a compressor, condenser and evaporator for each room or service. The evaporator, in which the refrigerant boils by absorbing heat from the medium it cools, may perform its cooling function, either directly by heat transfer, as with a fan and coil unit cooler, or indirectly by cooling a low-temperature heat-transfer fluid such as ethylene glycol or brine.

The most commonly used refrigerants are the "Freons"; the type used depends upon the temperature and degree of control required of the system. Refrigerant compressors are normally of the positive displacement piston type, the belt being driven by electric motors. Compressors may be installed singly or in series. For ultra-low-temperature work the practice is toward series installation due to the greater efficiency of this type of installation. Although usually water-cooled, occasional use is made of air-cooled or evaporative-type condensers. Water-cooled condensers use either domestic cold water which is subsequently wasted after passing through the condenser, or recirculated water which is cooled in a cooling tower. Frequently, local codes, which govern the use of domestic cold water, require a cooling tower or some other method of condenser water recirculation.

Often built as integrated units on a common base, compressors and condensers should be located in a space separate from the room which they serve and, if several systems are required, an attempt should be made to group the compressors in a central location to facilitate service and maintenance. To avoid noise transmission, care should be taken to ensure that vibration eliminators are provided for each compressor. Compressor rooms should be adequately ventilated in order to dissipate the heat produced by motors or other heat-producing sources.

If cooling coils are to be at temperatures below $32°F$, it is necessary to provide some means of defrosting possibly by utilizing the heat of the refrigerant gas or by electric strip heaters. The defrost cycle is normally operated according to the buildup of ice thickness from a timing mechanism which can be adjusted to suit requirements; then the condensate is piped to the sanitary drainage system, where care should be taken to avoid freezing. The section of the drain pipe within the cold room should be soldered or brazed to the hot refrigerant gas-discharge line from the unit cooler or heated in some other manner.

The controls for direct expansion unit coolers normally consist of a room thermostat to operate the unit cooler fan and a thermostatic expansion valve to regulate the refrigerant flow to the evaporator; whereas, indirect expansion systems require a refrigerant expansion control valve regulated by a thermostat in the heat-transfer fluid return line to the heat exchanger. The control of the heat-transfer fluid through the cooling unit is by flow modulation through a pneumatically operated three-way valve.

For any installation involving several laboratory refrigeration systems a cooling tower should provide the most suitable means of refrigerant condensing. Self-containing air-cooled condensers reject heat to the compressor room and require the use of an excessive ventilation rate to maintain their performance and ensure relatively comfortable conditions in the compressor room. Seldom economical or desirable, remote air-cooled and evaporative-type condensors involve the extension of refrigerant suction and discharge piping. In most cases install separate cooling towers for the air conditioning and the laboratory refrigeration systems.

Refrigerant piping for "Freon" systems should be type K or L hard copper, with wrought copper fittings and sweat or flanged joints. Since it deteriorates at low temperatures, soft solder should not be used. Condenser water piping should be schedule 40 black steel with standard fittings. Unit coolers should be fabricated of corrosion-resistant materials, e.g., welded alumi-

num or stainless steel. Heat-transfer fluid piping must be suitable for the fluid in question. Most brines require the use of welded schedule 40 wrought iron piping. Ethylene glycol solutions can be piped through schedule 40 black steel pipe with standard welded fittings.

Cold rooms require insulated sides, floors, and ceilings. Despite the increased use of foamed plastic, cork remains as the most commonly used insulating material. Both the temperature of the room and the adjacent spaces will determine the thickness of insulation. Although the interior surfaces of cold rooms are finished with a special plaster applied over the insulation, floors are often finished with concrete. It is usual to install a floor drain to facilitate floor washing.

PART 5: ELECTRICAL SERVICES

ELECTRICAL LOADS

Electrical requirements for laboratories are varied and complex as will be shown by the data in Table 5.1 which lists electric loads supplied to research laboratories of several different industries. Because of this complexity, it is not possible to present a simple description of one or two possible systems which would satisfy general needs. Instead a rather complete discussion of the various possibilities has been outlined. In this way, the planning committee will be able to get a better understanding of available alternatives.

The subjects covered include possible systems which supply power to the facilities, those which distribute power within the facilities and those handling local power distribution. Other subjects covered are grounding, lighting, auxiliary systems and special requirements such as systems for refrigeration and electric heating, voltage and current regulation, high frequency power, variable frequency power, direct current and high voltage.

SUPPLY SYSTEMS

Purchased Power vs. Generated Power

Electric power for a laboratory facility is generally purchased rather than generated. For one

thing, the investment for generating equipment can be invested in other facilities to yield a better return. Likewise the problems involved in operating and maintaining generating equipment are avoided. The utility company is in a position to furnish less expensive power and can readily contend with price adjustments of fuel and labor, and finally purchased power affords economic flexibility to meet market changes and business cycles.

Important Considerations in Planning Supply Systems

Supply systems represent the electrical systems which carry incoming power from the utility company to a specific point or points in the new facility. Modern design dictates that careful consideration be given to the following items when supply systems are being planned.

Outdoor Substation Location. Locate the outdoor substation as near to the load being served as is feasible. The location, a compromise between the electrical load center and utility requirements, should be free from corrosive fumes and a source of residues which might settle on high-voltage insulators. If feasible, locate the substation to the windward side of potential sources of trouble.

Outage Expectancy. Investigate the utility

company service records for outage expectancy and reflect the findings in the design and location of utility feeders.

Reliability. Select a reliable supply system so that normal laboratory operation can be maintained. Since many laboratory experiments are conducted on a step-by-step basis, and any power outage can adversely affect the experiments, the supply system chosen must deliver a continual source of power.

Overhead and Underground Service. The initial cost of overhead service is less than that of underground service. Faults on overhead conductors usually last for a short time, and are easily located and cleared. Conversely, faults on underground services are difficult to locate and repair. Nevertheless, underground service is favored as the more rugged.

Dual Service. Current utility company practice is to offer one power service to the customer. However, if the customer requests a dual service,

it will charge him for the additional expense involved in bringing the second service to his premises. Depending on the load's size and the company's rate structure, a portion or all of this expense may be returned to him after a period of time.

System Factor. The demand, diversity and load factors required for system design are defined as follows: Demand Factor is the ratio of the maximum demand on a system to the total connected load of the system; Diversity Factor is the ratio of the sum of the individual maximum demand of the various parts of a system to the maximum demand of the whole system; Load Factor is the ratio of the average load over a designated time period to the peak load occurring in that period.

Safety. The protection of personnel engaged in the operation and maintenance of the supply system equipment is of utmost importance. Employ modern safety devices and techniques in the

TABLE 5.1
LABORATORY LOAD DATA TABULATION

LABORATORY TYPE	POPULATION	AREA IN SQUARE FEET GROSS	AREA IN SQUARE FEET NET	% AIR CONDITIONED	TOTAL CONNECTED LOAD IN KW	CONNECTED KW LOAD PER PERSON	CONNECTED LOAD IN WATTS PER SQ. FT. (GROSS AREA)	CONNECTED LOAD IN WATTS PER SQ. FT. (NET AREA)	MAXIMUM DEMAND LOAD IN KW	DEMAND KW LOAD PER PERSON	DEMAND LOAD IN WATTS PER SQ. FT. (GROSS AREA)	DEMAND LOAD IN WATTS PER SQ. FT. (NET AREA)	DEMAND FACTOR MAXIMUM DEMAND PER CONNECTED LOAD	HOURS MAXIMUM DEMAND PER MONTH	CONSUMPTION IN KWH PER MONTH	LOAD FACTOR AVG. LOAD PER MONTH/MAX. DEMAND	PERCENT POWER FACTOR
ic research	650	—	175,000	2	6,360	9.8	—	36.3	1,420	2.2	—	8.1	.22	350	500,000	.49	95
	800	313,000	150,000	20	10,000	12.5	32.0	66.7	1,850	2.3	5.9	12.3	.19	390	720,000	.54	97
tronics research	915	360,000	97,000	50	2,480	2.7	6.9	25.6	1,520	1.7	4.2	15.7	.61	384	584,000	.53	95
	331	122,600	71,000	20	1,590	4.8	13.0	22.3	850	2.6	6.9	12.0	.53	364	309,000	.50	90
nical research	424	197,000	161,000	7	2,990	7.1	15.2	18.5	1,100	2.6	5.6	6.8	.37	386	425,000	.54	77
	124	57,000	29,000	100	860	6.9	15.1	29.7	360	2.9	6.3	12.5	.42	420	152,000	.59	95
	600	235,000	115,000	50	—	—	—	—	2,000	3.3	8.5	17.4	—	400	800,000	.56	80
oleum research	356	115,514	73,917	100	1,780	5.0	15.4	24.1	958	2.7	8.3	13.0	.54	290	275,970	.40	90
lear development research	1,700	1,500,000	500,000	67	57,545*	33.8	38.4	115.	14,386	8.5	9.6	28.8	.25	536	7,705,608	.75	80
l products research	585	252,000	150,600	60	5,500	9.4	21.8	36.6	1,500	2.6	6.0	10.0	.27	403	605,000	.56	80
ber industry research	371	182,000	127,000	2.75	2,350	6.3	12.9	18.5	775	2.1	4.3	6.1	.33	390	300,000	.54	90
ical research	675	116,900	60,000	25	—	—	—	—	518	.78	4.4	8.6	—	500	258,300	.69	—
rmaceutical products research	170	95,400	76,900	85	750	4.4	7.9	9.8	188	1.06	1.97	2.45	.25	610	115,250	.85	95

* Transformer Capacity

design of the system. Adhere to the rules and regulations as set forth in the national and local codes and manufacturers' recommendations. The rules and regulations which are the minimum standards designed for personnel and equipment protection are contained in the following sources:

National Electrical Code

American Institute of Electrical Engineers Publications

National Electrical Manufacturers Association Publications

Insulated Power Cable Engineers Association Publications

Associated Edison Illuminating Companies Publications

National Safety Handbook

Basic System Design. Incorporate into the design of the system all present and future requirements for proper laboratory operation; include the equipment necessary for simple operation but avoid the pitfalls encountered by the use of unnecessary "frills." These additions tend to complicate the system's operation and maintenance.

Cost Comparisons. In the preparation of engineering cost comparisons for system selection include all equipment, e.g., switchgear, cable, conduit, grounding, control, and alarms, as well as their installation.

System Voltages. The following are system voltages in common use:

120/208 WYE
480
2,400
4,160
6,900
13,800

The voltage selection will depend on the utility company's supply, the size and type of the load and special equipment requirements.

Voltage Spread. Utilization equipment will determine and limit the amount of voltage spread allowed in the system design. Poor regulation can hamper operation and decrease the life of the electrical equipment. Where voltage spread is high, the use of load tap changing equipment, regulators, and switched capacitors can be used to correct this condition.

Flexibility. In order to meet load growth as well as load relocations, stress flexibility in the supply system equipment's design. Allocate space for present equipment and anticipate future equipment requirements. Provide empty conduit systems for future equipment and size feeder cables so that new loads will not require major changes in the cable system. Money spent initially for system flexibility is considerably less than that required after the building's completion.

Utility Company Service. Consult with the utility company on the following characteristics of incoming service:

Supply voltage

Number of phases

Short circuit current available

Power factor

Frequency

Overhead or underground service

Type of metering and location of the same

Service contract (power factor and demand clause)

Coordination with utility company relaying

Feeder capacity and location

Packaged Substation. Because of the installation cost, packaged substations are preferable to field-constructed substations. Although the initial equipment expenses are higher for the packaged substation, equipment coordination is greatly reduced with its use resulting in a good looking custom installation.

Grounding. Good grounding in the supply system improves personnel safety, protects equipment in the system by limiting voltage between uninsulated conducting objects in the local area and provides both an indication of fault and a method for locating faulty systems. Generally the system's neutral is grounded by solid resistance, reactance or ground fault neutralizer grounding. System grounding should be coordinated with the system of the utility company. In addition to grounding the system, any equipment forming part of the system (steel structures, switch gear, conduit, fences and control equipment enclosures) is also grounded in the interest of personnel safety in the manner specified by the National Electrical Code and the National Electrical Safety Code. Grounding to provide protection against lightning for the supply system should be included in the planning for this system.

Coordination of Supply and Distribution Systems. Coordination of supply and distribution systems must take into account the following: The location of incoming feeders and means of access into the building—the number and sizes of incoming conduits—the number, size and type of incoming cables—and the short circuit current available.

Emergency Power. Depending on the size and nature of the load, emergency power can be provided by a utility company trailer, a diesel or gasoline engine generator or by battery supply. Sufficient space should be allocated in the initial plan to provide space for emergency power equipment sized both for the present and future.

DISTRIBUTION SYSTEMS

Basis for System Selection

The power distribution system must serve a wide range of loads both safely and economically. Concentrated loads may shift from one part of the system to another as projects are completed and new ones initiated.

The system finally selected should comply with the following criteria.

Safety. Safety deserves the foremost consideration. In an electrical system, the majority of the safety features must be built in and not left to safe operating practices. Accidents or malfunctions resulting from a hazardous installation are usually violent and instantaneous; therefore, no time is available for preventive action. The potential hazard must be eliminated in the planning stage or by preventive maintenance.

What are some of the potentially hazardous conditions? In addition to exposed live parts, location of equipment or wiring where it may be subject to mechanical or water damage is one. Subjecting insulations to fluctuating temperatures that will cause gradual deterioration and eventual breakdown is another. Obvious only to the system designer is the danger of using equipment lacking the mechanical strength to withstand the stresses imposed upon it during the short interval between the time a system fault may occur and the protective devices clear the fault. The high values of short circuit current present can induce strains that may shatter the equipment. There-

fore, the equipment must be selected with the knowledge of possible currents at each point in the system.

Reliability. If a system is safe, one of the major requirements for a reliable system has been met. A reliable system depends upon a number of factors such as the source of power, the system for distribution, the load capabilities, voltage variations, frequency variations, power factor and wave form.

In the case of purchased power, review with the utility company the past history of outages to determine the reliability of the service to the site. Designing an elaborate system for reliability will be of little use if the site does not have a reliable source of power or its own stand-by generating facilities. At the same time, frequency and voltage variations, wave form and power factor of the supply may also be checked. In general, these factors are kept within well-defined limits by the utility company thereby becoming important only when planned tests or experiments require that rigid standards be maintained. Under these conditions, the owner will usually need auxiliary apparatus to provide the necessary supply reliability.

In the following discussion of the various types of distribution systems, note that as reliability becomes more important the system becomes increasingly complex and expensive. The real need for extreme reliability should be carefully analyzed before the selection of the system. The penalties that would be paid for loss of power, even for as short a time as one or two cycles, must also be evaluated.

Flexibility. The required flexibility of a system depends largely on the type of laboratory it is to serve. It is a rare installation that can be designed for precise requirements. The system should provide for shifting of load requirements with a minimum of service disruption, cost, and time. Planning for possible load shifts may only entail providing space for future equipment and distribution lines but this early-stage planning can eventually pay for itself.

Durability. Beside selecting good quality equipment, it is equally important to choose components suitable for their designated use. To illustrate, the best quality insulation for dry locations will not serve in a damp location; furthermore, ambient and operating temperatures must be considered. Frequency of operation of control and protective devices is an important consideration in their choice since savings can often be made in this respect, e.g., a seldom operated switch can be just as reliable in a less expensive unit than one designed for constant operation.

Ease of Maintenance. Generally a durable system is also easy to maintain. In addition to accessibility of parts for inspection and maintenance, the system should be designed with the quality of maintenance personnel in mind. Unfortunately, a system can have an excess of safeguards which in the hands of relatively inexperienced personnel can become trouble spots. Therefore, a minimum of shut-downs for preventative maintenance is a basic consideration.

Expansibility. Requirements for expansion can be an extension of the provisions for flexibility. A similar approach can be used in planning for expansion as is used in locating and laying out the primary supply and main substation.

Low Initial Cost. Initial cost is the factor that limits or modifies all of the previous criteria excepting safety; however, this need not be detrimental to the system's design. The factor does, however, underline the need to examine the features of the plan to see whether all are really needed. Often at the outset of a project, many apparent requirements are based upon vaguely conceived features which are not basic to the system and will be used infrequently. In some cases it would appear that special arrangements made when the need arises would be cheaper and almost as satisfactory as including them in the design. Still another way to save money is to limit excessively rigid specifications to such parts of the system as need them. However in limiting initial cost, the future penalties that have to be paid in maintenance, flexibility and ease of expansion must be carefully considered.

Requires Minimum Space. Since space is usually at a premium, selection of main distribution routes, especially in low buildings, can be made utilizing storage and equipment areas with small but frequent takeoffs to individual use points. This will limit space requirements in laboratories and permit ready accessibility to equipment in areas assigned to building maintenance and operation. Distributing at higher than use voltages to load centers limits feeder space requirements in large installations, which may also be an important cost factor.

Satisfies Owner's Standards. An important and often troublesome feature of system design is that it satisfy the Owner's standards. This means that the Owner must clearly establish the standards in order that a system may be designed to satisfy his operating methods and needs. It is equally important that the objective of the standards be made clear to the designer. So often, standards have grown during the years of operation, and are either outmoded or designed for a different type of a system than that contemplated for the new construction. Finally a clear understanding by the designer of the intended method of operation can only result in the development of a more satisfactory and economical system.

Types of Systems

Conventional Simple-Radial System. This system accepts the primary supply at one point, steps down the utility company voltage to the use voltage through one transformer and later distributes power to utilization points by means of low-voltage feeders, which originate from a single substation. The advantages in this system are all in the interests of economy. A single source permits taking full advantage of diversity among the loads. The transformer hence can be of minimum size. The space requirements are also minimum. Among the disadvantages are the following. The system is limited to installations requiring short feeder runs and a maximum demand in the order of 1,000 KVA. Voltage regulation is poor, and little flexibility is possible. Furthermore, a fault on a feeder will interrupt service to all loads and a fault on the main low-voltage bus, transformer or primary supply will interrupt service to the entire installation until repairs are made.

When used within its limitations, this system requires the smallest initial outlay.

Modern Simple-Radial System. As its name implies, this system is an improvement on the conventional system since power is distributed directly at primary voltage to load centers located

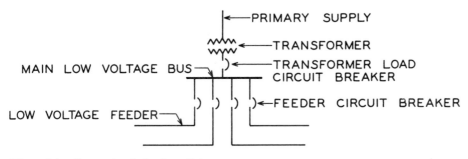

Figure 5.1 Conventional simple-radial system.

to minimize the length of low-voltage feeders. Thus, the building has been broken down into a number of areas each served by a conventional simple radial system.

Advantages include better voltage regulation, suitability, and lower original investment for loads in excess of 1,000 KVA. The simple radial system has the same disadvantages as the conventional system, namely poor reliability and a lack of flexibility. Stepping down from the primary voltage to a use voltage at a number of substations increases the required transformer capacity for a given load because only the diversity of the loads connected to each substation is considered. Each substation must be sized to handle the peak load of its area.

The initial investment will in general be lower for loads in excess of 1,000 KVA with this system than any other.

Modified Modern Simple-Radial System. Although initially more expensive, this system features refinements of the first two basic systems which are not found in the simpler systems.

Since separate feeders are run from the primary service gear to each substation, the costs are greater. However, the following advantages counteract this: improved voltage regulation, greater flexibility and reliability. Moreover, a fault on a primary feeder will only cause a service failure to the particular load center served.

Loop-Primary Radial System. A cheaper method of providing more reliable primary serv-

Figure 5.2 Modern simple-radial system.

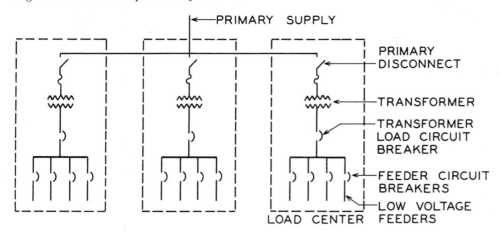

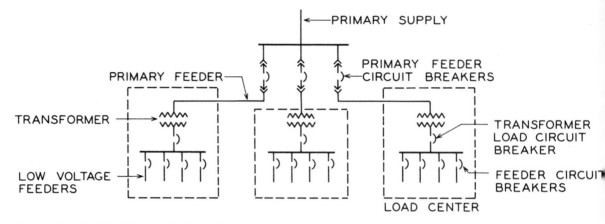

Figure 5.3   Modified Modern Simple-radial system.

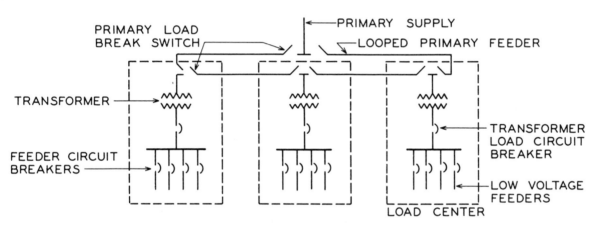

Figure 5.4   Loop-primary radial system.

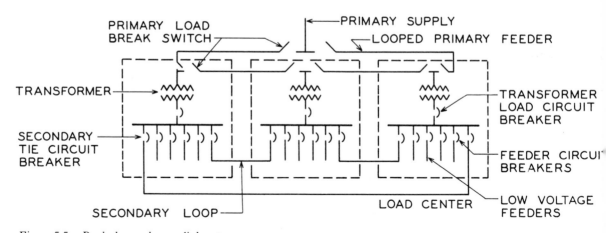

Figure 5.5   Banked-secondary radial system.

ice is by means of a sectionalized loop since a transformer failure or fault in any part of the primary distribution loop will interrupt service to the entire installation. However, service can be restored to the entire system by isolating the faulty section of cable or to all of the system except one load center in the case of transformer failure. This is done by the correct positioning of the various sectionalizing switches. Since full load capacity is present in the primary around the entire loop, they can be shifted without adding to the primary system. This illustrates this system's flexibility.

Banked-Secondary Radial System. A secondary loop may be placed between load centers as an added refinement to the loop-primary radial system. In the case of a transformer failure, the associated loads can now be fed through the secondary loop. An added feature in this system permits uniform sizing of transformers and their operation in parallel. With this arrangement, transformers may be sized based on the diversity of the entire system thereby eliminating the need for an individual load center sized to handle a peak occurring only in its load which is balanced over all of the load centers. Starting of large motors on such a system will present much less of a voltage dip problem and motors that otherwise might require reduced voltage starters may now be started across-the-line with a savings in starter equipment.

Primary-Selective Radial System. With the exception of the modified modern simple-radial system, all systems interrupt service to the entire installation when a fault in any one transformer or any part of the primary feeder system occurs. To prevent this, the primary-selective radial system provides two, full capacity primary feeders to each load center of which one-half will be connected to one primary feeder and one-half to the other. Consequently, in the case of a fault in a transformer or primary feeder, only one-half the load is interrupted. In the case of a primary feeder fault, power may be restored to all load centers by transferring from the defective feeder to the other.

Secondary-Selective Radial System. The secondary-selective radial system provides duplicate service not only for the primary bus bar but in the transformer capacity to the secondary bus bar as well. A transformer or primary feeder fault will interrupt one-half the load at each substation instead of all the load for one-half the load centers. Service can be restored by switching all load centers to the remaining primary service and shutting the bus-tie breakers or switching a faulty transformer off the line and closing the bus-tie breaker in that load center. Additional transformer capacity is required for this system, but in most applications this system will be as reliable and more economical although not as flexible as the banked-secondary radial system.

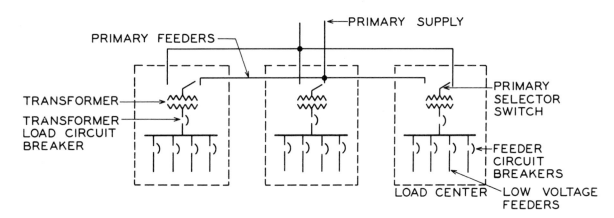

Figure 5.6   Primary-selective radial system.

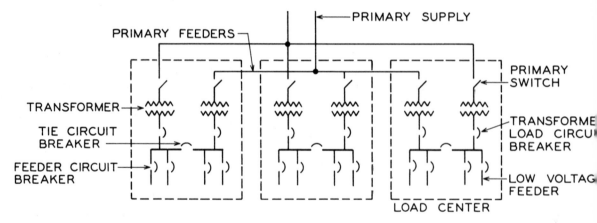

Figure 5.7   Secondary-selective radial system.

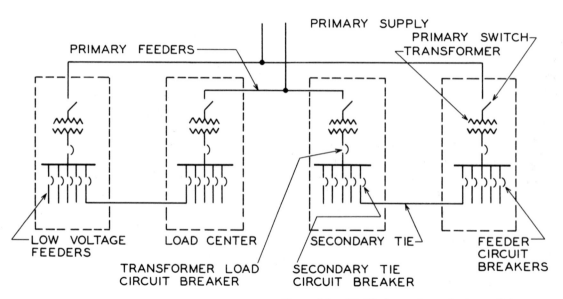

Figure 5.8   Modified secondary-selective radial system.

Figure 5.9   Simple network system.

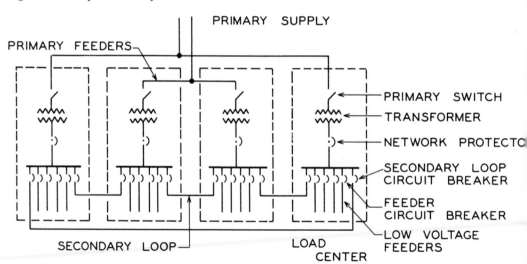

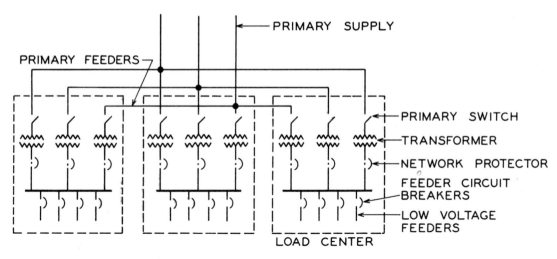

Figure 5.10   Simple spot network system.

Modified Secondary-Selective Radial System. In some instances, the more economical method of incorporating the features of the secondary-selective radial system in an installation is to provide transformers capable of handling twice the demand load and then tieing the pairs of load centers together.

Simple Network System. This system is designed so that either primary line will carry the entire load and, in the event of an outage of any two transformers, the other two will carry the load. In the place of transformer load circuit breakers, network protectors are used; therefore, this combination of primary feeder breaker and network protector will remove automatically a faulted primary line or transformer without any cessation of service. This is important where an interruption of just a few cycles may completely disrupt an experiment or data-processing thereby making necessary the repetition of a lengthy operation. This system is the most flexible and expansible of the systems described herein; loads may be shifted or added within wide limits in any part of the system without significantly changing the system or affecting its operation. Moreover, the system provides adequate, uniform voltage regulation. Although this system represents the highest initial cost, this is offset by the continuity of service anticipated.

Simple Spot Network System. A modification of the previous system, it is more economical in cases where there are heavy concentrations of load with considerable distances between them. Except that two of the three transformers in each load center are capable of handling the entire load, the automatic operation is similar to that explained above; however, it is not as flexible.

Primary-Selective Network System. Because this system has two primary feeders available at each transformer, it is the most economical of all the network systems when two or three primaries are needed. The use of two primaries at each transformer permits the elimination of spare transformer capacity and results in other savings in size and capacity of secondary switchgear.

Primary-Selective Spot-Network System. This system is the same as the simple spot network system except that each transformer has two primary feeders and each load center has two transformers. As a network system, it is economically attractive; however, extended outages such as infrequent transformer failures, require the reduction of load at the load center affected.

Transformers

One of the prime factors in designing an economically feasible distribution system is to distribute large quantities of power at higher-than-use voltage by transformers and step-down to use voltage near the utilization points.

The higher the voltage, the less copper is required for a given size load.

The three basic types of transformers are the oil-filled, the "askarel" filled and the dry type.

Lowest in initial cost, the oil-filled transformer operates well in wet, dusty and in most corrosive atmospheres, has a high impulse level to withstand lightning surges from outside overhead lines. But it does require some maintenance, is heavy and must be installed in a fireproof vault because the oil is inflammable.

The "askarel"-filled transformer is similar but uses a non-hazardous cooling liquid thereby not requiring a fireproof vault.

The dry type uses air cooling, either of the self-cooled or forced air cooled type. Light weight, safety, and minimum maintenance are a few of its favorable aspects. However, it must be used in a dry location and is susceptible to dust.

Transformers may be purchased in either three-phase or single-phase units. Except for small loads or special applications, the three-phase unit is generally preferred because of its higher efficiency, lower cost for equivalent capacity, need for less space and ease with which it can be installed.

Noise, an unpleasant feature of transformers, is transmitted either by air or through a structure and the audible hum proves to be annoying to most people. Whenever a transformer is to be located in the same building with areas having a changeable noise level comparable to a normal office, care should be taken in choice of location and methods of mounting. Low noise level transformers are available at additional cost.

Since transformers have been known to cause noise in extremely sensitive electronic equipment, keep them separated as far as possible from the equipment because the interference is inversely proportional to the square of the distance. Another method of eliminating interference is to shield the transformer room, but this is costly and not always reliable.

Overload and Short Circuit Protection

There are a wide variety of protective devices. Each has a specific application depending upon the size and types of equipment, loads to be protected, frequency of operation (manual or automatic, local or remote). In addition to preventing damage to equipment, property and human life, the correct application and coordination of protective devices can contribute materially to the reliability of a system by limiting or localizing malfunctions that otherwise could cause major interruptions or outages.

The five basic groups of protective devices include: air circuit breakers, plastic case circuit breakers, fuses (including the standard, the dual element which act instantaneously on short circuits with delayed action for short time overloads, and the current limiting), a combination plastic case circuit breaker with current limiting fuses and finally sectionalizing switches.

Low-Voltage Distribution

Two methods are available for the distribution of power: conduit and wire, and busway.

For individual loads that are not extremely large, concealed distribution and inaccessible feeder runs, use the conduit and wire method.

Busway has the advantages of lower voltage drop and smaller space requirements for heavy feeders, availability of the entire capacity at preselected points along a feeder with plug-in type busway, and the convenience of easy and continuous movement of devices connected to trolley duct.

Standard Use Voltages

The higher the voltage the smaller the circuiting wiring required for a given load is applicable to use voltages as well as distribution voltages; therefore, the highest use voltage that is economically feasible and safe for the purpose intended, the less the cost of the branch circuit wiring. The most commonly used voltages are:

(1) 120/208 volts, 3 phase, 4 wire

(2) 120 volts, single phase, 2 wire

(3) 208 volts, single phase, 2 or 3 wire

(4) 208 volts, 3 phase, 3 wire

(5) 227/480 volts in combinations as under (1), (2), (3), and (4)

(6) 120/240 volts in combinations as under (1), (2), (3), and (4)

(7) 240/480 volts in combinations as under (1), (2), (3), and (4)

LOCAL POWER DISTRIBUTION
General

Local power distribution systems consist of laboratory panel feeders, the panels themselves, and laboratory branch circuits and outlets. Adequate capacity and maximum flexibility should be the major considerations in the design of this portion of the electrical system for here is where the ability to change laboratory functions will be determined.

Panel Feeders

The conventional manner of running separate feeders to groups of panels is not very well suited to laboratory distribution since capacity and flexibility are to be primary considerations. A more suitable means might be providing a series of horizontal plug-in bus duct units which would feed large groups of panels because this type is adaptable for supplying relatively large blocks of power on a single feeder, is easily extended or contracted at a minimum of cost and inconvenience, and permits a larger diversification of electrical loads. Final wiring to panels is made by means of cable and conduit subfeeder connections from plug-in circuit breakers on the bus to the panels.

Panels

The most practicable means of controlling and protecting laboratory branch circuits is by the use of small individual laboratory panels, which should be designed with space provisions to handle the initial and foreseeable future conditions of their respective laboratories. Panels should be located on convenient and permanent structural members of the laboratory building such as columns and shafts to minimize disturbance if wall partitions are rearranged. For easy control in nonhazardous areas, circuit breaker handles should protrude through panel covers.

Branch Circuits

From the individual panels to the laboratory bench and wall outlets, the branch circuit wiring can be accomplished in several ways. Individual receptacle outlets may be mounted exposed on racks below reagent shelves, in pedestals on bench tops, flush in bench aprons, or in wiring channels above bench tops. Outlets in wiring channels are most flexible since receptacles can be added or replaced with a minimum of effort. Another advantage of this system is that it is easily adapted to re-use by merely disconnecting at one location and remounting and connecting in desired lengths at any new location.

GROUNDING OF ELECTRICAL SYSTEMS

A grounded system is one in which the common or neutral conductor is intentionally grounded. The reasons for grounding an electrical system include the following:

(1) Greater service continuity is available with a grounded system.

(2) Faults are more readily determined on a grounded system. On an ungrounded system, a ground fault does not open the circuit which makes fault detection difficult unless some means of detection is installed. In contrast a fault is indicated and located immediately on the grounded system since the respective circuit protective device opens the circuit and thus demands correction.

(3) A grounded system likewise provides better protection for personnel during a period of a ground fault. On an ungrounded system under the same conditions, personnel contacting another phase and ground are subjected to full line-to-line voltage instead of the lower line-to-neutral voltage experienced on a grounded system.

(4) Among the other factors making grounding desirable are the reduction of switching surges, overvoltage due to accidental contact with higher voltage systems, transient voltage build-up due to intermittent ground faults, and the prevention of static voltage build-up.

Laboratory planners as they deal with electrical system grounding should be familiar with code requirements. Local codes follow the National Code but should be checked individually. The latter code makes the following provisions:

(1) Grounding is mandatory for alternating current systems if this can be done so that the maximum voltage to the ground does not exceed

150 volts; grounding is recommended where the voltage to the ground does not exceed 300 volts.

(2) For direct current systems, grounding is mandatory for the neutral conductor of three-wire systems supplying interior wiring as well as for two wire systems operating at not more than 300 volts between conductors unless used for supplying industrial equipment in limited areas and equipped with a ground detector.

(3) Grounding is not required for circuits of less than 50 volts, unless stipulated in the code.

(4) Grounding is not required for furnace circuits.

(5) Crane circuits should not be grounded where the cranes operate over combustible fibers in hazardous locations.

(6) Finally, circuits which supply operating rooms or other places for surgical treatment in which there exist the hazard of igniting flammable mixtures or combustible anesthetic agents should be ungrounded. This may be accomplished by the use of isolation transformers whose secondaries have been removed from the system ground. Ground detectors are required which indicate by a warning buzzer and light accidental ground contact.

Grounding of the system may be accomplished generally by one of three methods. The first called solid grounding, is generally used for building systems; it involves a direct, minimum impedance connection to the ground. Its disadvantage is the generation of high ground fault currents which occasionally require circuit breakers of higher interrupting capacity. A second method is called resistance grounding; in this the system is connected to the ground through a resistor. This results in lower ground fault currents but is used mainly for systems over 15 kilovolts. The final method, reactance grounding involves connection to the ground through a reactor. This is mainly used to ground generator neutrals.

Equipment Grounding

The main purpose of equipment grounding is to safeguard people coming in contact with electrical equipment. All exposed metal parts subject to accidental contact with a live conductor are required to be grounded in order to prevent having a conductor above the potential of the person touching the equipment. Among such equipment are switchboard and panel board enclosures, metallic raceways, motor frames, and portable equipment.

Location of System Ground Connection

Connection to ground shall be at the point of service entrance on the supply side of the service disconnecting means. For an isolated interior wiring system, ground connection shall be made at the transformer or generator, or at the switchboard on the supply side of the first switch controlling the system.

Methods of Grounding

Where possible, system grounding shall be made to a metallic underground water piping system and connected to the supply side of the piping system at its entrance into the building. If this is not feasible, the connection may be made to the metal frame of the building if it is effectively grounded, or to other local metallic underground systems approved by the inspector. Where these grounds are unavailable, an electrode—such as a driven pipe, driven rod, or buried plate—may be used provided their installation and resistance follow code requirements.

Dependent upon the entire system's capacity, the size of the ground connection is fixed by code. Neutral wire should be identified throughout the electrical system by using the color white for its insulation.

The system ground connection is also used for the equipment ground because ground may be carried to miscellaneous equipment by the continuous metallic raceway wiring system (conduits, EMT, or busways with metallic enclosure) and does not require a separate conductor. Grounded connections can be accomplished by contact between raceways and switchboard enclosures, panel boards, and transformer housings; by a jumper between raceway and motor frame; or by a separate ground wire in the cord between raceway and enclosure for portable equipment. In order to provide for the ground wire, receptacles and plugs can be the polarized type, i.e., equipped with a grounding pole in addition to poles required for electrical conductors. Green insulation identifies ground wires.

Laboratory Equipment Grounding and Shielding

The availability of good ground connections for laboratory instruments may be important, since a good connection will measure a minimum resistance to ground. To accomplish this, quite elaborate grounding systems may be necessary. Typical provisions for larger laboratory buildings may consist of a continuous loop of ground conductors throughout the building tied to the building steel, or a combination of both interconnected and connected to the electric system ground. The choice of the magnitude of the system will always depend upon specific requirements.

Certain areas in laboratories containing high-sensitivity electronic instruments may require shielding against outside interference which may be accomplished by wire grids, meshes, or even solid metal shields around walls, floors, ceilings, and around any opening such as doors, all of which must be interconnected and connected to ground at one or more locations. Again the choice of protection will depend upon specific requirements and care should be taken to avoid interference by electrical equipment, e.g., transformers or fluorescent lamps.

Static Grounding

Static charges are the accumulation of electric potential when dissimilar substances are brought into contact with each other. Under these conditions, negatively charged particles will accumulate on one substance and positively charged particles on the other. Separation of the oppositely charged substances results in a static discharge.

Since the danger due to explosions or fires resulting from a static discharge may not always be eliminated by simple grounding, it is necessary to study each installation where static charges may accumulate to select an adequate method of control.

Conditions affecting the production of static include: the characteristics of the materials, the speed of separation between the substances, the area in contact, the relative motion between the substances and the atmospheric conditions.

A number of procedures and devices have been designed to control static. In one, the system is grounded by bonding the various parts of the equipment and grounding the entire system. In a second, the relative humidity is maintained above 60%, under which conditions static accumulations are not likely to reach dangerous proportions. Yet another uses static collectors. Belts made of insulating materials have been replaced by conductive belts and by direct drives. Floors have been made to be conductive. Finally in the case of personnel, wearing apparel of low static-producing qualities, conductive shoes and the establishment of rigid operating procedures are important.

Hazardous Locations

Special wiring and electrical equipment are required for hazardous areas containing explosive vapors or flammable equipment. Any electrical equipment used should be of the explosion-proof type, making it impossible for sparks generated in the equipment to spread to the outside. Wherever it enters the area or where electrical contact is made, wiring such as at switches, receptacles, or at equipment connections should be sealed, i.e., it should pass through a sealing compound which will prevent any sparks from traveling further. In all specific cases, local electrical code requirements should be consulted.

Lightning Protection

In determining the extent of lightning protection required for a specific structure the frequency and severity of thunderstorms in the area and the location of the structure should be considered. The need for protection varies with its location. For example, in large cities, hazard to individual buildings is small except to the highest structures in the area; in open country, a prominent structure may be a frequent target for lightning; in mountainous districts, a building upon high ground is usually subject to greater hazard than one in a valley. Generally, a building can be considered safe if all its parts are lying within a "cone of protection" enclosing about 45° from the high point which is provided by a higher grounded structure.

Fundamentally, lightning protection is a means by which a discharge enters or leaves the earth by passing through a nonconducting part of the structure. In metal structures, lightning effects are negligible if the metal has sufficient cross-section area and is ultimately grounded.

The following components comprise a lightning protection system.

Air terminals of heavy-gauge metals are provided for all structural parts likely to receive a discharge; special attention should be given to projections such as gables, chimneys, parapets, and edges of flat roofs. By a continuous heavy guage metal coping or grid of interconnected terminals around the roof edges and projections maximum protection may be obtained.

At least two down conductors, separated as much as possible, should be provided on any protected building. The number of conductors will depend on the degree of protection desired. In the case of steel-frame buildings, the vertical steel members, if located at the periphery of the building, may serve as down conductors.

A ground connection shall be provided for each down conductor placed if possible in permanently moist soil, unless potentially corrosive, at uniform intervals around the building. These down conductors should be interconnected. Where a metallic water pipe enters the building, at least one down conductor shall be connected to it.

In deep soil, electrodes may be made by extending a rod 10 ft. into the ground. Where soil is largely sand, gravel or stones, more extensive electrodes may be made by adding metal in the form of driven rods, pipes, strips, or plates. In shallow soil, with bedrock near the surface, ground connection may be made by trenches radially from the building and burying the lower ends of the down conductors.

LIGHTING

Due to the special type of work, design conditions for a laboratory lighting system are quite different from those encountered for other types of applications.

Recommended levels of illumination may be found in any number of lighting handbooks. The Illuminating Engineering Society recommends 50 footcandles for work benches and 100 footcandles for close work areas. Other factors to consider are brightness, glare and location of light sources in relation to work areas.

Brightness should be avoided as in most other types of installations, but glare presents a little different problem. Since glassware graduations and other measuring lines must be continuously read, some reflected glare is desirable and should be considered in a well-designed lighting system. Fluorescent lighting fixtures suspended from the ceiling with metal sides, louvered or baffled diffusers, and top openings for ceiling lighting are better suited for laboratory lighting than other more elaborate and expensive systems suggested.

Care must be taken in locating the lighting fixtures not to place them where they will cast shadows on the bench top from shelves, cabinets or the experimenter himself. Where center islands are used, fixtures should be located on either side of the island, particularly when the benches contain reagent racks.

It is good practice to have all metal parts of the fixtures finished in porcelain enamel for these will be easier to clean and will have longer life in the presence of corrosive gases than will the uncoated metal parts.

For the sake of flexibility, fixtures and wiring should be arranged to facilitate the removal and relocation of partitions with little loss of time and money.

Since standard fluorescent fixtures may interfere with the operation of electronic devices, laboratories where these are used should be equipped with incandescent or interference-free fluorescent fixtures.

Where experiments with explosive or combustible materials are conducted, or where products of this nature are formed, the lighting fixtures as well as the wiring, switches and receptacles must meet the requirements as defined in the local or National Electrical Code for "Hazardous Locations." Both incandescent and fluorescent fixtures meeting these requirements are available.

Dark rooms must be given special consideration to protect the film which is being handled; therefore, fluorescent lighting should be avoided since the enclosed phosphor will continue to emit light for some time after the lamp has been extinguished thereby possibly damaging exposed film. Safe lights, with interchangeable filter provisions, should be provided for film handling. Switches controlling dark room lighting should be located to minimize accidental operation. Additional means of protection would be interlocked doors to prevent light leakage into the dark room when doors are opened.

Experimental work involving color matching, such as is carried on in textile and paper color matching laboratories and in microanalysis of fibers by staining, will require a light source of suitable color content.

Emergency lighting may be required for safety and economic reasons. When expensive experiments must be uninterrupted or where expensive rental equipment would be inoperative without lighting, emergency lighting should be considered.

The most common sources of power for emergency lighting include packaged battery units with sealed beam head lamps, central battery installations, engine-generator systems, alternate Utility Company service and network distribution systems. There are often other lighting problems faced by the planner and these will become apparent to the experienced engineer as each individual laboratory is being designed. The above, however, will serve to point up some of the more pertinent considerations.

AUXILIARY SYSTEMS

Auxiliary systems can cover a multitude of interrelated wired equipment, but we shall confine ourselves to the clock systems, sound systems and alarm and supervisors devices and systems.

Clock Systems

There are three basic types of clocks incorporated into four basic types of clock systems. The three basic types of clocks are the minute impulse, the single-synchronous and the dual-synchronous.

The four types of clock systems are the centrally wired minute impulse, the centrally wired single-synchronous, the locally wired electronic single-synchronous and the centrally wired dual-synchronous.

The centrally wired minute impulse clock system is operated and corrected by impulses from a master clock and is usually recommended where only direct current is available or where local power frequency is unreliable; however, clocks with sweep second hands are not available in this system.

Both locally and centrally wired single-synchronous clock systems have single-synchronous motor clocks which are corrected each hour by their respective master clocks through advancing gear arrangement in each clock. Where there is available alternating current and reliable local power frequency, these systems are to be recommended. Since wiring has to be provided only to the nearest 120 volt outlet, the locally wired electronic system is usually more economical than the centrally wired system particularly in large installations where expansion is contemplated.

The dual-synchronous clock system has similar characteristics to those of the single-synchronous system. Each clock has dual-synchronous motors, one of which is for normal operation while the other is for corrective purposes.

Time clocks can be incorporated in any of the systems mentioned above, and master clocks can be furnished with programming drums capable of actuating program-signaling devices.

Electronic clock systems, with appropriate auxiliary equipment, can operate other electrical systems and equipment by remote control. Thus, by setting up the proper pegs on a program drum and furnishing pick-up relays, other systems or equipment can be turned on or off automatically for any predetermined time. Illustrative of this application is the remote-control operation of ventilating equipment, heating and air conditioning equipment, water and steam valves and lighting fixtures.

Alarm and Supervisory System

Alarm and supervisory systems are available to meet almost any conceivable condition of which the most recently developed are:

Closed Circuit TV Systems. A simple closed circuit TV system might consist of a compact TV camera and receiver with interconnecting cable. Such a system is used for at least two purposes: to supervise dangerous procedures (e.g., for handling of radioactive materials) and as part of an instructional system (e.g., a telecast of an intricate operation or experiment). Applications of closed circuit TV are increasing constantly in number and are found both in industry and in teaching.

Automatically Operated Vibrating Alarm Systems. As a means for indicating mechanical troubles from peripheral areas of a laboratory to a central supervisory location, float switches and pressure switches separately wired to a central alarm board can be employed. Consequently, when an alarm condition actuates any one of these switches, an alarm is set off at the central alarm board and the specific switch is indicated.

Watchman's Tour Systems. Available in the wired, manual, short-wave, or combination wired and manual forms, these systems permit after-hours laboratory surveillance to detect burglary, fires or laboratory accidents.

As the simplest, cheapest, and most practical for small laboratories, the manual system consists of coded keys located throughout the laboratory in a predetermined sequence. Accordingly, a watchman makes his rounds following a prescribed route and punches his recording clock by inserting the coded key which records the station and time on a paper tape reel.

Somewhat similar to the manual system, a wired system may be furnished where the size and complexity require it. In this case, recording is done electrically at a central location. When a watchman's portable key is inserted into a fixed watchman's station along his route, the station code and time are recorded. Moreover, failure to complete a trip between stations within an established time limit will sound a delinquency alarm. Also, facilities for telephone conversation between station and central location are available.

Special or remote laboratory layouts may dictate the use of shortwave equipment or a combination of a wired and manual watchman's system.

Photoelectric Systems. For turning on outside lighting or turning off recirculating air conditioning equipment, a photoelectric system can be most useful. The system basically consists of a light sensitive photoelectric cell and control equipment. Thus at the end of the day, the reduced natural illumination deactivates a photocell which subsequently, through contacts and relays, closes

a switch thus causing the street lights to come on. For still another application, smoke in a recirculating air duct of an air conditioning system indicative of a fire condition, breaks a beam of light and causes contacts to stop fan motors thereby producing a dual effect: the prevention of the spread of smoke to other areas and the reduction of the air supply to the danger area.

Window and Door Supervisory Systems. Similar to an Automatic Vibrating Alarm System, a Window and Door Supervisory System provides a means of protection against burglary or unauthorized intrusion in areas where confidential research is in progress or where there is costly equipment. Contact switches which are activated by the opening of doors or windows sound an alarm indicating the location of entry.

Ultrasonic Surveillance System. A more highly sensitive means of supervising a remote area against unauthorized intruders is the Ultrasonic Surveillance System which utilizes a device that saturates an entire enclosure with a high-frequency signal; this in turn triggers an alarm whenever something within the enclosure moves. The essential components of the system consist of a very compact and easily hidden transmitter, receiver, master control and remote monitor.

Sound Systems. In addition to furnishing a facility for sound reinforcement, a sound system can be utilized for the purposes of public address, programmed music or for intercommunication.

There is no more useful facility for general and emergency announcements and paging than a simple public announcement system; a few speakers in central corridors and selected rooms are generally adequate, although the system should have capacity for expansion.

Provisions for receiving AM and FM programs or leasing Music Systems Co. facilities can easily be incorporated in a basic sound system. This will transmit background music or programs of special interest generally or to selected areas.

With minor changes and additions, further versatility can be incorporated permitting a two-way conversation between outlying speakers and the central control rack. A slight modification of this system involves the use of a call system; a coded system of bells can provide for a large number of staff people. The call system is handled from the switchboard and local telephones are used for establishing contact with the board.

SPECIAL REQUIREMENTS

Because of the large number of individual research projects going on in a laboratory building and the special electrical requirements related to each of these projects, it is impossible to list all possible requirements; this section, therefore, is devoted to a listing and summary of some of those which may be encountered.

Equipment

Refrigeration Equipment. The requirements for a refrigerator system in a laboratory have already been discussed under Special Laboratories. The equipment usually consists of a thermostatically controlled compressor to circulate freon gas thereby cooling a given enclosure. Provision should be made for adequate electrical capacity to provide for future additions.

In this connection, in many smaller laboratories such as those in college science buildings household refrigerators are installed to provide some degree of cooling capacity. Reference is made on page 237 to the precautions which need to be taken in order to make these installations safe.

Electric Heating Devices. These provide desirable heat sources for laboratory experiments for they make precise heat control possible, combustion and the products of combustion are eliminated from the laboratory and there is no reasonable limit to the temperatures obtainable.

Examples of types of electric heating devices include those utilizing resistance heating, dielectric heating and induction heating.

Resistance heating, the most common application of electric heating, is used for hot plates, sterilizers, stills, ceramic ovens, electric furnaces, and heat lamps.

Dielectric heating is used for heating between all electrically charged metal plates as well as for low thermal conductivity materials as wood, rubber, and textiles.

Induction heating is quite similar in principle to the induction motor, i.e., a magnetic field is utilized to induce a current which in the case of the motor causes a shaft to rotate; in the induc-

tion device, the current, by virtue of the resistance of the material through which it is flowing causes heating. Principally, it is used in heating steel for hardening, metals for forgings, and metal parts in glass bulbs for degassing during evacuation.

Battery Chargers. In order to prolong the normal life of a storage battery, it is necessary at intervals to recharge it. Charging may be carried out either by disconnecting the battery from its load and charging, or charging the battery while it is connected and supplying its load. The rate of charging is an important consideration in prolonging battery life. Any installation with battery-supplied direct current will require a battery charger.

General

Voltage Regulation. In the absence of corrective equipment, the voltage generated at the power station will always be higher than the voltage delivered to a load: the greater the distance between the two, the greater the load; the poorer the power factor, the greater the difference between the voltages. Voltage regulators are used to eliminate this condition. Most laboratories require permanent or portable means for the regulation of voltage. Such equipment includes transformer top changers, synchronous condensers, switched capacitors, induction regulators and electronic regulators.

Constant Current Regulating Equipment. For street lighting, battery charging, electrolysis and electroplating, constant current must be employed. For this purpose, either constant current transformers having movable cores which adjust themselves to maintain constant output current with varying load, or constant current generators which have an output which automatically adjusts itself to the load it is supplying may be used.

High Frequency Power

Spark-discharged generators, vacuum-tube oscillator circuits, and mercury arc rectifiers may be used for purposes which require high-frequency power such as brazing, soldering, plastic molding, induction heating, drying penicillin and diathermy.

Motor speeds up to 120,000 rpm are also possible utilizing a two-pole motor with 2,000 cycles per second power applied to its terminals.

Special Work Shops

In order to save time and money and encourage coordinated effort, many laboratories include provisions for workshops besides the conventional metal and woodworking shops. Some of the equipment and tools that might be encountered are:

Woodworking and metalworking machinery and tools which can add up to considerable electrical loads: 10 to 20 kv of connected load in an average size shop are not uncommon. This means that safety provisions should be considered in the early planning stages, e.g., safety push buttons which de-energize all electrical equipment in an emergency, should be provided at several locations throughout a shop.

Welding, with its high electrical capacity requirements for short periods of time, must also be considered in the early electrical planning.

Electric furnaces or kilns for porcelain enameling and various other glass heating treatments also require more power than needed for an average electrical appliance. For this reason their capacity and location should be considered in the planning.

Direct Current

Direct current for laboratory use can be obtained from batteries, static rectifiers or motor generator sets.

The original, and for many years the most practical source of a limited direct current, was from a battery. Today, except for very small isolated direct current requirements, the battery has been replaced in laboratories by the static rectifiers of the selenium of copper oxide type. For larger power requirements, the motor-generator direct current source is the more practical where direct current requirements are extensive. Some consideration should be given to central distribution systems.

Variable Frequency Control

Since railroad equipment operates at 25 cycles, European electrical equipment at 50 cycles, airlines at 400 cycles, electronic equipment at almost any frequency and direct current and other special equipment at frequencies deviating from the usual Utility Company 60 cycles, the need for means to convert frequencies is apparent. Common equipment utilized for frequency conversion include motor-generator sets, induction motor frequency changes, electron oscillators and mercury arc rectifiers.

High-Voltage Laboratories

Insulation tests, electron accelerators, induction heating and other high-voltage requirements are usually handled in a separate area in a laboratory set aside for high-voltage producing and test equipment. A typical high-voltage laboratory might include the following: transformers, impulse generators, capacitors, induction coils, power rectifiers and control equipment and conductor.

CHAPTER VI

Laboratory

Furniture

M. M. SOLOMON

General Electric Company
Philadelphia, Pennsylvania

FACTORS AFFECTING SELECTION OF FURNITURE

Ideally, women should have a hand in the selection of laboratory furniture because of the diversity of available items in a wide range of materials, colors and finishes. Practically speaking, however, the choice of laboratory equipment is primarily governed by two basic considerations:

(1) The money and space available, which is usually established by Administration action prior to the actual planning.

(2) The type of work to be done in the various laboratories; this in the final analysis falls broadly within the statement of purpose outlined by Administration when the decision to build has been reached.

If we break these basic considerations down into specific factors, we find many influencing the equipment to be ordered. Among these are the following:

(1) The fields of science and technology being studied or investigated, e.g., chemistry, chemical or other engineering, physics, mathematics, biology. Within these fields are narrower sub-disciplines, e.g., in chemistry there are inorganic, organic, analytical and physical chemistry. Analytical chemistry has crossed the physics border to include instrumental analysis. Biology and chemistry have biochemistry, biology and physics, biophysics. For a combination of all three, there is molecular biology. Modern mathematics depends heavily upon computers. These all have specific laboratory requirements and influence the choice of furniture selected. The leveling of barriers between disciplines is one of the important signs of the times. The inevitable effect in the academic world will be that biology departments will be installing some chemical furniture, chemistry departments will need instrument rooms for work with electronic equipment, and physics departments will need laboratories designed for use with expensive and sophisticated equipment.

(2) The nature of the work; will it be research, development, quality control, engineering design or a combination; or will the laboratories be used for teaching?

(3) The type of materials being investigated:

special precautions must be taken if these are flammable, odorous, unstable or generally hazardous. They may influence hood design, the type of electrical fixtures, the location of equipment where particularly hazardous reactions are being studied.

(4) Special storage facilities: hazardous materials will require special storage facilities.

(5) The people using the facilities: these may be high school and college science students, graduate students and faculty, technicians and professional chemists having varying levels of competence and furniture needs. What is adequate for one may well be inadequate for another.

(6) The working space allocation per scientist, or linear feet of bench space per student: these govern the general bench design and width of drawers and cabinets.

(7) The quality of maintenance: there is wide variation in the standards of maintenance; frequently those in industrial and government laboratories excel those in academic laboratories. This will influence the type of furniture and related facilities.

(8) Appearance or function: somewhat related to maintenance is the importance placed upon designing for function or designing for appearance. A number of college and university science buildings have been designed to match existing architecture with a loss in effective use of the space in the building. For somewhat different reasons, some industrial research buildings have been planned with advertising value rather than utility in mind. In either case the design of the laboratories and selection of equipment is influenced by the particular situation.

(9) Permanence of the installation: in some cases laboratories are located temporarily on a site with the expectation that they will be relocated as the long-range plan is developed.

MATERIALS OF CONSTRUCTION

Steel Furniture or Wood

In general, industrial companies tend to favor steel furniture while academic institutions favor wood. The proponents of both present valid arguments for their choice. Those who favor steel argue that:

(1) It has greater fire resistance.

(2) The new baked-on epoxy-type finishes are impervious to a wide variety of acids, bases and solvents.

(3) It is easier to clean than wood and requires less maintenance.

(4) It has greater flexibility. Steel furniture featuring interchangeable cupboard and drawer sections is available.

The advantages of wood are presented as:

(1) It is a "warmer" type of material, both in feel and appearance.

(2) In crowded classrooms and laboratories the closing of metal doors and drawers creates a high noise level, especially when compared to the sound-deadening power of wood.

(3) Although wood is easier to damage, it is also easier to repair. This can be done by a maintenance man experienced in working with wood. Metal workers would be harder to find on the maintenance crew of a college.

(4) It is easier to refinish furniture made of wood than of steel. Finishes for the latter require baking to have chemical resistance equal to the original finish.

Obviously both materials have their good points; personal opinion often is the deciding factor. It is wise to consult insurance authorities for any possible effect the selection may have on rates.

In general, cost of wood *vs.* steel furniture for orders over $10,000 are usually comparable, or can be made so by competitive bidding.

If the decision favors steel, several features should be checked.

(1) Although most manufacturers use comparable gauges of steel in fabricating the unit, it is important to investigate the reinforcement of critical corners and sides as well as the strength of drawer suspension and stops. Pull a loaded drawer out to the stop and see how well it takes the strain. Swing back and forth on a cabinet door; students do! Will the hinges take the treatment? In case of breakage, can parts be obtained and repairs made by local labor, or must a factory representative be called in?

(2) Consider the hardware, particularly strength, metal composition, ease of replacement and appearance. The use of aluminum fixtures is

questionable in laboratories where alkalies are used frequently. Plastic fittings have found some use, but must be checked first against the particular conditions.

(3) A final point deals with the protective treatments given steel before or after fabrication. In the early days of steel laboratory furniture, the units were fabricated from sheet steel and then were sprayed with a paint which would provide a hard surface, good appearance and some degree of chemical resistance after baking. The paint film provided the sole barrier between steel and corrosive chemical. Any condition which would remove even a small area of paint initiated corrosion, e.g., scratches on outside surfaces and drawer and cabinet bases, accidents with hot concentrated acids or film softening by solvents particularly where the film might be thin as in the corners of drawers.

To provide a second barrier, the more progressive manufacturers some time ago turned to the use of a lead-coated steel, and this is still used in small volume for certain applications. Although an improvement over unprotected steel, the lead-coated steel laboratory bench had certain weaknesses. Where these were spot-welded in fabricating, the lead was removed and such spots were corrosion sites. In addition, the adhesion of paint to the lead surface was not as good as desired.

The units are now fabricated from sheet steel and the entire unit is then given a phosphatizing treatment (often spoken of as "bonderizing") which provides a non-reactive corrosion-resistant surface to which paint adheres firmly. When a scratch goes through the double protection of paint and bonderizing film, corrosion is said to be confined largely to the area of the scratch rather than creeping under the adjoining film. There are a variety of types of treatments and the degree of resistance imported is influenced by the conditions of treatment.

The combined efforts of research and development work in the laboratories of the paint, resin and laboratory furniture manufacturers has produced better and better finishes. Currently there are available high quality epoxy resin paints which yield extremely tough, resistant coatings when baked on a "phosphatized" steel surface. Such finishes will continue to be improved, and

planners are urged to test-check proposed new finishes. Tests at the Silicone Products Department of the General Electric Company at Waterford, New York, have shown that two coats of epoxy resin paint baked on "bonderized" steel will resist solvents such as acetone, ethyl alcohol, and various aliphatic and aromatic compounds and strong acids and alkalies. Neither the common organic solvents nor dilute and concentrated sulfuric and nitric acids affect the finish under the test conditions. Only concentrated hydrochloric acid when left for two days in contact with a painted surface having exposed edges destroyed the coating. If a question remains as to the suitability of the finish, the planner should ask for a list of users of the same furniture and contact several whose needs are somewhat in line with his own.

For those who are planning to use wood furniture the following considerations are important. The fabrication of wood furniture differs from that of steel in one respect. Almost every community, regardless of size, has some kind of a wood work shop and in view of the relative cost of laboratory furniture, there will be a temptation to save money by having the laboratory benches made there. The plumbing and electrical work for the benches will generally then be let out to local plumbers or electricians. Unfortunately the average layman does not realize that there are other considerations than mill work, plumbing and electrical fixtures before a laboratory is in good working order. A complete laboratory furniture installation requires, besides the above, decisions as to hardware and fittings, the type and quality of wood for outer and interior surface*, and the design of the furniture to ensure free movement of drawers and doors under laboratory conditions. The moisture content of the wood at the time of fabrication will influence the latter. Someone must design the service arrangements on the benches and plan for service hookups so that the different units will fit together

---

* There are many different kinds and grades of both hardwood and softwood. Generally, the hardwoods used for exterior surfaces include top-quality oak, maple, or birch. Plywood cores should be rotary cut poplar; interior plywood should be Douglas-fir. Beware of the general use of the term "hardwood" for all deciduous trees are classified as hardwoods regardless of the characteristics of the wood.

accurately. Not many institutions will have available individuals who are capable of this type of planning.

If local construction of wood furniture is considered, the building committee should investigate in some detail the matter of relative costs involved in having furniture designed, built, assembled, and installed locally or in having a laboratory furniture manufacturer design, fabricate, and assemble the furniture in his plant and install the equipment on the job under a performance guarantee such as the local group cannot provide. The more complex the job, the more important it becomes to place the furniture order with a reputable laboratory furniture manufacturer, to ensure proper coordination of planning, production and installation.

Wood furniture finishing is entirely different from steel finishing, and the steps followed depend on whether the finish is to be clear or enamel. A clear finish generally is applied in the following manner.

(1) The wood surface, prepared earlier for finishing, is stained, unless the finish is to be natural, with a stain which will not lift the fiber surface.

(2) After drying, a mineral filler is wiped across the grain.

(3) When this also has dried, the surface is given a sealer coat and is sanded to a smooth finish after the sealer has dried.

(4) A chemical-resistant synthetic varnish is then applied.

A laboratory furniture manufacturer should at least be able to provide a clear finish which will give *good* resistance to all acids with the exception of 70 per cent sulfuric acid and 50 per cent nitric acid. With the former, the surface is altered in appearance but still retains its chemical resistance; the latter discolors and slowly etches the surface. Resistance is *good* in the case of 10 per cent sodium hydroxide and concentrated ammonium hydroxide, and also with solvents such as ethyl alcohol, xylene, benzene, naphtha and carbon tetrachloride. The terms excellent, good and fair have the following meaning: (1) *excellent* implies that the test leaves no visible effect on the finish film; (2) *good* means that while the test solution may cause a slight discoloration or change in gloss, there is neither loss of film adhesion nor loss of film protection; (3) *fair* is used when the film shows moderate etching and discoloration without loss in film adhesion or protection.

Research during the past few years however has led to the development of new, chemically resistant synthetic resins of the polyurethane type which are coming into use in finishes for wood laboratory furniture. There they impart improved resistance to deterioration by a wide variety of organic solvents and strong alkalies and acids. The planner should be aware of the availability of such finishes. Spot tests will identify the relative resistance of submission samples. Today's research may bring forth even better finishes.

These same new resins are finding application in the field of enamel finishes for wood. To produce an enamel finish, the surface is treated first with a primer-surfacer, followed by sanding and dusting. Two coats of pigmented, chemical-resistant enamel are then applied; after each coat, the surface is sanded and dusted. Generally speaking, the pigmented enamel finishes are not quite as resistant as are clear finishes.

The quality and appearance of the wood finishes are dependent not only on the composition of the finishes but also on the excellence of the workmanship used in their application. The same holds for the cabinet work. Programmed maintenance should be started as soon as the new facilities are put to use; in this way, the new furniture will retain its appearance for many years. Often it is good policy to discuss with technical men or teachers and students the proper care and maintenance of laboratory furniture and facilities; in some companies maintenance handbooks are passed out after such a meeting, together with bench top waxes to be applied by the user of the furniture. Unfortunately, there seems to be no correlation between the professional level of the individual and the care with which he treats his laboratory furniture, hence a precautionary word is desirable.

Worktops

Having chosen the materials of construction for the case or cabinet work, the next consideration is the specific work top to be used in each location. To do this properly we need to examine each situation so as to establish what type of work the top will handle. What are the hazards in terms of chemical corrosion or fire? Will the top be expected to support unusually heavy equipment? Will it involve extreme working conditions such as large differences in working temperatures? As illustrations, wood tops would not be suitable in locations in analytical laboratories where the reflected heat from Meker burners and blast lamps might char the top or blister the top finish; laboratories using concentrated hydrochloric acid in quantity should stay away from stainless steel tops, while those using perchloric acid should consider stainless steel. In fact, serious thought must be given to a low absorption coefficient of the top material, especially when perchloric acid is used, in the interest of safety of workers. Finally there are cost considerations.

An examination of the various types of tops lists the following as the most popular:

(1) *Natural stone.* "Alberene," quarried in Virginia, is a silicate with or without talc. It has structural strength, a low coefficient of absorption and is resistant to most of the reagents normally found in the chemical laboratory. With proper housekeeping, "Alberene" tops will be useful for the life of the furniture.

(2) *Natural stone, impregnated.* Within recent years, impregnated hard sandstone tops have become popular. These also have great structural strength and are highly resistant to chemical attack. They are not recommended for use where they will be subjected to high continuous localized heating unless protected by a sheet of asbestos. The over-all excellence of other properties makes it a most desirable top material. This type of top goes under the trade names of "Kemrock," "Labrock," "Imperial Stone," "Shelrock," "Metrock," etc.

(3) *Cement asbestos compositions.* "Kemstone" and its next of kin, "Colorlith" are cement asbestos, monolithic compositions. They are excellent in most ways outlined above except for a rather high coefficient of absorption which can be lessened somewhat by impregnation with certain sealers. "Colorith," a modification of "Kemstone," has the additional advantage of

color to brighten laboratory areas. It too suffers from poor coefficient of absorption (hence causing some staining); however, there are available promising fillers which should cut down on this deficiency. To date, the other major deficiency of "Colorlith" is a cost approximately 50 per cent higher than the black "Kemstone."

(4) *"Transite."* Probably the poorest of the synthetic stones is "Transite," which is excellent where heat resistance and physical toughness is desired but is not satisfactory in chemical resistance and high absorptivity. One big advantage is lower initial cost.

(5) *Wood.* Of the wooden tops, cored birch or surface-treated plywood are most often encountered. Both make particularly attractive tops, excellent for use on physical test tables, and are known for their surface warmth. Carbonized (black) wood finishes and other type wood tops, properly treated with acid- and alkali-resistant finishes, make for very serviceable working areas.

(6) *"Textolite."* "Textolite" guarantees ease of cleanliness, brightness of decor, and gives moderate chemical and heat resistance.

(7) *Stainless steel and "Porocel."* Stainless steel and "Porocel" (enameled steel) make excellent work surfaces when radioactive research is being conducted.

In summary, where cost differences are not critical and maximum resistance to all types of chemicals and environmental conditions is desired, stone tops either natural or synthetic are the materials of choice. Again the planner is urged to look into the new and modified materials emerging from the research laboratories of equipment manufacturers and chemical companies. Improved products are presently on test.

Cabinet Work

The number and type of cabinet units and drawers put in the laboratory bench is independent of the choice of wood or steel for the bench and the type of top selected; rather they depend upon the type of work for which the bench will be used, the space and funds available and in the case of schools and colleges on the distance to the stock or dispensing room. Thus is an analytical laboratory, miscellaneous long, narrow drawers for burettes and large cupboards for

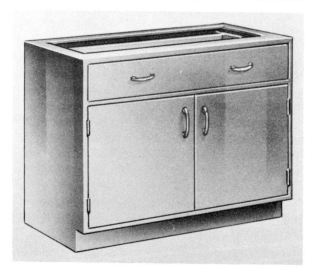

burners and desiccators might be specified. About the same unit might also prove useful for an organic chemist with condensers, stirrers and ground glass fittings requiring length rather than depth. Figure 6.1 shows a popular multi-drawer unit with a variety of drawer sizes: the small deep drawers are particularly adapted for cork and tool storage, as well as for filter papers and other small items and the larger deep drawers are useful for beakers, stirring motors, heating mantles, smaller flasks and distillation columns. Figure 6.2 is a base cabinet with maximum cupboard space for bulky equipment.

Teaching laboratories call for two different types of storage space.

(1) In the personal storage area the student keeps under lock pieces of equipment assigned his personal use. At the end of the term, he is responsible for its return clean and ready for reassignment. Customarily the facilities assigned to the student are of such size as to handle his equipment requirements for the period of the course (see Figure 6.3). In teaching laboratories of the type described in Figure 12.10, the dispensing rooms opening on to the laboratories will issue as needed for day to day use, larger glassware, e.g., large beakers, flasks, condensers, and desiccators. In this way, the storage requirements for the student lockers are reduced in size and the desk capacity in terms of sections is increased at little extra cost.

(2) The other type of storage furniture is that which is to be used for general storage. This includes the shelving on the walls of the room for the storage of large supplies of acids and alkalies of different concentrations, or for larger amounts of certain solvents. Likewise there would be cabinets with sliding or swinging doors for the storage of equipment used in common. Part of either shelving or cabinets could be set aside for the storage of desiccators when not in active use.

Figure 6.1   Multi-drawer base cabinet.

Figure 6.2   Base cabinet with maximum cupboard space for bulky equipment.

Figure 6.3   Base cabinet with one large drawer and a double cupboard.

Reagents and solvents for immediate use by the students in carrying out assignments are generally kept on the reagent shelf above the service pipes on the desk top as illustrated in Figure 6.4, or are placed in an indicated space at the center of the table top of benches without reagent racks. While the storage of bottles on the shelf of a reagent rack is rather inexpensive and handy, such shelves never the less are difficult to keep clean and neat. Moreover they can be a safety hazard from three points of view.

(1) Reagents (most of which, if handled improperly, are very dangerous) are left within easy reach of unauthorized individuals. Here they are open to contamination, sometimes to the detriment of the equipment.

(2) Often the reagent shelf fails to have a "stop" in the center. It is easy to push a bottle off such a shelf while replacing a bottle on the opposite side with subsquent breakage and spillage of dangerous chemicals.

(3) The reagent shelf with its bottles and service piping makes it almost impossible for the instructor to check the techniques of class members for unsafe practices and incipient accidents. Furthermore it rules out the side wall as a chalk board location unless the latter is equipped with sash weights for raising and lowering.

A better but more costly method is to provide every worker with his own supply of reagents which can be kept under lock and key, and this is easily accomplished with acids and bases by means of polyethylene reagent bottles. Another way is to provide storage space for stock reagents —preferably in the stockroom—to be dispensed by the attendant or kept in lockable sliding door cabinets illustrated in Figure 6.5, which are maintained by the instructor or attended in some other way thus providing a check on contamination or unauthorized use.

For storage of corrosive or extremely valuable materials a modified storage cabinet idea is shown in Figure 6.6. Note that this cabinet is lined with chemical-resistant material such as "Kemstone," "Transite," etc. as shown in Figure 6.7. It is vented via a top-housed fan, fresh air being drawn through louvers in the door. Free air circulation, important in preventing accumulation of corrosive or toxic fumes, is provided by

Figure 6.4   Use of reagent shelf over laboratory bench for storage purposes.

Figure 6.5   Sliding door case for storage of reagents and long glassware.

using perforated storage shelves. These cabinets quickly pay for the extra cost of fabrication by the increased longevity brought about by these methods and materials of construction.

Wherever possible it is desirable to keep to the larger size units such as the 35 or 47-in. wide types because these cost less per square feet of cabinet and per cubic feet of storage space. However, this is again dictated by the size of the laboratory area and the number of different varieties of units actually required. Certainly the small units are handy for fitting into corners.

In recent years a number of major manufacturers have fabricated equipment which makes possible the interchange of drawers and cupboards for the replacement of a large drawer by two small ones. A cutaway of this type of unit is shown in Figure 6.8. This could be important for small laboratories where the emphasis on the type of work being done changes, thus requiring changes in size, quantity and design of experimental equipment and hence in the size and type of storage units.*

* In view of the many proposals for modifying the undergraduate curriculum in chemistry, as much flexibility as can be achieved in one way or another is desirable in undergraduate laboratories. Somewhat the same is true in high school science laboratories.

Another way of obtaining a degree of flexibility is to have all units fitted with integral tops, i.e., each unit is fitted with its own individual top. Then the units are put into a row and the tops cemented together preferably with a semi-permanent cement. Should it be desirable to change types of units, the top joints are broken (by a power saw with a masonry cutting blade) and the entire unit replaced with one to meet the new requirement. Since it has its own top, the replaced unit then can be used in any location immediately. If no place is available for it in front of a service strip, it can be used as a table top where few or no services are required. This type of system requires service distribution by means of a separate service strip. Ways of distributing services and the types of service strips available are discussed at length in a later chapter (Chapter 8).

Figure 6.6　Modified storage cabinet.

Figure 6.7　Modified storage cabinet, interior details.

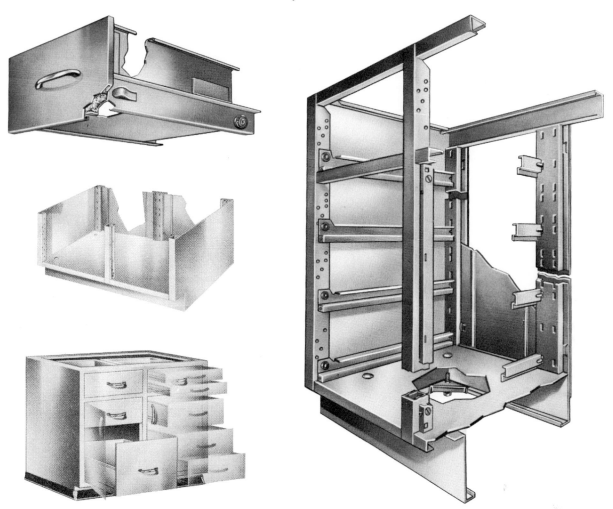

Figure 6.8   Bench drawers showing interchangeable construction.

Hoods

Because of the importance of hoods to working safety and comfort, it is deemed desirable to devote a separate section to the discussion of them.

One of the most important pieces of laboratory equipment is the hood. Almost every type of scientific study and endeavor requires that a portion of work, because of heat, odor, or toxicity, be performed in a hood. Thus, the hood serves as a marked safety device and in many instances is the sole means for removing air in the entire laboratory. Yet the design and proper operation of this most important unit is most often compromised or improperly handled. One cardinal principle to remember when considering the installation and number of hoods is that one can always use a hood as regular bench space with little if any loss in area or efficiency but no plain bench can serve as a hood! Moreover, when a hood is required, there is no safe substitute.

In recent years we have seen great progress in hood design. The old box-type hood with protruding sides was replaced by the flush wall design as illustrated in Figure 6.9 which in turn faces active competition from the air flow or streamlined type of hood, two types of which are shown in Figures 6.10 and 6.11. The last two permit the efficient operation of fume hoods with

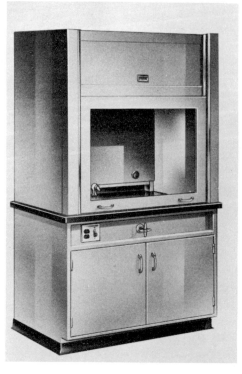

Figure 6.10   *Airflow fume hood with type "A" sash.*

Figure 6.9   *Box type fume hood with flush interior.*

reduced face velocity which results in a great saving in the cost of the ventilating system due to the reduced capacity needs.

New installations like those at the General Electric Company's Silicone Products Department, Waterford, New York, exemplify the achievement of the ultimate in hood design, efficiency, and safety. In close cooperation with the manufacturer, these hoods were designed to include all the salient features desired by chemists in various other laboratories throughout the country. The result: an excellently operating hood system. The 8-ft section pictured in Figure 6.12 provides:

(1) Option to use 4 ft of hood as walk in and/or 4 ft as a bench height hood.

(2) Option to use two 4 ft hoods as one 8 ft bench height hood.

(3) All remote controls.

(4) Built-in safety shields via horizontally sliding panes within the main vertically sliding sash.

(5) Continuously vented corrosive storage cabinet which is lined with chemically resistant material.

(6) Color-coded, corrosion-resistant fixtures.

(7) "Colorlith" walls for light reflection.

(8) Much greater head height compared to previously designed hoods.

(9) Simple and useful storage for the removable shelf in the walk-in hood section.

(10) Place for mounting of racks and rack space.

(11) Good lighting by two 30-watt (totally enclosed) fluorescent bulbs.

Hoods of all types and varieties can be fabricated to meet special needs, e.g., a hood is available with glass partitions or sashes on all three sides to allow demonstration which may be seen by a large audience as illustrated in Figure 6.13.

Walk-in (Figure 6.14) bench height, and intermediate height hoods are available (Figure 6.15) as are table-top hoods and hoods that double as dry boxes (Figure 6.16). There are hoods with a

Figure 6.11   Double compartment, Floline fume hood, H-200 series.

Figure 6.12   Modified fume hood.

Figure 6.13   Demonstration fume hood, glass on three sides.

Figure 6.14   Airflow walk-in hood.

variety of built-in installations, such as hot plates and built-in variable voltage transformers, as well as portable hoods. Long hood sections without posts to interfere with the free work surfaces may also be obtained (Figure 6.17).

Hood Interiors: Materials of Construction. More often than not, the hood's interior will be lined with a thinner version of the materials used for work tops. However, there is no reason why the lining should be made of bench top material. A case in point is that of a hood in which there will be extensive use of perchloric acid. This requires careful design and construction because perchloric acid generates perchlorates which detonate easily in the presence of organic matter. Collections of the residues must be carefully removed and contact with organic materials in the hood, duct, and fan avoided. Materials used in the construction of the hood and its exhaust system should be inert, non-absorbent, and free of any organic impregnation. All joints should be made liquid- and gas-tight with an inert cement. Water-spray pipes may be installed for washing

Figure 6.15   Intermediate height hood with work surface 18″ from the floor.

Figure 6.16   CBR type hood used as a dry box.

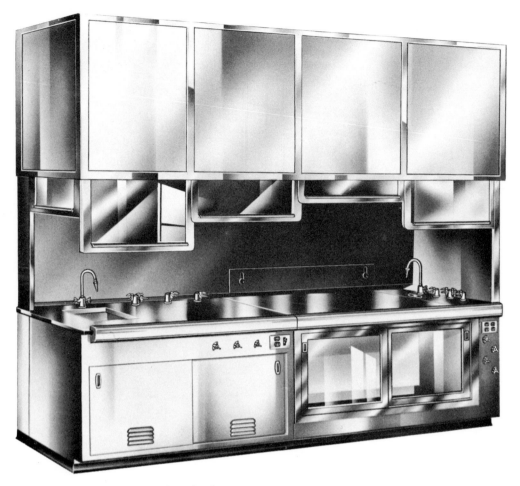

Figure 6.17   Multi-purpose fume hood.

down the back surfaces of the baffles in the hood, and provision should be made for carrying away this flushing water. In some hoods the baffles are removable so that the hood's entire interior may be easily cleaned. If hot plates are installed in such a hood, it is advisable to provide removable liners or shields of asbestos, composition, or tempered glass across the end and back of the hood structure where the hot fumes strike. This procedure protects the hood structure itself, and new liners are easily and inexpensively installed.

It is recommended that separate fan and duct systems be installed for perchloric acid hoods and that these be arranged to achieve easy, thorough, and frequent cleaning. The vent duct should be made of corrosion-resistant welded metal arranged preferably as a vertical stack. Draft may be supplied directly by a cast-iron fan with bot-

tom horizontal discharge for easy cleaning, or it may be induced. Access panels should be provided so that steam or air may be used to loosen and drive out collections of materials that may contain perchlorates. Occasionally vent systems are cleaned by water-spray nozzles installed at the top of the duct and at bends. Similarly, materials of construction for sash frames and guides present a problem in the presence of large amounts of substances like hydrochloric acid. The sash frames and guides in the hoods in our laboratories at Waterford already show signs of stainless steel corrosion. The use of painted plastic-coated or structural plastic such as epoxy-coated fiber might have been a better choice.

Lastly, all exposed fasteners inside the hood should be so covered as to render them as chemically resistant as the interior itself.

Figure 6.18   Organic chemical laboratory.

Hood Systems for Air-Conditioned Buildings.
While the subject of air conditioning in the laboratory has been covered elsewhere, some facets of this problem are so inextricably related to proper hood operation as to warrant some opinion and facts before leaving the subject of hoods.

Under average conditions, even the best of hoods will require a minimum of 50 cfm of air crossing the face at which rate the quantity of air removed by the hoods from an average laboratory can be quite large and costly—perhaps surprisingly so to the uninitiated, particularly if the laboratory is air-conditioned. Often the architects or ventilation engineers will suggest a scheme to recirculate part of the exhausted air back into the room. It is the author's personal opinion, as well as that of many other laboratory designers with whom he has talked, that this is a *most* dangerous practice from the standpoint of health, fire and explosion hazard as well as discomfort due to odors. One must realize that in a

laboratory the high cost of air conditioning is one of the unavoidable business expenses, but one that can more than pay for itself by increasing the effectiveness of the laboratory staff during the unbearably hot humid days of summer.

After one reaches an advanced stage of planning and has a good idea as to the facilities needed, it is advisable to call the area representatives of several reputable laboratory furniture companies who are most capable, willing, cooperative, and helpful. Frequently, they can help reduce the expenditure by suggesting standard units of different types capable of doing the required jobs at lower costs.

When all individual planning has been integrated with the various suggestions of vendors and engineers, it is time to determine the method of purchase. As a rule of thumb, if the job is under $5000 for total installation, it is well to consider purchase of standard stock units to be engineered and installed by the vendor, since

Figure 6.19   Organic chemical laboratory.   *Figure 6.20   Organic chemical laboratory.*

they are considerably cheaper than custom installations. If the cost exceeds $5000, it usually pays to ask for bids on a set of written specifications and drawings. Choice of the purchase method may also be influenced by whether the furniture is needed quickly or whether there will be several months before installation. Final question which must be answered is: Which of the bidders are offering you furniture which meets your specifications?

This chapter would not be complete without a picture of what your laboratory might look like in its completed condition. A typical organic chemical laboratory at General Electric's Waterford Silicone Products Department is shown in Figures 6.18 through 6.22. Note particularly the long drawer sections for the storage of condensers and stirring rods.

Figure 6.18 is taken from the office area looking toward the exit into corridor. It shows one-half of the left side and all of the center bench including a dual sink—one section of which is a stainless steel sink for solvents, the other a general purpose ceramic sink. The fire extinguisher location is opposite the unshown hood. Figure 6.18 and Figure 6.20 show the left and right side, respectively, as photographed from just inside the door. Note technicians' lower table partitioned off from office area by the 3 x 7 sliding door storage cabinet.

Figures 6.21 and 6.22 show opposite sides of the center bench in greater detail. Note the larger extinguisher outside office area in Figure 6.19 and the fire blanket in Figure 6.20. Each side has the multiple drawer unit for storage of corks and sundry smaller items as well as the long four-foot drawers for storage of heating mantles, etc. Another useful unit has four drawers of filing cabinet size. This permits the safe, out of sight, storage of five one-gallon bottles per drawer or an equivalent amount of smaller bottles. Note the rather unique installation under the open benches

Figure 6.21   Organic chemical laboratory.

Figure 6.22   Organic chemical laboratory.

which was fabricated by an outside contractor but which, if a contract is to be let, should be done by the furniture manufacturer when the bench is built. The waste paper chutes on the side of the sink cabinets promote good housekeeping. One unique feature is the sink area for cleaning small parts and materials coated with silicone which can only be removed by alcoholic caustic solution. These special sinks are stainless steel and can be drained into a five-gallon can. The standard sink, a product of U.S. Stoneware, is a one-piece cast ceramicware which is cleaned easily.

Over each rack, connected into the hood duct work is a 2- to 3-in. tail piece containing a manually operated butterfly damper which can be connected by means of flexible hose to an air scoop and, in turn, can be used as a portable hood for rack-mounted equipment. The sliding door closets, two of which are present in every laboratory, provide adequate storage for chemicals and glassware. The 5-foot 30-in. high table can be used either for instrumentation or as a place where technicians can write and keep their notebooks. The variety of cabinets which we have used can be seen in this illustration. Other planners will in turn have special requirements for their particular laboratories.

The many other types of cabinets available are better seen in the catalogs of the furniture manufacturers, which should be obtained at the initial planning stage.

SECTION D

Health and Safety Factors

CHAPTER VII

Occupational Health and Safety

DONALD L. SNOW

National Institutes of Health
Bethesda, Maryland

HOWARD H. FAWCETT

General Electric Company
Schenectady, New York

"Safe" laboratory environments can be established with reasonable care, providing the nature of the chemical, biological or radiological agents to be used and the specific methods of research procedures to be conducted are determined. In actual practice, research techniques are subject to change, and particular emphasis should be placed on planning laboratory facilities which, with minor alterations, can be adapted for handling a variety of agents. It is not unusual to have plans for research and even routine procedures changed before construction is completed.

At the outset, it should be recognized that facilities are only one aspect of safety, health and fire protection. While a well-designed and constructed laboratory environment can make a major contribution to safe operations, it is the proper or improper practices, and how intelligently materials and facilities are used that exert the primary influence on safety. A vital factor in the entire equation is the insistence of the laboratory management that laboratory personnel observe safe practices. In the final analysis, people are responsible for safety. Facilities may aid, but they should not be expected to replace human considerations.

While the following sections outline some of the more significant items of health and safety concern in laboratory design, it is recommended that the references listed be consulted for details beyond the scope of this chapter.

FUNCTIONAL ARCHITECTURAL CONSIDERATIONS
Personal Hygiene Facilities

Ratios of employees to toilet fixtures have not been specifically developed for laboratories, but the office building toilet facilities standards of the American Standard Plumbing Code[1] or of the federal Public Buildings Service[2] may be used as general guides where local codes do not apply. Table 7.1 summarizes portions of the ranges of personal hygiene facilities recommended by these two authorities.

Requirements for lockers and showers depend directly on the nature of the laboratory investigations and the extent to which lab coats, cover-

TABLE 7.1

PERSONAL HYGIENE FACILITIES RATIOS

| NO OF PERSONS | Men | | | Women | |
	WATER CLOSETS	URINALS	LAVA-TORIES	WATER CLOSETS	LAVA-TORIES
1 to 8–15*	1	1	1	1	1
9–16 to 24–30	1–2	1	1–2	2	2
25–31 to 36–55	2	1	2	3	2
37 to 56	3	1	2	4	3
56–57 to 75–80	3–4	2	3	4	3
76–81 to 96–110	4	2	3	6	4

* Larger figures from A. S. A. Std Plumbing Code, smaller figures from Public Buildings Service Design Stds.

alls or other special protective clothing or clothing changes may be required. Where biological or radioactive agents are employed, locker, toilet and shower facilities may be interposed between contaminated and noncontaminated laboratory areas in an air lock or vestibule arrangement. Depending on the relative health hazards or laboratory product quality requirements, the use of protective clothing and routine showering may be required of personnel passing between these areas. Conveniently located grab bars in shower stalls are recommended together with abrasive-surfaced tile or other slip-resistant surfaces for shower-stall floors. Figure 7.1 shows one typical arrangement for locker-shower facilities designed to secure a reasonable degree of separation between "dirty" and "clean" or "maximum" and "minimum" hazard areas.

Lavatories, with or without foot-, knee-, or wrist-operated valve controls may also be required, not only in toilet rooms, but at strategic locations within laboratory areas. In larger toilet-room installations, ceiling or wall-hung partitions, wall-hung fixtures and adequate lighting will facilitate mopping and general sanitation.

Food Service and Drinking Facilities

Food vending and eating facilities in laboratory buildings may range from isolated vending machine stations, vending machine-lunch rooms, snack shops and coffee bars to cafeterias and dining rooms. Since local health departments have regulations which frequently govern the design and construction of food service equipment

and building details, these regulatory agencies should be consulted in advance. A number of recommended and nationally accepted sanitation standards are now available for food-service planning. Vending machines are covered in the Public Health Service publication "The Vending of Foods and Beverages—A Sanitation Ordinance and Code."[3]

Other pertinent design information is included in the food service equipment standards prepared under the direction of the National Sanitation Foundation.[4] Where laboratory investigations involve work with infectious agents or radioisotopes, or extremely toxic materials, food and beverage consumption within the laboratory should be banned to reduce the possibility of employee contamination or infection. Multipurpose rooms for the employee's lunch, conference or periodical reading requirements can be planned to keep these functions separate from, but reasonably close to work areas. Another type of informal lunch facility located adjacent to a locker room is shown in Figure 7.2. Corridor-

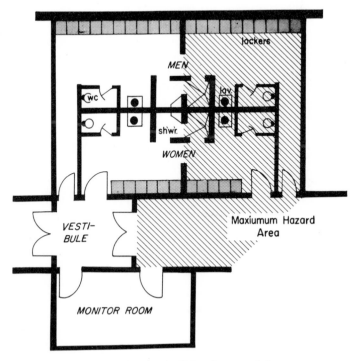

Figure 7.1 Locker-shower facilities interposed between maximum and minimum hazard areas.

located combination electric water heaters and coolers will help avoid the preparation of hot beverages immediately within restricted laboratories and eliminate any necessity to use laboratory water for drinking purposes. Moreover, organic chemistry laboratories are increasingly using automatic ice-making machines for their cubed, crushed and flaked laboratory ice needs. However, there are very real possibilities that the employees may contaminate the ice in these machines hence the latter should be conspicuously placarded to discourage the use of the ice for icing beverages.

Fire-Resistant Construction and Movable Partitions

Laboratory construction should be as fire-resistant as possible, since flammable and combustible substances and ignition sources are usually present. Local and state building codes, insurance carrier requirements and zoning laws should be consulted in the planning period as well as the NFPA National Fire Code[5] and pertinent handbooks.[6]

Any movable partitions used must comply with the required fire ratings of the local governing code. In the absence of these specific requirements, a principle to follow is: select partitions with a fire rating of sufficient duration to allow time both to actuate a local fire detection unit and to permit a local fire fighting crew to reach any specific laboratory before the fire can spread.

Figure 7.2   Employees' lunch facility adjacent to a locker area.

Noncombustible materials should be specified for movable partition filler panels; safety wire glass should be specified where glazing is required for laboratory and corridor doors.

Access-Egress Requirements

Every laboratory and work area where combustibles or toxic substances are used in even moderate quantities, or where a chemical fume hood is located, should have at least one alternate escape route. This second exit should preferably be a door, a "dutch" (half) door, or an escape panel positioned so it cannot be readily blocked. It should be uniquely colored or otherwise marked for ready identification. To achieve an unimpeded, quick escape from the laboratory in an emergency, doors should swing toward the corridor, but should not reduce the effective width of the corridor in the full-open position. This potential impasse is frequently resolved by creating a vestibule between the laboratory and corridor, the depth of which should correspond to furred-in space utilized for ducts, piping, "built-ins" such as clothes lockers, or recessed areas for desks. Laboratory and corridor door checks are useful. If checks are installed, they should be provided with fusible links. The necessity for laboratory door locks should be weighed carefully; although excellent for security purposes, they can cause the loss of valuable time by fire-control crews needing immediate access. Details on general access-egress requirements may be found in the NFPA Building Exits Code.[7]

Corridor Planning

Corridor space may be frequently occupied during the working hours by laboratory carts, platform trucks, animal cage racks, and other movable equipment. The maximum width of such equipment should be considered in determining the net corridor space available for personnel egress and fire-control purposes. Off-corridor space for storage of this equipment is recommended. Corridor niches for vending and ice-making machines, fire-fighting apparatus, and other emergency equipment have been used successfully to avoid corridor encroachment. Busy corridor intersections are hazards to personnel who may collide with moving carts and other equipment. Where possible, longer sight distances should be provided at these intersections by such devices as chamfered corners.

Room Layouts

Among other considerations, sizing the width of the laboratory module should be governed by the resultant net aisle space between bench units on opposite sides of the room. Too wide an aisle will offer possibilities for placing equipment in the middle of the room, resulting in narrow passages which increase accident potential. Blind-alley arrangements of laboratory benches and other equipment should be avoided, to maintain maximum possibilities for personnel escape.

Hood design criteria are discussed later in this chapter; hoods should preferably be placed to minimize such interferences as air disturbances from adjoining doors, ventilator units, and laboratory personnel traffic. Locating them as far from the exit as possible will increase the chance of personnel escape if a hood is involved in a fire; however, there are other considerations which will not always make this solution the best one.

Storage of Chemicals

Storage space for chemicals is potentially one of the most hazardous areas in a laboratory building due to the quantity of materials stored and the inability to completely segregate incompatible substances. Chemical laboratories have several distinct chemical storage needs, and one storage facility cannot be expected to meet them all.

Of immediate necessity in most chemical laboratories is a special locker or cupboard within the laboratory proper for storing limited quantities of solvents and corrosives in current use. A separately exhausted base cabinet in a chemical fume hood will usually serve this purpose. This arrangement is especially convenient for handling fuming or volatile reagents which otherwise might be stored directly in the fume hood.

There are two other needs for chemical storage space. One is an inside "ready" chemical storage area which should be centrally located for convenience and maximum use. It should be above ground level to expedite approach by fire-control personnel. As it is positioned above ground, natural ventilation can be resorted to in the event of failure of the ventilation system serving the room, and more adequate provisions for explosion venting are possible. A door fitted with a wire glass view panel is recommended for maximum visibility into the room. Furthermore, shelving and cabinet units should be positioned so as not to impede personnel escape. This type of storage space is not intended for the bulk storage of solvents or compressed gas cylinders. It may be set up as a self-service facility or, preferably, be manned by an attendant trained in the properties and hazards of the materials stored.

Another type of chemical storage is a "bulk" storage area, preferably located in a structure separate from the laboratory building, or in an appendage to it. Reserve quantities of liquid and solid chemicals as well as compressed gas cylinders should be stored here. What constitutes "safe" quantities of solvents or compressed gases to be stored in a laboratory will depend partly on their rate of use, e.g., no more than a three-day supply of a solvent should be stored.

In designing this latter facility, compressed gases and other materials that are incompatible or highly reactive, should be stored in separate enclosures; or, if in the same enclosure, they should be placed as far apart as possible. For example, alkali metals should not be stored near water or chlorinated hydrocarbons, and strong oxidizing agents should not be near organic liquids. Various references describe a number of incompatible substances.[8, 9, 10, 11, 11a]

The "bulk" storage area may be relatively simple in design with louvered walls or other "open" construction. If used to store materials subject to freezing, *e.g.* benzene and glacial acetic acid, its design will be more substantial and will require minimum heating and ventilation. For summer conditions, it will require insulation from the sun, vents for gravity ventilation or special sparkproof-blade exhaust fans for mechanical ventilation.

Solvent-dispensing operations may be conducted at these locations if certain safety design details, such as sparkproof materials, electrical bonding of dispensing drums and solvent safety containers, are provided.[12] Maximum use of "bulk" storage facilities can be encouraged by designing them so that materials can be transported to the laboratory buildings on hand trucks or carts instead of motor trucks. The degree of accessibility and distance(s) from the building(s) they serve will largely determine the extent to which the storage facilities are used. Figure 7.3 illustrates a storeroom constructed in a series of cubicles for separating different classes of chemicals.

High-Pressure Processes

Equipment such as apparatus for hydrogenation and laboratory processes and pilot plant operations having explosive possibilities should be installed in isolated, protected areas. Designing facilities for these purposes is a highly specialized art. Generally, they will include blowout wall sections or rupture panels, and barricades intended to vent an explosion and deflect or intercept hurled objects, or they will be oriented to take advantage of hillsides and other natural barriers. Figure 7.4 shows one type of pilot plant building with large glazed and corrugated cement-asbestos board walls which rupture readily and relieve blast pressures. On request, manu-

facturers of laboratory high-pressure equipment can make specific recommendations regarding protective structures and related details such as remote-control features. In addition, there are a number of references on this subject. [13, 14, 15]

First-Aid and Medical Facilities

First-aid rooms or more elaborate medical facilities[16] should be provided for each laboratory building or associated groups of laboratory structures. Among the features recommended for such a facility is a shower where chemicals and radiological substances may be more thoroughly flushed from an employee's skin after an initial washing under a safety shower.

UTILITIES
Water Supply

One problem with water-distribution systems within laboratory structures is to design against the possibility of backflow or back-siphonage, which may result from one of the following conditions: (1) sudden break in the supply main,

Figure 7.3   Sectionalized bulk chemical storage building.

(2) shut-off of the building supply accompanied by an open discharge valve at a low point in the building distribution system, or (3) attainment of critical rates of flow in a supply line above its capacity to furnish under-positive pressure. All these conditions can and do exist occasionally, especially in laboratory buildings where temporary piping is frequently installed.

The consequences of any of these hydraulic irregularities are the same: (1) negative pressures or partial vacuums are set up in all or part of the building water system; (2) flow is reversed in the pipe lines, and (3) the contents of tanks, laboratory vessels and sinks can contaminate the potable water supply.

Various methods are used to break vacuums and avoid backflow conditions. The simplest and most foolproof is to provide an air gap between the outlet of the supply fixture and the receiving vessel. Minimum air gaps and the more common methods of backflow prevention are outlined in the American Standards Association publications Nos. A 40.4, and A 40.6. [17]

Plumbing design which was originally safe can be nullified by the not-infrequent practice by laboratory investigators of installing shut-off valves on the outlet sides of vacuum breakers, none of which are intended for those conditions. Also, laboratory equipment connected to vacuum breakers, but located higher than the vacuum breaker air ports, can cause these items to function improperly. If reduced-pressure zone backflow preventers can be used to isolate or industrialize the water supply system, no vacuum breakers are needed. Figure 7.5 shows a cross-section of this type of backflow preventer.

There is a loss in water pressure through these units; consequently, water pressures within the system should be carefully checked against manufacturers' flow-pressure loss curves for their equipment. Lines supplying drinking fountains, toilets, and fire apparatus should branch off ahead of the backflow units.

An entirely different safety problem is involved with distilled water handling. A distilled water distribution system with outlets located in individual laboratories will eliminate the hazards of personnel handling heavy distilled water carboys.

Figure 7.4　Pilot plant laboratory with rupture walls for venting blast pressures.

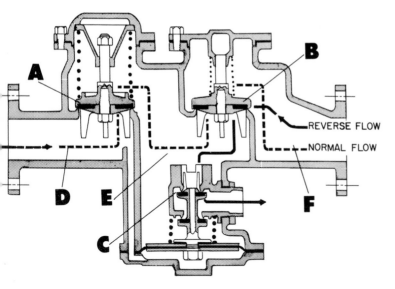

REVERSE FLOW

NORMAL FLOW

Figure 7.5   Cross section of reduced-pressure zone backflow preventer.

Drainage

Odors and fumes in laboratories frequently can be traced to sewer gas escaping through cupsink traps where the water seals have evaporated, or have been lost through unvented or improperly vented waste lines. Anti-siphon traps are sometimes employed to eliminate the need for vents; however, their use is prohibited in some localities and they are subject to several limitations. The National Plumbing Code, Illustrated,[18] lists approved types of plumbing trap installations.

Electrical Distribution and Convenience Outlets

The basic guide to both life and fire safety of electrical installations is the National Electrical Code.[19] In applying this code to laboratories, consideration should be given as to how the distribution systems are to enter each work area. For example, by using vertical risers with horizontal take-offs at each floor level, it is possible to eliminate overhead bus ducts and conduits, thus saving space and minimizing the hazards of overhead maintenance.

Frequently overlooked is the need for an absolutely independent electrical grounding system.

Water pipes and other metallic items are not dependable as grounds. One laboratory uses a ground network solidly connected to the steel work of the building frame, all metal pipes, and steel partitions at many locations throughout the building. The network is then connected to a grid of ground rods and cables extending into the ground outside the building.[20]

Water spilled on laboratory floors can be prevented from causing damage to electrical bus ducts by installing raised curbs or sleeves where the ducts pass through floor chases. Electrical outlets should be excluded in the immediate vicinity of sinks and similar grounded equipment. With 110-120 volt convenience outlets, the three-prong, American Standards Association-type grounded plug shown in Figure 7.6 should be used.[21] Maximum protection against electrical shocks from accidental grounding of laboratory personnel also requires constant surveillance of all electrical equipment as to the necessity for and adequacy of grounding.

Electrical outlets for chemical fume hoods occur in a number of positions both inside and outside hoods. Outlets in hoods are subject to accelerated corrosion. When placed outside, there are other hazards from dangling electric cords, and from unconfined solvents flowing over the

Figure 7.6   American Standards Association grounded plug.

edge of the work surfaces and igniting in outlets. In either case, it is recommended that each hood convenience outlet be separately switched from outside the hood. This will permit the hood sash to be closed before any electrical circuit is energized.

Compressed Gases

Gases which are most frequently used in laboratories in sufficient volume to justify piping distribution systems include natural gas, compressed air (ranging from 10 to 100 psi), hydrogen, helium, nitrogen, and oxygen. These piping systems are convenient, but they present a number of hazards including distribution of wrong gas in a distribution system, selecting unsafe piping materials for certain gases, and leaking, particularly within confined wall structures. Publications of the Compressed Air Association[22] offer recommended details and practices for safe distribution system installations.

Some laboratory designs include special conveniently located corridor lockers for individual gas cylinders or limited numbers of cylinders. These lockers should be well ventilated.

Piping Identification

The American Standards Association piping color scheme assigns a distinctive color for the piping of five main classes of materials. The five pipe colors (red, yellow, green, blue, and purple) may be supplemented by stenciled legends indicating the precise materials carried in each pipe. The value of this system lies in its relative simplicity and quick recognition by maintenance employees and emergency crews. Whenever possible, this uniform method of pipe marking should be applied.[23] This piping color system is not related to the color scheme for identifying plastic insert discs used in laboratory benchtop fixture valve handles.

Fire Detection and Extinguishing

The diversity of chemical, electrical and other fire hazards associated with laboratories, plus differences in the requirements of various fire insurance carriers, make most generalizations on the above subjects of little value. Details of recommended practices are usually available from the laboratory's insurance carrier. In addition, the NFPA "Handbook of Fire Protection"[24] offers considerable coverage of this subject.

Except for chemical storerooms or laboratories using large quantities of solvents and other flammable materials, it has not been universal practice to provide automatic sprinkler or carbon dioxide extinguishing systems. Each laboratory or chemical storeroom may present a special case, since sodium, for example, will react violently with water. Rate-of-rise fire detection units are relatively inexpensive and are recommended for continuous surveillance of laboratory and storeroom areas. Locations of these units should be planned to avoid possible accidental actuation by various heat-producers, such as sterilizers and ovens.

All fire-line control valves should be of the outside stem and yoke (O.S. and Y.) type and at least the main valves should be electrically supervised. Residual pressures at the extremities of fire lines should be sufficient to operate a "fog" or spray nozzle to combat fires of flammable liquids and to minimize water damage. Outside pumper connections should be considered wherever standpipe or sprinkler systems are installed, particularly where there is any possibility that water pressures can fall below the desired range.

Safety Showers and Eye Irrigators

Safety showers are essential in or near chemical laboratories. Their number, location, distinctive marking and type of design are necessarily subject to individual interpretation. Features which are helpful for laboratory personnel attempting to locate them include: (1) a standardized, repetitive location with relation to each laboratory, or chemical fume hood; and (2) a pull chain and/or pull chain handle placed where it can be quickly located by the smallest employee groping for it.

Floor drains may be utilized under these showers where there is danger of water damage in the surrounding areas. Unless their traps are regularly filled as a result of a rigid maintenance program, they can present nuisance and possible explosion hazards by venting gas from the laboratory drain system. However, floor drains permit the selection of shower head valves which will stay in an open position. This is an important detail since it allows an employee to use both hands to remove his clothing. Flushometer-type shower valves allow a time lag before closing and thus to a considerable extent obviate the need for floor drains, since both hands can be used for a few seconds before the valve must be re-actuated. Water damage is thus partially controlled and minimized.

A good eye protection program is basic to any laboratory, but eye irrigators or fountains may also be necessary. Generally these should be located convenient to or within laboratory sinks where there is less opportunity for water damage. Recommended installation features are foot-operated or similar types of valves which leave the operator's hands free.

EXHAUST VENTILATION
Explosion, Fire and Smoke Control

In any ventilation duct, and in chemical exhaust ducts in particular, there exists the possibility of an explosion or fire. Small radius bends and abruptly expanded sections of ducts should be avoided in duct design, as they tend to build up chemical precipitates and deposits in ducts. Where strong oxidizing agents such as nitric acid and perchloric acid are used, there is always the possibility of igniting dusts or vapors composed of organic substances. Perchloric acid is especially critical in this respect: it can explode upon shock as well as detonate spontaneously by reaction with organic condensates. If perchloric acid is to be used more or less continuously, a separate hood built of impervious material such as stone and designed with a water-tight floor and sides should be specified. The hood and its connected duct should be equipped with water sprays set at strategic points to flush down all surfaces.

Laboratory exhaust ventilation usually involves the problem of designing ducts for which the various types of materials to be exhausted are not known in advance, and which can be expected to change from time to time. Hence, there may be conflicting criteria for an ideal chemical exhaust system. For example, one frequently advocated principle is that each laboratory chemical fume hood exhaust duct should be separately ducted and exhausted to the roof or other discharge point by the shortest possible route. The advantages here are the convenience to the operator in the complete control of his hood; the better control in monitoring what materials are used in a hood and whether or not they are compatible; and restriction of the operations to only one laboratory in the event of duct or exhaust blower repairs.

There are equally good reasons for collecting the exhausts from a number of hoods into common exhaust headers, especially if these headers are served by dual exhaust fans to increase the reliability factor of the system. For example, common exhaust headers can terminate at the most favorable points for discharge from the building to minimize chemical exhaust short-circuiting to fresh air intakes. Where individual outlets are provided, short-circuiting from a discharging exhaust to an adjacent non-functioning hood exhaust outlet is a possibility. Further, large ducts can be more readily inspected and cleaned. Fume hoods which are individual-operator controlled pose special air-balance problems in large air-conditioned laboratory buildings unless supplementary air can be provided. Hence, the desirable feature of flexibility in hood exhaust control must be weighed against the undersirable alternative of unbalancing the ventilating system.

Another duct design principle which may have certain disadvantages is the general requirement of fire codes for fire dampers in ducts passing between floors. Difficulties may be expected if the design specifies automatic fire dampers in chemical exhaust ducts without anticipating what might be the practical effects of a fire within the hood. With dampers of conventional design, chemical corrosion or encrustment surrounding the damper may cause it to fail to operate when needed. On the other hand, serious problems may result if an automatic fire damper should be actuated. These include backup of smoke and possibly of highly hazardous chemical fumes from the hood into the laboratory. Continuous blower operation in such cases minimizes personnel exposures in the building and enables fire control crews to approach the hood safely.

Laboratory ventilation design should not utilize the corridors as return or balancing spaces. Failure to provide for ducted exhaust from each laboratory will impair its unrestricted use for various laboratory processes and agents.

Dust, Fume, Mist and Gas Control

Effective containment and safe removal of laboratory vapors, gases, mists, and smokes are the dual objectives of a laboratory exhaust ventilation system, and a properly designed chemical fume hood is the most important element in the exhaust system. "Safe" hoods require good design, plus careful operation to compensate for any design limitations in the hood and the toxicities of the materials they handle.

The stability of the air flow into hoods has been studied when subject to random air movements and cross currents in the laboratory. Under normal conditions of cross drafts from personnel movements in the laboratory, influence of air currents from diffusers, and normal hot plate or burner usage in the hood, an average hood face velocity of 100 feet per minute is recommended.[25] Hood design features, and control concentrations and volatilities of the materials used are other factors which must be considered in more closely approximating the design air velocity at the hood face.[26] Where no release of materials to the room can be permitted, such as with alpha emitters and pathogenic agents, gloved boxes or safety hoods must be provided to preclude escape of any possibly contaminated air.

An air foil design at the hood entrance and the avoidance of excessive depressions, such as sinks, in the hood floor are other details which contribute to improved hood performance.[25] Laminated safety glass has good breakage control properties when subject to explosions and is recommended for hood sash construction.

A number of safety-related design details associated with hood exhaust problems are recommended. Mechanically operated balancing dampers or by-pass dampers are superior to the gravity-operated type on hood exhaust ducts because of their tighter seal against fumes and better control over face velocities.[25] Since fumes can escape through pressurized ducts of conventional design, hood exhaust blowers should be located at the point of exhaust from the building, rather than directly on top of a hood. In no case should exhaust blower motors be enclosed in an exhaust duct.

Restricted room air turnover rates, if proposed for laboratory air conditioning, will impose difficult if not impossible conditions for effective operation of a hood in the average size laboratory module. Hood designs with lower air velocities at the face to meet these arbitrary limitations on their use will usually result. Hoods for which supplementary tempered outdoor air is introduced at the face in a peripheral arrangement have been designed and are in use. However, they are less satisfactory than hoods of conventional design which use larger quantities of conditioned air. With these special designs, the hood operator is frequently forced to work with the sash in a partially closed position.

Special design hoods which have glazed, movable panels the full height and completely enclosing the hood, such as the "California-type" hoods, are useful for fractionation columns and other tall apparatus. Their good visibility minimizes the need for the operator to enter the hood enclosure during periods of actual operation.

Regardless of design criteria, too much emphasis cannot be placed on a plant maintenance program for regularly checking hood performance under actual operating conditions.[26]

Laboratory uses for paper chromatography cabinets and jars and other large, fume-producing apparatus which cannot be conveniently located in hoods of "standard" design are increasing. Walk-in hoods and special local exhaust scoops designed to handle solvent fumes from this equipment may be needed, particularly in air-conditioned laboratories operating with minimum volumes of air for dilution purposes.

Figure 7.7 illustrates how chromatography jars can be vented, using a flexible hose connected to a movable, slotted air scoop. Also shown is a ventilated cabinet for evaporating solvents from paper chromatograms. As a safety detail, the air scoop is fitted with sparkproof rollers running on well-mounted rails.

Another design solution for handling excessive fume or heat-producing laboratory apparatus in air conditioned structures is to establish strategically located special rooms provided with high rates of ventilation. While the locations of these rooms may be somewhat inconvenient to the individual laboratory worker, they can accommodate this special equipment with the maximum possible safety and comfort to the operator.

Household refrigerators are frequently used in laboratories for storage of chemicals. Unless properly modified to remove all internal ignition sources, they may be the cause of fires or explosions.[26.1, 11] Details for modification[26.2] include the following:

(1) Relocate the control thermostat system to the exterior of the box, preferably on top;

(2) Disconnect and abandon the wiring to the light socket, door switch, butter cooler, and any other internal services;

(3) Relocate starting relay of the compressor motor to a location near the top of the box;

(4) In older boxes, substitute a magnetic door closure for latch closers to permit venting in case of pressure build-up.

A refrigerator, specifically designed for storage of solvents and other chemicals, has been given a Class I Group C & D rating by Underwriters Laboratory.[26.3]

Walk-in constant temperature or cold rooms also present possibilities for personnel asphyxiation and explosions where laboratory procedures involving solvents and flammable or toxic gases may be conducted within them. Illuminating gas should not be piped into these rooms; if solvents

are to be used, the rooms should contain provisions to include an air supply and exhaust for them. Air heat economizers can be designed to make this practice economically feasible. Fans or evaporator units, electrical convenience outlets and laboratory equipment such as stirrers and shakers are potential ignition points. Hence, the ventilation design of these rooms is a critical item and should be carefully considered. Features such as the air scoop above, or small hoods, can also be used to reduce the air supply requirements for these special rooms. A four-inch minimum diameter port-hole with an insulated plug located near the top of the walk-in room door and a similar one located near the bottom of the door will permit the use of a portable blower to evacuate the room in the event it is accidentally contaminated.

Exhaust Gas Short-Circuiting

Both building exhaust and intake air locations should be planned to minimize the possibility that fumes exhausted from the building or effluents from nearby incinerators may short-circuit to the fresh air intakes. The configuration of the laboratory building, its distances from surrounding buildings, the character of surrounding terrain, and seasonal wind directions are among the factors which must be taken into account. Very little authoritative information having immediate

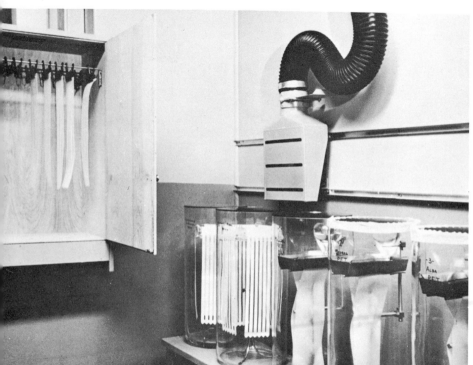

Figure 7.7   The air scoop of a flexible exhaust duct for ventilating paper chromatography processes.

design application is available on this subject. Meteorological data on such local conditions as temperature inversions and "windless" days may be secured from local U. S. Weather Bureau offices. These will help serve as a general guide in evaluating the possibilities for short-circuiting. The ventilation design of a low-silhouette laboratory structure having multiple roof-top chemical exhaust outlets and fresh air inlets should be approached with a good deal of care. Chemical exhaust collector ducts, developed as an integral part of the building architecture and extending above the zone of influence of the building, are one solution. These may terminate in one or more chimneys.

ILLUMINATION

Recommended Lighting Levels

Lighting, both from the standpoint of distribution and intensity, should be given careful consideration. New data on recommended lighting levels have been obtained on both seeing task and lighting level interrelationships; seeing tasks are ranked between the extremes of "easy" and "most difficult".[27] To minimize eyestrain in the laboratory, the basic approach is to maintain the same rates of adjustment of the human eye between the "more difficult" seeing tasks as between the "easy" seeing tasks. This requires higher brightness values for the "more difficult" work. In turn, required brightness, coupled with light-reflectance values of the materials used in the task, provides the basis for determining the required level of illumination.

Although no formal recommendations based on the new method described above have been made for laboratory lighting, good present-day lighting needs for laboratory procedures can be met with a general level of at least 50 footcandles at the work surface level. For close work, supplementary illumination is frequently necessary to increase the local lighting level to 100 footcandles or more. Lighting diffuser selection and location should avoid any shadowing of work by personnel stationed in seated or standing positions in front of the laboratory bench. Related problems and practices in industrial lighting are discussed in various informational bulletins.[28, 29, 30]

Safety Aspects

As with any other overhead item, an improperly secured lighting fixture or lamp may be a hazard. Specially designed locks are available to prevent the accidental dropping of fluorescent tubes. Louvers and other parts of overhead lights can fall, particularly during lamp replacement and, hence, should be carefully hinged or otherwise secured. Various devices are available to protect fluorescent light ballasts from failures which may result in fires or eruptions of their asphaltic or resin sealants on laboratory occupants.[31, 32]

LIQUID AND SOLID WASTES

Liquid Wastes, Toxic and Radiologic Agents

Neither large volumes of laboratory waste acids or solvents, nor even small quantities of certain highly reactive, toxic, radioactive, or potentially explosive chemicals should be indiscriminately disposed of via the sewer. These practices run the risk of sewer main explosions set off by an accidental ignition of high concentrations of volatile vapors, and exposure of maintenance workers to explosive and toxic atmospheres and chance mixtures of compounds which may form such products as hydrogen sulfide and hydrogen cyanide. Other hazards include the possible return of these toxic or explosive sewer atmospheres directly to the laboratory via drain traps with evaporated water seals. Further, there are splash, fume, violent reaction and container breakage hazards to personnel engaging in dumping and flushing these materials at the laboratory sink.

If the quantities of these waste materials, leaking gas cylinders, and unlabeled containers of chemicals warrant, it is recommended that a laboratory waste chemical collection service be planned, together with a waste chemical handling and disposal site. Solvents can be fed into domestic or industrial-size oil burners mounted in firebrick combustion chambers. By adjusting fuel-air ratios, smokeless combustion is readily obtained.

Corrosives may be collected and either diluted or neutralized to minimum pH levels required by the local sewer authority, if discharged to the public sewer, or health authority, if emptied directly into a public watercourse.

In handling toxic compounds and unlabeled bottles or containers suspected of containing peroxides, such disposal personnel safeguards as a safety barrier equipped with a bottle drop slot and a container breaking or crushing device should be planned. A sketch of a laboratory waste chemical disposal facility is shown in Figure 7.8.

Health authorities should be consulted for any local requirements for pretreatment of liquid in-

fectious wastes. Special conditions may sometimes require the installation of tanks or blow cases for "pasteurizing" such wastes by the use of steam.

Liquid wastes containing the short half-life elements, phosphorus-32 and iodine-131 can be disposed of by well-developed dilution methods.[33] Radioactive waste elements may be disposed of by dilution to levels of radioactivity specified in the U. S. Atomic Energy Commission regulations.[34]

Figure 7.8   Sketch of laboratory waste chemical disposal facility at National Institutes of Health.

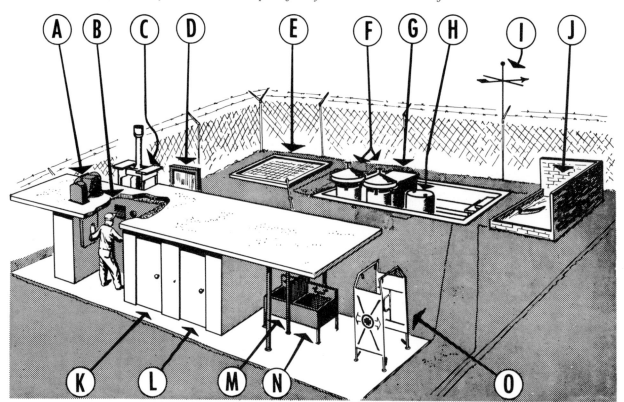

A. Exhaust fan for leaking gas cylinder enclosure.	E. Neutralizing tank.	K. Lime storage room.
B. Crusher loading and observation area.	F. Waste solvent storage tanks.	L. Pit controller and crusher pump room.
C. Bottle and can crusher.	G. Waste solvent burner.	M. Acid dump sink.
D. Observation mirror.	H. Burner starting fuel storage.	N. Solvent dump sink.
	I. Weather Vane.	O. Safety shower.
	J. Sludge burning pit.	

Solid Wastes Handling and Disposal

Combustible and noncombustible wastes should be collected, stored, and handled in separate receptacles starting at the laboratory. The well-designed laboratory should have adequate and convenient space reserved for both types of waste containers.

Where laboratories must dispose of contaminated biological products and sacrificed animals, it is strongly recommended that an auxiliary fuel-fired incinerator be provided. Only if the laboratory wastes present no hazards of infection should contract hauling and off-site disposal of these materials be considered. Information on the applications of basic classes of incinerators, including a check list to avoid common incineration design errors, is available from the Incinerator Institute of America.[35]

While incineration is the recommended method for the safe disposal of infectious solid wastes, the waste-handling system must safely convey these wastes to the incinerator. Disposable plastic or waterproofed paper liners fitted in metal waste cans, and gathered and tied when full, will safely contain these wastes until they are discharged in the incinerator. Waste-can washing facilities at the incinerator are also recommended. Hot water or steam plus suitable detergents should be used for cleaning, followed by a hot-water rinse.

Garbage grinders are being used increasingly to dispose of small volumes of organic wastes at locations where they are produced. Since aerosols can escape from such grinding operations, depending on the materials being ground, grinder covers or special enclosures should be used to prevent this.

Solid radioactive waste disposal procedures generally involve land burial or disposal at sea.[34, 35, 36] In either case, these wastes must be temporarily stored by the laboratory pending their removal. Wastes which may decompose can be bagged, marked and stored in deep-freeze units. Other wastes should be stored in whatever containers are required by the contract collector. If wastes are to be disposed of at sea, small concrete burial vaults may be used for their collection.[37] Areas for the temporary storage of these wastes are preferably isolated from the bulk of the laboratory operations. However, they should be convenient to a truck loading dock.

HOUSEKEEPING

Floor Materials and Maintenance

Floor cleaning and maintenance constitute the most important single activity in the laboratory routine cleaning. Other than appearance, few standards are available as to what constitutes a clean laboratory floor. Spilled mercury, radioactive substances and microbiological contaminants may be present on an otherwise clean-appearing floor; these will require special procedures or equipment for their detection. Tissue preparation and pathology laboratories commonly spill a good deal of wax in their operations, which contributes to floor slip hazards.

For most laboratory applications, composition tiles of asphalt, vinyl or rubber are generally favored over continuous sheeting material because of their easy removal and replacement if damaged. However, joints between the tiles still present problems, since they tend to permit lodgement for spilled mercury and allow radioactive materials in solution to penetrate into the tile base. Floor waxes in the joints between the individual tiles alleviate but not eliminate this problem. Concrete floors, treated with various dust-preventing sealers[38] are relatively impervious, although with wear, re-sealing will be necessary. Resilient rubber mats used on concrete floors should be selected with care to prevent trip hazards from upturned edges.

Construction Features

"Built-ins", such as clothes lockers, or sloping top wall-cases are typical construction details which will assist in maintaining neat and orderly laboratories. Unfortunately, these design details are still subject to individual misuse.

Air-conditioning diffusers or return grilles should be located where there is the least possibility of apparatus being stored and blocking their operation or routine cleaning.

Locking-type, grounded convenience outlets, located in corridors at frequent intervals, are recommended for operating floor maintenance machines, as they cannot be inadvertently disconnected. A central vacuum-cleaning system should be considered for laboratories where toxic dusts and other hazardous materials may be encountered. Dust-receiving hoppers for these control systems should be equipped with provisions for flushing their contents direct to drain, rather than risk exposing maintenance workers to the added hazards of cleaning them.

NOISE CONTROL

Noise in spaces occupied for about 8 hours a day and over a period of up to 30 years must exceed 85 decibels above threshold before any permanent hearing loss can be caused.[39] Since sound pressure levels in most laboratories rarely approach this figure, laboratory noise is not ordinarily considered a health hazard. Intermittent noise peaks, such as from elevator machinery, centrifuge and pneumatic tube operations, can be a source of annoyance to laboratory occupants.[40] Yet various studies have not been conclusive in demonstrating any significant reduction in office or industrial employee efficiency with these annoyance factors.[41] Where the laboratory design raises doubts concerning noise sources which may interfere with normal conversation or annoy laboratory occupants, plans should be reviewed by an acoustics consultant.

MICROBIOLOGICAL SAFETY

The hazards of infecting laboratory personnel are chiefly due to lack of control of the possibilities for escape of infectious agents from specific laboratory procedures. Hence, the design of microbiological laboratories is chiefly a problem of providing facilities for safely isolating processes where there are any hazards of personnel infection. Aerosols produced from homogenizing infected tissues have been known to cause difficulty in this respect.

Other design objectives are to: (1) select nonporous and readily cleaned materials or finishes for floors, walls, benchtops and other surfaces subject to soiling; and (2) specify or design equipment, such as light fixtures, with surfaces tending to minimize contamination and to facilitate cleaning.

Many microbiological laboratories handle, over a period of time, a variety of disease agents which have a wide range of potential contagion. Hence, it is good design practice to include at least minimum safety provisions for work with such agents in every microbiological laboratory. However, facilities themselves should not be expected to give complete assurance of safety. Judgement of the laboratory operator is still required as to whether a procedure can safely take place in the open laboratory, or within a bacteriological safety cabinet or hood.

Safety and Sterile Hoods and Cabinets

Some confusion exists between the basic functions and design differences of safety hoods or cabinets, as compared with sterile hoods or sterile cubicles. Safety hoods, or cabinets, are used to confine biological (or chemical or radioactive) agents and to protect the individual operator handling them. Sterile hoods or cubicles are primarily intended to minimize or eliminate contamination of bacterial cultures or tissue cultures.

Sterile cubicles may or may not have a bacteriological safety hood or cabinet within them. This decision depends on whether the principal problem is judged to be operator protection or prevention of overgrowths and other contamination in the cultures. If hazardous procedures are confined to them, sterile rooms can increase laboratory efficiency by reducing the area of potential contamination within a larger laboratory, and thus permit other activities to proceed concurrently in the remaining areas.

Maximum operator safety is obtained either by using a gloved box type of safety hood for manipulations, or a safety cabinet completely enclosing a hazardous process. Where more freedom of movement by the operator is needed, some compromising of safety is sometimes permitted by omitting the safety hood glove port panel. With this stripped-down safety hood, or inoculation hood, other adjuncts to the hood design are needed for safety purposes. These include positive air flow through the hood opening and ultraviolet radiation protection within the hood. The use of gowns, gloves and masks by the operator may also be required.

Maximum protection of the product or culture

may also be obtained with the same gloved box type of safety hood if operated under positive air pressure. If the gloved port panel is omitted, such culture protection features as an ultraviolet light within the hood and a positive air flow from the hood toward the operator should be provided. Successful work can also be accomplished by the careful operator with a sterile hood having a quiescent atmosphere rather than any air flow.

Safety Hood and Cabinet Design

There are a few important principles to observe in safety hood and cabinet design. Their materials of construction should be smooth, highly reflective to ultraviolet radiation and not subject to corrosion by cleaning and disinfecting materials. They should be designed to eliminate any sharp interior corners or crevices which cannot be readily cleaned or disinfected. In general, their interiors should be free of any obstructions where spilled materials might accumulate or otherwise escape notice. Gasketing of any removable or hinged view windows or panels must be tight-fitting, and the gasketing material itself should have a smooth, nonporous finish. Ultraviolet installations should have bare tubes. If reflectors are used, they should be located so as not to cast shadows. Ultraviolet safety precautions are discussed below.

While exhaust ventilation is required for the ungloved hood, it is usually also provided for the gloved port safety hood to remove excess heat and prevent collection of condensate from bunsen burner operation. Treating the exhaust for removal of infectious aerosols is accomplished by a number of methods involving either heat, filtration or ultraviolet radiation; these are separately outlined below. The degree of treatment required is a matter of both judgement and arbitrary decision. It involves possibilities for accidental contamination of service personnel who are charged with maintenance, possible exhaust air re-entry into the building, and the hazards to the building environs. Safety cabinets have one feature not normally provided in a safety hood. This is an interlocking switch arrangement so that in the event the access door or sliding sash is opened or raised, connected electrical equipment within the cabinet will stop operating.

Sterile Hood and Cabinet Design

As mentioned above, sterile hood design features, with the one exception of reverse air flow or a quiescent interior atmosphere, are identical with those for gloved safety hoods.

Sterile room design presents a number of architecturally related problems. There is no unanimous opinion on whether to provide hinged or sliding doors. Hinged doors are usually easier to gasket effectively. Another design detail to reduce contamination is to provide an ultraviolet light screen or barrier curtain at the door.[42]

Continuous, unbroken and easily cleaned floor finish materials should be provided within sterile rooms. Linoleum sheeting is frequently used for this purpose. Preferably, the walls and floors should be free of shelves and cabinet units, which are difficult both to clean and to clean around. Criteria for selecting benchtop materials are the same as those for the interiors of safety hoods.

The exhaust air from safety hoods handling infectious agents inside sterile rooms can be handled by methods outlined below. The degree of supply air treatment for a sterile room depends on the intended functions of the room. Treatment is usually accomplished by filtration alone, or by a combination of filtration and ultraviolet radiation or electrostatic precipitation. As these rooms are usually closely confined spaces, their air-inlet diffusers should be carefully designed and selected to minimize air turbulence and possible disturbance of contaminants on surfaces.

Air Sterilization

Heat. Air incinerators should maintain proper contact time-temperature relationships for effective sterilization of air. Critical contact times and temperatures have been determined for bacterial spores.[43] These incinerators will usually consist of an initial heating section, followed by a section of insulated duct to maintain the required contact time at elevated temperatures.

Filtration. Filters are available for removing air-borne microbiological agents down to sizes approaching the larger virus particles.[44, 45] Where virus particles may be involved, a fundamental consideration having practical design importance is whether the virus particles do exist by themselves or are found in aerosols of larger diameters, or in bits of tissue. Enormous energies, not normally developed in the usual laboratory processes or procedures, are required to produce particles in the sub-micron or virus-size range. Where filters are used, provisions must be made for sterilizing them in place before removal. This can be accomplished with built-in, thermostated filter heating elements installed in insulated filter housings. Time-temperature combinations for sterilizing filter beds, *e.g.* 338° F. for one hour, should be designed for.

Ultraviolet. Ultraviolet light installations can be designed for effective air sterilization. One of the prime safety considerations with these installations is the assurance that the ultraviolet lamps are always clean and operating at their rated efficiencies. Air filters placed ahead of the ultraviolet installations will help in this respect. Most important is to place the tubes in duct sections where they can be frequently inspected and cleaned when necessary.

Care must be exercised in designing ultraviolet installations for air or surface disinfection in inhabited areas. The maximum ultraviolet light intensity in the occupied zone of a laboratory should not exceed 0.5 microwatt per square centimeter, if the period of occupancy does not exceed 7 hours.[46]

When greater ultraviolet intensities are required for laboratory decontamination purposes, the ultraviolet and general lighting circuit switches should be interlocked to permit only one of these lighting systems to be energized at a time.

Air Balance

If adjoining laboratories or other work spaces differ significantly in their potentials for personnel infection, their relative air pressures should be unbalanced to promote a positive movement of air from the lesser hazard area to the greater.

Steam Sterilizers

Laboratory steam sterilizers or autoclaves present certain hazards which can be minimized by good design and constuction and proper maintenance and operation. Certification that a steam sterilizer has met the rules for the construction of unfired pressure vessels should be required in building construction or equipment purchasing specifications.[47]

The sterilizer temperature gage should be actuated by changes in temperature rather than by pressure converted to temperature as the important factor in sterilization is temperature. The gage should be located in the sterilizer steam return line.

Other safety features should include a positive action locking device to prevent accidental opening of the sterilizer door under pressure. If a number of laboratory personnel may use the same sterilizer, or if the sterilizer may be unattended for periods of time, the inclusion of automatic cycling features is recommended to reduce the human error in operation.

RADIOLOGICAL SAFETY

Selected aspects of radiological safety, such as liquid and solid waste disposal, and design features for hoods, personnel locker and shower facilities have been covered in preceding sections of this chapter. Many of the microbiological safety requirements in laboratory design are equally applicable in radiological laboratories. However, the outstanding differences from a design standpoint between these two types of laboratories lie in the problems of shielding ionizing radiation sources and the relative persistence of radioisotopes as contrasted with most microbiological agents. Several of the numerous excellent references on shielding and protection against X and gamma-rays used in hospital and commercial applications are listed at the end of this chapter. [48, 49, 50]

It is recommended that radiation facilities designers acquaint themselves with various publications on radiation safety techniques.[51] The services of a consultant in this specialized area of laboratory design is also recommended to insure both adequate and economical design, especially since earlier radiation laboratory design standards have been relaxed as additional experience has been acquired in this field.

REFERENCES

1. National Plumbing Code, American Standards Association Code No. ASA-A40.8-1955, American Standards Association, 70 East 45th Street, New York, 17, N. Y.

2. Mechanical and Electrical Engineering Handbook, General Services Administration, Public Buildings Service, Washington, D. C., June 1958.

3. "The Vending of Foods and Beverages—A Sanitation Ordinance and Code," (Public Health Service Publication), Supt. of Documents, Washington 25, D. C. (15¢).

4. Soda Fountain and Luncheonette Equipment—Standard No. 1; Food Service Equipment—Standard No. 2; Spray Type Dishwashing Machines—Standard No. 3; Electric Commercial Cooking and Warming Equipment—Standard No. 4; Gas Commercial Cooking and Warming Equipment—Standard No. 4. National Sanitation Foundation, Ann Arbor, Michigan (50¢ ea.).

5. National Fire Code, Vol. III, "Building Construction and Equipment," 1958, National Fire Protection Association, 60 Batterymarch Street, Boston, Massachusetts.

6. Handbook of Industrial Loss Prevention, prepared by Staff of the Factory Mutual Engineering Division, McGraw-Hill Book Co., Inc., New York, N. Y., 1959.

7. Building Exits Code No. 101-1958, Fifteenth Edition, National Fire Protection Association.

8. National Fire Code, Vol. I, Flammable Liquids and Gases, and

9. National Fire Code, Vol. II, Combustible Solids, Dusts, Chemicals, and Explosives, National Fire Protection Association.

10. Nicholson, D. G., "Safety Practices. Industrial vs Academic Chemical Laboratories," Paper No. 3M, Abstracts of Papers, American Chemical Society Meeting, Chicago, September 1958, American Chemical Society.

11. Fawcett, H. H., "Chemical Booby Traps," *Ind. Eng. Chem.*, 51, 4, 89A-90A, (April, 1959).

11a. Sax, N. I., "Dangerous Properties of Industrial Materials," Reinhold, 1957. (Second edition in preparation)

12. "Static Electricity," Safe Practices Pamphlet No. 52, National Safety Council, Inc., 20 North Wacker Drive, Chicago 6, Ill. 14 pages. (55¢ ea., member price)

13. Loving, F. A., "Barricading Hazardous Reactions," *Ind. Eng. Chem.*, 49, 1744-1746 (1957).

14. "High Pressure Symposium," Papers Nos. 65L-66L and 70L-72L, Abstracts of Papers, American Chemical Society Meeting, Miami, April 1957, American Chemical Society.

15. "Safety in the Chemical Laboratory, Chapter X, Pressure Vessel Hazards," pages 162-179, D. Van Nostrand Co., Inc., New York, 1954.

16. Fulton, N. J., "Medical Department Layout and Design," Sections I, II, III, and IV, Industrial Medicine and Surgery, 27, 1, 2, 3, and 7 (Jan., Feb., Mar., and July, 1958)

17. "Air Gaps and Backflow Preventers in Plumbing Systems," American Standards Nos. A40.4-1942 and A40.6-1943, American Standards Association, ($1.50).

18. The National Plumbing Code, Illustrated, Manas Publications, 4513 Potomac Ave., N. W., Washington 7, D. C., (1952).

19. National Fire Code, Vol. V. (Revised 1958), National Fire Protection Association.

20. Race, H. H., "The Research Laboratory Builds a House," General Electric Review, November 1948, Reprint No. 1557, General Electric Research Laboratory, Schenectady, N. Y.

21. Fawcett, H. H., "Safety and Industrial Hygiene in the Laboratory," *Chem. Eng. News,* 30, 2588-2591 (1952).

22. Compressed Gas Association, Inc., 11 West 42nd Street, New York 36, N. Y.

23. "Scheme for the Identification of Piping," American Standards Association Code No. ASA-A13. 1-1956.

24. N. F. P. A. Handbook of Fire Protection, Eleventh Edition, Crosby-Fiske-Forster, National Fire Protection Association (1560 pages).

25. Schulte, H. F., Hyatt, E. C., Jordan, H. S. and Mitchell, R. N., "Evaluation of Laboratory Fume Hoods," American Industrial Hygiene Quarterly, 15, 3 (Sept. 1954).

26. Peterson, J. E., "An Approach to a Rational Method of Recommending Face Velocities for Laboratory Hoods," American Industrial Hygiene Association Journal, 20, no. 4, 259–265 (1959).

26.1. Fawcett, H. H., *Chem. Eng. News,* **27,** 2102 (1949).

26.2. Explosion-Proofing Instruction—conventional models, The Product Man, XXIX, no. 4, April, 1958, General Electric Co., Appliance Park, Louisville, Ky.

26.3. Underwriters Laboratory, Inc., 207 E. Ohio St., Chicago 11, Ill.

27. Report No. 1 of I.E.S. Committee on Recom-

mendations for Quality and Quantity of Illumination, Illuminating Engineering, LIII: 8, 422-424 (Aug. 1958).

28. "Footcandles in Modern Lighting Practice," Bulletin LS-119, Inquiry Bureau, Lamp Division, General Electric Company, Nela Park, Cleveland 12, Ohio.

29. "Twenty-Five Industrial Lighting Solutions," Bulletin 321-7138, General Electric Company.

30. "American Standard Practice for Industrial Lighting," American Standards Association Standard No., A11 1-1952.

31. "Fluorescent Ballast Protective Devices Bulletin," Ballast Department, General Electric Co., Danville, Ill.

32. Helm, Scott, "Fusing—An Answer to Positive Ballast Protection," Electrical Construction and Maintenance, 58:2, 84–87 (Feb. 1959).

33. "Recommendations for Waste Disposal of Phosphorous-32 and Iodine-131 for Medical Users," Handbook 49, National Bureau of Standards, Supt. of Documents, Washington 25, D. C. (10¢).

34. U. S. Atomic Energy Commission, Standards for Protection Against Radiation, Part 20, Chapter 1, Title 10, U. S. Federal Register, July 30, 1950.

35. "The Selection of Incinerators for Hospital Use," Incinerator Institute of America, 420 Lexington Ave., New York 17, N. Y.

36. Newell, John F., "Handling and Disposal of Radioactive Wastes," American Industrial Hygiene Association Journal, 19:1, 31–35 (Feb. 1958).

37. Powell, C. C. and Andrews, H. L., "Radioactive Waste Disposal," Public Health Reports, 67:12, 1214-1215 (Dec. 1952).

38. "Surface Treatments for Concrete Floors," Portland Cement Association, 33 W. Grand Avenue, Chicago 10, Ill.

39. "The Relations of Hearing Loss to Noise Exposure," Report by Exploratory Committee Z24-X-2, American Standards Association, Inc., New York, N. Y. (1954).

40. "Noise Control in a Research Hospital," Taylor, F. B., *Noise Control* 4: 5, 9–11 and 62, (Sept. 1958).

41. Handbook of Noise Control, Edited by Harris, Cyril M., McGraw-Hill Book Co., New York, N. Y. (1957) Chapter 10.

42. Wedum, A. G., Hand, Everett, Jr., and Phillips, G. H., "Ultra-violet Sterilization in Microbiological Laboratories" Public Health Reports, 71:4, 331-336 (April 1956).

43. Decker, H. M., Citek, F. J., Harstad, J. B., Gross, N. H. and Piper, F. J., "Time, Temperature Studies of Spore Penetration through an Electric Air Sterilizer," *Appl. Microbiology*, 2–1, 33-36 (Jan., 1954).

44. Decker, H. M., Geile, F. A., Moorman, H. E. and Glick, C. A., "Removal of Bacteria and Bacteriophage from the Air by Electrostatic Precipitators and Spun Glass Filter Pads," Heating, Piping and Air Conditioning, 23: 10 (Oct., 1951).

45. Decker, H. M., Harstad, J. B. and Lense, F. T., "Removal of Bacteria from Air Streams by Glass Fiber Filters," Annual Meeting Paper No. 56-1, Air Pollution Control Association, 4400 Fifth Avenue, Pittsburgh 13, Pa.

46. "Acceptance of Ultra-violet Lamps for Disinfecting Purposes," American Medical Association Council on Physical Therapy, *J. A. M. A.*, 122: 8 (June 19, 1943).

47. ASME Boiler and Pressure Vessel Code, Section VIII, "Unfired Pressure Vessels," The American Society of Mechanical Engineers, 29 West 39th St., New York 18, N. Y. (1952).

48. Price, B. T., Horton, C. C., and Spinney, K. T., "Radiation Shielding," Pergamon Press, 122 E. 55th Street, New York 22, N. Y. (1957).

49. Braestrup, Carl B. and Wyckoff, Harold O., "Radiation Protection," Charles C Thomas—Publisher, Springfield, Ill., pp. 361 (1958).

50. National Bureau of Standards Handbook No. 50, "X-ray Protection Design," (1952) Supt. of Documents, Washington 25, D. C.

51. Boursnell, J. C., "Safety Techniques for Radioactive Tracers," Cambridge University Press (1958).

Applications

in

Design

CHAPTER VIII

Facilities

for Scientific

and Technical

Functions

M. M. SOLOMON

General Electric Company
Philadelphia, Pennsylvania

DETERMINATION OF THE MODULE

If one is planning to build a new laboratory, a number of questions are likely to arise from general discussion: How big should it be? How much space is required to do a desired job adequately? These questions are some of the most fundamental in the entire job of laboratory planning. How is the size of the building determined? Is there any rule which says how much space is required per technical man? What is the most effective way of obtaining space at the lowest cost? Let us begin by looking into the last question, for it in turn will lead us to the answer to the others.

In an effort to keep costs down in both constructing and furnishing the building, most modern laboratories are arranged so that a definite unit of laboratory or office space repeats itself throughout the entire building. The smallest of such repeating units is defined, for the purpose of this chapter, as a module. Modular construction offers definite economic advantages in the initial planning and engineering of new constructions by permitting standardization of materials and larger-volume purchase of similar materials. Because of the repeating nature of modular construction, the estimating and engineering costs are more easily determined and are far more accurate. Lastly, this type of planning permits determination of total requirements by a simple multiplication operation.

While planning the new Product Development Laboratory of the Silicone Products Department, General Electric Company, at Waterford, New York, the author had the opportunity to visit many outstanding laboratories encompassing a variety of industries and geographical locations throughout the country. The laboratory buildings visited during this inspection tour housed individual laboratories which covered the entire gamut of sizes and shapes, with many different types of equipment, etc., all influenced by the type of institution and kind of work being done. Thus, the outside-to-inside wall distances or the depth on one side of the building, which may be considered as half of the modular dimension, was found to vary from 19 ft (Mellon Institute) to 52 ft (General Electric Company Chemical Products Department, Cleveland, Ohio); within this range were laboratories whose depths were 22, 26, 27, 28 ft, and so on.

The other dimension completing the module is that distance covered when walking parallel to the outside wall or corridor wall. The favorite distances here were found to be 8, 10 and 11 ft, many laboratories using a multiple of either two or four of these distances. Most laboratories were from 18 to 22 ft in width. The most usual area per occupant ran from 140 to 180 sq ft, although some had only 114 sq ft per individual while others had as much as 220 sq ft. Thus there is no magic number to help one determine what the depth and width of a typical laboratory should be. (Nor is the word "typical" here meant to be restrictive in any form.)

There is only one practical way to establish the size of a typical laboratory or, as it may be called, a modular laboratory, namely:

(1) Determine the type of work to be done in the laboratory.

(2) Determine the kind and amount of equipment required to do it.

(3) Determine the degree of flexibility that will be required in coming years (based on the best available data).

(4) Relate (1), (2) and (3) to amount of sq ft, i.e., (1) will determine (2) and (2) + (3) must be translated into sq ft necessary to house needed laboratory and office equipment supporting facilities.

(5) Allow an adequate overage for unforeseen contingencies.

Thus, for example, at Waterford we prepared block layouts using two-dimensional scale models of standard laboratory furniture units and established the most useful type of unit for various locales. We interviewed all the people who were going to occupy these laboratories to find out what they considered an adequate amount of storage space and table top and/or bench top space. We then proceeded to analyze the desires of all those questioned and divided the practical from the impractical, arriving finally at a tentative block layout embodying the most generally useful type of cabinets as indicated by the workers. Finally, we called in representatives of the various reputable laboratory equipment manu-

facturers and asked them for opinions on our plan.

One might argue the relative merit of the timing, i.e., whether it is better to call the laboratory furniture representatives in before these block layouts or after. We chose the latter so that the desires of our people would be unhindered by conventional thinking. Having taken the total number of desired units into consideration, we then used the graphic layout plans to determine the most economical and step-saving layout. When all the dimensions were added up and allowances made for the space required for service entrances, perimeter wall heating space requirements, office requirements (if present), door clearances, etc., the depth dimension was established.

The actual width of the laboratory is more readily decided once it is determined what aisle widths are desired. In general, we found that the minimum aisle width in a chemical laboratory should be 4 ft and the maximum 6 ft, the optimum and most generally used running from 4½ to 5 ft. This allows adequate room for two people to pass each other without danger of disturbing the equipment near the edge of any given bench. Adding the aisle space to the sum total widths of the laboratory benches gave the total width required. Thus the laboratory module size was determined. As a case in point, at our own laboratory at Waterford it was decided that the optimum depth was 28 ft and the optimum repeating unit 10 ft, and that each laboratory *per se* would house two 10-foot distances, i.e., each laboratory was 20 ft wide and 28 ft deep. Office areas where required, were 10 x 28 ft and capable of subdivisions into two 10 x 14's, etc.

By office areas we are referring only to office areas for management personnel, or other non-laboratory personnel who require working space. We found it most desirable not to disturb the module for the creation of "tailored" offices. Since a laboratory building is built essentially to house laboratories, not offices, and the dominant consideration must be given to that optimum modular size, office space being fitted in as well as possible. In almost all cases, multiple or fractional modules, partitioned by full height nonload-bearing walls or movable partitioning of varying heights, served most excellently.

The problem of offices in a nonsymmetrical

building (two different depths on either side of corridor) is discussed in greater detail under the subheading "Laboratory Offices."

Having established the size of the individual module, it was then merely necessary to divide the number of people occupying one module into the total laboratory personnel to determine how many typical laboratories were needed. Again in our case, a typical laboratory is occupied by two chemists and two assistants. To this was then added the so-called supporting facilities, which include the library, rest rooms, special test rooms, oven rooms, compounding rooms, sample storage areas, conference rooms, cafeterias, or rooms of other types.*

Having found the desirable size of a typical laboratory, the number of such units and supporting facilities required, one has automatically arrived at the total size of the building. How then is this house made a home, or more technically, how is this building equipped and serviced to make it an efficiently operating laboratory?

What type and quantity of services are required? How are they distributed most efficiently and at what magnitude?

DISTRIBUTION OF SERVICES

Several methods may be used to bring necessary services into a laboratory. The most popular is vertically through inside (corridor) or outside false walls, then horizontally through the inside walls directly into the bench service strip. These

---

*One might comment here that perhaps the most neglected sort of supporting facility are things such as the janitors' closets and adequate space for maintenance people and their equipment. It is ironical to note that while one will spend many thousands of dollars in building a magnificent laboratory building, frequently little attention is paid to how it will be maintained. Hence, skimpy janitors' closets and other storage areas necessary for the care and maintenance of the building are provided.

Included too in the supporting facilities should be mentioned the desirability of both freight and passenger elevators. The former is almost a necessity in any laboratory building. A passenger elevator, to a great measure, is a luxury if the building is three floors or less.

Figure 8.1   Construction view of piping shafts and corridor.

Figure 8.2   Completed pipe chase.

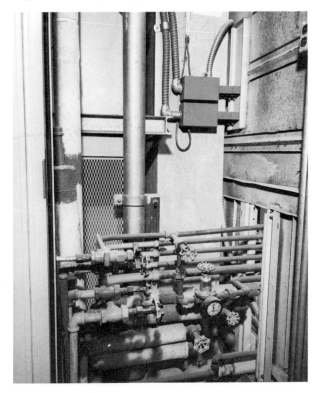

Figure 8.3   Ceiling distribution of services.

services may originate in a "pipe chase," basement, or service tunnel of other type.

A second way to bring the services into the building, which is particularly applicable if it is desired for one reason or another not to have a basement or underground "pipe chase," is through the ceilings in the corridors. From here, servicing of the individual laboratories is handled by "teeing off" of the main service arteries at right angles, going through the corridor wall into the laboratories proper at a specified height, dropping vertically, and going horizontally into the service strip or bench service lines, whichever is provided.

The first method, which is by far the more desirable from the point of view of appearance, over-all building maintenance, and serviceability, is also somewhat more costly because of the requirement that the building be made at least 4

to 6 ft wider than is necessary by the second method. In the second case, one does incur some cost because of the necessity of making the ceilings higher than would be required if the false wall method were used. However, it has been found by experience that in general the cost of making a building somewhat taller is less than that of making it wider; unfortunately the cost per square foot seems to progress geometrically while the cost per cubic foot increases at a somewhat slower rate. The greater the number of floors in a building, the narrower the cost gap becomes between the two types of major service distribution.

Figures 8.2 and 8.3 illustrate these two types of major service entrances. Figure 8.1 shows the pipe "chase" during construction. In Figure 8.2 a complete job is shown. The piping, electrical conduit and fume duct exhaust all run vertically

Figure 8.4   Services in conventional reagent rack.

Figure 8.5   Services in pedestal or service island.

Figure 8.6   Services in box curb.

in this shaft. Figure 8.3 shows ceiling distribution of services. Whichever method is finally used, the basic method of "teeing off" of service mains and going through a wall into the laboratory itself remains essentially the same. Once the "tee-offs" are made, they should be "valved off" immediately, so that in the event of any breakages within the laboratory proper, etc., only one or a small area of laboratories is incapacitated, rather than the entire building.

Within the laboratories themselves, methods of service distribution are manifold. Some of the more popular ways to distribute services are shown in Figures 8.4 through 8.8. The method illustrated in Figure 8.4 suffers from the disadvantages of being undesirable in the esthetic sense. The exposed piping makes for loose housekeeping and hinders the passage of materials from one side of the bench to the other between co-workers. In recent years a large number of industrial laboratories have done away with this exposed type of service distribution piping.

The pedestal or service island type illustrated in Figure 8.5 makes for an interesting and more esthetic installation, but is also somewhat restrictive in that the location of services may at one time or another be inconvenient to apparatus etc., mounted in other parts of the work surface. Thus lengths of hose, wire, etc., are likely to clutter up the work bench and cause accidents.

A modified form of the pedestal or turret form of service distribution has been working most effectively since December, 1956. Mr. D. P. Krotz, of California Research Corporation, notes:

"Laboratory plumbing is one of the most expensive single items in laboratory construction. It is also the principal source of major maintenance costs. Considerable thought should be given the plumbing design before a final solution is developed. The initial cost, ease of maintenance, provisions for alteration or addition, and appearance must be considered. Emphasis on any one of these criteria depends on the policies governing the design of the laboratory.

Figure 8.7   Services in flush type plumbing island.

Figure 8.8   Services strip supported on partition walls.

"In the last ten years many laboratories have used a system of utility racks (Figure 8.4) to hold the laboratory utilities (plumbing, electrical, and sewage disposal). These racks, either against a wall or as a free-standing center island, are independent of the laboratory bench and provide the services at a relatively low cost, permit changes and/or additions, and present a good appearance. However, it is necessary to move the laboratory bench and, therefore, disrupt the chemist every time that work is performed on the utility lines.

"To avoid this problem and keep the advantages of the utility rack system, the California Research Corporation (Richmond Laboratory) used a modified service turret, straight through piping and the union connections as shown in Figure 8.9. To work on the piping in this system, it is only necessary to close the branch service valve, unscrew the special turret (*accessible from the top of the bench*), break the union, and disconnect the pipe and turret. The pipe may then be pulled up into the laboratory or lowered into the basement or service space between floors.

"Removal of the waste disposal line is similar. The union is broken, and the riser is unscrewed from the tail-piece of the bench fixture (cup or regular sink)."

New utility service and turrets may be added to the system as the floor slot allows space for the additional pipe. The completed bench using the service arrangements in Figure 8.9 are shown in Figure 8.10.

In recent years the two popular methods of service distribution on the bench are those illustrated in Figures 8.6, 8.7, and 8.8. These not only offer a more esthetic installation, but also facili-

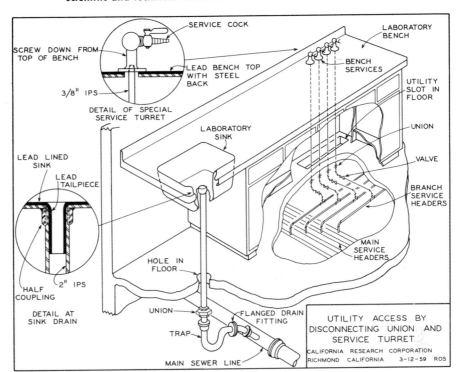

Figure 8.9 Utility access by disconnecting union and service turret.

Figure 8.10 Completed bench using the service arrangements.

tate flexibility in interchange of various furniture units, etc. As noted by California Research experience, however, the service strip is not without problems. To minimize inconvenience, all the backs of the cabinets should easily be removable if line breakage should occur in a service strip type of installation. Often breaks can be repaired through these openings. To ensure complete exposure of the piping for its entire length, drawer units on one side should have cupboard units opposite and *vice versa*. This will frequently give full coverage.

The arrangements illustrated in Figure 8.7 and 8.8 permit the free passage of equipment, etc., from one side of the bench to the other. The slight disadvantage of less accessibility to service piping, in case of breakages, etc., is more than offset by the advantages cited. The inclusion or exclusion of a reagent shelf is easily accomplished, as is shown in Figures 8.4 and 8.5. If, however, it is desirable from the esthetic sense and good housekeeping not to have a reagent shelf, then the type illustrated in Figure 8.7 is preferable.

Having determined how to bring in and distribute the services, one must next proceed to the detailed planning of what types and quantities of services are required. These can only be determined by individual needs. For example, the following quantities and types of services were distributed in the new Product Development Laboratory, Silicone Products Department, General Electric Company, Waterford, New York.

Nitrogen at 60 psi from a central source was originally available from two pedestals on every outer bench (13 ft long). The advisability of distributing such high-pressure nitrogen was questioned for safety reasons. In addition, careless use could result in greater losses through wastage. It was decided to lower the pressure to 10–18 psi. After one year of operation the lower pressure has answered all the needs of the workers for an inert gas.

Compressed air at 60 psi was available from a central plant system. This is adequate for most laboratory air stirrers and for drying. It should be stressed that adequate precautions should be taken to install equipment which generates dry, oil-free air.

Steam at 10 psi was distributed only to the hoods in order to minimize the danger of live steam burning someone and also the chance of making the atmosphere too uncomfortable. Where necessary, 150 psi process steam was distributed to special areas.

Natural gas was brought in at standard pressures usually ranging around ½ psi.

City water was brought in at 60–80 psi to the cup sinks on each bench. In this regard it should be noted that it is well worth while to provide individual traps for each cup sink. The type of service distributed, illustrated in Figure 8.7, permits installation of a more efficient and esthetically pleasing sink than those illustrated in Figures 8.4 and 8.5. Type 8.4 usually utilizes a trough-type sink.

One might also consider in this regard the use of some of the newer plastic materials such as medium- and high-density polyethylene (to obtain higher softening points) or polyvinyl chloride drain piping, provided in the first case that no solvents are disposed of via the sink so equipped. The installation and maintenance costs of these materials in many cases are lower than for conventionally used lead-lined steel. In addition, the construction of the polyethylene traps makes for exceedingly easy cleaning compared to the great difficulties of removing and cleaning lead-lined traps. (The latter requires a lead burner or skilled craftsman, whereas the former merely requires that someone unscrew the bottom section, clean and merely retighten.) After 15 months of operation, the polyethylene drain pipe in the service strips is in perfect shape. One small difficulty arose initially when leakage occurred where the horizontal polyethylene drains went into the main vertical cast-iron drains. This was remedied by replacing ordinary putty-type caulking compound with a special mastic, recommended by the polyethylene pipe manufacturer, after the trouble had occurred. Some six months later, no leakage had recurred.

In joining any two dissimilar materials, special care must be given to effect a leakproof joint.

Distilled water was distributed to each laboratory via a gravity feed system. The still itself was purchased with more than adequate present and anticipated needed capacity. In this case it is a low-pressure steam-heated still, 10 gph capacity, with a 50-gallon storage tank and fully automatic controls. This, to the author's way of thinking, is the only way to purchase a still. Reliance upon manpower should be kept to a minimum when it comes to the distribution of services.

Electricity for equipment was distributed in three forms, 110 V single-phase, 208 and 440 three-phase. Nonelectrically oriented planners should note that splitting of 440, 3-phase yields 208—*not* 220 V current.

For illumination, electricity was distributed at 227 V for the newest type of fluorescent lighting. The lighting itself was installed at 75 foot candles incident on the bench, which can be maintained at 57 foot candles, to give a comfortable illumination on the work surface. Fixtures were placed approximately 4 ft apart, running perpendicular to the axis of the benches proper. The light fixtures themselves were of the baffled type to prevent glare.

Depending upon the type of work being done, distribution of additional services, other gases such as oxygen, argon, helium or acetylene may be desirable. In most cases, the general plan is the same as for the distribution of the more popular gases, such as nitrogen and natural gas. Precaution must be taken, however, to regulate the pressures entering each laboratory so that safety regulations can easily be enforced. Again it should be pointed out that individual needs must be considered and the quantities, pressures, etc., should be varied to meet them.

In terms of the number of actual service outlets per bench and their location, it was found to be an almost universal opinion that the number of electrical outlets always seems insufficient. In planning the new laboratory at Waterford, therefore, we made sure that the number of outlets was adequate. Hence, each 20 x 28 foot laboratory has more than 100 individual laboratory outlets connected to a total source of power of 200 amps with a 50% diversification factor for the entire building; thus each laboratory can draw a maximum of 200 amps at any given time. However, if all the laboratories were to draw maximum power, each could only obtain a maximum of 100 amps per unit. Each duplex was fused to a 15-amp circuit-breaker switch.

In planning the services, one should remember that the cost of an additional size pipe or the installation of a larger capacity is a relatively minor part of the total cost of the service installation. Hence, one should allow a minimum of 50% excess capacity over immediate established needs, and preferably should extend this to double the capacity. One must also make provisions for sufficient service to take care of known future needs, as for example, in the electrical connection and cooling water for air-conditioning to be installed at a later date.

The service distribution on the bench top of the typical organic chemical laboratory at Waterford Silicone Products Department Development Laboratory is shown in Figure 6.21 Note how the pylons or pedestals are so arranged that one may turn any ground key cock to any position without danger of pinching fingers on adjacent handles, etc. In the hoods, where the greatest concentration of corrosive chemicals is used, one should consider the idea of protective coatings on the internal fixtures. Thus, for example, color-coded fixtures may be obtained which are baked-on chemically resistant paints having maximum corrosion resistance. These may simultaneously serve for easy identification of the remote-controlled service by affixing to the control handle a button of the same color as the service nozzle. Similarly, even the pipes running through the service "chase" and "strip" should be color-coded.

To further ensure safety, the nozzles dispensing high-pressure or high-temperature liquids or gases should be angled toward the back of the hood or down toward the bench to minimize accidental scalding or other injuries.

LABORATORY ARRANGEMENTS

Basically, laboratories can be arranged in two ways—those having island benches and those having peninsular-type benches. Figures 8.11 and 8.12 illustrate the two basic types of installations. Note that the actual form or direction in which the benches go can be modified, but that the basic principle of island or peninsular-type bench still holds true. Figure 8.13 shows the arrangement at the General Electric Research Laboratory in which the work stations are more or less formed by the U or L type of bench arrangement.

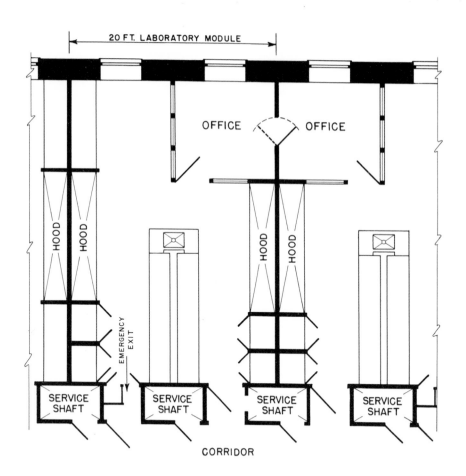

Figure 8.11   Typical peninsula bench laboratories.

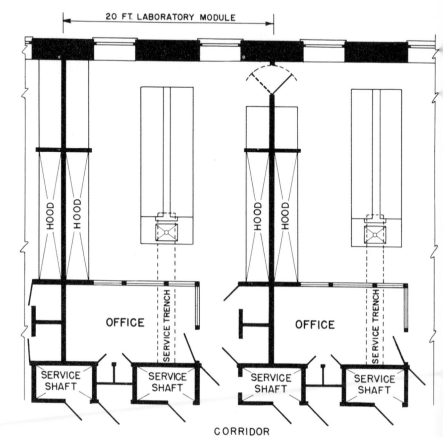

Figure 8.12   Typical island bench laboratories.

The tables on the U are replaced by fully serviced benches in organic laboratories. Note, however, that it is still a peninsular type of service distribution. Figure 8.12 shows that typical laboratories at the Texas Company have an island-type distribution. Again the benches could be curved or turned at any angle desired, but the basic service distribution is still of the island type.

The more popular arrangement seems to be the peninsular type of service distribution. This is probably due to the lower cost of this type of servicing and the general ease of installation. The island type requires a trench under the floor, as shown in Figure 8.14, thus adding to the cost. It can also create a problem in that the floors, which are seldom perfectly level, do not provide a suitable covering for the pipe trench. The advantages of the island arrangement are those of

Figure 8.13   Arrangement of benches.

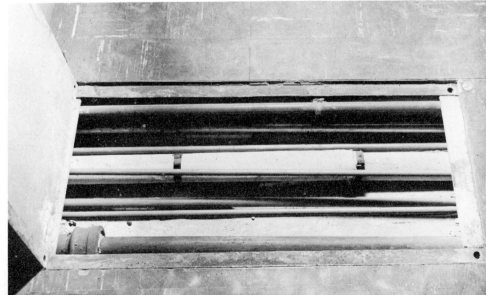

Figure 8.14   Pipe trench for lines serving island type bench.

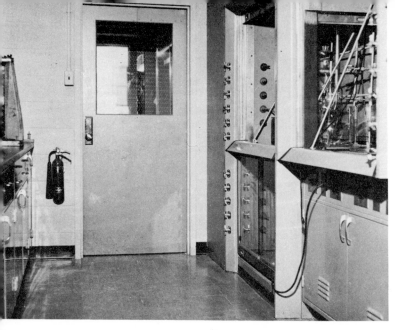

Figure 8.15   Door arrangement into peninsular laboratory.

Figure 8.16   Schematic of partitioning.

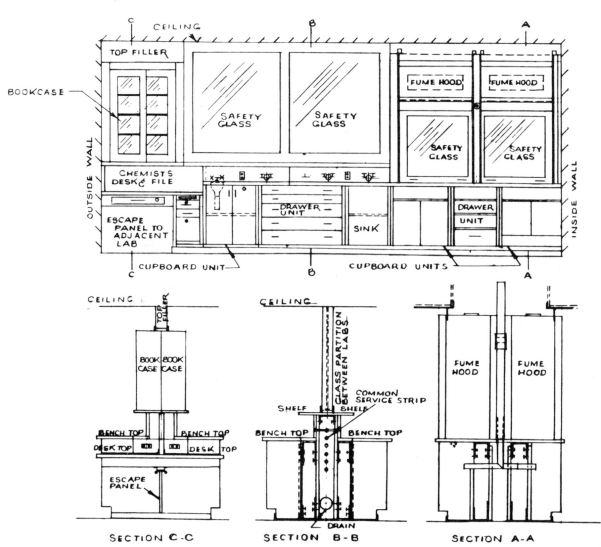

safety and convenience: it does not impede emergency exit and also saves steps, for the personnel can walk around either side of the bench.

The peninsular bench is appropriately named, as is obvious from Figure 8.11. It is certainly the less expensive method of distribution but suffers from the drawback that workers cannot go around one end of the bench. This can somewhat be alleviated by providing an adequate number of entrance doors as illustrated in Figure 8.15. A great deal more can be said about the advisability of both types of arrangements. However, individual taste is the deciding factor in most cases.

The type and distribution of laboratory furniture has already been adequately discussed in Chapter 6. However, Figure 6.18 is shown merely as an illustration of one way in which a typical laboratory has been set up. Note here that the size and distribution of drawers and cupboards can be easily changed without changing the general distribution of cabinetry *per se*.

The laboratory furniture itself can be arranged in a number of ways. As pointed out in the foregoing, the General Electric Research Laboratory utilizes a U-type. The most popular arrangement seemed to be that involving the use of two wall benches and one center bench, which was usually double-size. Thus, for example, Figure 6.18 shows the typical arrangement at Waterford in which there are two wall benches with their own service strips and one center bench which has a common service strip and two individual work surfaces. A novel way to distribute services and partition laboratories without loss of efficiency was observed at the G. D. Searle Company in Skokie, Illinois, schematically illustrated in Figure 8.16. This involved the use of a single-service strip between two laboratories. In this case the wall benches are actually the same as the center benches, i.e., they are double benches with the single-service strip running down the middle. The bench itself serves as the wall for a distance of 3 ft or 37 in. high. On top of it rests a dividing curtain wall which can be fabricated of almost any type of durable nonflammable construction material, which is usually supported from overhead steel, which in turn is part of the building skeleton. This allows considerable saving in the cost of service distribution by permitting use of only four main service line entrances for two laboratories instead of the usual six.

One interesting point to consider in the arrangement of laboratory furniture is the location of the hoods. It has been observed that they can be placed almost anywhere. Some laboratories have them on the center benches, some farthest from the corridor, others closest to corridor, and on the wall benches. In considering this matter for our own laboratory, it was decided to place them on the wall benches closest to the entrance doors. This was done for several reasons.

(1) To minimize the length of duct runs, which makes for a less expensive installation, more efficient hood operation, and a more easily balanced ventilating system.

(2) To enable one person to observe both hoods while in operation. Thus, in case of emergency, a man's co-worker could see anything happening from his side of the bench. Figures 8.17 and 8.18 show the arrangement of the hoods on the center benches and wall bench, respectively. Note by the position of the man, that if he were suddenly overcome by gas or rendered unconscious, he would be out of sight of his co-workers in the laboratory. While this is highly unlikely, such possibilities should be avoided.

One might initially question placing the hoods so close to the doorway for fear that people entering and leaving might set up adverse currents which would affect proper operation of the hood. We have found, particularly when the doors open outward, that is, away from the hoods, that the type and magnitude of the air currents set up are too insignificant to affect hood operation to any extent. In addition, if the laboratory is equipped with a proper ventilating system, the bulk of the supply air should come through some entrance duct above the height of the hood sash. This opening should be equipped with an adjustable grill so that the air can be directed away from the face of the hoods. When this is done, location of the hoods close to the door is satisfactory from all points of view.

At the risk of being overly repetitive, it would pay to repeat here that hoods, their proper operation, sizing, etc., are a most essential part of the laboratory and hence great care should be paid

Figure 8.17   Arrangement of hoods on center benches.

Figure 8.18   Arrangement of hoods on wall bench.

to their proper selection and installation. Once again we must remember the very important general principle that hoods can always be used as a work surface even though a hood is not required, but the opposite is not true.

Another consideration in the arrangement of laboratory furniture is the location of some of the safety features. Many laboratories have safety showers within the laboratory proper. The location of these is usually at the exit doors or near the office area. In an increasing number of laboratories additional safety showers are being installed in the corridors. Thus, if an injured worker should panic and run into the corridor, his co-workers can stop him and get him to the closest shower in the corridor, without having to pull him back into the laboratory. Figure 8.19 shows the distribution of safety showers in the typical laboratory corridor at the Product Development Building in Waterford. Figure 8.20 shows a similar arrangement in the Minnesota Mining Manufacturing Laboratory, St. Paul, Minnesota.

Note in Figure 8.15, of the Waterford Laboratories, the location of the fire extinguishers opposite the hoods, wherein it is generally conceded that the more dangerous operations usually take place. Note, too, the location of a much larger extinguisher on the office wall as shown in Figure 8.21. Last, also note the additional escape door which is a necessity for any laboratory. This permits exit from either extremes of the laboratory in case of emergency. It is of the utmost importance that none of the doors be blocked in any way during laboratory operation.

Returning to the hoods momentarily, two other safety features should be pointed out: sliding glass within the sash gives one a double pane of safety glass which can be used as a shield; also, the exclusive use of remote-controlled handles permits the worker to operate services without endangering himself by opening the hood sash or reaching in.

LABORATORY OFFICES

The question as to whether chemists should be provided with laboratory offices, or for that matter with any offices at all, has been one that has been debated pro and con for many years. It is

Figure 8.19 *Distribution of safety showers in laboratory corridor.*

Figure 8.20 *Location of safety shower.*

Figure 8.21 *Location of large fire extinguisher on office wall.*

the author's unshakeable belief that the provision of an office will make for a more productive person. Not only does it give a good "shot in the arm" for morale but it provides a certain amount of privacy within the laboratory proper which creates an environment conducive to writing and reading. At Waterford we feel that this has been particularly proved as a result. Many comments have been forthcoming that, after one got used to the "quiet," the degree of efficiency and work output went up by leaps and bounds. Far-seeing and progressive laboratory managers will probably agree that offices for the individual chemists are highly desirable.

The question as to whether an office should be provided within the laboratory proper or at a different location has also caused considerable debate. One must concede that the most efficient way of writing or reading is in a spot completely away from the distractions of the laboratory. Thus, for example, at the Esso Research and Engineering building in Linden, the building is an off-center one, i.e., on either side of the corridor are two rooms of different size (one for laboratories, one for offices) so that if the chemist wants to write or read, he must go across the hall. The arguments for offices in the laboratory seem a bit more persuasive in that there are many times during the day when a reaction is going or time must be given for reactions to take place during which a chemist can write while keeping an occasional eye on his experiment. The office-laboratory is a compromise, therefore, in giving the worker degree of privacy, yet permitting him to observe the workings of the laboratory at frequent intervals.

Thus, it was the general consensus of opinion of laboratory personnel contacted that laboratory offices were more satisfactory than out-of-laboratory offices, but both are quite acceptable. An important point to remember is that if glass partitions are installed in the laboratory, safety glass should be used. Experience has shown that doors for in-laboratory offices are totally useless and in fact may be a great hindrance to the efficient and safe operation of the laboratory. Figures 8.22 through 8.33 at the end of this chapter give vital statistics and floor plans for various laboratory arrangements.

SPECIAL FACILITIES

In the past years more specific types of facilities for such things as calculations, record storage, and so on have been becoming prevalent in laboratories. For occasional calculations, etc., the portable calculator, of course, is invaluable. However, when a great deal of statistical work is to be done, consideration may well be given to the inclusion of a small calculating room, preferably sound-proofed to minimize machine noise. The location of this should be somewhat central so as to permit its convenient use by all personnel. If the business or laboratory has an IBM set-up for its bookkeeping center, it may be well to discuss with the people operating this center the use of their facilities and equipment for calculations relating to laboratory work.

In planning a laboratory building, record-storage facilities should be considered, particularly for those which might be valuable in the prosecution of patents. Thus, for example, completed notebooks of active workers, notebooks of workers who are no longer associated with the laboratory, and data on important processes must be safely preserved. The record-storage room should be fireproof, and if possible it should also have a controlled atmosphere with respect to temperature and humidity in particular. Many laboratories have gone to an extreme and actually set off a portion of the building to be fabricated in a vault-like manner. The necessity of this is questionable from the point of view of protecting the contents from theft. It would seem to the author a greater need to protect the records from the ravages of time than from depredations of the personnel. The size and type of vaults or record-storage facilities depends greatly on whether or not Microfilm or a similar process is being used to record notebooks and other literature. Modern miniature copying machines can, of course, conserve a great deal in the way of space, but the use of material in patent proceedings, etc., should be investigated with a patent attorney. It is conceivable that the storage of records should come under the supervision of the library where frequently the photocopying machinery is already installed. Similarly, the library staff are exceedingly capable in the cataloging and safekeeping of valuable records. This again, however, would depend upon the size of the library and the staff available.

STOCK AND STORAGE ROOMS

It is the consensus of opinion that there is seldom enough planned storage space. Space should be provided for storing samples that must undergo long shelf-life tests, and materials purchased in bulk, or are themselves quite bulky, are best stored in nonlaboratory space. This space should be adjacent to two functions, that of shipping-receiving and the stock room. Space for storage and dispensing of chemicals and equipment is also neglected or compromised. Yet failure to provide enough needed materials can be a source of much wasted time.

The following is a suggested breakdown into smaller functional units within the stock room:

(1) Flammable solvent storage. This should be made of a material like "Pyrobar" and must be equipped with an automatic alarm and extinguishing system. An automatic door closer which can always be opened from either side is advisable. It should have an effective exhaust system, changing the air completely at least once every two minutes.

(2) A room for the storage of chorosilanes or other materials having similar chemical properties should definitely be provided. Special care should be taken to have materials which are impervious to hydrochloric acid. This room should also have a high-capacity exhaust system so that the air can be changed from 30 to 60 times per hour. Materials such as "Transite" or panel-type enameled steel should be particularly good for the wall coverings of such types of rooms.

(3) There should be a chemical storage area, subdivided for the storage of organic and inorganic chemicals.

(4) The stockrooms must be the center for receiving and shipping materials to and from the laboratory. They should be equipped to send and keep records of shipments of laboratory samples, as well as distribute incoming materials. An essential part of this function is a truck dock equipped with a ramp so that hand trucks can go up and down with ease.

(5) Adequate office space for the storeroom supervisor should be provided. He should have the proper filing equipment to maintain a perpetual inventory of the contents of his domain.

DISHWASHING

A four-foot section of locker or drawer space under the bench top for storing scrap solvent, safety cans, and baskets for dirty glassware is adequate for a laboratory 20 by 28 feet in area. Thus, when the time comes to remove the solvent and glassware, the service personnel will know exactly where to go. Dirty glassware may be:

(1) cleaned in the laboratory by a technician or handyman and hung on peg boards or placed in heated ovens to dry;

(2) placed in containers to be carried to a central washing area by laboratory personnel;

(3) placed in containers and collected periodically by service personnel, who leave a clean container. The dirty glassware is transported to the cleaning area and from there returned to stock.

The housekeeping keynote of any laboratory is "keep it neat." It is both inefficient and untidy to have dirty glassware all over the place.

GLASS BLOWING

Many laboratories have found the need for a full-time glass blower. Many chemists have their own ideas on how some of the equipment should be made. If this practice is prevalent, it is certainly much cheaper to hire a full time glass blower. The size and shape of the shop and the extent of equipment will depend largely upon the amount of custom fabrication required. The glass blower has his own ideas on the equipment with which he would rather work. The room should be well ventilated, since much heat will be dissipated through glass lamps and annealing furnaces.

LABORATORY FLOOR PLANS AND STATISTICS

The following floor plans were constructed and used in the planning of chemical laboratories. This system, however, can be easily converted to the planning of other types of laboratories, i.e., physical, mechanical, electrical, etc. In order to accomplish this, substitute work benches for fume hoods and sinks. The statistics would then apply to the type of laboratory under consideration.

These layouts represent a good cross section of information concerning size, personnel, and floor plan layouts of industrial laboratories today.

Figure 8.22

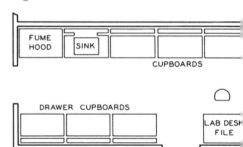

LABORATORY STATISTICS

Laboratory Dimensions	10 × 20
No. of Sq. Ft./Laboratory	200
Personnel/Laboratory	2
Technical	1
Assistants	1
No. of Sq. Ft./Person	100
No. of Linear Feet of Bench/Person	16
Size of Office	
No. of Sq. Ft./Office	
Personnel/Office	
Assistant Report Writing Space	No

Figure 8.23

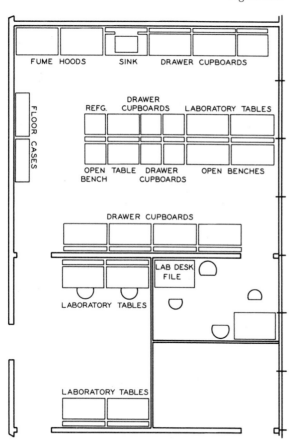

LABORATORY STATISTICS

Laboratory Dimensions	20 × 24
No. of Sq. Ft./Laboratory	480
Personnel/Laboratory	4
Technical	2
Assistants	2
No. of Sq. Ft./Person	165
No. of Linear Feet of Bench/Person	18
Size of Office	7-6 × 12
No. of Sq. Ft./Office	90
Personnel/Office	2
Assistant Report Writing Space	No

Figure 8.24

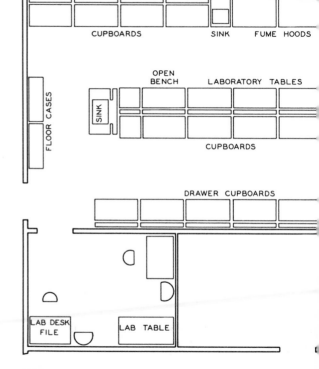

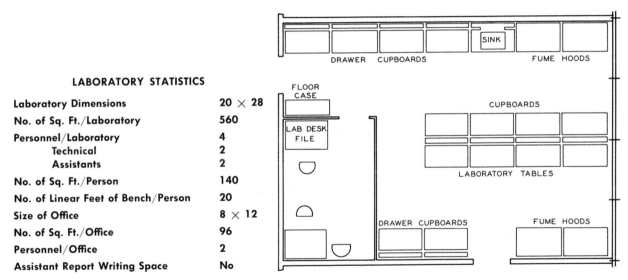

LABORATORY STATISTICS

Laboratory Dimensions	20 × 28
No. of Sq. Ft./Laboratory	560
Personnel/Laboratory	4
Technical	2
Assistants	2
No. of Sq. Ft./Person	140
No. of Linear Feet of Bench/Person	20
Size of Office	8 × 12
No. of Sq. Ft./Office	96
Personnel/Office	2
Assistant Report Writing Space	No

Figure 8.25

Figure 8.26

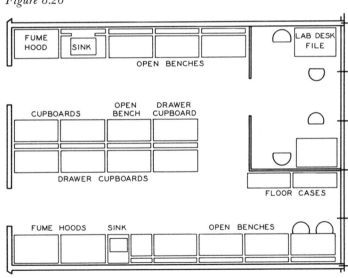

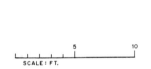

SCALE: FT.

LABORATORY STATISTICS

Laboratory Dimensions	20 × 30
No. of Sq. Ft./Laboratory	600
Personnel/Laboratory	4
Technical	2
Assistants	2
No. of Sq. Ft./Person	150
No. of Linear Feet of Bench/Person	20
Size of Office	7-6 × 8
No. of Sq. Ft./Office	60
Personnel/Office	1
Assistant Report Writing Space	Yes

LABORATORY STATISTICS

Laboratory Dimensions	20 × 26
No. of Sq. Ft./Laboratory	520
Personnel/Laboratory	4
Technical	2
Assistants	2
No. of Sq. Ft./Person	160
No. of Linear Feet of Bench/Person	22
Size of Office	10 × 13
No. of Sq. Ft./Office	130
Personnel/Office	2
Assistant Report Writing Space	No

LABORATORY STATISTICS

Laboratory Dimensions	20 × 30
No. of Sq. Ft./Laboratory	600
Personnel/Laboratory	4
Technical	2
Assistants	2
No. of Sq. Ft./Person	150
No. of Linear Feet of Bench/Person	18
Size of Office	7-6 × 8
No. of Sq. Ft./Office	60
Personnel/Office	1
Assistant Report Writing Space	Yes

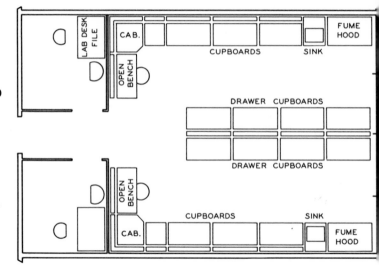

Figure 8.2

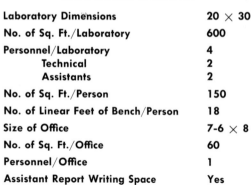

Figure 8.28

LABORATORY STATISTICS

Laboratory Dimensions	20 × 30
No. of Sq. Ft./Laboratory	600
Personnel/Laboratory	6
Technical	3
Assistants	3
No. of Sq. Ft./Person	100
No. of Linear Feet of Bench/Person	13
Size of Office	6-6 × 7-6
No. of Sq. Ft./Office	49
Personnel/Office	1
Assistant Report Writing Space	No

Figure 8.2

LABORATORY STATISTICS

Laboratory Dimensions	20 × 30
No. of Sq. Ft./Laboratory	600
Personnel/Laboratory	4
Technical	2
Assistants	2
No. of Sq. Ft./Person	150
No. of Linear Feet of Bench/Person	23
Size of Office	6 × 7-6
No. of Sq. Ft./Office	45
Personnel/Office	1
Assistant Report Writing Space	Yes

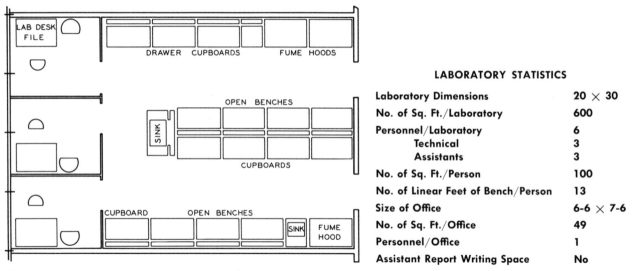

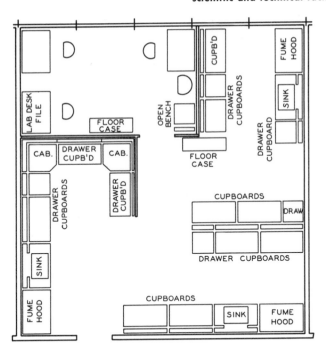

Figure 8.30

LABORATORY STATISTICS

Laboratory Dimensions	25 × 26
No. of Sq. Ft./Laboratory	650
Personnel/Laboratory	3
Technical	3
Assistants	
No. of Sq. Ft./Person	216
No. of Linear Feet of Bench/Person	26
Size of Office	9 × 15-6
No. of Sq. Ft./Office	140
Personnel/Office	3
Assistant Report Writing Space	

LABORATORY STATISTICS

Laboratory Dimensions	26 × 28
No. of Sq. Ft./Laboratory	728
Personnel/Laboratory	6
Technical	3
Assistants	3
No. of Sq. Ft./Person	121
No. of Linear Feet of Bench/Person	16
Size of Office	7 × 7
No. of Sq. Ft./Office	49
Personnel/Office	1
Assistant Report Writing Space	Yes

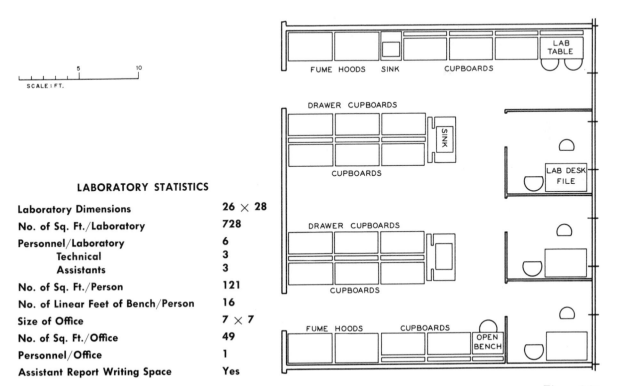

Figure 8.31

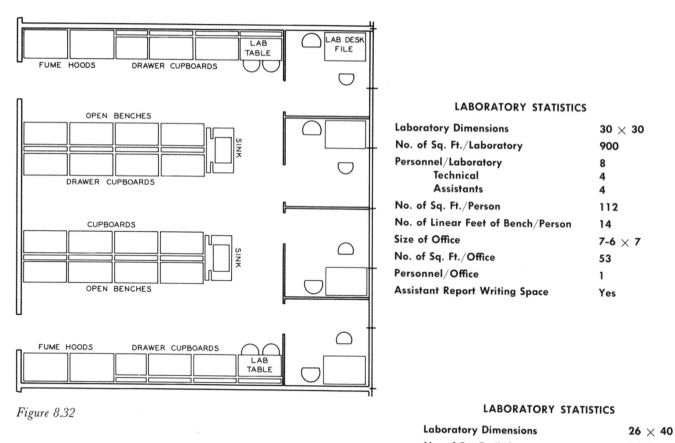

LABORATORY STATISTICS

Laboratory Dimensions	30 × 30
No. of Sq. Ft./Laboratory	900
Personnel/Laboratory	8
Technical	4
Assistants	4
No. of Sq. Ft./Person	112
No. of Linear Feet of Bench/Person	14
Size of Office	7-6 × 7
No. of Sq. Ft./Office	53
Personnel/Office	1
Assistant Report Writing Space	Yes

Figure 8.32

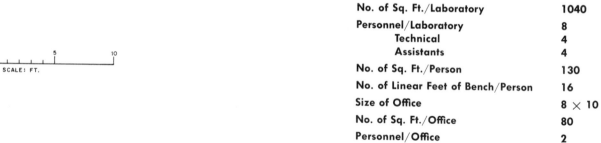

LABORATORY STATISTICS

Laboratory Dimensions	26 × 40
No. of Sq. Ft./Laboratory	1040
Personnel/Laboratory	8
Technical	4
Assistants	4
No. of Sq. Ft./Person	130
No. of Linear Feet of Bench/Person	16
Size of Office	8 × 10
No. of Sq. Ft./Office	80
Personnel/Office	2
Assistant Report Writing Space	Yes

Figure 8.33

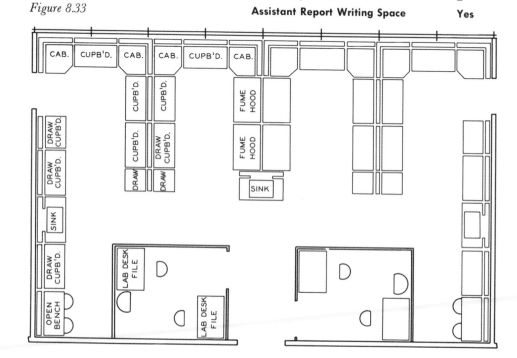

CHAPTER IX

Common Denominator Facilities

R. F. CONKLIN

General Electric Company
Liverpool, New York

Whether you are planning an industrial research laboratory, a university chemistry or chemical engineering building, a college science building, a high school, or a nonprofit research foundation laboratory, you will find numerous common functions. The lobby, offices, file rooms, conference rooms, and record vaults belong in the category of *administrative services,* while employee services such as cafeteria, auditorium, library, rest rooms, etc., are classed as *common denominator facilities.* In many cases the latter are afterthoughts and consequently are either forgotten or reduced to a minor function.

It is difficult to measure these common denominator facilities in terms of return on investment; however, they do much to promote good employer-employee relationship. Budget-minded management is always ready to chop away at such employee fringe benefits, but to do so is false economy and begins to lay the foundation for decreased worker efficiency, increased absenteeism and employee turnover. The payroll is the largest single expense of any laboratory. Top-notch research and development personnel do not come cheap. These facilities are a small investment in comparison.

RECEPTION ROOM

First impressions are very frequently lasting ones with many people, whether they are customers, visitors, or job candidates. Their first impression of the reception area may influence them in their dealing with your company. Music, natural planting, drapes, and large glass areas do much to promote a feeling of warmth and informality. Size, decor, and facilities will depend largely on the type and volume of visitor traffic. Adequate coat storage facilities should be provided, and there may be a tasteful display of company products and projects. A public pay phone and internal phone should be available for the use of visitors. In large reception areas, men's and women's rest rooms should be located at a convenient distance from the lobby. Several small conference rooms immediately off the lobby should be considered, to provide for cases when it is not desirable to take a visitor into the laboratory area. Comfortable divans, magazines, ash trays,

Figure 9.1   Reception room.

etc., should be plentiful (Figures 9.1 and 9.2). Switchboards should be installed in or near the reception areas. Additional space must be provided for installation of automatic telephone switching equipment.

Since the first contact with any company is via the receptionist, she should be placed so as to command a clear view of the lobby and be easily seen by visitors. The receptionist should have adequate, convenient storage for badges, visitors'

cards and incidentals. In case of small operations, the receptionist's extra duties should be of a nature that can easily be interrupted, as her first duty is to the visitor. The use of a lock, electrically controlled by the receptionist, on the door leading from the lobby into the building proper should be considered.

Figures 9.3, 9.4 and 9.5 depict typical reception area layouts for small, medium and large laboratories.

The reception area is a product of the company's progressive design and planning, but it should never be *overdone* to the extent that the rest of the laboratory appears inferior by comparison.

OFFICES

The planning of offices is a complex task which must be given careful consideration to assure that the final layout will afford not only adequate office operation for the present but for the future as well. Attention must also be given to the layout of each employee's work area with respect to itself and to the office as a unit. Over-all appearance of the office must be planned to offer both functional and attractive working conditions. As the final office layout must fall within the limits of a financial budget, these different phases of planning must be interrelated to incorporate the most practical ideas of each development phase. If a thorough understanding of the requirements of each phase is first gained, the final correlated layout will be better suited to meet the requirements of the office.

Space is the initial consideration. The question is asked: "How many square feet per person are required?" The answer may range from 60 to 160 square feet net, depending on such variables as:

(1) Job responsibility
(2) Number of people in general office areas

Figure 9.2   Reception room.

(3) Number of individuals in private offices

(4) Size and shape of existing buildings.

Therefore, any attempt to set an arbitrary standard figure would only be misleading.

Even after developing a method of determining the square footage required for each person, the job of planning for the necessary space is not completed. Foresight must be given to future alterations necessitated by changing office needs, with particular emphasis on the time and cost required to effect them with the least disturbance. An office without flexibility can quickly become outmoded. A program as extensive as this cannot be effectively developed without a plan, written as a procedure or method. Survey, Analysis and Planning are the three essentials for a systematic approach and should be included in every program.

Private Offices

The subject of private offices has always been of much concern in planning a laboratory layout. Such questions as: "Should we have private offices?", "Who gets a private office?", "How big should the office be?", "Where should they be located?", are but a few that arise. An advocate of private offices will say that the justification for private offices rests on these factors:

(1) Job responsibility.

(2) Mental concentration.

(3) Confidential or secret work.

(4) Increased significance of private offices during manpower shortage.

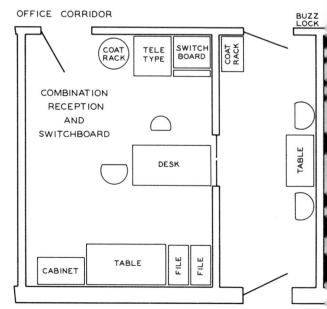

Figure 9.3   Layout of reception and vestibule combination for a small plant.

An opponent of private offices will point out:

(1) Poor space utilization when compared to as open area arrangement.

(2) Higher cost due to buying, erecting, and maintaining partitioning.

(3) Loss of informality, closeness, effectiveness.

(4) Complicated facilities planning in regard to heating, lighting, air-conditioning, and communications.

Whatever the arguments are, you are sure to be faced with the problems of planning for offices.

Table 9.1 recommends standards for offices and lists examples of office sizes which correspond to the position of an individual. Naturally, these recommendations will not apply to all cases but they will help avoid nebulous estimates. Offices designed to these sizes will efficiently and adequately fill the needs of 80 per cent of the offices in a laboratory. Formulate and standardize a scheme for office sizes. Get top management to accept it, and much time will be saved.

Consultant's Office

A facility lacking in many laboratories is a general type of unassigned office space which can be used occasionally by consultants, visitors,

TABLE 9.1

RECOMMENDED STANDARDS FOR
PRIVATE OFFICES

	SIZE OF OFFICE*	SQUARE FOOT OFFICE†
Office worker	Open area	60–80
Chemist, sales engineers, etc.	Open area (8′ x 9′)	70–90
Manager-operation (other)	9′ x 12′ to 12′ x 16′	108–192
Manager-operation (section level)	16′ x 16′	256
Department general manager	16′ x 20′	320
Division general manager	20′ x 20′	400

* Bay or column spacing and window location will, of course, influence the eventual size of the office.

† These space allocations should in all cases be made in accordance with operational requirements.

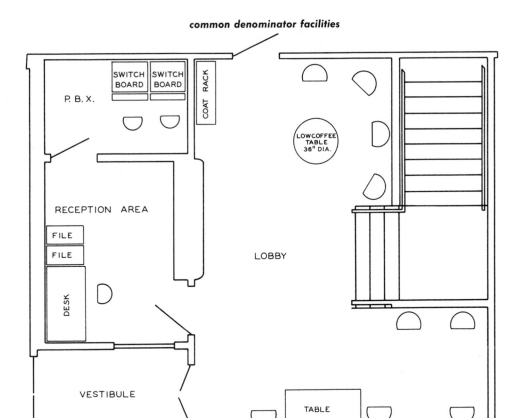

Figure 9.4   Layout of reception and lobby for a medium size plant.

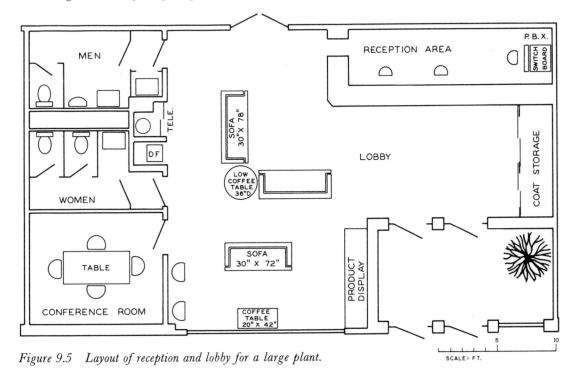

Figure 9.5   Layout of reception and lobby for a large plant.

licensees, auditors, and special company officials. An office not more than 150–200 square feet equipped with phone, desk, chairs and writing equipment should be planned.

Office Area for Chemists

Pros and cons of various types of office arrangements, as well as the arguments for and against office space for chemists, are many. It is the writer's opinion that office space for chemists is desirable and that a 7 to 8 foot semi-partition is adequate. This provides sufficient privacy, reduces the noise level, and tends to discourage prolonged and unnecessary "bull sessions." The office is a distinct morale booster to the technical man and makes a good impression on visitors. Most important, offices provide an atmosphere conducive to writing and reading within the laboratory. It is recommended that an office for two technical men cover an area of 95 to 110 square feet. It should be located on an outside wall to make service distribution easier, to provide an outside view, and to discourage unnecessary visitors. (See also discussion in chapter VIII.)

Location of the Secretary

Secretarial and typing duties can range from that of a private secretary to a steno-clerk, the space required usually varying in proportion to the responsibility. However, other factors which influence space requirements are filing requirements, reception or waiting area, personalities, and type of work performed. Figures 9.6 through 9.9d suggest several types of layout arrangements.

In many cases the secretary's location depends upon the number of linear feet of outside wall area. If you compare Figures 9.6 and 9.7, you will find that Figure 9.6 requires one-third less linear wall space than Figure 9.7. This is a good guide to remember when outside wall space is at a premium.

The private or confidential secretary is responsible for the secretarial duties of one man. (See Figures 9.9a through 9.9d.) However, these systems use more floor space. Figure 9.8 requires less floor space and presents a close-knit operation. Figures 9.9a and 9.9c permit occupancy by at least two secretaries, each serving an individual, and thus facilitate continuity of service to both

Shown here and on the facing page are various arrangements for secretarial offices.

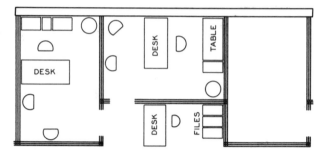

Figure 9.6

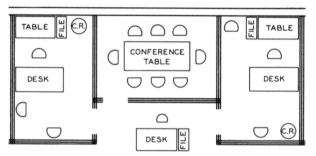

Figure 9.7

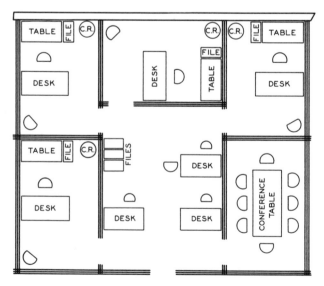

Figure 9.8

men when one girl is out of the office due to sickness or vacation.

To ensure privacy a wall should separate the manager's office from the secretary's. However, a sliding panel or intercom system should connect the two offices. The secretary's office should be arranged so that she has the following:

(1) An unobstructed view of the doorways.

(2) Adequate file space for work performed.

(3) Room for storage of a small supply of stationery and often-used supplies.

(4) One or two chairs for visitors.

To be efficient a secretary must have adequate work space. Consult with her and find out her specific requirements—only then can you formulate your approach to the space requirements.

NETWORK DICTATION SYSTEM

In most cases the installation of a secretarial pool is based on the economics of lower operating costs, that is, it takes less people to do the same amount of work. However, there are other benefits to be derived. An efficient general filing system can be set up and adhered to by a group, instead of each girl setting up her own system. Typewriter noise—always a nuisance in the general office area of a laboratory—can be eliminated if centralized typing is adopted. Since the typing activity will be localized, the typing area may well be enclosed in acoustic tile.

There are essentially two types of dictating-transcribing facilities. The major manufacturers of dictating machines supply separate hand sets with wiring from the private office to the steno pool. This separately wired instrument system is more expensive. By using the existing internal telephone system, no extra wiring is necessary, and maintenance of the telephone instrument is the responsibility of the local telephone company. No extra charges will be incurred as a result of office or laboratory rearrangement, for as soon as the internal telephone is reconnected, you are back in business again. Work loads can be redistributed by assigning alternate numbers on the telephone in case the general number is in use. Additional recorders can be added at the switchboard at any time without having to rewire the system to balance the work load.

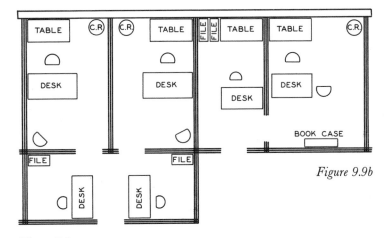

Figure 9.9b

Figure 9.9a

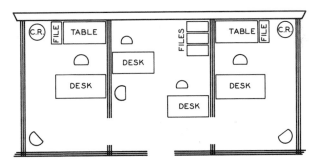

Figure 9.9c

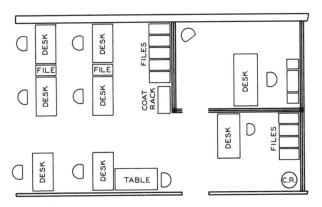

Figure 9.9d

One group leader and four typists can handle from 60 to 70 people. Equipment for this group would include four voice-actuated recorders connected to internal telephones, four transcribing units and five electric typewriters. All work coming into steno pool should be handled and distributed by the group leader. If there are individuals who cannot adjust to this system, provision should be made for accepting letters in longhand. A series of baskets or pigeon-holes can be labeled according to time required. Records from the dictating machine should have priority over all other typing. The typist should service the recorders, such as removing used discs and reloading fresh ones, and answering telephone calls concerning dictated material. If a good job of scheduling is done, work should be completed within two hours after it is received in the stenographic pool.

A network dictating system with proper study and management should prove to be a substantial cost reduction plus providing better service.

CONFERENCE ROOMS

The location and number of conference rooms is always a hotly debated question. Many base their argument for an individual office on the need of privacy for meetings. While those who have been assigned a private office need one big enough to contain a table, a conference room is still the best place for a conference. The meeting can be held in a business-like atmosphere. A greater number of people can be accommodated, and each individual has a convenient place to sit, write, or take notes. All these conveniences can be had with a minimum of distraction and interference. There are no standards suggesting the number of conference rooms based on the number of people in the laboratory. However, there are several arrangements and sizes that may prove helpful.

A suggested size of an individual conference room is 12 by 18 ft. This will comfortably seat ten people. If more are to be seated, add 2 ft 6 in to the table and room length for every two people —5 ft for four more people, etc.

It is sometimes necessary to hold large group meetings. If no cafeteria or auditorium is available, an arrangement such as Figure 9.10 may prove useful. A folding partition offers the greatest amount of flexibility in such an area. Its use will permit two or three conferences to run simultaneously, and folding it to one side will open the entire area to accommodate company discussions or lunchtime movies. This arrangement is definitely advisable if no cafeteria or canteen service is available.

Very often there is a need for small or informal conferences within the private office. Recognizing this fact, desk manufacturers have designed a conference desk (See Figure 9.11). There are many sizes and shapes, but all have the overhang on three sides of the desk to provide knee space for comfort while taking notes.

The location of conference rooms is too frequently an afterthought prompted by the need to utilize excess space. Advance consideration should be given to location, number, and size of conference rooms.

AUDITORIUM

The auditorium is definitely an area that has to be closely evaluated from the standpoint of per cent of utilization. The conducting of sales meetings, training courses, community and technical meetings are a few uses to which this area can be put; but the size and frequency of such meetings must dictate the need.

There are two basic types of auditoriums— those having permanently fixed chairs on a sloped or tiered floor— approximately 15 sq ft per person including stage area is allowed—and those having movable chairs on a level floor with a raised stage and projection booth; for these, approximately 10 sq ft per person, including stage area, is generally allocated. The sloping auditorium is definitely restricted in its use. However, the level-floor auditorium with removable chairs shown in Figure 9.12 is flexible, as it can be used to accommodate large meetings or employee and communal programs.

The following Tables (9.2 and 9.3) are designed to determine the seating capacity of auditoriums. Table 9.2 shows the total number of chairs per row that can be placed across the width of the room. Table 9.3 shows the number of rows in the

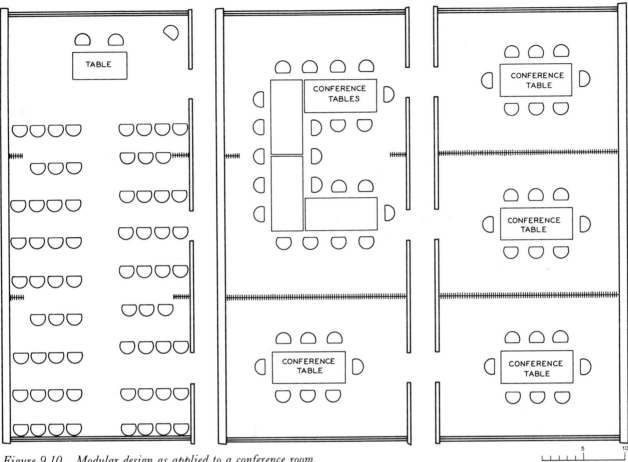

Figure 9.10 Modular design as applied to a conference room.

SCALE : FT.

depth of the room. Total seating capacity may be obtained by multiplying the number of chairs in width by the number of rows in depth.

CAFETERIA

If it is envisioned that an auditorium would be in use 30 to 40 per cent of the day, it should certainly be constructed. This may be the case at research laboratories where the number of personnel is high. Most operating plants cannot justify the expense of an auditorium. However, most laboratories do need a lunch room or cafeteria. To answer the needs of both an eating and meeting room, it is recommended that a cafeteria-type room be planned. This room should be decorated so as to promote a definite change of pace. Provision should be made for a projection booth, stage, projection screen, blackboard, podium,

Figure 9.11 Private office with conference desk.

Figure 9.12 Auditorium arrangement.

TABLE 9.2

ROOM WIDTH		LAYOUT							TOTAL NO. OF CHAIRS IN ROW
18" CHAIR	24" CHAIR	NO. CHAIRS	AISLE SIZE	NO. CHAIRS	AISLE SIZE	NO. CHAIRS	AISLE SIZE	NO. CHAIRS	
18'	23'	5	3'	5	—	—	—	—	10
21'	27'	6	3'	6	—	—	—	—	12
24'	31'	7	3'	7	—	—	—	—	14
30'	38'	4	3'	8	3'	4	—	—	16
33'	42'	5	3'	8	3'	5	—	—	18
33'	41'	—	3'	8	3'	8	3'	—	16
36'	46'	6	3'	8	3'	6	—	—	20
39'	50'	6	3'	10	3'	6	—	—	22
41'	51'	—	3'6"	10	4'	10	3'6"	—	20
47'	59'	—	3'6"	12	4'	12	3'6"	—	24
56'	71'	5	3'6"	10	4'	10	3'6'	5	30

TABLE 9.3

NO. OF ROWS	*DEPTH IN FEET
10	39
12	45
14	51
16	57
18	63
20	69
22	75
24	81
26	87
28	93
30	99

Above depth in feet is figured on the basis of 3-foot back to back spacing between chairs.

The seating capacity of an auditorium may be determined from these tables. Table 9.2 shows the total number of chairs per row that can be placed across the width of a room. Table 9.3 shows the number of rows in depth of the room. Total seating capacity is obtained by multiplying the number of chairs in width by the number of rows in depth. Table 9.3 is based on a 3-foot back-to-back spacing between chairs and includes a 4-foot cross aisle in the back of the auditorium and a 5-foot cross aisle in the front.

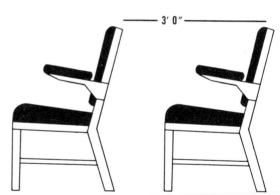

*The depth includes a 4-foot cross aisle in back and a 5-foot cross aisle in front.

Figure 9.13a   Cafeteria with a recessed stage.

Figure 9.13b   Cafeteria serving area.

public address system and other props necessary for the presentation of lectures, movies, etc. Folding panels, partitions, or drapes can serve to change the decor from that of a cafeteria to that of an auditorium. Such an area should be augmented with other rooms, to be used for chair and prop storage and coat closets, especially for outside guests. An example of a general eating and meeting room is seen in Figures 9.13a and 9.13b. The following formula can be used for preliminary estimation of the amount of space required for a cafeteria.

$$T = \frac{1.25 \ (N \times 17)}{NS}$$

where T = total space required
1.25 = 25% of total area for kitchen and related services
N = number of people served
17 = 17 sq ft per person (seating, serving and aisles)
NS = the number of eating shifts

Remember, the above formula is for a quick estimation of space requirements. An excellent book entitled "In-Plant Feeding" by C. W. Schroeder of the Hotpoint Division of the General Electric Company will give enough information to plan a cafeteria adequately.

CANTEEN

The canteen or automatic food service is an excellent idea which is gaining popularity (Figure 9.14). Many of the older established firms have complete cafeteria facilities and today because of increased overhead are operating at a loss. The canteen service is operated by industrial food caterers. The only cost to management is floor space. Maintenance, stocking of machines, and general cleanliness of the area are taken care of by the vendor. The selection of food is limited, however. Wrapped sandwiches, pastries, soups, ice cream and beverages are usually the extent of the menu. Occasionally, these mechanical vendors do not operate the way in which they were designed. The idea is, however, appealing to management from the standpoint of economy of space and money.

Figure 9.14   Canteen servinette installation.

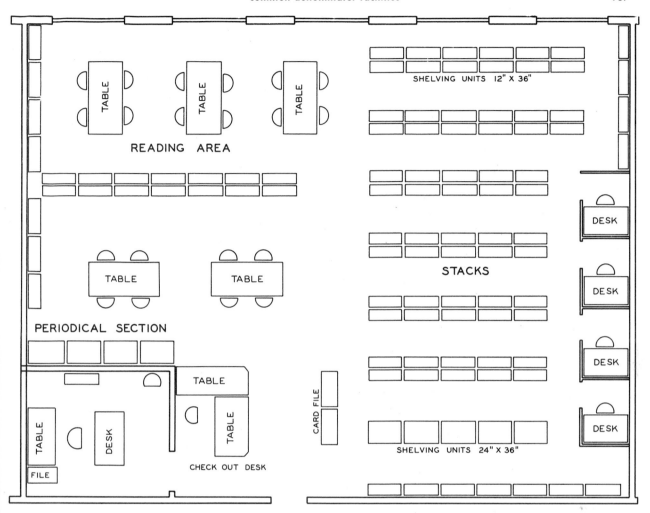

OFFICE CORRIDOR

LIBRARY LAYOUT—1900 SQ. FT.

Books	• Vols/Ft of Shelf	Shelf Depth
Law	4	8″
Public Documents	6	8″
Reference	8	10″
Technical	7	10″
Bound Periodicals	5	12″
Periodicals, Atlases, Etc.	-	18″

Allow One-third Shelf Space For Expansion

Figure 9.15 Library layout.

LIBRARY

The library has assumed an increasingly important function in the operation of research and development laboratories. No longer does it serve merely as a dispenser of books and periodicals, but has come to be looked upon as a technical information center. The chemist, whose time schedule is forever being tightened, is becoming more and more pressed for reading time. The

Figure 9.16   Arrangement of library carrels.

library is the source of abstracting services, obtaining of reprints, aid in the duplication of journal articles, translations, obtaining of copies of patents and maintenance of an index thereof, filing of inside reports, notebooks and other important departmental papers. These duties, plus giving general assistance to the individual in keeping abreast of recent events, have made the technical library a *must*. The layout (Figure 9.15) suggests the various components common to most libraries and shows their interrelationship. The use of carrels is exceedingly helpful to the chemist who is engaged in deep thinking (Figure 9.16).

A service desk for checking volumes in and out of circulation is essential for good control, and should be located near the exit-entrance.

Some excellent examples of wise library planning can be seen at the B. F. Goodrich Laboratories (3,500 sq ft), the 3-M Research Laboratory (7,000 sq ft), and the Esso Research and Development Laboratory (over 7,500 sq ft and currently being expanded).

The print reproduction room is an all-important part of the library activities. It should be equipped with a sink, storage, work cabinets and hanging wall cabinets to utilize all possible space. The graphic reproduction equipment is often extensive. A Microfilm reader-printer, a photocopying machine and a diazotype printing machine are essential for a start. This room should be constructed like a photographic darkroom with light traps and safe lights. Consideration should be given to integrating the graphic reproduction and photographic activities into the same general area, as the facilities and services required are the same. The need for additional work rooms is a function of the type and size of the library. Industrial laboratory libraries are usually modest in size and require a minimum amount of equipment. Research and development libraries often require more extensive facilities for journal circulation, binding and cataloging. This makes it desirable to subdivide the library area into separate rooms to reduce noise and eliminate distractions.

Much can be done to reduce noise in the library: cork floor tiling, acoustic ceiling tile, window drapes, wooden furniture, rubber instead of metal tipped chair gliders, and sound-absorbing partitions are a few of the materials that can be used. The arrangement of equipment can also be used to control the noise level. The reading room can be isolated by periodical display racks and book stacks. Work and typing activities should definitely be within an enclosure.

EMPLOYEE STORE

Many industrial firms having research laboratories offer an employee service commonly called the employee store. Individuals may purchase company products at a discount.

The employee store should be convenient to all employees. Since the bulk of sales is transacted during lunch hour, a suggested location would be in the vicinity of the cafeteria. Another possible location would be near the exit where the employees can shop before leaving the plant.

One of the best locations, from the standpoint of merchandising, is on a heavily traveled corridor; however, lines may form at a service window or counter which may hamper office traffic in main corridors. It is thus advantageous to locate the store at the junction of intersecting corridors, where there is more space for product display windows, and where the line could form in the less traveled corridor.

The size of the employee store depends on the type of merchandising, number of employees and planned sales volume. Space requirements can be calculated by dividing the planned sales volume by 100, the answer being the approximate number of square feet of space required to carry on store activities.

DISPENSARY

A laboratory having more than 200 people should maintain a dispensary. The specific needs will, of course, have to be determined by the functions performed in the laboratory. Figure 9.17 gives an example of a dispensary layout showing the various rooms and their relation to one another. Several factors must be kept in mind when trying to determine the dispensary's location with respect to the over-all operation. It should be so located as to provide easy access from all points of the building, and the emergency door should be so placed that confusion when a stretcher or ambulance is needed will be

minimum. Employee relations offices should have access to the desired medical information; therefore, it is recommended that the dispensary be near the employee relations function. Space allocations, selection of equipment, and planning should be a combined effort of management, the doctors, and nurses. It is advised that the planning engineer consult with all three groups in order to get all the necessary information on the facilities and equipment required.

FILE ROOMS

Centralized vs. decentralized filing is a problem to be studied and evaluated by your particular operation. If centralized filing is accepted, 5 to 7 sq ft for letter-size files and 6 to 8 sq ft for legal-size files may be used to calculate the size of the file room. A 5-drawer filing cabinet, if substituted for a 4-drawer file, will save 20 per cent of the filing space, that is, four 5-drawer files have the same filing capacity as five 4-drawer files. This allows a greater concentration of effort in large file rooms. Although one would expect the 5-drawer file to be a full drawer higher, design changes have made it only one-

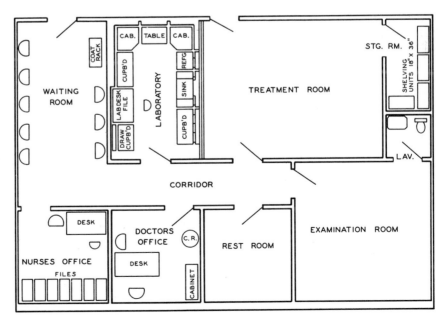

Figure 9.17   Layout of a 1350 Sq. Ft. dispensary.

half drawer higher. Wise filing practices suggest the use of the top and bottom drawers for less active papers. A 4 to 5 ft aisle is recommended where rows of filing cabinets face each other.

TOILET AND JANITORIAL SERVICE AREAS

The necessity of provision for adequate toilet and janitorial facilities is self-evident. The best location is in interior space; in multi-storied buildings, they should be located over one another. Ordinary travel to the toilet location should not be in excess of 150 feet. Of course, state and local codes must be met, but for preliminary planning the following guide is generally acceptable:

Water Closets	Persons
1	1–15
2	16–35
3	36–55
5	81–110

Add one water closet for each additional 40 persons over 190. Subtract one water closet from the above number for each urinal used. Allow one wash basin for each 20 persons.

For the preliminary planning of men's toilet rooms 2 to 3 sq ft per person should be allowed, and for women's toilet including rest rooms approximately 7 sq ft is necessary. The wisdom and/or need for shower rooms and lockers for technical personnel falls into the class of items which must be determined by management, in light of the work performed. A lounge for women employees is ordinarily required. Provisions for a janitor's sink adjacent to the toilet area must be made, and a room for the storage of janitorial supplies should be provided. Since an abundant supply of water is available within this area, consideration should be given to installing a water cooler or a drinking fountain recessed into the corridor wall.

STAIRWAYS

Exits and stairways should be designed with reference to state and local codes. The width of the stairwell has a definite relationship to the number of people on the floor. Travel to any exit should be limited to 150 ft. Stairways should be placed over one another in a multi-story building. Since stairwells create a natural draft between floors, many state and local building codes require that the stairway enclosure be of fireproof construction. In many cases, decorative stairways are planned for the lobby area but should not be considered as one of two necessary exits for multi-story buildings.

ELEVATORS

In large multi-story laboratory buildings, consideration should be given to the installation of passenger and freight elevators. Passenger elevators should be located at the vertex of travel between corridors and reception rooms. The freight elevator should be located near the receiving-shipping area on the first floor and, if possible, next to the stock or supply rooms on the second floor. In many cases, for the sake of economy, passenger and freight functions can be combined in one elevator. In this case, thought should be given to the use of an elevator cab having a door on both sides. Hydraulic-type elevators have proved an economical installation in two-story laboratory and office buildings.

MODEL AND MAINTENANCE SHOP

The development of space and facilities requirements for shops must be planned for in the early stages of layout and building design. Quite frequently this area requires special services, excessive headroom, floor loading considerations, and extensive exhaust and dust-collecting systems. The decision as to whether to air-condition this area is based on the type of work and the amout of heat generated by the equipment. A good ventilation system separated from the main air-conditioning system would seem advisable if a considerable amount of outside air is necessary to replace process exhausts.

The location of this area with respect to the total planning should be considered during the layout phase. Because of the nature of the work performed here ground-floor location adjacent to the shipping and receiving area is desirable. Sheet metal and special metal shapes should be handled with a minimum amount of transportation.

New equipment can be pretested in this area before permanent installation. The shop should have an area large enough to accommodate large pieces of equipment. This would allow the removal of equipment which is in need of repair from the laboratory to the shop. This repair area should be supplied with all types of services and with flexible service connectors to facilitate speedy repair and return. Any machines which produce considerable noise should be mounted on shock-absorbing floor pads.

The shop's responsibility is to keep the present equipment in repair, provide special prototype work, build special glassware-holding devices for the chemist, pretest new equipment, and keep service facilities in operating condition. The proper amount of space, equipment and trained personnel are the important factors involved in keeping the laboratory in top working order.

SHIPPING AND RECEIVING AREA

In many laboratories the shipping and receiving activities are combined in one area; however, this is not true if the laboratory is of a product-oriented nature, and in this event care must be taken to integrate these areas with the manufacturing plant. A combined area is definitely economical from the standpoint of facilities duplication. Its size and equipment requirements are based on the volume of traffic. Certain considerations must be prepared for whether it is a large or small installation.

The size (height and width) of outside doors should conform to commercial carrier dimensions. In many cases, doors are too narrow for full loads and overhead clearance is too low for trucks to enter the building. If frequent opening and closing of doors is necessary, thought should be given to doors equipped with electric openers actuated by pull rope, push button or a photoelectric eye. An air lock or a double set of doors is often used to facilitate loading or unloading of trucks during inclement weather. An overhead monorail and hoist system is often installed for unloading heavy apparatus. The rail should extend beyond the face of the building and over the truck bed, as well as into the unloading area. This system allows the receiving personnel to lift the equipment from the truck bed, transport it via the overhead monorail and lower it in the receiving area.

Aisles within this area should be marked, and must be of sufficient width to facilitate constant material flow. Elevator entries and aisle intersections should be of ample width and clearance for the largest loaded truck to be used.

Floor loading is another factor to be considered. If proper load-bearing capacities are not provided for, frequent use will cause rough floors which in turn will cause slow travel. Different floor levels should, if possible, be avoided.

The expansion of this area is in direct proportion to business forecasts. It is wise practice to integrate the space planning with future business volume in order to anticipate storage capacity, number of receiving and shipping docks, elevator capacities, floor loading and type of storage racks.

CHAPTER X

Specific

Applications

B. F. JAEGER and CLIFFORD C. JAPS
Minnesota Mining and Manufacturing Company
St. Paul, Minnesota

The term "pilot plant" has been in common use for some twenty to forty years. During this time, architects and engineers have studied and evaluated a wide variety of building designs, both on paper and by actual construction. Analysis of pilot plant buildings erected over the years shows that almost all of them can be classified as described below. No attempt will be made here to include those pilot plants which are constructed in operating plants as individual process setups for either convenience of communication with operating personnel, proximity of raw material supply, or other reasons. The same applies to special pilot plant setups erected in buildings mainly devoted to laboratory work.

MAIN TYPES OF
PILOT PLANT BUILDINGS

Regional Laboratory (or Outer Balcony) Type

This is usually a two- to four-story building, three or four bays wide, with balconies around three or four sides and a full height open area in the middle. The name is derived from the USDA Regional Research Laboratories which have used this construction in a number of their industrial laboratories, or pilot plant wings. This is probably the most common form of building currently being erected for data-taking, pilot plant scale operations. The design is a compromise to provide adequate high bay area with maximum floor space. A disadvantage is that seldom, if ever, is any great portion of the high bay area actually used for installation of tall equipment. It is generally conceded to have some failings; nevertheless, it appears to be the best compromise design worked out to date.

Center Balcony Type

As implied by the name, this is a building open to the ceiling next to the outer walls with one or more balconies in the center. However, this type of building is not very common, but may have some advantages for combining process development and rather large semiworks operations under one roof.

Modular Type

This is generally a series of rooms with high ceilings, located side by side, with individual operations or equipment setups in each room, and with partial balconies in each room of the size and height required for installation and operation of necessary equipment. This type is adaptable to work comprising larger-scale organic preparations and purifications wherein equipment setups can be either permanent or temporary, but will never be so large as to require more than one module. It has the advantage of isolating each setup when this may be desirable.

Multi-Story Type

Typically, this is a rectangular building, more than three bays wide in both directions, with all floor areas decked over with solid floor or grating and with large-size reactors, receivers, mix tanks, etc., mounted in the upper decks. This type is generally used for semiworks scale pilot plants as well as many full-scale production plants. It is one means of packing the largest possible number of pieces of process equipment into the smallest possible volume.

Individual Small Building Type

The major advantage ascribed to this type of pilot plant is safety in case of fire or explosion from the standpoint of preventing spread of fire and keeping personnel concentrations to a minimum. Also, operations with toxic or nuclear materials can be isolated by this arrangement. It is probably the most expensive design to execute for any given total pilot plant floor area, from the standpoint of total cost of the enclosing wall areas as well as the cost of utility distribution systems.

Open (Barn) Type

This building is generally up to 80 feet wide, completely open, at least two stories high, and has a typical barnlike appearance in cross section. It is especially well suited to house a variety of different size semiworks setups. Each setup can be built in a line with no limit on the length or width of the complete unit. Operating balconies and steps are erected of any required size and height for each individual unit.

Open Air Type

A number of chemical and many petrochemical pilot plants are constructed entirely in the open, exposed to the elements, process equipment being hung on a structural steel frame and operating platforms and steps installed where needed. Generally, these pilot plant setups are continuous processes, highly automated and instrumented, so that little attention is required at the equipment. A small instrument or control room may be enclosed and located convenient to the open structure. Whenever it is practical from the standpoint of climatic conditions and type of operation, this kind of construction is highly desirable to reduce initial cost.

Make-Do Type

The only generalizations one could make on this type of pilot plant would be that it has been in quite common use for years, and that it has housed the inauspicious beginnings of many very fine pilot plant groups. It may be located in a basement, storage room, garage, warehouse, tent, or any unused area relinquished by another division of the company. No more need be said.

PILOT PLANT FUNCTIONS

The term "pilot plant" means many things to many people, and there is wide variation among companies in respect to pilot plant philosophies. A pilot plant may be organizationally under a Central Research Department, an Engineering Research Group, a Production Division, an Engineering Department, or any other company subdivision. Also, many companies have two or more pilot plant departments, each handling different functions and reporting to different corporate divisions. In each case, the particular company organization responsible for pilot plant operations will determine, to a great extent, which pilot plant functions will be emphasized. In other words, no discussion of a particular design for a pilot plant building would be meaningful unless that design had been examined in the light of how well the requirements for the company subdivision were served. Consequently, it is seldom, if ever, that a specific pilot plant building could well serve more than the one company for which it was designed. However, it is obvious that many general features of construction and layout may be common to different pilot plants.

Since a pilot plant building must be designed to accommodate specific functions which differ from one company to another, we will briefly examine and list, in arbitrary terms, some of the more important functions of chemical pilot plants. Naturally, no one pilot plant will ever have all the functions listed and others may have functions which are not included in one list.

(1) Bench Scale Process Development or Process Improvement (implies bench work in glass or metal equipment).

(2) Pilot Plant Scale Process Development or Process Improvement (implies work in small-scale replicas of standard production equipment, for instance, 5- to 50-gallon reactors).

(3) Research Samples Preparation (generally up to one pound and often handled by a research laboratory or technical service group).

(4) Application or Market Sample Preparation (10 to 1000 pounds or more).

(5) Semiworks, Semicommercial or Interim Production (any conceivable scale necessary to handle production requirements until full-scale plant is built and operating).

(6) Basic Engineering Research.

(7) Applied Engineering Research.

(8) Cost Estimating (for any stage of research or development).

(9) Consulting Work (may be for operating divisions, or sometimes, for guidance of research work in other laboratories).

(10) Special Services (includes the application and operation of specialized pilot plant equipment).

MINNESOTA MINING AND MANUFACTURING COMPANY — CENTRAL RESEARCH PILOT PLANT

To illustrate the design and layout of a pilot plant to serve specific functions, let us consider the requirements for a particular pilot plant in a specific company, and examine in detail the manner in which these requirements were met. For our example, we will take the pilot plant of the Central Research Department of the Minnesota Mining and Manufacturing Company. This is a "data taking" pilot plant and process development group whose main purpose is to provide a smooth flow of economical chemical processes from the laboratory to the semiworks and production groups. Operating policy is to obtain scale-up data on the smallest practical scale, both in bench and pilot plant work, to conserve manpower and materials and to minimize capital investment. Consequently, equipment sizes are kept as small as practical and emphasis is placed on versatility, flexibility, and portability in equipment selection.

The function or requirements for this pilot plant, which were considered in determining the layout and final building design, are briefly stated below, along with an approximate per cent figure which reflects the amount of the total effort devoted to each function.

(1) 20% bench scale process development work.

(2) 20% pilot plant scale process development work.

(3) 30% preparation of chemical samples for evaluation of new materials by other groups in the company, especially coming from Central Research Laboratory. Sample sizes are small, generally in the 10 to 100 pound range.

(4) 15% research on new and varied chemical processes.

(5) 15% special services, i.e.,

    a. economic analyses of proposed processes designed for research guidance to Central Research Department.

    b. operation of specialized processing equipment for other groups in the company.

    c. consultation service for other laboratories and divisions.

Preliminary Planning

Primary responsibility for providing a suitable building for this pilot plant department was assigned to 3 M's Staff Laboratory Engineering Department. A project engineer of this department acted as project coordinator during both planning and construction stages. It was his responsibility to provide the liaison between the operating department and the architectural firm contracted to the project.

A member of the Pilot Plant Department was designated as spokesman for his group. He established both the general and many of the detailed requirements for the building, such as the approximate size and type of working area, the number of offices and laboratories, etc. Visits were then made to several of the leading pilot plants throughout the country. Detailed discussions with operating and design personnel resulted in a good understanding of the planning, features, and failings of each of these facilities. For anyone planning a new laboratory or pilot plant, an inspection trip of this nature is a "must"; many companies are proud to display their modern facilities to their industrial neighbors.

Building Location

The Central Research Pilot Plant Building is located in the Pilot Plant and Central Utilities area of the 3M Research Center. This location, approximately one-half mile from the main research laboratory building, has not proved to be a disadvantage, as first feared. The highly desirable day-to-day communication between the pilot plant engineers and laboratory personnel has been maintained by various means, including informal luncheons at the cafeteria.

On the other hand, the relatively remote pilot plant location does have distinct advantages; visitors usually come only on business and the department is generally free to operate quite independently. Furthermore, such accidents as fume leak, for example, cause far less disturbance than they might in a more congested area.

Building Type

The building, designed to accommodate the functions mentioned previously, is a combination one-story modular laboratory and office area and a three-story regional laboratory hazardous pilot plant area. In addition, a small three-story nonhazardous pilot plant area is provided. By way of definition, hazardous areas are those in which no spark-producing operations are permitted, in which highly flammable materials are used, and which are restricted to Class I, Group D electrical equipment. Conversely, nonhazardous areas are those where sparks are permitted and the operations are relatively safe from fire hazard.

Outside views of the building are shown in Figure 10.1. The building is fireproof design and of brick and steel construction. All outside walls are concrete block faced with brick to blend with other buildings on the site. A touch of external color is added by green-enameled panels on the face of the building surrounding the entrance area. In designing the building, every effort was made to maintain previously established 3M standards for new laboratory construction. The building design emphasizes functionality, safety, and pleasant working conditions. A generally cheerful atmosphere is created through the use of good lighting and a wide selection of gay colors. The structural steel in the process area, for example, is painted varying shades of green while all balcony and staircase railings are light yellow.

Building Arrangement

In locating the working areas within the building, every attempt was made to satisfy the following general considerations:

(1) Related working areas should be located convenient to one another.

(2) Paths of travel should be the shortest possible.

(3) Service areas should be aside from the process areas.

(4) Building design should permit future expansion.

(5) High safety standards should be maintained.

(6) Location and layout of working areas should be conducive to good housekeeping.

(7) Building services should be inconspicuous but readily available and easily maintained.

Figure 10.1   Central research pilot plant, front view.

(8) Personnel should be dispersed to minimize congestion.

At this point, by a process of trial and error, floor layouts were made, each being tested for the above requirements. After many layouts, the plans shown in Figures 10.2, 10.3, and 10.4 evolved. This floor space was allocated as follows:

	Sq. Ft.	% of Total
Laboratory and office	2820	12.1
Non I-D process area (see p. 145)	2360	10.2
I-D process area	5115	22.0
Service areas and corridors	8500	36.6
Storage area	4420	19.1
Total	23,215	100.0
Available by Decking (future)		
I-D process area	3400	
Non I-D process area	1000	

Development Laboratories

Two double laboratory modules were provided for bench-scale engineering operations. Since the people associated with these laboratories normally do not utilize the three-story pilot plant area, they are placed far from this area.

One double laboratory is located near the process area and is used primarily as a scale-up laboratory. Here the development engineer will generally verify a chemist's procedure prior to scaling up to pilot plant units. This laboratory also is used in conjunction with the normal pilot plant operations; for example, frequently it is more convenient to study variables on a small scale where several flasks can be operated at one time than to operate a pilot plant reactor.

Each single laboratory (Figure 10.5) is provided with an 8-foot, high velocity fume hood and a 10-foot chemical bench at the outer wall. A

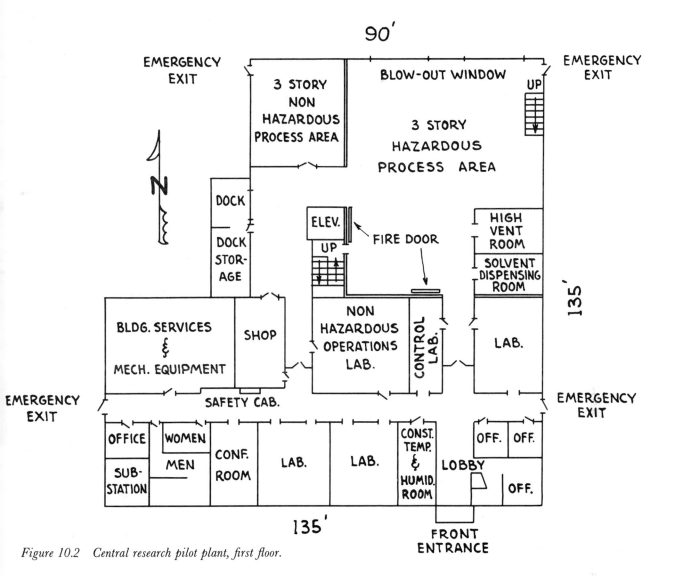

Figure 10.2   Central research pilot plant, first floor.

Figure 10.3   Second floor plan.   Figure 10.4   Third floor plan.

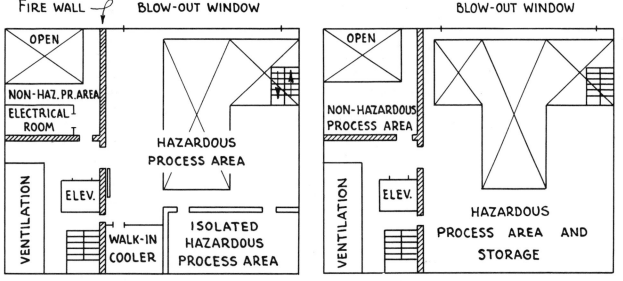

chemical rack with services occupies the center area of each double module.

Each single module is designed for a technical man and his assistant. Desk space for the technical man is provided in a glass partitioned area at the outside wall of his module. This arrangement provides a measure of protection from the laboratory hazards and affords some degree of privacy. Multiple unit offices have been avoided whenever possible.

Each double laboratory is 24 by 26 feet in size with a 14-foot ceiling—ample headroom for most operations. All modules have two exits, one leading to the corridor and the other into the adjoining laboratory.

Control Laboratory

A control laboratory is centrally located in the building with short routes to the hazardous process area and all laboratories. The area was set up to house such commonly used equipment as is used for the determination of solids, melting points, viscosities, pH, titrations, etc. Anyone is

Figure 10.5 Engineering laboratory. Single module with chemical bench, hood and desk area.

free to use the facilities as required; however, the responsibility for maintaining this equipment is delegated, as a part-time job, to one technician.

Occasionally, it has been advisable to move or duplicate a piece of test equipment to make it more convenient to an operation. This does not detract from the value of having a selection of test equipment assembled in operating order in a central location. This has encouraged the engineers to try simple tests which otherwise might have been overlooked or neglected.

Constant Temperature-Humidity Room. A 14- by 26-foot module is set aside for use as a constant temperature-humidity room, needed for such instruments or operations as require controlled conditions of temperature and humidity. The room has no windows, is well insulated, and has a self-closing door. Original equipment in this room includes a chemical table along one entire wall and a partitioned desk space at one end. The room is so designed that it can be used as a standard laboratory module when not required for its original purpose.

Nonhazardous Operations Laboratory (one story)

A single-story nonhazardous operations laboratory was provided for those operations which could not be conveniently handled in the normal laboratory module. Its larger size (20 by 30 feet), concrete floor, and supplementary ventilation make it well suited for many operations including, at present, all nonhazardous drying and furnacing operations.

Office Area. The main office area is immediately inside the front entrance, which is offset to one side of the building. Building expansion to the right (Figure 10.1) would place the offices and entrance at the front, center of the building. Private offices have been provided for supervisors only. The operating personnel, as previously pointed out, are located near their work wherever possible. A secretary-receptionist is located in an open office facing the front entrance; the main panel of the intercom system and the telephone switchboard are located at her desk.

Locker Room. The locker and wash room is located in the general service area of the building, aside from the working areas. The subdivided room contains toilet facilities and a large semi-circular wash fountain in one area and shower stalls and lockers in the second or inner area. The wall lockers, provided for 35 people, have a small bench permanently attached at the lockers' base as a means of conserving space.

A small women's rest room is provided for the secretary and other female employees in an adjoining area.

Receiving Area. All service areas, including the main receiving area, are located at one side of the building or to the left as is shown in Figure 10.1. The dock, which is built at truck height, and protected by an over-hanging canopy roof, is 12 by 36 feet in size. An 8 by 8-ft overhead service door and standard-size personnel door serve this area. The far end of the dock is used for general cylinder storage and a nitrogen manifold system from which the gas is piped throughout the building. No other storage is maintained on this dock.

The inside receiving area is spacious and connects several key areas including the main entrance to all process areas, the maintenance shop, elevator and stairwell.

A 6½- by 7½-foot freight elevator serves the upper floors and opens into service areas on all levels. A 12- by 18-foot walk-in cooler (40°F), is located on the second balcony convenient to the elevator.

Nonhazardous Pilot Plant (3 story)

A three-story nonhazardous operational area (28 by 32 feet) was provided for those operations for which considerable headroom would be required and which could not be safely carried out in the hazardous operation area. These would include all operations which do not conform to the Class I Group D electrical code and which do not involve the use of flammable solvents and gases.

Locating this area in the corner of the building had two main advantages. First, it permits an expansion of the area with a building expansion to the north, and second, a location adjacent to the hazardous pilot plant area (block fire wall between) suggests the possibility of a combination hazardous and nonhazardous pilot plant operation by installation of an integrated unit on both

sides of the fire wall. For example, non-Class I Group D instrumentation might be located in the nonhazardous working area while a process system involving flammable solvents is located in the hazardous area.

The present floor plan of this three-story area provides a minimum working space at the upper levels. Four-foot and ten-foot balconies serve two sides, the remaining area being open. If additional single story operating space is required in preference to three-story space, the plan permits the upper decks to be extended and used as separate floors. The first floor presently is used primarily for single-floor operations (Figure 10.6) in much the same manner as the other single-story nonhazardous laboratory.

Permanently installed facilities include an 8-foot walk-in hood and an 8-foot chemical bench at first-floor level. Service stations are conveniently available at numerous locations on all levels.

Good ventilation is provided, the normal air charge being once every five minutes. A supple-

Figure 10.6 Nonhazardous three story pilot plant area.

mentary floor fan increases this level to once in three minutes. For process work, spot ventilation is available to all points in the area.

Hazardous Pilot Plant Area

The hazardous pilot plant area, provided for the processing of flammable or otherwise hazardous chemicals, consists of a three-story regional laboratory-type construction made up of nine 20- by 24-foot bays. The second and third levels are balconies above the outer bays, the center bays being open from floor to ceiling (Figure 10.7).

As shown in Figure 10.2, several entrances serve this process area. The front entrance leads directly to the scale-up laboratory, control laboratory and offices. The main side entrance is convenient to service area, elevator and maintenance shop.

Two stairways lead to the upper levels, the first an enclosed stairwell adjoining the elevator and the second, an open staircase located directly in the process area. Since this is a hazardous operational area, no spark-producing operations are allowed and good ventilation is provided. To ensure the former, all electrical equipment con-

Figure 10.7   Hazardous pilot plant area.

Figure 10.8   Central research pilot plant, rear view.

forms to the Class I Group D code and proper measures have been taken to prevent static sparks, etc. The open bays provide for a comfortable and roomy working area, as communications between floors, lighting and ventilation are facilitated.

The area was so designed that most of the initial operations could be conducted at first-floor level. The upper decks, originally useful for storage, in the future could provide additional space for either single- or multiple-floor operations.

Headroom for the first, second and third floors, is 14, 14, and 12 feet respectively, the 40-foot total being adequate for anticipated operations. Initially this height is being utilized by two fractionating columns and a barometric condenser.

Structural steel was designed with the thought that the open bays might at some future date be decked over. All upper floors are constructed of

¼-inch steel plate and covered with a protective floor coating. These floors are considered to be expendable, allowing for greater flexibility in the installation of equipment. A three-inch angle iron is welded around the outside balcony edge below the hand rails to prevent spills or falls to the lower levels. An expanded metal screen faces the guard rails to further protect the lower levels from falling objects.

One outside wall of this process area is composed entirely of windows (Figure 10.8) to provide daytime lighting and explosion relief if necessary. A large door (12 by 12 feet) at ground level in this wall was provided for possible truck deliveries directly into the building. A swinging type door was installed in preference to the overhead type inasmuch as this was not to be a frequently used entrance and the overhead tracks could be eliminated.

The ground floor is poured concrete pitched (½″/foot) to open floor trenches. A 2-foot wide trench runs the length of the middle three bays while 9-foot wide trenches serve each of the side areas. Permanently installed chemical reactors are located immediately above these wider trenches.

Hazardous Isolation Room. A two-bay section of the second floor area is walled off from the main process area to provide an enclosed space for those operations which for any reason might require isolation. The room is currently used to house dusty operations (grinding, screening, and mixing), but conceivably could also house special pilot plant setups.

High Ventilation Room. An inside bay in the hazardous operational area is subdivided to form a high ventilation room and a solvent dispensing room. The high vent room (12 by 20 feet) is provided to permit isolation of operations (usually toxic or obnoxious) from the rest of the working area. It is merely a walled-off area with open doors and ventilation which provides a one-minute air change. Two-thirds of the floor area is covered with open grating to provide good drainage. Service outlets are available at two walls. Equipment is temporarily installed and removed when the job is completed.

Solvent Dispensing Room. This room is provided as a dispensing station for drum quantities of the commonly used solvents. A double tier rack provides space for 24 drums, laid on side by means of a hand lift truck. All drums are grounded and spigots and vents are safety approved. The floor is pitched with a rise at the doorway and scupper through the outside walls; a fire door, normally open, protects the entrance. The room is centrally located and is convenient to laboratories as well as process areas.

Building Services

Considerable attention was given to the proper distribution and location of services within the building. (No compromise was made on the number or type of services which would be included in the initial layout.) Furthermore, it was considered essential that these services be conveniently accessible to both operation and maintenance, but yet inconspicuous and noninterfering with process setups.

A mechanical equipment room was established to serve as the heart of this distribution system. This room contains the service entries and reduction stations for 290 pound steam, city water, natural gas and 100 psi air as well as auxiliary equipment for the handling of process water. This includes a 1500-gallon water storage tank, a 35,000-gallon softener, a hot-water heater and condensate return pumps. The storage tank is equipped with two feed pumps to ensure an adequate water supply at all times; a warning device sounds if (for any reason) the water level falls below the desired level.

A small room was provided as an electrical substation and main distribution center for electric power. Initial power requirements are met through a 300 KVA transformer, but in anticipation of expansion at a future date, space has been provided to house an additional power

Figure 10.9 Distribution of services.

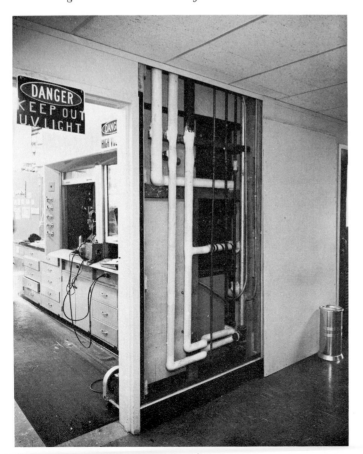

supply. This area is walled off and initially is being used as an office.

Distribution of services can best be followed by referring to Figure 10.9. The main laboratory distribution system for all services is located above the false ceiling in the 8-foot wide corridor. Services branch from these headers and follow a downward path through the corridor side wall to the proper elevation for distribution into the laboratory. Easily removed "Transite" panels provide an easily maintained installation with no sacrifice in appearance. Services which are distributed to the laboratory in this manner include cold water, hot water, distilled water, 100 psi air, natural gas, 15 psi nitrogen, 15 psi steam, and 110- and 220-volt electric power. These services are available at stations conveniently located in the hoods, chemical benches and center equipment racks.

Distribution of inlet air ducts follows the same general pattern, the exception being that they are placed at ceiling height in all laboratories and offices. The main supply system heats the air to 65°F prior to distribution. All laboratories and offices have individually operated thermostatic controls which operate steam heaters in the supply ducts. Wall-mounted fin-type steam radiators are located below all outside windows to maintain a balanced temperature. All air is exhausted from the laboratories by means of the fume hoods which serve as individual exhaust systems. All hood blowers and motors are mounted on the open roof, thereby minimizing the noise level in the laboratories and placing the units in an easily maintained position. A parapet around the roof hides these units from ground level view.

The building is served by two drainage systems. The first is a sanitary system which enters directly into the city sewer, and the second is a chemical system which manifolds into a lime-

Figure 10.10   Distribution of building services.

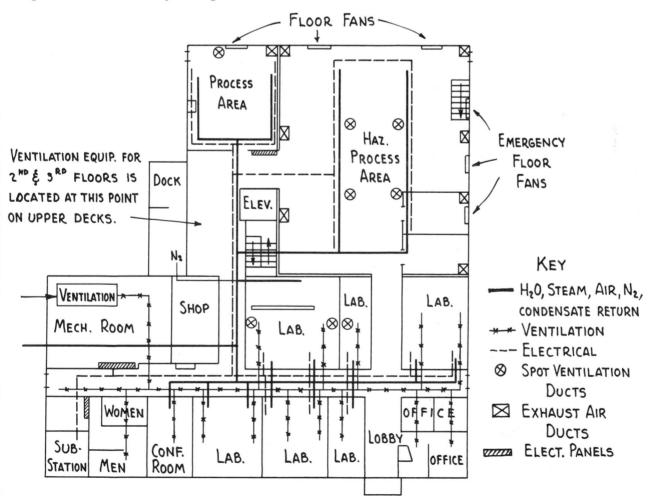

treating pit, located beside the building, before spilling into the same municipal system. Distribution services to the three-story pilot plant areas follows the route also shown in Figure 10.10. Headers are supported below the first balcony adjacent to the open bays (Figure 10.11). This pattern permits direct service runs to any position on either the first or second floors. The third floor, not presently used for process work, has a single service station on each balcony. Future distribution can follow the same pattern as set for the lower balcony.

In addition to the services found in the laboratory, soft water, 250 psi steam, 100 psi nitrogen, and vacuum are available to the pilot plant area.

Conduits for permanent equipment and lights follow the same general pattern as shown for other services. Convenience outlets, located at many points throughout the working area, are generally served by conduits permanently buried beneath the concrete floor. One hundred and ten, 220 and 440 volt power is available at most locations.

All light switches are located in panels placed immediately outside the hazardous working area, eliminating the necessity of providing the costly I-D switches. Switches for process equipment are Class I Group D and are located directly on the equipment. Special effort was taken to locate switch and heater boxes on wall areas where there would be no possible conflict with future process operations.

Concrete floors in the process areas are pitched to open floor trenches covered with steel plate or grating. Reactors are permanently mounted above 9-foot wide trenches ensuring immediate flushing of spills and a dry floor. All such trenches are ventilated to prevent the accumulation of heavy vapors.

The normal total volume air change in both hazardous and nonhazardous process areas is one in five minutes. Intake air is filtered and heated to 65°F at the stations shown, similar blowers being located on and serving both the second and third floors, respectively. Inlet air ducts are confined to the service areas, the inlet vents being mounted in the wall separating service and process areas.

Air is exhausted from both three-story process areas by means of individual exhaust system ducts located at several points along the outer walls. Motors and blowers are located on the roof, a single vent dropping from each to ground floor level where the air is removed.

Supplementary ventilation provided by floor fans in the outer wall can increase the air change to once in three minutes. Multiple fans are interlocked with a mechanical device which automatically opens the windows at third-floor level to maintain a balance pressure.

Spot ventilation is available at any point in the process areas by 6-inch flexible hoses connected to four separate 1500-cfm exhaust systems. Vapors emitted during draining or charging operations, or through inadvertent leaks of noxious chemicals can thereby be very adequately controlled.

Over-all, a balanced air pressure is maintained to ensure a positive pressure in the nonhazardous and laboratory areas at all times. No flammable gases can flow from the hazardous areas where they are used to other areas where they might be ignited.

Special Safety Features

Since the building was designed to accommodate numerous types of operations, many of a hazardous nature, all possible safety features have been included.

(1) Adequate ventilation, approved electrical installations and specially designed working areas provide maximum protection against the accidents.

(2) An automatic water sprinkler system covers the entire building, each spray head being individually operated. For fire fighting, dry chemical and CO_2 fire extinguishers are strategically located throughout the building, the largest being a 300-pound cart mounted unit in the hazardous process area.

(3) Fire blankets, safety showers, and eye wash fountains are also located in all working areas. The showers and fountains are provided with 90° F water, as it has previously been found that 40-50°F was unbearably cold on prolonged flushing. A portable bathtub is also available for submerged flushing of chemical burns.

(4) For protection of personnel in operation, complete safety suits, gloves, masks, boots, etc., are available. Fresh air masks are located in several areas and are frequently used when handling noxious or toxic materials.

(5) Alarms are used to indicate failure of any of the ventilation units during operation. Alarms are also used to indicate overheating of the chemical storage cooler.

(6) Battery-operated lights are placed at strategic locations to flash on in event of power failure.

(7) For communication between individuals, specifically during shift work when only two or three people occupy the building, an intercom system has been provided so that personnel may safely work in isolated areas of the building without loss of contact. On the day shift this intercom system serves as a paging system.

(8) Safety signs governing procedures are spotted throughout the building as reminders to safe operation. Special safety regulations have been set up as guides to the use of all operating areas and equipment.

Process Equipment

While no attempt will be made to describe all the equipment available to the operating department, it can be said that batchwise process equipment is normally kept small and sized, in general, to the requirements of a 20-gallon reactor. The policy of operation emphasizes both portability and flexibility of equipment, and therefore most of the units can be considered "multi-purpose." When not in use, all portable equipment is moved to the second- and third-floor storage areas.

Chemical reactors of 5 to 20 gallons in size are permanently installed in the hazardous operating area. These units vary in pressure rating, material of construction and auxiliary equipment, for example, some being equipped with distillation systems, feed tanks, receivers, etc. Portable equipment is assembled for special conditions, i.e., refrigeration for low-temperature cooling, hot oil heater for high-temperature reactions, and pumps for continuous addition of reactants.

Of special interest is the method used to mount reactors. While probably not original, the technique lends itself very well to the installation of small units. As shown in Figure 10.11, a cantilever support holds the kettle, eliminating all legs and providing maximum utilization of the unit. All service piping has been assembled behind the control panel and is easily maintained. This unit is equipped with a steam water temperature control system complete with circulating pump.

Figure 10.11   Five gallon cantilever kettle and service headers.

SUMMARY

Many types of pilot plant buildings and engineering laboratories are in common use today, each fulfilling in its own way the specific requirements of the operating department. No single design can be recommended as a universal design since each type has inherent advantages and disadvantages. If a building is to be built for a specific and well-defined operation, a review of the features of the various types will probably identify the construction best suited to the need.

Frequently, it is desirable to design a general-purpose pilot plant building, hoping to provide for almost any eventuality which might arise in the future. This can be a difficult assignment, and frequently can be done no better than the objectives and functions of the operating department can be defined. Realizing that operating departments can change with a company's growth or management, this might appear to be a hopeless task; but this need not be true. An appraisal of the history of a department's operation and growth, together with an intelligent projection to the future can generally define the basic space requirements. The following general rules can serve as a guide for the planning of any pilot plant.

(1) Define your department's objectives. Do they fulfill your company's requirements? Do you anticipate these to change with time?

(2) Define your detailed space requirements. Consider hazardous and nonhazardous areas, areas of varying head room, laboratory requirements, service areas, offices, etc.

(3) Plan to inspect other pilot plants and talk with the personnel associated with these facilities.

(4) Give adequate thought to the overall layout of the building. Do not settle on a plan until you are absolutely convinced it is the best possible for your needs.

(5) Design your building to provide for reasonable departmental growth. The basic plant should be one which can be easily expanded externally.

(6) Provide adequate storage and service areas. In many pilot plants these areas are equal to the process area.

(7) Design for safety—it will pay off.

(8) Select adequate service facilities and give careful thought to their distribution within your building. Again, sufficient time spent in reviewing preliminary electrical and mechanical prints will pay rich dividends. Make sure such items as electrical boxes, service headers, and ventilation ducts are mounted where they are not likely to interfere with future process installations.

(9) Design maximum versatility into the building. It is difficult to anticipate the future, so give a little extra thought to the location and design of supporting walls, structural steel, etc. Open areas may eventually require decking. Will the beams support the extra loads? What will this do to your ventilation?

Planning an engineering laboratory or pilot plant can be a demanding, time-consuming assignment. However, it does have its rewards—as a job well done can prove to be very satisfying as well as producing a monument of which you can be justly proud.

PART 2: HIGH AND LOW LEVEL RADIOACTIVITY LABORATORIES

a. LOW-LEVEL RADIOISOTOPE LABORATORIES

DONALD R. WARD

Oak Ridge National Laboratory*
Oak Ridge, Tennessee

Radioisotopes are useful because of the radiation they emit, yet this same radiation presents a potential hazard to the isotope worker and in certain instances to the general public. Many experiments have been performed with animals to determine the extent of these hazards. Maximum permissible radiation exposure limits for isotope workers have been established on the basis of these tests, consideration also having been given to possible long-range genetic effects. The excellent safety records at Government and

* Operated by Union Carbide Nuclear Company for the U. S. Atomic Energy Commission.

private laboratories have shown that radioisotopes can be handled safely if the proper facilities and techniques are used. Radiation should not be feared, but it should be respected.

Laboratories for using microcurie and millicurie quantities of isotopes generally do not need the elaborate concrete cubicals, remote manipulators and massive lead shielding frequently found in high-level laboratories. There are, however, certain design features which should be observed when a low-level laboratory is being planned, and these features will be discussed in this chapter.

TYPES OF RADIATION HAZARDS

Since the special design features of radiochemical laboratories are for the purpose of protection against radiation hazards, it is in order to review the precise nature of these hazards and the radiation constituting them.

Radiation hazards may be divided into two groups: (1) Those which may injure personnel, and (2) those which may invalidate technical results. These two groups, in turn, may be further subdivided into (a) trouble caused by external irradiation, and (b) trouble caused by radiochemical contamination.

External Irradiation of Personnel

The hazards of external irradiation can be minimized by the proper use of shielding barriers, by maintaining adequate distance between the isotope user and the active material, by keeping the length of exposure time to a minimum, and by using no more active material than the least quantity necessary for performing the work.

Radioisotopes available through the Atomic Energy Commission isotope-distribution program[1] emit beta rays or a combination of beta and gamma rays.* The nature of these rays and the distance or the shielding sometimes suggested for protection against external irradiation by the most commonly used isotopes are described in Figs. 10.12, 10.13, and 10.14.

Beta rays (high-velocity electrons) have a finite range and will be completely absorbed by

* The one exception is Polonium 210, an alpha-ray emitter, which is available from the Atomic Energy Commission only as a radioactive decay product of Bismuth 210.

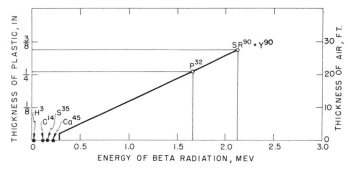

Figure 10.12   Thicknesses of plastic shielding and air used for protection against Beta radiation.

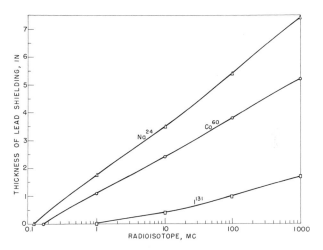

Fig. 10.13   Thicknesses of lead required to reduce Gamma-ray intensity.

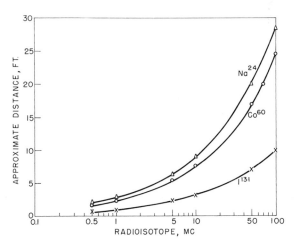

Figure 10.14   Distances required to reduce Gamma-ray intensity.

the shielding or thickness of air shown in Figure 10.12. Beta rays below approximately 0.3 Mev will be completely stopped by the container walls or by the hornified outer layers of skin. Consequently, special shielding (except for eye protection) is not needed for work with isotopes emitting only weak beta rays. It should be noted that absorption of beta radiation by material produces secondary radiation known as "bremsstrahlung." This secondary radiation has the characteristics of soft X-rays, and additional shielding may be needed. If beta shielding material of low atomic number is used, the amount of bremsstrahlung will be minimized.

Gamma rays (electromagnetic waves) cannot be completely absorbed, but their intensity can be reduced to any desired value by means of a sufficient thickness of shielding material. The intensity of gamma radiation varies inversely as the square of the distance between the radioactive material and the point at which it is measured. Practical gamma-ray protection is generally a combination of both shielding and distance.

TABLE 10.1
RELATIVE RADIOTOXICITY OF VARIOUS ISOTOPES[2]

GROUP 1: SIGHTLY HAZARDOUS

Sodium 24*	Arsenic 76*
Potassium 42	Arsenic 77
Manganese 52*	Krypton 85
Copper 64	Mercury 197*

GROUP 2: MODERATELY HAZARDOUS

Hydrogen 3	Tellurium 127
Carbon 14	Tellurium 129
Sodium 22*	Iodine 131
Phosphorus 32	Cesium 137*
Sulfur 35	Barium 140*
Chlorine 36	Lanthanum 140*
Manganese 54*	Cerium 141
Iron 59*	Praseodymium 143
Cobalt 60*	Neodymium 147*
Strontium 89	Gold 198*
Niobium 95*	Gold 199*
Ruthenium 103*	Mercury 203
Ruthenium 106	Mercury 205

GROUP 3: VERY HAZARDOUS

Calcium 45	Zirconium 95*
Iron 55	Cerium 144
Strontium 90	Promethium 147
Yttrium 91	Bismuth 210

* Principal gamma-ray emitters.
[2] Refers to reference #2 at the end of the chapter.

Any alpha or beta radiation present will be completely absorbed by gamma-ray shields.

Ingestion of Radiocontamination by Personnel

It is possible for radioactive materials to enter the body by inhalation, by swallowing, and by absorption through the skin. The likelihood of taking radioactive matter into the body can be minimized by careful control, and proper techniques and adequate laboratory equipment will assist in this effort.

The radiotoxicity of various isotopes when taken internally depends upon several factors, such as: (1) degree of selective localization of the isotope within the body; (2) biological rate of elimination of the isotope from the body; (3) half-life of the isotope; (4) energy and character of the radiations (i.e., beta or gamma). A partial list of radioisotopes grouped according to the degree of internal hazard which they present may be found in Table 10.1.

Stray Radiation Pick-up During Technical Measurements

The final operation in many laboratory experiments using radioisotopes is to measure the amount of radioactivity present in a particular specimen or group of samples. The radioisotope content may become greatly reduced during the course of the experiment and the final radioactive intensity to be measured may be extremely small. Thus it is imperative that the amount of background radiation not related to the experiment be minimized.

Technical Contamination of Experiments

The contamination control required during precise experimentation may be much more rigid than that required by safety. Proper laboratory facilities, careful isotope handling techniques, and good housekeeping habits will serve to minimize the likelihood of unwanted cross-contamination.

THE RADIOISOTOPE LABORATORY

To an institution contemplating the use of radioisotopes, economic considerations in establishing the laboratory will undoubtedly be of prime importance. A review of the anticipated

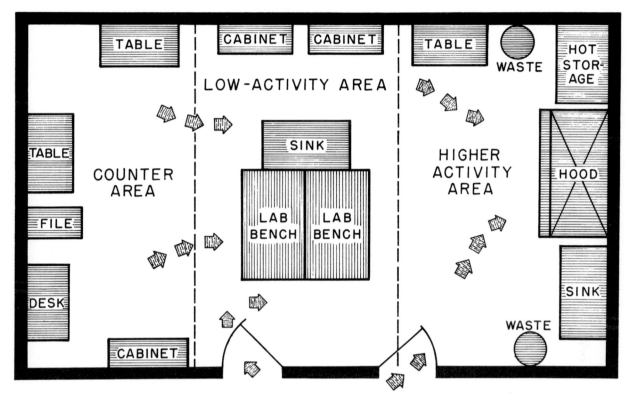

Figure 10.15   Low-activity radiochemical laboratory showing arrangement of areas and ventilation pattern.

usage and work load factors will dictate whether the facility is to make use of several existing altered rooms, a new wing on an existing laboratory or a new laboratory building.

General Laboratory Features

Arrangement of Rooms. All rooms of a radioisotope unit should be grouped together to reduce the likelihood of spreading radioactive contamination to nonradiochemical areas. Locating the laboratory on the top floor of a building offers the advantage of requiring short exhaust ducts from the fume hoods to the roof. A ground-level location, on the other hand, will require shorter drain lines from sinks to the sewer.

Radiochemical work has little in common with X-ray work, and the two programs should not be carried on in the same rooms. Since stray radiation from X-ray machines may interfere with radiation counting equipment, the two operations should be widely separated. Also, similar precautions should be taken against possible interference from radium sources, particularly if they are routinely moved from one location to another, as in certain hospital work.

In a radioisotope laboratory the operations should be segregated according to levels of radioactivity.[2] The plan shown in Figure 10.15 illustrates this segregation. The areas that have little or no activity are at one end of the laboratory, the areas that have large amounts of activity are at the other end, and the intermediate levels are located in between. Wide separation between the counting area and the high-activity area will minimize the chance for the counting instruments to record stray radiation from the high-activity area. The use of separate areas and separate facilities for high-activity and low-activity work will reduce the likelihood of accidental cross-contamination of experimental samples. The decision as to whether these various areas should occupy separate rooms or different portions of the same room will depend upon the nature of the isotopes and the type of program.

The single-room laboratory, shown schematically in Figure 10.15, is suitable only for work at microcurie or tracer levels of activity. For work at higher levels of activity, more complete segregation of the operations into rooms instead of areas is suggested. Space is not shown for an office, storage facilities for glassware and non-radioactive chemicals, lecture room, shop, electronic repair room, etc., but the possible need for such space should be borne in mind in designing a particular laboratory.

Ventilation, Heating and Air Conditioning. The flow of ventilating air in the radioisotope unit should be from rooms or areas of no activity to rooms of higher activity as illustrated in Figure 10.15. This air pattern will help prevent the spread of radioactivity to the counting room, offices, and other "nonactive" rooms. It is not meant to imply, however, that radioactive materials should be permitted to enter the air in the "active" rooms. If proper facilities and techniques are used, all the air-borne radioactivity will be confined to the hoods. During the span of several months or at the time of an accidental spill, however, it is conceivable that active particles might enter the atmosphere of the room. The exhaust fans of the fume hoods should withdraw air from the high-activity rooms at a fairly rapid rate and help to produce the desired direction of air movement through the building.

The air in the radioactivity rooms should not be recirculated. The relatively large volumes of air required by the fume hoods should be kept in mind when the heating and air-conditioning system of a building is being designed.

It has been found that certain scalers and other electronic counting equipment (particularly the earlier models) are sensitive to changes in moisture and temperature. Air conditioning is therefore recommended for the counting room, especially in regions of high humidity.

Laboratory Equipment and Facilities

Many of the design features of radiochemical laboratories and the equipment items are similar to those found in ordinary laboratories. Only those that are different will be discussed.

Laboratory Surfaces. Rooms where radiochemical work is performed should be made readily cleanable so that any radioactive material that is spilled or deposited gradually over a period of time may be removed without difficulty. The proper choice of surface materials is highly important in this regard.

Floors should be covered so that spilled radioactive liquids cannot reach the underlying wood or concrete, since these two materials are quite porous and it is practically impossible to decontaminate them once the radioactive chemicals have soaked in. Asphalt tile, rubber tile, vinyl tile, rubber runners, linoleum, and other common types of floor covering have been found suitable for use in radiochemical laboratories. The cracks between adjacent blocks or pieces can be satisfactorily filled by waxing the surface. These floor materials do not exhibit outstanding ease of decontamination, but their chief merit lies in the fact that, if radioactive materials penetrate the waxed surfaces and cannot be removed by rinsing and scouring, contaminated portions of the floor covering can be replaced rather easily. Wooden and concrete floors can be varnished or painted, but these surface coatings usually do not have the desired service durability and resistance to chemical attack.

Walls are much less likely to become contaminated than floors, yet certain precautions should be taken at exposed wall areas, such as near sinks. Porous wall materials such as wood, concrete, or cinder blocks should be coated with nonporous washable paint at locations where wall contamination is most likely to occur.

Other laboratory surfaces, such as the interior of fume hoods and the tops of laboratory tables, may be covered with removable paint[3, 4] which may be peeled off to remove contamination if washing the surface is not effective. Although stainless steel is subject to attack by halogens, it is generally useful in radioisotope laboratories for sinks and work surfaces in fume hoods.

Isotope Storage Facilities. Radioisotopes should be stored in such a manner that the radiation will not present a hazard to personnel and will not fog film or interfere with delicate measurements being made in the counting room or elsewhere. It is generally recommended that they be stored in the "hot" laboratory or in a small room adjoining this laboratory and isolated from the counting room.

The special containers used for shipping isotopes are designed to reduce the radiation intensities at their surfaces to safe, predetermined levels. Such containers are also suitable for storing isotopes in the laboratory (see Figure 10.16). The concrete containers in which beta-ray emitters are shipped are nonreturnable and may be used for storage purposes. The heavy lead containers in which gamma-ray emitters are shipped, however, must be returned to the supplier, and it is suggested that gamma-ray emitters be stored in lead (or cast iron) pots owned by the institution and patterned after the shipping containers used for the respective isotopes. The pots may be stored on the floor or on a bench in an unused portion of the laboratory room. Monitoring the area with radiation survey instruments will show whether additional shielding barricades are required.

A vault may be used for storing materials at a high level of activity. Such a vault (illustrated in Figure 10.17) may consist of a bank of vertical or horizontal holes cast in a concrete block. The bottled isotopes are placed in the holes, which

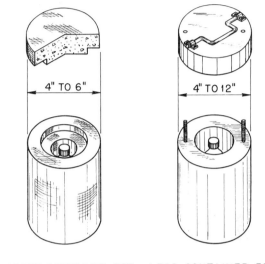

CONCRETE CONTAINER FOR
PURE BETA-RAY EMITTERS

LEAD CONTAINER FOR
GAMMA-RAY EMITTERS

Figure 10.16 Isotope shipping containers.

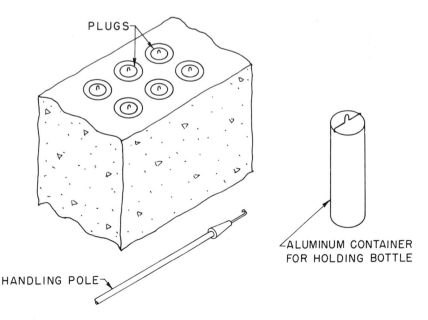

Figure 10.17 Storage vault for radioactive materials.

PLUGS

HANDLING POLE

ALUMINUM CONTAINER
FOR HOLDING BOTTLE

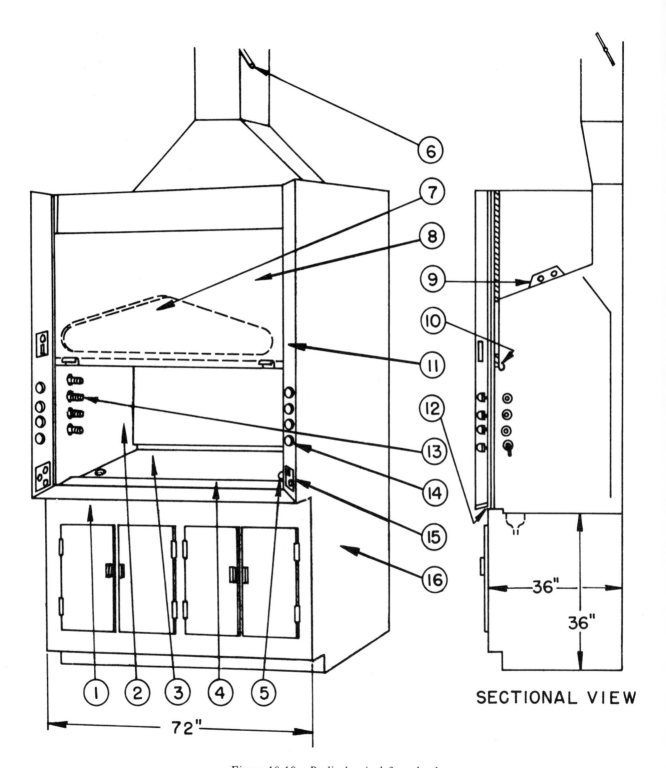

Figure 10.18   Radiochemical fume hood.

are plugged with shielding blocks of concrete, iron, or lead. Storage of isotopes in pots is more flexible and generally less expensive than in a special vault. Either the vault method or the pot method may impose a considerable load on the floor of the room, and safe load limits should be determined and respected.

Shielding. In X-ray work it is customary to line the walls of the room with sheet lead for the protection of persons outside the room, and it is sometimes erroneously thought that similar protection against gamma radiation from radioisotopes is sufficient. However, no thickness of lead at the wall will protect workers within the room. For this reason, local shielding enclosing the radioactive material is essential.

The recommended safety procedures are (1) to shield the active material locally on all four sides (and top and bottom, if necessary) and (2) to check the radiation intensities inside the room and in adjacent rooms (including those above and below), using a suitable radiation survey meter. Local shields, such as barricades of lead,

iron, or stone blocks placed around the active material, are relatively inexpensive, and their thickness can be increased or decreased to suit the particular shielding requirement merely by restacking the blocks in a different configuration.

Radiochemical Fume Hoods. The purpose of the radiochemical fume hood is to prevent contamination from escaping into the laboratory. Although this function is basically the same as that of ordinary fume hoods, smoke and odor tests have shown that many of the older hoods are rather ineffective in preventing the spread of fumes. Considerable development work has been undertaken in recent years by hood manufacturers and by Government and private laboratories.[5] As a result, hoods designed specifically for radiochemical operations are now commercially available.[6]

The hood design shown in Figure 10.18 illustrates many of the special features found desirable for radiochemical work at millicurie levels. It should be pointed out that the air by-pass feature of the hood (item 7) wastes air. But laboratory

Special Features of Fume Hood Shown in Figure 10.18

1. The hood should be resistant to heat and chemical action and may be made of stainless steel. In some cases less expensive materials such as plywood, "Transite" or furniture steel may be used if carefully coated with a suitable protective covering.

2. It may be advisable to give the interior of the hood a final coating of washable, strippable paint, which may be peeled off and replaced with a fresh coat if it becomes seriously contaminated.

3. A layer of replaceable absorbent paper may be used to cover the working surface of the hood. Trays, preferably of stainless steel, may be used for additional spillage protection.

4. All operations should be performed beyond a ½-inch ledge extending 6 inches inside the face of the hood. Smoke tests have indicated that this is important for proper fume control.

5. Easily cleaned cup sinks, located near the front of the hood, are recommended in place of a less accessible trough sink located at the back.

6. An air velocity of from 70 to 100 linear feet per minute at the face of the hood is recommended at all usable sash positions. An exhaust duct damper can be preset as required.

7. The lintel behind the sash contains an air by-pass opening which becomes exposed when the sash is lowered. This by-pass prevents excessive velocity of air at the

work surface when the sash is in its lower positions. An earlier design links the sash to the exhaust duct damper so that lowering the sash reduces the damper opening.

8. The counterbalanced hood sash is made of tempered safety glass.

9. Fluorescent lights, shining through a glass pane, are changeable from outside the hood.

10. In accordance with general practice, a trough is located behind the bottom edge of the lintel to carry any condensate to the sides of the hood.

11. Turbulence of the air entering the hood should be reduced as much as possible. Tests with smoke indicate that 6-in. "picture-frame" air guides at the sides and bottom of the hood assist in reducing turbulence and air flow back into the room.

12. Smoke tests also indicate that the air flow characteristics are improved by the use of a vent space between the bottom air guide and the hood body.

13. Service outlets (gas, water, vacuum, etc., as required) are located near the front of the hood so the operator will not have to reach far into the hazardous zone to make hose connections.

14. Service handles and electric outlets are located outside the hood.

15. The base structure is strong enough to support a ton of shielding. It is not recommended that shielding be incorporated in the hood structure itself.

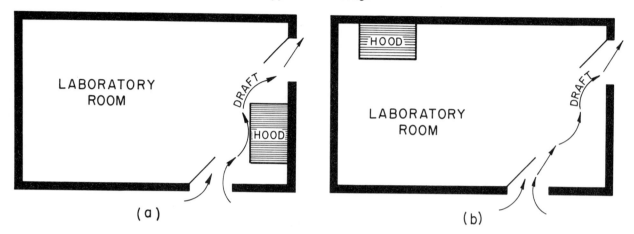

Figure 10.19   The desirability of a draft-free hood location. (a) poor hood location; (b) good hood location.

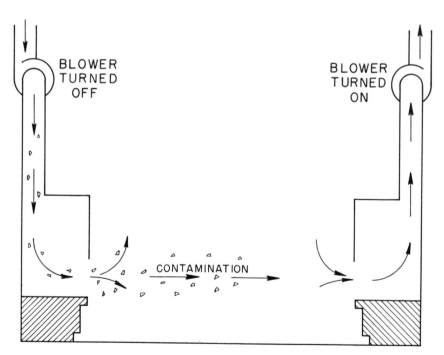

Figure 10.20   The hazard of spreading contamination in a laboratory if one hood is turned off and another is on.

authorities generally believe that this waste is more tolerable than the wide load fluctuations which would be imposed on the heating and air-conditioning system if the by-pass were omitted and the rate of air flow through the laboratory were governed solely by the random position of the fume hood sashes.

Even properly designed hoods are vulnerable to the effects of strong drafts of air, and the proper choice of hood location is important (see Figure 10.19). Hoods should not be placed near doorways, windows, ventilator outlets, or other sources of strong air currents. Because shielding and some hood materials are quite heavy, the matter of floor loading also should be considered when selecting a hood location.

If two or more fume hoods are in the same room, the blowers of the hoods should be controlled by a single switch. If the blowers are on separate switches, it would be possible for an operating hood to draw contaminated air from a nonoperating hood into the laboratory room (see Figure 10.20). Hood sashes should be closed when the hoods are not in use to prevent drafts from spreading contamination.

Air exhausted from a fume hood should be discharged at a point where the gases will be thoroughly diluted and dispersed before they can reenter a building. It is generally recommended that the point of discharge be safely above the roof level of the building.

The exhaust blower should be located near the roof so that the exhaust duct between the hood and the blower will be maintained at a slightly negative pressure. If the blower is located down at the hood, the duct leading to the roof may be above atmospheric pressure, and active matter may leak through holes in the duct work and escape into the building (see Figure 10.21). If the blower is at the top of the exhaust duct, the stack

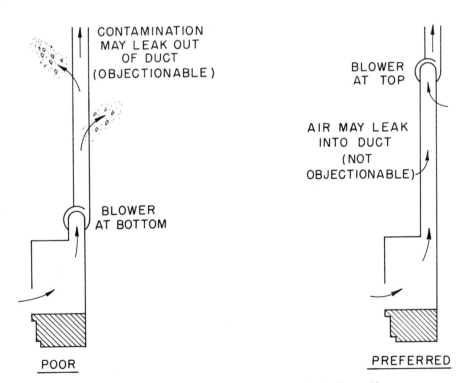

Figure 10.21   Poor and preferred locations for hood exhaust blower.

will be below atmospheric pressure, and any leaks in the duct work will merely allow a little air to be drawn into the duct.

Opinion is divided on the question of whether or not the hood effluvium from low-level laboratories should be filtered. Some believe that the hazards associated with changing and disposing of filters are greater than those resulting from discharge of untreated air. Coarse filters are not very efficient and fine filters become clogged quickly (mostly by lint and ordinary nonradioactive dust) and must be changed frequently. If proper laboratory techniques are used, there will be little likelihood that radioactive particles will be discharged up the hood stack.

If the type of isotope program or the location of the laboratory make the filtering of the hood effluvium advisable, simple mechanical filtering through a dry type of filter medium is suggested. Glass wool is superior to cloth or paper as a filter

medium for this application because of its better resistance to ordinary chemical attack. Inexpensive glass-wool filters of the disposable type are commercially available in several grades of porosity. The cleaning and re-use of contaminated filters are not recommended. Large budget institutions may prefer to use electrostatic filters. These offer the advantage of low initial resistance to air flow and very slow pressure build-up with time.

Hoods for Work with Carbon 14. Weak beta-ray emitters, such as carbon-14 or sulfur-35, may be manipulated in a glassed-in hood (illustrated in Figure 10.22) without the use of special radiation shielding, since the glass walls of the apparatus will stop these low-energy radiations. Beta-ray emitters of high energy, as well as certain gamma-ray emitters, may also be used in a hood of this type if suitable shielding material is used in strategic places.

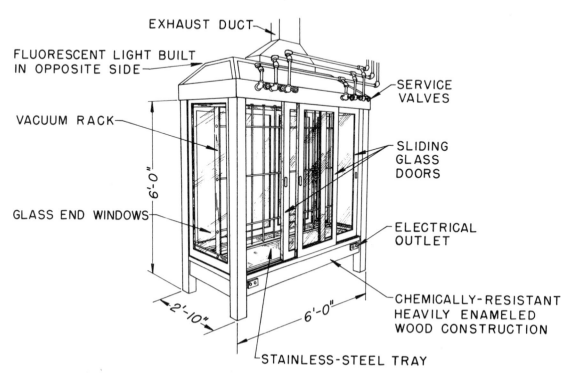

Figure 10.22 A glassed-in hood.

This hood is a cabinet-like structure specifically designed to house a glass reaction train containing radioactive chemicals. The glass system is mounted on a metal rack, and the chemicals in the system may be manipulated by changing pressures or temperatures at various points in the system. During a typical reaction process the chemicals may be in the gaseous, liquid, or solid phase. If the glassware breaks and radioactive matter escapes into the hood, any hazardous radioactive fumes will be drawn out the exhaust stack instead of being permitted to escape into the laboratory. The system is accessible through sliding doors on both the front and the back of the hood, thus facilitating the assembling, operation, and repair of the system.

Gloved Box. The gloved box or dry box (illustrated in Figure 10.23) is a small closed box of wood or metal, in which work may be safely performed with radioactive materials that present a hazard from the standpoint of contamination. Weak beta-ray emitters, such as carbon-14 and sulfur-35, can be readily handled in such gloved boxes. A small blower operated by a fractional horsepower motor may be used to keep the box slightly below atmospheric pressure, and the exhausted air may be drawn through a small filter to remove contamination before it is passed into the main hood stack. The gloved box will keep the contamination localized, and it is much easier to decontaminate a small gloved box than a large hood. For some types of work, a simple box without an exhaust blower may be adequate.

Laboratory Bench

The laboratory bench for radiochemical work is similar to an ordinary chemical bench except that exposed surfaces should be nonporous, chemically resistant, and decontaminable. Peelable paint may be used, or the top of the table

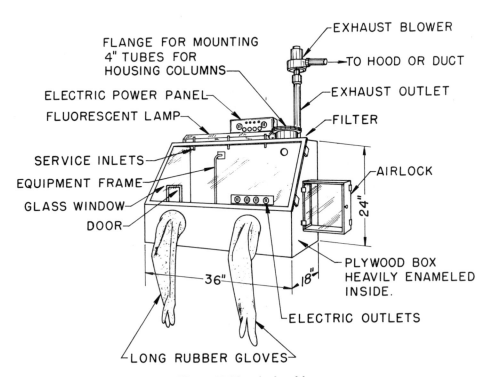

Figure 10.23   A gloved box.

may be covered with absorbent paper. Additional protection may be afforded, if necessary, by the use of stainless steel trays to catch any spilled materials. The bench structure should be sturdy enough to support whatever heavy shielding will be required. The usual service outlets should be available (gas, hot and cold water, electrical outlets, etc.). All vacuum lines should have traps to catch any radioactive liquids that might accidentally be drawn into the vacuum system. Cup sinks are recommended instead of the usual long trough sinks. The latter often accumulate extraneous materials and detract from the good housekeeping, which is so important in maintaining proper contamination control.

For certain operations not requiring the use of service facilities (gas, water, etc.), a satisfactory laboratory bench can be made by covering a sturdy table with a decontaminable surface.

Laboratory Sinks

Stainless steel sinks offer certain advantages over those made of soapstone or porcelain for washing glassware in radiochemical laboratories. The resilience of the sheet metal is more desirable than the rigidity of soapstone or porcelain-covered cast iron, and breakage of glassware will be lower. It is recommended that the sink be fabricated without sharp corners in order to facilitate cleaning. A drainboard on each side should be provided, one side to be used exclusively for dirty glassware and the other for cleaned glassware. Such an arrangement will reduce the likelihood of contaminating freshly washed glassware. Foot-, knee-, or arm-levers are suggested for controlling the hot and cold running water at the sink. The usual type of wooden pegboard for drying glassware is somewhat porous but may be used if coated with heavy layers of nonporous paint and washed occasionally to remove any traces of radioactivity.

Sinks designated to receive appreciable amounts of radioactive waste material should have a minimum amount of exposed surface. It is suggested that small cup sinks draining into shielded carboys rather than into the sewer lines be used for this purpose. The carboys can then be stored until sufficient radioactive decay has occurred or until an approved method of disposal has been worked out. The absence of faucets at these sinks will help to prevent rapid and needless filling of the carboys.

Drains and Traps

Drain pipes which handle low-level radiochemical wastes can be made of conventional laboratory construction materials and connected directly to the nearest drain piping in the customary manner. Although unnecessary bends, junctions, etc., should be avoided, there is no need for a separate drainage system leading directly to the sewer line. Normal wastes will assist in diluting and washing out any radioactive material remaining in drains and traps. The desirability of placing radiochemical drains in accessible locations for radiation monitoring, cleaning and (if necessary) replacement should be kept in mind when a new radioisotope laboratory building is being designed.

Miscellaneous

Many other pieces of apparatus and equipment are necessary in a radiochemical laboratory.[5] Items such as beta- and gamma-ray shields, tongs, radioactivity survey instruments, personnel monitoring devices, and counting-room equipment, although required for most radiochemical work, are not ordinarily regarded as part of the problems of laboratory design and therefore are not included in this discussion.

RADIOCHEMICAL WASTE DISPOSAL

Radioactivity cannot be destroyed nor can the radioactive decay process be altered by heating, chemical treatment or by any other known method. At present there are only two general methods for taking care of radiochemical wastes: (1) dilute and disperse, or (2) concentrate and store. As most isotope users will be faced with the problem of radioactive waste disposal, some of the equipment for this purpose will be discussed briefly.[7]

Storage Tanks for Liquid Wastes

Because it is considered permissible, under controlled conditions, to discharge certain limited amounts of short-lived radioactive materials into public sewers,[7] most institutions will not find it necessary to install special waste-storage tanks. If, however, the amount of waste requiring disposal is large and a tank system is believed necessary, careful calculations should be made of the amount of radioactivity and the volume of liquid requiring disposal each day (or each week), the decrease in activity due to radioactive decay during storage, the ratio of fresh waste to stored waste to be discharged each day, and similar factors. Such calculations may reveal that hold-up tanks are of marginal value except to take care of peak loads, and that such peak loads may be more easily handled by storing the wastes in carboys behind temporary shielding.

Burial of Wastes

Isotopes with long half-lives present a difficult waste-disposal problem. One solution is to concentrate and contain the radioactive material in solid form and bury it. The burial ground should be located on the property of the institution using the isotopes and should be fenced off and plainly marked with the name of the institution and warning of possible radiation hazards. In locations near the seacoast arrangements may be made with concerns specializing in picking up radioactive waste on a regular basis for burial at sea. Federal[7] and state laws regarding the disposal of radioactive materials must be observed.

Incinerators

Waste incinerators of standard commercial design are generally satisfactory if operated carefully.[7] The incineration of contaminated paper, clothing, and other combustible material is a convenient way to reduce its bulk. Much of the radioactivity is concentrated in the ash, but some escapes in the flue gases. Care must be taken to avoid the discharge of radioactive ash particles through the smokestack into the atmosphere. The ash that accumulates should be checked for activity and disposed of in an approved manner.[7]

GOVERNMENT PARTICIPATION

There are Federal laws governing the procurement, use, and disposal of radioactive materials. Title 10 of the Code of Federal Regulations concerns atomic energy. Two sections of particular interest to those establishing radioisotope laboratories are: Title 10, Part 20, "Standards for Radiation Protection"; and Title 10, Part 30, "Licensing of Byproduct Material."

Advisory service is available from the Isotope Branch, Division of Licensing and Regulation, U. S. Atomic Energy Commission, Washington 25, D. C. The Isotopes Branch can be of considerable consulting assistance in such matters as radioisotope laboratory design, radiological safety,[7] licensing procedures,[8] radiochemical waste disposal[7] and other related subjects. There is no charge for this advisory service.

CONCLUSION

Typical design features of low-level radioisotope laboratories have been presented in this chapter, along with certain background material regarding the nature of radioisotopes, the radiations they emit, the hazards associated with these radiations, and the Federal Government's participation in the interest of radiological safety. Emphasis in this chapter has been on the laboratory features found desirable because of the radiation and contamination hazards expected when working with radioisotopes. It should be noted, however, that there are other important design considerations not associated with radiation, and the planners of a laboratory should seek advice from professional architects who are laboratory specialists regarding modular construction, methods of installing utility services (water, vacuum, electricity, etc.), lighting, heating, ventilation, floor loadings, and other details of normal laboratory construction.

REFERENCES

1. Catalog and Price List: "Radioisotopes—Special Materials and Processes," available from Oak Ridge National Laboratory, P. O. Box X, Oak Ridge, Tenn.
2. "Safe Handling of Radioactive Isotopes," *National Bureau of Standards Handbook* 42, (1949).
3. P. C. Tompkins, O. M. Bizzell, and C. D. Watson, "Working Surfaces for Radiochemical Laboratories," *Ind. Eng. Chem., 42:1469* (August 1950).

4. S. E. Eaton and R. J. Bowen, "Decontaminable Surfaces for Millicurie-level Laboratories," *Nucleonics*, 8: No. 5 (May 1951).

5. K. L. Powlesland and G. T. Saunders, "A Constant Volume Radiochemical Hood," Livermore Research Laboratory of the U.S.A.E.C., Livermore California, 1954.

6. "Equipment Guide" (R-1) and "Buyers' Guide" (D-1), supplements in *Nucleonics*, 7: No. 5 (November 1950).

7. "Standards for Protection Against Radiation," *U. S. Federal Register,* Title 10, Part 20 (January 1957).

8. "Licensing of Byproduct Material," *U. S. Federal Register,* Title 10, Part 30, (January 1956).

9. J. R. Bradford (editor) "Radioisotopes in Industry," Reinhold Publishing Corporation. New York, N. Y. (1953).

10. E. H. Quimby and C. B. Braestrup, "Planning a Radioisotopes Program in the Hospital," *Am. J. Roentgenol, Radium Therapy, 63*: No. 1 (January 1950).

11. H. A. Steiner, "Establishing a Hospital Laboratory for Radioactive Isotope Therapy," *Hospitals, 24*:37 (1950).

12. F. C. Henriques and A. P. Schreiber, "Administration and Operation of a Radiochemical Laboratory," *Nucleonics,* 2: 1–15 (1948).

13. A. D. Mackintosh, "The Architectural Approach to Radiochemical Laboratory Design," *U. S. Atomic Energy Commission Report AECU-210 (ORNL-335),* 1949.

14. *Symposium on Radiochemistry Laboratories, Ind. Eng. Chem.,* 41: 228 (1949): P. C. Tompkins and H. A. Levy, "The Impact of Radioactivity on Chemical Laboratory Techniques and Design"; W. P. Norris, "Radiobiochemical Laboratories"; J. W. Swartout, "Research with Low Levels of Radioactivity"; N. B. Garden, "Semihot Laboratories"; P. C. Tompkins, "A Radioisotope Building"; C. N. Rice, "Laboratory for Preparation and Use of Radioactive Organic Compounds"; H. A. Levy, "Remodeling a Laboratory for Radiochemical Instruction or Research."

15. L. E. Pruess and J. H. L. Watson, "Design and Construction of a Small Radioactivity Laboratory," *Nucleonics,* 6 No. 5, 11–26 (1950).

16. J. R. Zacharias et al., "Laboratory for Nuclear Science and Engineering," *MIT Progress Report,* 1947, 49 pages.

17. C. H. Guest and L. G. Cook, "Design Auxiliary Equipment and Services for a Radiochemical Laboratory," *National Research Council of Canada, Atomic Energy Project Report CRHR-368,* 1948.

18. "Design and Construction of Radiochemical Laboratories," a selected list of unclassified references (TID-3013) Technical Information Services, Oak Ridge, Tennessee (1951).

19. R. J. Millet, "A Selected Reading List on Radiological Protection and Laboratory Design—1946 to 1956," Isotope Division A.E.R.E., Harwell, England (1956).

b. STRUCTURAL ASPECTS OF HOT LABORATORIES

H. M. GLEN
Oak Ridge National Laboratory
Oak Ridge, Tennessee

The term "hot laboratory" is applied to a facility for the safe handling and processing of high radiation level sources of radioisotopes including, (a) naturally occurring, (b) neutron-activated, (c) cyclotron-activated, (d) fission products. Such a facility differs completely from a laboratory designed solely for the safe handling and processing of small quantities of radioisotopes.

In general, a typical hot laboratory is composed of either a single hot cell or of a bank of these cells, with the area surrounding them divided into a semihot charging area and a cold operating area. Hot cells should be so designed as to permit great flexibility as to usage. The designations "semihot" and "cold" refer to the permissible background level of contamination present in these areas.

An ideal "hot" laboratory, whose design and construction are theoretically possible, would meet the criteria of 100% containment of harmful radiation and contamination; 100% safety for operators in both its charging and its operating areas; 100% safe handling of the source material as it is introduced into the cell and as the end products and wastes are removed from the cell; and easy manipulation of the radioactive material while it is being processed and analyzed within the cell. The hot laboratories now in existence and on the drawing boards, however, represent compromises involving generally accepted permissible radiation dosages for operating personnel, space limitations and cost.

Present hot laboratory designs compared to those of even several years ago reflect the phenomenal growth and development of atomic energy. Many of the hot laboratories built several years ago are being taxed to handle some of the high-intensity gamma radiation sources now available.

Hot laboratories and their cells are designed and constructed for many purposes, such as for remote chemical analysis, physical and metallurgical tests, metallography, corrosion examination, loop segmenting, pilot plant operation, chemical separations, machine shop work, etc.

The known uses at the time of design will have considerable effect on the design of the hot laboratory building structure and services and on the hot cells.

Since it is the purpose of this section to discuss the various structural aspects of hot laboratories in general the design features of a hot laboratory for handling gamma type radioactive material will be used for illustration. Individual hot laboratory structural features such as shielding wall materials, cell liners and floors, viewing facilities, access doors, ports and plugs, building crane, change rooms, and building floors will be discussed in detail.

Figure 10.24   A self-contained Beta-Gamma hot laboratory.

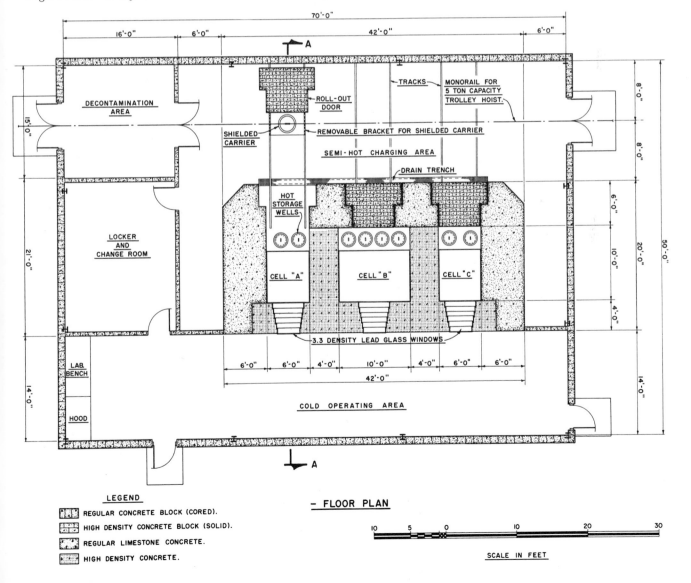

LEGEND

REGULAR CONCRETE BLOCK (CORED).

HIGH DENSITY CONCRETE BLOCK (SOLID).

REGULAR LIMESTONE CONCRETE.

HIGH DENSITY CONCRETE.

– FLOOR PLAN

SCALE IN FEET

HOT CELLS FOR HANDLING BETA AND GAMMA RADIATIONS

This type of cell is used for handling the radioisotopes of elements 1 to 82, inclusive, in both a dry or liquid state. Radioisotopes of those elements above 82 are usually handled only in a liquid state.

Since practically all the gamma radiations emitted by radioisotopes fall within the energy range of 0.07 to 3.0 million electron volts (Mev), the Compton scattering effect (absorption process) is the most important factor in the design calculations for shielding against the gamma emissions of these radioisotopes. Below 0.5 Mev, steel and lead are better shielding materials than concrete. In the 0.5 Mev to 3.0 Mev range of gamma energies the materials used as biological shielding are, in general, interchangeable on the basis of equivalent weight. For example, in the place of a calculated required shield thickness of 6 inches of lead, 31 inches of limestone-Portland cement concrete or 8.65 inches of steel may be substituted. In the case of X-ray shielding, lead is by far the best material to use.

Figure 10.24 shows the plan of the self-contained beta-gamma hot laboratory under discussion. Note the bank of three hot cells consisting of fixed equipment cell B flanked by two typical manipulator cells A and C, with its cold operating area and semi-hot charging area separated from each other by a concrete block partition wall. In this instance the shielding walls are composed of three distinct materials. The front or operating wall of the cell is of poured barytes-Portland cement concrete to permit the operator to be 2 feet closer to the slave ends of his through-the-wall type manipulators than would be the case had limestone-Portland cement concrete been utilized in this wall. This reduced front wall thickness tends to improve the viewing and the remote manipulation. Since space is not critical in this case, limestone-Portland cement concrete has been used to fashion the shielding walls on the side and back walls.

This design calls for roll-out type access doors constructed of stacked solid concrete blocks, within a structural steel framework. Solid limestone-Portland cement concrete blocks are used,

since they equal the shielding value of the rear or charging wall. The partitions between cells are of barytes-Portland cement concrete of a thickness equivalent to the front or operating wall. The size of cells A and C is 6 x 10 feet and cell B is 10 x 10 feet. Each of the two manipulator cells A and C in this bank is equipped with a 3.3 density lead-glass window, a pair of Model 8 through-the-wall mechanical manipulators, and a General Mills type electric rectilinear manipulator. Cell B is equipped with a similar window and is provided with plugged sleeves for mechanical type manipulators if required. Note that the only personnel access between the operating and charging areas is through the locker-change area, to impress on the operators the fact that it's better to wash off contamination than spread it. To do the same, as far as contaminated equipment is concerned, a decontamination area is provided within the charging area. The tracks for the roll-out type access doors extend almost to the building wall to permit a fork-lift truck to enter any cell when its door is in a completely open position. The monorail, as shown, is provided to service the decontamination area and the semi-hot charging area and/or to handle the shielded material carriers used to introduce source material into the cells. This charging is accomplished by placing the carrier on a removable shelf-like bracket located on the hot, or cell side of the roll-out doors. After closing the door, the source material is removed from the carrier by remote manipulation. Obviously, the reverse operation may be used to remove hot wastes, hot scrap, and other radioactive materials from the cells. Ample space is provided in the cold, operating area to permit entry and removal of the through-the-wall type manipulators (in this case 13 ft. is necessary). Laboratory hoods and benches are provided in the operating area for chemical make up or chemical analysis.

Figure 10.25 is a section cut through one of the manipulator cells in the above facility. Note the relative thicknesses of cell walls and removable roof plugs or slabs, the location of manipulator sleeves, the 3.3 density lead-glass window, the raised work level, the roll-out type door and the monorail. The removable roof slabs are lifted by a mobile crane from outside the building.

BIOLOGICAL SHIELDING WALLS OF LESS THAN 255 LBS/CU FT DENSITY

When the required density of a shielding material is less than 4.1 gm/cu cm, or 255 lbs/cu ft, the cost per pound of the materials making up the concrete remains relatively low (¼¢ to 1½¢), since this density may be obtained in concrete by using mineral aggregates alone. For limestone-sand-Portland cement concrete (generally referred to as normal concrete) it is usually satisfactory as well as economical to utilize the conventional mixer-gravity placement. This is also true of barytes-Portland cement and magnetite-Portland cement concretes, with the following exceptions. If the form work of the biological shield is relatively free of inserted fixtures, yet of such complicated geometry that access to certain areas is difficult, placement by pressure grouting should be considered. Or if the quantity or arrangement of the inserted fixtures in the forms is such that placement from above is difficult beyond the point of positive control, placement by pressure grouting should be specified.

Let us examine barytes-Portland cement

Figure 10.25   Cross section A-A of Beta-Gamma hot laboratory.

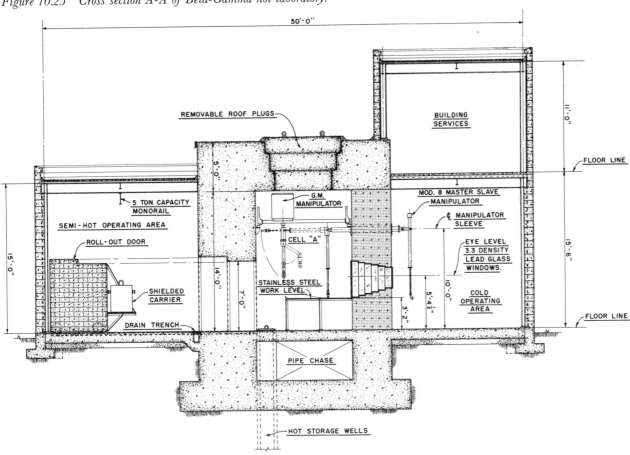

SCALE IN FEET

concrete. The density of dry-rodded barytes aggregate is approximately 156 lbs/cu ft. The density of a grout made of barytes sand and Portland cement for conventional placement is about 158 lbs/cu ft and the resultant concrete has a density of about 215 lbs/cu ft. Grout made of sand and Portland cement has a density of about 131 lbs/cu ft, grout made of barytes sand and steel shot (50% each) and Portland cement has a density of 219 lbs/cu ft.

In all the following concretes using Portland cement, approximately 2 gallons of water are needed to produce a complete chemical reaction for one sack (1 cu ft) of cement. This portion of the water becomes an actual chemical component of the concrete. The rest of the water (approximately 4 gallons per sack) used to make the concrete workable is held as captive moisture and its continued presence tends to vary according to the curing process, humidity present, etc. In all the following concretes using Portland cement, this 4 gallons of water is disregarded in considering shielding value and only the 2 gallons of water per sack of cement as noted above is used in computing the weights of the various mixes. The rest of the water is omitted, since it is a moot question how much of it remains within the concrete under varying working conditions.

As mentioned earlier, biological shielding walls should be so constructed and of sufficient thickness and density to reduce the radiation intensity of the source material below the prescribed permissible tolerance for operating personnel. The selection of the shielding material for any prescribed facility should be made by a considered comparison of the various available materials on the basis of the following desirable properties that should be included in a gamma shield: high density to minimize wall thickness, high content of heavy elements for the capture of gamma radiation, economical cost, ease of placement or fabrication, and structural strength and stability under nuclear radiation as well as high-temperature moist or high-temperature dry conditions.

Presently available direct-viewing windows and mechanical remote manipulation devices dictate a maximum operating wall thickness limitation of about 5 feet.

Care should be taken to prevent any voided

spaces in the shielding walls in the first 8 feet above the walking floor levels immediately around a cell structure. Hence, all the through-the-wall sleeves, inner wall piping, conduit and duct work should be kept above this level if at all possible. All pipe sleeves below this elevation should be adequately shielded at all times. Any vertical or horizontal runs of inner-wall piping, of any considerable size, below the 8 ft level should have localized shielding of a denser material than that used in the wall itself. Voids in the basic shielding wall due to poor concrete placement cannot be tolerated.

Biological shielding walls for hot cells handling beta and gamma radiations may be constructed of many dense materials. Among these are the following: Portland cement concretes of limestone-sand, barytes, magnetite, ilmenite, barytes-iron shot, ferrophosphorus and metallic iron-iron shot. In addition steel plate or bricks and lead sheet and bricks may be used.

Limestone-Sand-Portland Cement Concrete for Conventional Placement

This shielding material has a specific gravity of 2.2 gm/cu cm and weighs 140 lbs/cu ft or 3780 lbs/cu yd. The mix used to obtain this density is 1806 lbs of coarse aggregate, 1388 lbs of sand, 496 lbs (5¼ sacks) of Portland cement and 32 gallons of water (use 2 gallons of water per sack of cement in computing weight of finished concrete). The approximate cost of materials alone is $10/cu yd or ¼¢/lb.

This type of concrete is extensively used for shielding walls in hot cells and caves where space limitations are no factor in their construction. Where the proposed shield wall is extensively cut up by access ports, lead doors, viewing windows and pipe sleeves, poured concrete is used. However, in shields that are relatively free of inserted fixtures, mortared solid concrete block (staggered to prevent beaming) may be economically used. Where the quantity or arrangement of inserted fixtures in the forms, or the complicated geometry of the shield structure is such that gravity placement is difficult beyond the point of positive control of voids or pockets, placement by pressure grouting (Prepakt or equal) should be specified.

Zinc bromide solution viewing windows are

normally best used with this type of shielding material.

Limestone-Sand-Portland Cement Concrete for Pressure Grouting Placement

This shielding material has a specific gravity of 2.4 gm/cu cm and weighs about 152 lbs/cu ft or 4,100 lbs/cu yd. The theory behind pressure grouting placement is to pack and tamp as much coarse aggregate into the shield wall forms as possible then introduce grout, under pressure, from the bottom of the forms to fill all the voids and air pockets. The proportions used are 2956 lbs of coarse aggregate with the voids filled with 1144 lbs of grout composed of 557 lbs of sand, 367 lbs of cement (4 sacks), 145 lbs of "Alfesil"*, 5 lbs of intrusion aid and 245 lbs of water (use 2 gallons of water per sack of cement in computing weight of finished concrete). The approximate cost of material alone (Oak Ridge) is $12/cu yd or 0.29¢/lb. Note that the use of a larger proportion of coarse to fine aggregates results in a denser concrete.

Barytes (barium sulphate)-Portland Cement Concrete for Conventional Placement

This shielding material has a specific gravity of 3.4 gm/cu cm and weighs about 215 lbs/cu ft or 5800 lbs/cu yd. The mix used to obtain this density is 2915 lbs of coarse aggregate (¾ in), 2183 lbs of barytes sand, 590 lbs (6¼ sacks) of cement and 36 gallons of water (use 2 gallons of water per sack of cement in computing weight of finished concrete). The approximate cost of materials alone (Oak Ridge) is $60/cu yd or 1¢/lb. Barytes-Portland cement concrete placed by the conventional gravity method is extensively used for shielding walls in hot cells and caves. At Oak Ridge National Laboratory this type of concrete has become the favorite shielding material since it embodies high density with low cost. Even when the shielding wall is cut up by access ports and doors, viewing windows, pipe sleeves and inserts, the conventional gravity method of mixer placement (vibrated) is used. 3.3 gm/cu cm non-browning laminated lead

glass viewing windows are used with this type of shielding material.

Barytes-Portland Cement Concrete for Pressure Grouting Placement

This shielding material has a specific gravity of 3.4 gm/cu cm and weighs 215 lbs/cu ft or 5800 lbs/cu yd. The theory behind pressure grouting placement is to pack and tamp as much coarse aggregate into the shield wall forms as possible, then introduce grout, under pressure, from the bottom of the forms to fill all the voids and air pockets. The proportions used are 4150 lbs of coarse aggregate (¾ in.) with the voids filled with 1650 lbs of grout composed of 870 lbs of barytes sand, 470 lbs (5 sacks) of cement, 187 lbs of "Alfesil," 32 lbs of hydrated lime, 7 lbs of intrusion aid and 320 lbs of water (use 2 gallons of water per sack of cement in computing weight of finished concrete). Approximate cost of materials alone (Oak Ridge) is $63/cu yd or 1¢/lb.

Barytes-Portland cement concrete placed by pressure grouting is used where the quantity or arrangement of inserted fixtures in the shielding wall forms is such that gravity placement from above is difficult beyond the point of positive control.

Barytes-Portland Cement Concrete Blocks (solid)

This shielding material has a specific gravity somewhat less than 3.4 gm/cu cm and weighs somewhat less than that concrete as described above. The mix used in fabricating these solid barytes block is 94 lbs (one sack) of cement, 424 lbs of coarse aggregate (¾ in.), 321 lbs of barytes sand and 5½ gallons of water. Delivered cost of a 6 x 6 x 12 inch solid barytes block (Oak Ridge) is 99¢ (wt. 55 lbs), or at the rate of $4/cu ft.

In extensive biological shielding walls that are relatively free of openings or inserted features, staggered, mortared, solid, barytes, concrete block may be economically used. Unmortared, stacked barytes blocks are often used to plug seldom-used access ports while the cell is activated, and to provide temporary inner cell partitions. A facility constructed of mortared solid barytes block would lend itself to relatively easy and economical alterations in size and shape. In large complex cells, it is often economical to combine the use of

---

* A pozzolanic material, reported to be fly ash, required for use with the Prepakt method—Concrete Chemical Company, Cleveland, Ohio.

both forms of barytes concrete, limiting the poured form to those parts of the shielding wall where the inserted features are concentrated.

Magnetite Iron Ore-Portland Cement Concrete for Conventional Placement

This shielding material has a specific gravity of 3.59 gm/cu cm and weighs 228 lbs/cu ft or 6160 lbs/cu yd. The mix used to obtain this density is 2833 lbs of coarse aggregate (⅜ to ¾ in.), 2575 lbs of fine aggregate (#4 sieve and smaller), 639 lbs (6.8 sacks) of cement and 39.8 gallons of water (use 2 gallons of water per sack of cement in computing weight of finished concrete). The approximate cost of materials alone (Los Angeles) is $91.30/cu yd or 1½¢/lb. The delivered cost of a 9 x 9 x 18 inch solid block (wt. 194 lbs) is $5.35 each (Los Angeles). This is at the rate of $6.33/cu ft. A viewing window composed of 3.3 gm/cu cm non-browning lead glass of a thickness slightly in excess of the shield wall thickness, is normally used in conjunction with this shielding material.

The fact that aggregates from rich magnetite iron ores are sharp and angular in shape and possess magnetic properties make this material particularly adaptable to dry placement between steel sheets for use as shielding walls. The angle of repose of the aggregates of magnetite ores appears to be quite steep and its resulting horizontal pressure on side wall plates is somewhat less than that exerted by other comparative dry materials. This fact could result in the use of somewhat thinner side plates in a facility requiring this shielding material. This fact could be translated into a considerable cost saving, particularly in the stainless steel or hot side liner. Care should be used in the placement of dry magnetite ores to prevent cavities and voids from forming within the shielding walls. This shielding material is widely used, but the availability of large quantities of barium sulphate ore in the vicinity of Oak Ridge has given preference to this material over magnetite ores at O.R.N.L.

Ilmenite-Portland Cement Concrete for Pressure Grouting Placement

This shielding material has a specific gravity of 4.1 gm/cu cm and weighs 255 lbs/cu ft or 6900 lbs/cu yd. The theory behind pressure grouting placement is to pack and tamp as much coarse aggregate into the shield wall forms as possible, then introduce grout under pressure, from the bottom of the forms to fill all voids and air pockets. The proportions used are 1700 lbs of coarse aggregate (3 to 1½ in.) and 2306 lbs of medium aggregate (1½ to ½ in.) with the voids filled with 2894 lbs of grout composed of 2200 lbs of fine aggregate (4m to 100m), 460 lbs of cement (5 sacks), 175 lbs of "Alfesil," 25 lbs of hydrated lime, 7 lbs of intrusion aid and 300 (approx.) lbs of water. The approximate cost of materials alone in Oak Ridge is $69/cu yd or 1¢/lb.

BIOLOGICAL SHIELDING WALLS OF GREATER THAN 255 LB/CU FT DENSITY

Concretes using a metallic aggregate or aggregates are necessary to produce densities in excess of 4.1 gm/cu cm, which is about the maximum economical density that can be obtained with mineral aggregates alone. These metallic aggregates add appreciably to the over-all cost of the finished shield wall.

However, the unit cost of the materials used to make these concretes, per pound of shielding, may not vary greatly between, e.g., concrete using barytes with a density of 3.4 gm/cu cm at 1¢/lb and concrete using metallic steel coarse aggregates and metallic iron shot with a density of 6.18 gm/cu cm at 2.62¢/lb. Concretes containing iron shot as their fine aggregates and placed by pressure grouting will have a material cost of $40 to $50/cu yd less than concrete of an equivalent density placed by conventional methods. This cost differential is due to the lesser amount

TABLE 10.1a

	Aggregates Cost			Concrete Cost				
COARSE	PER TON	FINE	PER TON	PER YD.	PER TON	SP GR GM/ CU CM	CON. DENSITY
Barytes	$20	Shot	$160	$242	$69	4.15	265
Steel	40	Shot	160	314	63	6.18	385
Steel	50	Shot	160	354	71	6.18	385
Steel	60	Shot	160	394	79	6.18	385
Steel	80	Shot	160	474	95	6.18	385

of voids present in the coarse aggregate during pressure grouting placement. For this reason less grout is required, which contains the expensive fine iron shot.

Table 10.1a, shown on the previous page, may prove of interest; it applies to pressure grouting placement only.

Grouts made of fine iron shot and Portland cement have a density (average) of 275 lbs/cu ft. The above costs of steel coarse aggregates vary according to whether steel punchings, steel stars or steel chips, etc., are used.

Barytes-Iron Shot-Portland Cement for Pressure Grouting Placement

This shielding material has a specific gravity of 4.15 gm/cu cm and weighs 260 lbs/cu ft or 7020 lbs/cu yd. The procedure used to obtain this density is to pack and tamp as large a quantity of coarse aggregate into the shield wall forms as possible, then introduce iron shot grout under pressure from the bottom to fill all voids and air pockets.

The proportions used are 4260 lbs of coarse barytes aggregate (¾ in.) with the voids filled with 2760 lbs of grout composed of 2165 lbs of fine iron shot (1/32 and ⅛ in. dia.), 371 lbs of cement (4 sacks), 149 lbs of "Alfesil," 8 lbs of intrusion aid and 241 lbs of water (use 67 lbs or 2 gallons of water per sack of cement in computing weight of the finished concrete). The approximate cost of material alone (Cambridge, Mass.) is $242/cu yd or 3.4¢/lb.

This is a most practical concrete from the standpoint of both density and economy. It should be noted that while the barytes used as coarse aggregate has a dry-rodded specific density of about 160 lbs/cu ft., it has a bulk density of about 260 lbs/cu ft. The density of the grout is about 275 lbs/cu. ft. The resulting density of a mixture of barytes and this heavy grout will vary only slightly as the relative proportions of the aggregate and grout are varied. However, since the grout is the expensive item in this concrete, the most economical mix would be that which has least voids in the coarse aggregate. This would tend to keep the concrete density close to the 260 lbs/cu ft limit for the barytes coarse aggregate. In conjunction with a shield wall con-

structed of this material, a composite viewing window composed of 6.3 gm/cu cm and 3.3 gm/cu cm densities of lead glass or one using Penberthy 4.05 gm/cu cm density lead glass would be used.

Barytes-Iron Shot-Portland Cement Concrete for Conventional Placement

This shielding material has a specific gravity of 4.3 gm/cu cm and weighs 268 lbs/cu ft or 7240 lbs/cu yd. The mix used to obtain this density is 3695 lbs of coarse barytes aggregate (¾ in.), 3045 lbs of fine iron shot (1/32 and ⅛ in. dia.), 313 lbs of cement (3 + sacks), 126 lbs of "Alfesil," 6 lbs of intrusion aid and 208 lbs of water. (Use 55 lbs or 2 gallons of water per sack of cement in figuring weight of the finished concrete. The approximate cost of materials alone (Cambridge, Mass.) is $313/cu yd or 4.3¢/lb.

Had the placing of the above mix been by pressure grouting placement, a saving of $70/cu yd in materials alone could have been realized. The reason for this savings is that less grout is needed in the pressure grouting method than in conventional placement. And since the expensive phase of this mix is the iron shot grout, it follows that a savings in cost will result even when additional amounts of the barytes coarse aggregates are required. Of course, the over-all density of this concrete is greater by 220 lbs/cu yd than that placed by pressure grouting, but the cost of the material is disproportionately greater.

Ferrophosphorus-Portland Cement Concrete for Conventional Placement

This shielding material has a specific gravity of 4.7 gm/cu cm and weighs 293 lbs/cu ft or 7900 lbs/cu yd. The mix used to obtain this density is 4212 lbs of coarse aggregate (¼ to ¾ in.), 2804 lbs of fine aggregate (less than ¼ in.), 752 lbs of cement (8 sacks) and 46 gallons of water (use 132 lbs or 2 gallons of water per sack of cement in computing weight of finished concrete. The approximate cost of materials alone is $277/cu yd or 3½¢/lb. The viewing window used in conjunction with this shielding material is a composite type using both 6.2 gm/cu cm and 3.3 gm/cu cm densities of lead glass, or one using Penberthy 4.8 gm/cu cm density lead glass.

Iron or Steel-Iron Shot-Portland Cement Concrete for Pressure Grouting Placement

This shielding material has a specific gravity of 6.18 gm/cu cm and weighs 385 lbs/cu ft or 10,400 lbs/cu yd. The procedure to obtain this density is to pack and tamp as large a quantity of steel pebbles or punchings and iron stars into the shield wall forms as possible, then introduce grout under pressure from the bottom to fill all the voids and eliminate air pockets. The proportions used are 6195 lbs of steel pebbles or punchings, and 1895 lbs of iron stars, the voids in the coarse aggregate being filled with 2310 lbs of grout composed of 1811 lbs of iron shot (1/32 and 1/8 in. dia.), 312 lbs of cement (3+ sacks), 125 lbs of "Alfesil," 6 lbs of intrusion aid and 208 lbs of water (use 56 lbs, or 2 gallons of water per sack of cement in computing weight of concrete). The approximate cost of materials alone (Cambridge, Mass.) is $363/cu yd or 3.5¢/lb. Placing the above mix by pressure grouting permitted the use of a smaller quantity of grout and a larger quantity of coarse aggregates than would other placement methods for equivalent densities. The viewing window normally used in conjunction with this shielding material is one using 6.2 gm/cu cm density lead glass.

Iron or Steel-Iron Shot-Portland Cement Concrete for Conventional Placement

This shielding material has a specific gravity of 5.9 gm/cu cm and weighs 370 lbs/cu ft or 10,000 lbs/cu yd. The mix used to obtain this density is 5109 lbs of steel punchings (1/4 to 1 in. dia. and thick), 2304 lbs of iron shot (1/8 in. dia.), 1536 lbs of iron shot (1/32 in. dia.), 896 lbs of Portland cement (9½ sacks), and 39 gallons of water (use 155 lbs or 2 gallons of water per sack of cement in computing weights of finished concrete.) The approximate cost of materials alone is $452/cu yd or 4.5¢/lb. Care should be used to prevent segregation of aggregates during the conventional gravity placement of this material. Had the above mix been placed by pressure grouting, thus permitting the use of a smaller quantity of grout and a larger quantity of coarse aggregates than by the above mixer placement

in obtaining equivalent densities, a saving of $50 per cu yd, in materials alone, could have been obtained, since iron shot is relatively more expensive than iron punchings.

Steel or Iron

This shielding material has a specific gravity of 7.8 gm/cu cm and weighs 490 lbs/cu ft or 13,230 lbs/cu yd. Because of its relatively high cost (8¢/lb for plate stock and 10¢/lb for bar stock bricks), iron or steel plates or 2 x 4 x 8 inch bricks are seldom used as a shielding material in new (as opposed to the renovated or altered) facilities. The main usage of steel as a shielding material is in the alteration and/or modification of existing hot cells or caves to permit handling of more intense radiation sources. In facilities (other than those to shield X-rays) where 2 in. of lead (or less) is required, it is usually both economical as well as good practice to substitute for it the equivalent thickness of steel plate. Besides being more economical, the fabrication problems incidental to the supporting of vertical steel plate are trivial compared to those encountered in supporting sheet lead, which has a tendency to slump and creep.

Some specific applications of steel shielding (aside from access doors) that the author has witnessed first hand are as follows: (1) In a metallographic cell where, because of both space limitations and structural support problems, the shield walls were fabricated, within an existing facility, of laminated steel plates; and (2) in a sampling facility servicing several existing in-line hot cells, the bottle capper, filler and positioner with eye level viewing windows at each cell, as well as the intercell conveyor, with necessary piping and instrumentation were shielded with laminated cold-rolled steel plates each 1½ in. thick. Cold-rolled steel plates were specified because of the close tolerance, as to thickness, inherent in this material. Steel bar-stock bricks 2 x 4 x 8 inches may be coated as follows (with the cost of painting as unity): painting (3 spray coats) 1.0; plastic coating 1.25; galvanizing 1.0; cadmium plating over copper 4.10; and chrome plating over nickel over copper 6.0.

The viewing window normally used in conjunction with this shielding material is one using

6.2 gm/cu cm density lead glass. In this case, it must be somewhat thicker than the shield wall, with supplementary shielding around its perimeter on the cold side.

Chemically Pure Lead

This shielding material has a specific gravity of 11.3 gm/cu cm and weighs 706 lbs/cu ft or 19,062 lbs/cu yd. Of all the readily available shielding materials lead tops the list. This element is an excellent shielding material, especially where space is at a premium. It is widely used in the alteration and modification of existing facilities where localized shielding is desirable. Its normal usage is in the form of stacked brick. The relatively high cost of lead is the primary reason for the substitution of other materials whenever possible. Doors and access ports in hot cells and caves are generally composed of steel-encased poured lead. For X-rays and very low energy gamma rays, lead is almost always used because of its superior shielding properties in this energy range. For temporary or localized shielding, lead brick (2 x 4 x 8 inches) is the ideal material. The bricks are easy to handle and place and are almost completely salvageable. For altering existing hot cells or caves to permit the use of more intense radiation sources, sheet lead or homogeneous lead covering on steel plates is ideal, since it provides maximum shielding protection without appreciably decreasing the inside usable volume of the cell or cave.

In X-ray facilities, because the required thickness of lead is usually quite small, the sheet lead must of necessity be supported before being utilized. Steel plates (¼ in. thick) with homogeneous lead covering on the facility side (manufactured by Knapp Mills) or sheet lead laminated to plywood (Ray Proof Corporation) are both excellent shielding materials. Lead is particularly effective against X-rays and low-energy gammas because of its high photoelectric absorption and also against high-energy gammas (over 3.0 Mev) because of its high pair-production cross section.

In certain large or complicated structural steel door frames, used with lead doors in hot cells or caves, lead shot has been substituted for poured lead, as the shielding material, so that the door frames could be fabricated, shipped and erected empty, rather than filled with poured lead. Tests indicated that the shielding value of lead shot varies greatly with the shot size and their mix. The results of these tests were evaluated; to minimize voids, the following mix was specified: 56.2% of ⅞ in. lead balls, 28.2% of 0.22 in. buckshot, and 15.6% of #12 shot. Care should be used in the placement of these shot in the steel box frames to prevent segregation. The usual procedure is to pour relatively thin layers of the large lead balls. To these is added the proper percentage of buckshot, which is gently vibrated until the large balls begin to appear. Then the same procedure is followed to disperse the #12 shot in the voids of the buckshot. If extreme care is used to prevent the large balls from floating on the fine shot, densities in excess of 8.5 gm/cu cm may be obtained. Lead may be used as shielding in the following forms:

	Relative Cost (lb)
(1) 2 x 4 x 8 inches cast lead brick	1.0
(2) 2 x 4 x 8 inches machined lead brick	1.25
(3) Sheet lead, normally for horizontal shielding	1.0
(4) Homogeneous lead covering on steel plates for vertical shielding	1.25
(5) Sheet lead laminated to plywood for vertical shielding	1.25
(6) 6 in. lead, encased three sides by ¼ in. mild steel plate, the fourth or hot side by ¼ in. stainless steel plate	1.6
(7) 6 in. lead encased four sides by ¼ in. stainless steel plate	1.9
(8) 4 in. lead encased four sides by ¼ in. stainless steel plate	2.3

The viewing window normally used with lead is one of 6.3 gm/cu cm density lead glass. This viewing facility must be considerably thicker than the shield wall with a supplementary shielding "blister" around its perimeter on the cold side.

INTERIOR TREATMENT OF HOT CELLS

The interior of hot cells (walls and floors) are usually lined with a nitric acid-proof, impervious material, such as stainless steel sheets, seam-welded to form a vapor-tight box. In some cases a suitable alternate may have the concrete walls coated with a plastic coating system such as "Amercoat" and the floor and cove base covered with stainless steel. The reason for these expensive surface treatments is to permit easy decontamination of the cell interior when in-cell operations generate fumes, vapors, splashes and particles which cause surface contamination. When the source material is of high radiation intensity, stainless steel liners are almost universally used.

In the application of this type of lining there are two distinct schools of thought. One of these contends that the stainless steel liners should be of sufficient thickness to permit their utilization as the inner form in pouring the shielding walls. Whether the exterior or cold surface of the hot cells be composed of mild steel plate or merely exposed concrete is not definitely stated. The argument for the mild steel exterior plate covering is the relative ease with which all types of inserted fixtures may be welded in position between these two metal surfaces prior to the placement of the concrete. In addition, a metal exterior surface lends itself to simple attachment of brackets, service piping, etc. The only argument for exposed concrete on the cell exterior is its lower cost.

The other school contends that stainless steel liners should be only thick enough to resist repeated nitric acid decontaminations, and that any additional thickness to provide the rigidity necessary for a skin plate on concrete forms is an unwarranted expense. In this second instance, the poured floor and walls of the cell contain stainless steel angles, bars or some other method of subsequently fastening the thin stainless liner in position. Note that stainless steel liners are never directly welded to a mild steel framework or anchors. This is to prevent a mixture of mild steel with stainless at the point of weld, which would cause a weak spot in the liner insofar as corrosion and decontamination with nitric acid are concerned.

The effectiveness of a stainless steel liner is in direct proportion to the excellence of the seam welds involved. A poor weld will permit seepage of the decontaminants between the liner and concrete wall, and gradual buildup of radioactive contamination. Or, in an extreme case, the spill itself might occur at the faulty weld, and the cell becomes unusable by the personnel necessary to set up the chemical or physical equipment for further experiments, until the liner around the leak had been removed and the concrete chipped out and replaced.

Because nitric acid is often used as a decontaminant, it is not good economics to specify an expensive mirror finish on the stainless steel liner. This type of finish lasts only until the first decontamination. In addition, there is the possibility that the operator may be troubled by the reflected inner cell lighting on such liners. A 2B finish is very satisfactory and constitutes a distinct saving in initial cost.

Thin Stainless Steel Wall Liners

Wall liners of 11 gage Type 347 or 307L stainless steel sheets are extensively used. These sheets (in 2B finish), 4 x 8 feet in size, are affixed to a grid of 1½ x 1½ x ³⁄₁₆ inch Type 347 stainless steel angles anchored into the poured concrete walls with mild steel "Nelweld" stud anchors. This angle grid is at 2 ft. centers both horizontally and vertically and the 11-gage sheets are affixed to this grid by vapor-proof perimeter seam welds using shielded arc. This 11-gage sheet is then plug-welded at 12 in. centers to all grid angles not used to back up the perimeter seam weld. Seam welds are also used to join this liner to all stainless steel pipe inserts, manipulator or periscope sleeves, and the stainless angle framing around the formed openings contains viewing facilities as well as personnel and material access ports and doors. The four corners of this cell liner are normally coved at 2 in. radius to expedite decontamination. A nominal 4 x 8 ft sheet of 11-gage stainless steel is so bent that this coved portion straddles the cell corners so that all vertical welds are made against a wall with angle backing.

Thin Stainless Steel Floor Liners

In conjunction with the 11-gage stainless wall liners, ¼ in. thick sheets of Type 347 or 307L stainless steel are utilized for the floor pan. These sheets, nominally sized 4 x 8 feet, are affixed in the same manner as the wall liners to a grid of 1½ x 1½ x ¼ inch Type 347 stainless steel angles set to provide proper sloped drainage away from the walls to the centrally located semi-hot drains. This angle grid, which is also at 2 ft. centers (both ways), is anchored into the poured concrete floor slab with mild steel "Nelweld" stud anchors. Seam welds are also used to join this floor liner to the thinner wall liners, as well as to the stainless semi-hot and hot drains. The edges of this floor pan are also coved at 2 in. radius and a back-up angle provided (6 in. above high point of floor pan) behind the seam weld connecting this pan to the thinner wall liner. In practice, this stainless steel floor liner is at nominally the same elevation as that of the operating and charging areas. However, a supplementary table-top-height work area is normally provided within the cell.

Thick Stainless Steel Wall and Floor Liners

As mentioned earlier, there is a difference of opinion concerning the ideal thickness of stainless steel liners. We will now take up the case of those who contend that these liners should be of sufficient thickness to permit their being welded into a vapor-tight, topless box and used as the inner concrete form for placing the poured shielding walls. It has been found from experience that even stainless steel cell liners ¾ in. thick need an extensive supplementary grid of timber bracing when used as a concrete form, particularly when high-density concrete is involved. Experience also reveals the fact that it is very difficult to adequately place the concrete base slab beneath the floor liner once it has been welded in place to the wall liner, and that objectionable voids and hollow areas beneath the floor liner are the inevitable result. To prevent this, it becomes necessary to use the same procedure in affixing the thick floor pan to the base slab. This consists of seam and plug welding this floor pan to a grid of stainless angles anchored into the existing base slab. This coved floor liner is then seam-welded to the thick wall liner, which is then braced with a network of timbers and used as the interior concrete form for placing the poured shielding walls.

Thick Stainless Clad Wall and Floor Liners

For stainless liners less than ½ in. thick it is uneconomical to consider the use of stainless cladding on mild steel as a substitute. However, for thick liners fabricated before the placement of the concrete in the shield walls and used as the inner form for their placement, stainless clad plates about ¾ in. thick are employed. In using thick stainless clad wall and floor liners, extreme care must be taken in welding the plates into a vapor-tight liner. In fabricating this material the first seam welds are made on the mild steel side. This, however, leaves a crack between the plates on the stainless clad side, necessitating back-chipping of the clad side with a sharp round-nose chisel, or grinding. Then two seam-weld passes are made on the clad side, using stainless steel welding rods. It is extremely difficult not to dilute the stainless welding beads with base metal from the mild steel side. The dilution of this stainless steel clad side seam weld with base metal could cause weak spots as far as decontamination is concerned. In addition, it is extremely difficult to provide coved corners in the thick stainless clad wall liners and around the perimeter of the stainless clad floor pan.

Liners of Plastic Coatings

"Amercoat" 33, "Nukemite" 40 and "Corrosite" 22 are recommended air-dried vinyl coatings in general use as liners for concrete or steel cell wall and floor surfaces. "Amercoat" 33 or 33 HB is quite extensively used as cell liners when stainless steel has not been specified. This material can be used to cover every one of the shielding materials listed so far. Three coats of "Amercoat" 33 or two coats of "Amercoat" 33 HB are needed to provide a nitric acid-proof, impervious lining 5 mils thick. "Amercoat" 86 primer is used with both. "Boltaron" 6200 sheets are sometimes used as cell wall and floor liners. This material is weldable with a hot-air torch or cemented with epoxy resin.

Under certain conditions the interior surfaces of unlined cells are coated with a "strippable" plastic "Cocoon" type disposable finish. The theory behind the use of this material being that the "Cocoon" localizes and contains the spill or splash or other type of liquid surface contamination and can be stripped locally and replaced by remote manipulation. Recommended "strippable" coatings are G. E. Cocoon, Brevon, Monsanto D-100 and Gordon Lacey A89 A.

Ceilings of Plastic Coatings

Normally, in stainless-lined cells the undersides of both the removable roof slabs and the fixed portion of the cell roof, supporting these slabs, are coated with either "Amercoat" 33 or 33 HB systems to a thickness of 5 mils. If the entire roof of the cell is composed of removable slabs, the stainless wall liner is normally lapped over and welded to the mild steel angles that frame the roof opening.

VIEWING FACILITIES

Viewing means may be roughly divided into three categories: liquid-filled windows, solid windows and non-shielding types. Typical liquid-filled windows contain a solution of zinc bromide. The solid category is typified by windows composed of laminations of lead glass usually in a bath of mineral oil. The non-shielding types include periscopes and mirrors.

Viewing facilities may be rectangular, circular or stepped. Liquid windows are usually either rectangular or so fashioned with sloped sides that the area of its hot side face is greater than that of its cold side face. Both liquid and solid viewing facilities may be fashioned so as to have circular hot and cold faces. Solid windows, because of the necessity to economize on lead glass, are normally stepped outward on all four sides at each increase in area of the lead glass components. Usually these steps are of greater depth on the bottom than on its top or sides.

The size and configuration of the viewing window, its location with respect to the horizontal and vertical dimensions of the cell, and the horizontal and vertical taper of the window container are best determined by a full-scale mockup of the proposed hot cell. A selection of manufacturer's standard size glass window assemblies usually results in some savings in cost.

After the viewing facility is installed within its formed opening in the concrete shielding wall, the cracks around its perimeter, on both hot and cold faces, are filled with compacted lead wool. In high radiation level cells the perimeter of the hot face is flashed to the stainless steel liner to prevent contamination within the cell wall due to "breathing" of the viewing facility due to changes in atmospheric pressure as well as seepage of decontaminants.

Liquid-Filled Windows

The density of the 60% zinc bromide solution in this type of window is 2.52 gm/ml (plus or minus .02 gm/ml). The four inner-wall sides of the window container for this solution may be of welded mild steel plates (1 in. thick) internally painted with seven coats of black "Amercoat" System #31. This consists of a prime coat, three body and three seal coats over a sandblasted surface. The hot or cell side of this window is composed of a laminated pane made up of a sheet of tempered, non-browning glass ("Herculite") between two sheets of select quality, annealed, polished, non-browning lime glass (Corning type 8365 of 2.7 gm/cu cm). The cold or operators side of the container is composed of a laminated pane made up of two sheets of select quality, annealed, polished plate glass (2.5 gm/cu cm) with an interior sheet of tempered ("Herculite") glass. Glass panes are laminated with polyvinyl butyral.

Keeper plates holding both glass panes in position should be securely bolted to the zinc bromide container plates. Gaskets between these plates, the keeper plates and the glass are of "Koroseal" No. 116. A partially filled expansion tank containing the terminals of both the Amercoated fill pipe and the ¾ in. vent pipe, are provided above the window on the cold side to compensate for changes in atmospheric pressure.

Zinc bromide solution is in the same density range as concrete made of limestone—sand—Portland cement, and is normally used in windows for cells with shielding walls of this material. The relative economy of zinc bromide solution (60¢/lb) compared to even the cheapest lead glass ($2.40/lb) permits the use of extremely large, liquid-filled windows if needed. The zinc bromide should be purchased under specifications for optical clarity, etc. These specifications are available at Argonne National Laboratory, Lemont, Illinois.

Solid Windows

The densities of the viewing windows in this group vary from 3.3 to 6.2 gm/cu cm, which corresponds roughly to the densities of the shielding materials beginning with barytes (barium sulphate)-Portland cement concrete at 3.4 gm/cu cm and including steel at 7.8 gm/cu cm. The total effective window density should be in the same density range as the shielding wall.

The 3.3 gm/cu cm density non-browning lead glass (Corning No. 8362, Pittsburgh No. 4966) is usually used in conjunction with barytes-Portland cement concrete when designing cell shielding. It is normally used in plates 8 or 9 in. thick (to decrease the number of surfaces) laminated in a bath of mineral oil and housed in a stepped container that may be constructed of either welded steel plates or cast metal. The interior of this container should be coated with baked epoxy resin. The hot or cell side of this window is usually composed of a 1 in. thick sheet of select-quality, annealed, polished, non-browning lime glass (2.7 gm/cu cm, Corning No. 8365 or Pittsburgh No. 6740). The cold or operator's side of the window is usually composed of a 1 in. thick sheet of select quality, annealed, polished plate glass (2.5 gm/cu cm). Keeper plates holding both cover glass sheets in position must be securely bolted to the container plates or casting. Gaskets between these plates or casting, the glass and the keeper plate are of "Koroseal" No. 116. Thin, stainless flashing is provided if necessary. An expansion tank partially filled with clear, water-free mineral oil, and containing the terminals of both the Amercoated stainless steel fill and vent pipes must be provided above the viewing facility on the cold side to compensate for changes in atmospheric pressure. The present cost of 3.3 gm/cu cm density lead glass is approximately $2.40/lb.

A typical 3.3 gm/cu cm solid window as used in a 36 in. shield wall of barytes-Portland cement concrete, to service a cell 6 ft. 6 in. wide by 8 ft. deep, may well conform to the following criteria: the lead glass plates shall be (beginning with the cold side) 18 x 30 x 9 inches, 22 x 32 x 9 inches, 26 x 34 x 9 inches, and 30 x 36 x 7 inches, all of 3.3 gm/cu cm density. The hot-side cover glass shall be 34⅛ x 38⅜ x 1 inches of 2.7 gm/cu cm density non-browning lime glass and the cold-side cover glass shall be plate glass 21⅝ x 32⅜ x 1 inch. From this we note that while the lead glass plates increase 6 in. in width (from cold to hot side) the increase in height is 12 in. Note, also, that of this 12 in. increase, 9½ in. are below the centerline of the cold-side lead glass plate and the remaining 2½ in. is above this centerline. The centerline of the hot-side lead glass plate should be located 5 ft. 3 in. above the floor of the operating area.

For use in the intermediate density range, Penberthy Instrument Co. has available two additional lead glasses for general use. These are 4.05 gm/cu cm high lead content glass (Penberthy ME-D 4.0) with an index of refraction of 1.66 and 4.8 gm/cu cm high lead-content glass (Penberthy ME-D 4.8) with an index of refraction of 1.76. The first type could well be utilized in conjunction with barytes-metallic iron shot concrete (4.15 gm/cu cm) and the other type with Ferrophosphorus-Portland cement concrete (4.7 gm/cu cm). For other intermediate densities between 3.3 and 6.2 gm/cu cm not specifically covered by the above two materials, a combination of the various densities may be used. Additional shielding should be provided around the perimeter of the cold (operator's) side of the window if smaller and denser glass is placed on this side. Note that this is the normal place for the denser and more expensive glass component, since the area and volume of the glass panes increase in steps from the cold to the hot side.

At the top of the lead glass density range is the 6.2 gm/cu cm high lead-content glass (Corning No. 8363 or Penberthy HiD 6.2; present cost about $8.50/lb.) with an index of refraction of 1.97. This material is used in conjunction with shields of steel and iron, although the window must, of necessity, be slightly thicker than the shield wall itself to match the mass shielding effect. This necessitates the use of supplementary shielding in the form of a "blister" on the wall around the cold side perimeter of the window. This type of glass has a 75% lead content and 1 inch of it is the equivalent of .55 inch of lead. Like the 4.0 and 4.8 densities, it is very soft, easily scratched or etched, and in addition discolors more easily under radiation exposure. Hence, it is good practice to have one or several panes of 3.3 glass at the hot side of the window to protect the 6.2 glass. The type of container housing the intermediate and high densities of lead glass are similar to that described under the 3.3 gm/cu cm type.

Non-Shielding Viewing Facilities

In low radiation level cells having relatively thin walls (12 in. or less) mirrors are sometimes used. This, of course, necessitates viewing slots or openings in the walls. In higher radiation level cells, mirrors are sometimes placed within the cells to permit observation of gauges and processes that would otherwise be masked from direct sight through windows or periscopes.

Periscopes are normally used in conjunction with stainless steel pipe inserts through the shield walls. The elevation of these periscope sleeves is usually above the heads of the operating personnel, for it is almost impossible to satisfactorily shield the opening through the sleeve while the periscope is in use. When a periscope has been moved to a new position or its use discontinued, the unused sleeve should immediately be shielded with a plug made of the same material as the shield wall itself. Kollmorgan Optical Corporation wall periscope Model 301 with through-the-wall sleeve located 7 ft. above the floor of the operating area, and with supplementary radiation shield on its cold side, is recommended.

When a straight-line-viewing periscope is utilized, its sleeve should be located at a 45° angle to the cell faces and its hot end should terminate at one of the front corners of the interior of the cell. This type of periscope should be provided with a remotely adjustable mirror for scanning the interior of the cell.

DETERMINING THE SIZE OF A HOT CELL

Determining the size of a hot cell is an important factor of hot laboratory design. It is based on three important considerations. The nature of the function, size of the work and equipment, and the process to be performed within the cell is the most important. The other two considerations, namely, suitable viewing and remote manipulation of inner-cell equipment and material are also important. The cell should not be so wide that it cannot be viewed easily and without distortion, or so large that objects can roll out of reach of the available manipulation. It is a generally accepted practice to limit cell area to about 6 ft wide by 8 ft deep for one viewing window and one pair of mechanical master slave manipulators. When width and depth dimensions are greatly in excess of 6 x 8 ft. more viewing windows and additional or different types of manipulators should be considered. Here again the construction of a plywood mockup will greatly assist in selection and placement of such equipment.

When neither viewing nor remote manipulation is critical (or in some cases necessary, as in some radiochemical process installations) normal concrete walls are the most economical. General viewing through lower-cost, larger-size zinc bromide windows is satisfactory for walls up to 5 ft thick. General-purpose remote manipulation may be substituted by specific remote controls in most cases for repetitive operations. However, with normal concrete, the structure housing the hot cell and its operating and charging areas, must be proportionally larger and more costly.

In general, thicker walls aggravate viewing and manipulation problems.

Both the liquid filled and solid windows have in common the property of "round-the-corner" viewing. The index of refraction for zinc bromide is 1.51 and for 3.3 density lead glass it is 1.59. Experience indicates that where the angle of refraction on the hot side of the viewing facility is less than 50°, the distortion may be disregarded as far as direct viewing is concerned; but when the angle of refraction is in excess of 50°, distortion becomes excessive. However, when a photographic record of the function performed within the cell is required, the camera must be positioned so that the photographs are taken straight through the viewing window, with absolute minimum of deviation from the horizontal plane or from a path perpendicular to the cold side of the viewing facility. Hence, rectangular viewing windows provide a greater area for photographic work.

ACCESS DOORS AND PORTS IN HOT CELLS

Access doors and ports are roughly divided into two categories: the personnel-material and the material-equipment types. The former are usually heavy doors of a size that permit relatively easy entry by an operator. The material-equipment types may vary in size from a small shielded transfer drawer, pipe sleeves normally kept plugged, and small openings through the shielding walls equipped with hinged or sliding doors of materials of very high density (such as lead or steel), to movable roof slabs that leave the entire cell open when removed. The latter arrangement is provided so that the equipment within the cell may be handled by a bridge type building crane.

Personnel—Material Access Doors

These may be as follows: (1) hinged, sliding, lift and drop doors of lead or steel; (2) hinged and roll-out doors of the same material as the wall itself; and (3) a lift type composed of a lower portion of laminated steel plates and an upper portion so fashioned of steel plate encased concrete that it will provide adequate shielding in the vertical lift cavity while the steel door is in its normal closed position. This type, preferred by the author, is used for beta and gamma cells.

Hinged Doors of Lead or Steel. This type is normally located on the charging area side of the hot cell and mounted flush with the cold side of this wall. Being flush-mounted, these doors are used in conjunction with an extensive stepped frame of the same material at the top and sides of the door opening provided through the shielding wall. This costly door frame is used to prevent radiation from beaming through the weak shielding around the perimeter of the door opening. Hinged doors are usually constructed of poured lead. The hot side stainless steel plate and the mild steel structural shapes that are utilized in fashioning the stepped edges of the door are used as the mold for the lead core. Doors of this kind are either single or bi-parting, and, for ease of opening are provided with a "Butcher Boy"

type of door starter. Hinges are a problem and may vary from those available commercially, such as Stanley Co. No. BB-852½, to the specially designed pin-thrust bearing types. The hinge leaves are shop-welded to the door and field-welded to the door frame. The contact edges of the bi-parting doors are stepped or curved to prevent radiation beaming through the crack. Care should be taken always to mount hinged doors to their frames after the walls are poured. This makes it possible to shim the door correctly in position before the hinges are welded in place, thus preventing binding between the door and frame which can be a serious problem with such heavy doors. Hinged doors are apparently the easiest of all types to seal adequately with gaskets against the leakage of decontaminants. Steel-hinged doors are usually of laminated construction to provide the stepped edges without costly machining.

There are occasions when an inner or hot side gasketed door of stainless steel is provided to minimize splashes and seepage beneath and around the shield door when cell decontamination is performed.

Hinged Doors of Concrete. This type of door is fastened to the cell wall with pin-thrust bearing type hinges, but the weight of the door itself is supported, in large part, by wheels running on a circular track or plate. Like hinged doors of the denser materials, this type can be gasketed to prevent leakage of decontaminants. In addition, this type of door does not require chopping up the floor of the charging area to nearly as great an extent as do roll-out doors of the same material. (See roll-out type doors for the possible use of a carrier bracket on the hot side of this door.)

Horizontal Sliding Doors. Horizontal sliding doors are normally of steel, although they may be of steel-encased lead. This type of door may be either single-leaf or bi-parting, and may be manually or hydraulically operated. Surface-mounted on track and guides, they are normally designed somewhat oversize to prevent radiation from beaming through the weak shielding around the perimeter of the door opening. Horizontal sliding doors recessed back into the cell wall necessitate the addition of supplementary shielding of a greater density than that of the shielding wall to compensate for the loss of shielding material incidental to forming the recess. All sliding doors are extremely difficult to seal against the leakage of decontaminants.

Vertical Lift Doors. Vertical lift doors may be either surface-mounted, flush-mounted or located in a cavity formed within the shield wall itself. This type of door may be either hydraulically or manually operated or positioned by a building bridge crane, in which case the door is simply lifted and then held in an open position by a pin or pins, thus releasing the crane for other duties. As mentioned earlier, this writer thinks highly of a certain modification of vertical lift door. In this case the vertical formed cavity containing the door is located slightly on the hot side of the center line of the shielding wall so as to minimize the width of the door, in excess of the formed door opening through the wall that is required to prevent gamma radiation from beaming around its perimeter. This vertical formed opening in the shield wall necessarily extends all the way from the floor through the roof of the cell. However, to avoid adding a supplementary shield of denser and more costly material on the hot side of this vertical formed opening to compensate for the cavity, the door itself is constructed so that its height is roughly equivalent to that of the cell from floor to roof. However, only that portion of the door which is actually needed to shield the horizontal door opening through the wall at personnel level is of expensive steel or steel-encased lead. That part of the lift door which is above the horizontal door opening is composed of steel-encased concrete to match the shield wall. The relatively thin, mild-steel plates used to enclose this poured concrete are also used to tie the high-density lower portion and the concrete upper portion into a liftable unit. The steel plate that would normally cover the top edge of this lift door is omitted so that the upper portion may be filled with concrete. Lifting eyes are provided at the top for raising by the bridge crane and a pin slot or slots are used to hold the door in an open position. If due care is taken in forming the vertical slot and in fabricating the door, this type should prove both efficient and economical.

Vertical Drop Doors. Vertical drop doors that necessitate pockets in the floor seem to this writer to present contamination problems that are all too numerous even under ideal conditions. This type of door is normally hydraulically operated.

Roll-out Doors. This type is normally of the same material as the shield wall itself and is another solution to the personnel-material access problem. While economical, these access doors are bulky and, when open, occupy valuable space on the floor of the charging area. This door may either be of 3- or 4-point suspension; to be specific, it may have either two wheels (on the hot side of door) on two tracks with the front, or cold, edge of the door suspended by a monorail hoist, or four wheels on two tracks either electrically or manually operated. Roll-out doors of the latter type are extensively used at ORNL. Such doors may be sealed against perimeter leaks of liquid decontaminants. In normal usage 4 point suspension roll-out doors are provided with a removable, load-bearing bracket on their hot sides for the purpose of introducing and removing lead carriers containing source material into the cell. In practice the carrier is placed on the bracket by a monorail hoist, the door closed and the carrier opened and its contents removed by remote manipulation. This source material is then placed within an inner cell, shielded container while the door is opened and the carrier removed. Of course, the reverse operation may well be used to remove waste and/or end product material from the cell. NOTE: If the 3-point suspension type is used it will be impossible to utilize the monorail hoist method of placing the shielded carrier on to the door bracket.

Material and Equipment Access Ports

As stated above, these ports may vary in size from small transfer drawers, pipe sleeves normally kept plugged and small openings through the shielding walls that are equipped with hinged lead or steel doors, to large movable cell roof slabs. The small material-equipment access ports are provided through the cell shielding wall for the primary purpose of introducing or withdrawing cold (non-radioactive) materials into the cell.

Transfer Drawer. A transfer drawer is simply a rectangular shielding plug somewhat longer than the thickness of the shield wall. It is usually mounted on slides or rollers so that it may be easily pushed partially into the cell or pulled partially out into the charging area. Located at the center of this plug is a cavity to hold the small piece of material or apparatus to be transferred. On both the cell and the operating side of this drawer is concentrated enough lead or steel to provide adequate shielding for the operator whether its cavity be exposed within or without the cell. Supplementary high-density shielding is necessary around the cold side perimeter of the framed, through-the-wall opening to prevent radiation beaming while the transfer drawer is extended into the operating area. With this type of access port it is possible to safely transfer relatively small pieces of material or equipment into and from even high radiation level cells, the procedure being simply to pull out the transfer drawer as far as possible, place the object within the cavity, and push the drawer forward as far as possible, so that the operator of the manipulator may remotely remove the object from the drawer within the cell.

Double-door Material and Equipment Access Ports. For larger pieces of equipment or material than can be handled by transfer drawers, a double-door access port has been developed for high-level hot cells. This type of port is very flexible and can be utilized both as an inner-cell or inter-cell facility. Each of the pair of doors is bi-parting vertically and of a high-density material. The two halves of this door are linked together so that the lower portion acts as a counterweight in lifting the upper half. A rod mounted on bearings activates each door manually from outside of the cell, thus leaving the slave end of the manipulator free to introduce the object into or remove it from the cavity. These two bi-parting doors are flush-mounted on both hot and cold sides of the shielding wall. Supplementary shielding is necessary around the cold side perimeter of the framed opening to prevent gamma radiation beaming around the bi-parting door.

Pipe Sleeves. In low radiation level cells, pipe sleeves are sometimes used to perform the same function as the transfer drawer. In this case the shielding plug is removed from the pipe sleeve and an operator either introduces apparatus or material into the cell using a pair of long tongs or removes the object from the slave end of a manipulator. Great care must be exercised by the operator to prevent exposure of his person to direct gamma radiation during this operation.

Access Ports. For larger pieces of equipment or material, access ports of greater size (2 x 2 ft) with hinged doors of lead or steel on the cold side of the cell wall are used to perform the same function as the pipe sleeves above. In this kind of access port a lead or steel frame must be provided around the perimeter of the formed opening to prevent gamma radiation from beaming around its edges. Here also the operator must exercise extreme care during the actual transfer operation while the door is open. Both pipe sleeves and the larger access ports with single hinged lead doors should be avoided in high radiation level cells. If necessary special carriers or coffins should be used to provide supplementary personnel shielding while material or equipment is put into or removed from the cell.

Removable Roof Slabs. Removable roof slabs are normally stepped around their perimeters as well as at the joints between slabs to prevent direct gamma radiation from beaming through to operating personnel who might be on the cell roof. These slabs are primarily for use in setting up the initial installation of equipment within the cell before it has become activated. These slabs are seldom removed while the source material is un-shielded within the cell or until the cell walls and floor have been checked and decontaminated. Of course, when a series of experiments have been completed, or should the usage of the cell be changed, these removable roof plugs would be used for removing the old equipment and for installing the new. These roof slabs are normally somewhat thinner than the shielding walls on the assumption that no operator will be on continuous duty above the cell. Lifting eyes, either fixed or removable, are provided for lifting these roof slabs by the building or mobile crane.

SPECIAL STRUCTURAL FEATURES IN HOT CELLS

These include an inner-cell raised working level, shielding plugs containing either building service piping, electrical conduit or instrumentation lines, sleeves containing periscopes or manipulators, overhead tracks for an electric rectolinear manipulator or bridge crane, and storage wells. NOTE: The side walls of all through-the-wall stainless steel pipe sleeves should be of sufficient thickness to resist bending or deformation during the pouring of high density concrete, as well as to permit boring to the required roundness and trueness necessary for the insertion of the shielded plugs.

Raised Working Level Within Cell

Since personnel operating the manipulators and other inner-cell equipment usually do so in a standing position, a raised platform or working level should be provided within the cell for effective viewing and normal handling of its contents. And since most cells have their coved floor liner at the same elevation as the operating and charging areas, a secondary floor pan must be provided about 38 inches above this elevation and approximately 24 inches below the center line of the cold side pane of the shielding facility. This working level is usually provided by fabricating a suitable stainless steel angle framing to support a heavy stainless grating. To this frame is fastened a secondary stainless steel floor pan with coved edges which is seam-welded to the stainless steel cell liners on both sides as well as the operating wall. This leaves the personnel-material door on the charging side free to open. An operator standing in this doorway would be confronted by a waist high working level below which is a cavity that is normally used for the hot and semi-hot drain lines for the working level. Having this cavity available makes the cell quite flexible as to usage for it can easily be modified into a full-height process cell. Usually the inner or stainless steel side of the personnel-material access door is provided with a drip strip so located that any liquid used to decontaminate the cell will be contained within the coved edges of the raised work level.

Shielding Plugs Containing Service Piping, etc.

Shielding plugs containing service piping, etc., that are located less than 8 ft. above the operating floor shall have a shielding value equivalent to that of the shielding wall. This is accomplished by using in these plugs a shielding material of greater density than that of the shield wall. Those service plugs to be used in pipe sleeves located 8 ft. or more above the floor may simply be filled with the same material as the shield walls.

Sleeves Containing Periscopes and Manipulators

Since the amount of shielding material possible to be provided within pipe sleeves containing periscopes or manipulators is all but negligible, it behooves the designer to keep both types high enough in the cell wall to eliminate as far as possible any direct gamma radiation beaming upon an operator.

Tracks for Heavy Duty Manipulators or Bridge Crane

Since inner-cell components are frequently of stainless steel, tracks for any supplementary manipulation, such as a G. M. Electric Arm and/or air or electrically operated bridge crane, are no exception. The tracks are either supported on shelves provided for them in each side wall or bracketed to the face of the cell liners with seam welds. Often both types of supplementary manipulation utilize the same track system, which is located above the through-the-wall manipulator sleeves.

Storage Wells

Storage wells of stainless covered lead are often provided within cells for the dual purpose of storing hot waste and temporarily shielding source material while operating personnel enter the cell, or material and equipment are introduced or removed from the cell.

CHARGING AREAS FOR HOT LABORATORIES HANDLING BETA AND GAMMA RADIATIONS

Since the charging area wall of the cell bank contains the personnel-material access doors as well as the material-equipment access ports, the possibility of the charging area becoming contaminated is greater than that of the operating area. This is the reason for its designation as a semi-hot area where protective clothing is required. Usually this area is isolated from the cold operating area by both the cell bank itself and a concrete block partition wall. It is good practice to limit the access between these two areas to personnel doors located on the operating and charging area sides of the change-locker room. In this charging area are located the decontamination facility, the locker, change area, and the terminus for whatever method devised for introducing and removing both cold and radioactive material into and from the cell bank.

The critical feature of any semi-hot area is its floors. This is because of the continuing necessity of clean up spills and the contamination spread by the shoes of those who enter the cells, so as to maintain as low an overall background radiation level as possible. In Figure 10.24 we note that this floor is cut up with the three pairs of tracks for the roll-out doors. And, although these tracks are recessed into the floor slab so that the top of rail is flush with the finished floor, they pose a four-way problem. The first is the amount of otherwise valuable space they reserve for the use of the roll-out doors in open position, the second is in forcing the elimination of the normal slope provided for drainage of the floor, thirdly, the groove in the floor along the tracks for the wheel flanges somewhat impedes the free rolling of heavy dollys across this area and finally, it has its decontamination problems. However, these disadvantages are more than offset by the great advantage possessed by doors of this type in being able to simply introduce and remove shielded carriers into these cells. This advantage is only fully appreciated when one considers that about the only alternate methods of introducing radioactive material into a cell bank and of removing the radioactive waste and/or end product from it, are by an elaborate tunnel system containing a transfer device, or by the time-consuming roof plug method.

A transfer tunnel would be designed as an in-line facility with the outer-cell, charging-unloading station so located as to necessitate a single run of straight tunnel from it to the stations within the cells.

The Decontamination Facility

Decontamination may be defined as the removal of radioactive by-products of nuclear fission from the parent substance. This definition should be enlarged to include the removal of radioactive by-products of nuclear fission from any surface where they might have been introduced by a chemical spill, by dust, by gas or by the spreading of contamination by tracking or localized explosion. All walls and floors subject to contamination should be finished in an acid proof (nitric), impervious material to permit the decontamination of these surfaces. In addition to nitric acid, which is the strongest decontaminant used short of sand blasting or grinding, many liquids, starting with warm water with detergent and continuing through acids and caustics of increasing strength to nitric acid are utilized, depending on the type and scope of the surface contamination.

The decontamination area is a necessary adjunct to a hot laboratory set up. This facility is usually a three walled room that is serviced by a monorail hoist. This facility is utilized to decontaminate any hot objects that leave the cell bank, be it a shielded carrier containing hot waste or radioactive end product, or a piece of contaminated equipment or perhaps a contaminated lead brick from the localized shielding in one of the hoods or work benches in the operating area. The ⅜" thick, Type 347 stainless steel floor pan slopes from its coved edges to the semi-hot drain located at the center of this facility. The walls of this decontamination area are of concrete block. The interior surfaces of these walls are water proofed by sacking with thin grout, rubbed to a smooth finish with a carborundum stone, then, with the ceiling, given an impervious, nitric acid proof, coating composed of two coats of "Amercoat" 86 primer, one coat of light gray "Amercoat" 33 HB and one finish coat of white "Amercoat" 33 HB in accordance with manufacturer's recommendations. Around the entire perimeter of the three walls of this facility, and 8" off of the floor one leg of a 1½ x 1½ x 3⁄16" stainless steel angle is embedded in the mortar joint of the concrete blocks. To this angle is seam-welded the coved edge of the ⅜" thick, stainless steel, floor pan.

Formerly, decontamination areas were constructed of acid proof brick, both floors and walls, but in this writer's opinion, after seeing several that have been in usage for years, one cannot beat stainless steel for this purpose both in initial cost and in economy of maintenance. And if there is enough money available the walls of a decontamination facility should be lined with stainless also.

The Track-Charging Area

Upon the usage of the particular cell bank depends in large part how the floor slab containing the track system should be treated. It could be that the possibility of contamination is so remote as to justify leaving the concrete slab exposed in the track area. But one must remember that the counter-sunk track system with its flange groove along the tracks is another case of begging for trouble in the event of possible contamination. However, in this particular facility the track area is given the following treatment. The flange grooves along the tracks slope from a high point at their far end to a grating covered trench located at the face of the cell bank (see Figure 10.24). These grooves are given a plastic coating consisting of one coat of "Amercoat" 86 primer and two coats of "Amercoat" 33 HB. The floor slab, between and around these tracks, is covered with vinyl plastic floor tile laid in large sheets or rolls, to minimize cracks; and in conjunction with a coved base around the exterior walls and cells (omit at area serviced by drain trench). The interior of all wall surfaces in this area shall be given the normal interior building treatment.

The Change-Locker-Toilet Room Facility

The floor covering within the change-locker room should be vinyl plastic floor tile in large sheets or rolls used in conjunction with a coved base around the perimeter walls. This facility contains not only the toilet facilities and individual lockers for the operating personnel but fresh supplies of protective clothing and foot covers, a hand and foot counter, soiled clothing hamper, showers, gang-type hand washing facilities, etc. The walls in this change locker area should be waterproofed then covered with any good washable paint, except the shower stalls and walls behind the lavatories, etc., which should be covered with wall tile or some comparatively impervious material.

OPERATING AREAS FOR HOT LABORATORIES HANDLING BETA-GAMMA RADIATION

This area contains the viewing and manipulating facilities for the cells as well as hood and laboratory bench space for on the spot analysis of specimens removed from the hot cell. Another possible cause of contamination in the operating area is during the removal of through-the-wall manipulators from their sleeve. As mentioned earlier, under material equipment access ports, great care must be taken to prevent the spread of contamination at this time.

The floor covering within this operating area should be vinyl plastic floor tile in large sheets or rolls used in conjunction with a coved base of the same material around the perimeter walls and cell block. The interior surface of all walls in this area should be waterproofed, and the ceiling painted.

c. MECHANICAL ASPECTS OF HOT LABORATORIES

A. B. FULLER,
Oak Ridge National Laboratory
Oak Ridge, Tennessee

It is the purpose of this section to describe the mechanical aspects of the design of high level radiation hot laboratories. The design features of piped services, heating, ventilating, air-conditioning, air handling and cleaning, and fire protection for the three classes of hot laboratory areas (the laboratory or operating area, the hot cell area and the service areas) are discussed. The description and discussions are best suited to gamma and alpha-gamma type hot laboratories of high levels of radioactivity which in general require relatively massive cell structures for confinement of radiation and associated toxic air-borne radioactive particles.

The design of mechanical aspects must assist

in achieving the required safety of operations. It is essential the designer commands a full and clear understanding of the hazards associated with radioactive work. A basic purpose underlying any design is in providing needed facilities to do certain prescribed work in the safest and most reasonable manner. All operations must be achieved without over-exposure of radiation of personnel involved. No compromise can be made in this respect. The recommendations of the "National Committee on Radiation Protection" establish current permissible limits of exposure to radiation. The designer must respect the safety of others in the locale through proper handling of radioactive wastes, radiation fields, etc. The remarks following in this chapter do not cover the scope of all hot laboratory designs. As new needs arise and potential hazards increase, the designer is compelled to pioneer new approaches which can best suit his particular requirements. Problems associated with confinement and containment can only be fully evaulated on an individual basis.

PIPED SERVICES

The requirements of piped services for the laboratory and service areas reflect closely the needs of an up-to-date chemical laboratory. However, some further considerations are required when provisions are being made to handle radioactive or contaminated material within these areas.

The Laboratory Area

The laboratory areas would normally be expected to be provided with adequate bench space, fume hoods and tables, all of which may be equipped with supply services of the following types:

Hot and cold potable water
Cold filtered water (cooling and process uses only)
Low pressure steam (5 psig)
High pressure steam (125 psig)—limited uses
Natural gas, or bottled gas (used as fuel)
Vacuum
Instrument air (15 to 60 psig)—dried and filtered
Low-pressure air (5 to 15 psig)

High-pressure air (80 to 125 psig)
Demineralized water (or distilled)
Off gas (radioactive waste gases)
Bottled gases, flammable (hydrogen, oxygen, acetylene, etc.)
Bottled gases, non-flammable (nitrogen, argon)
Electrical services (see other portions of this chapter)

Not all the above services would be provided in each case; only those for which there is a known or probable need should be considered. Virtually all laboratories require the basic piped services of hot and cold water, steam, air and gas.

Drains of a special type are normally provided where wastes are or could become contaminated by radioactive material. Wastes that are highly radioactive are best confined in the most concentrated form for the most convenient and economical handling. As in any chemical laboratory, a hot laboratory must accommodate corrosive wastes. Stainless steel lines are common for the most severe corrosive conditions and high silicon iron for moderately corrosive conditions. Hot drain lines are seldom trapped because of the tendency of highly radioactive material to be retained, and of the corrosive attack in the trapped area of the drain line. Plastic piping would be suitable for most exposed waste lines for slightly corrosive and/or radioactive wastes at room temperatures. Other materials, such as lead, glass and plastic-coated materials, can be utilized to advantage under specific circumstances. The decision is usually based on a compromise between length of service, what material best serves the expected life, and lowest initial cost for a given installation.

Table 10.2 is a rough guide that may be used to form a decision on material choices for hot laboratory drains inside buildings.

Stainless steel pipe has been preferred for most radioactive drain lines during recent years. Such lines are relatively expensive to install. Under the more severe conditions of service it usually is found that an expensive stainless steel line is no better than the poorest weld that exists in it. Therefore, it is good practice to employ the best welding techniques where severe conditions will be met and as few welds as possible for installation. When embedding pipe in concrete or installing in an inaccessible location it is best to use one continuous length of seamless pipe, free of all welds and joints, wherever this is at all possible.

It should be clearly understood that stainless steel does not satisfactorily meet the requirements of all corrosive conditions. A careful study should be made to best determine the material needs for each situation.

When stainless steel is chosen for drain and waste transfer lines, welding is the most widely used means of connection and jointing. Seamless pipe of Type 347 stainless steel (ASTM A312-56T) is the first choice, using the inert-gas shielded-arc method of welding. Only experienced welders can produce the quality of weld required. Whenever possible, radiographic inspection should be practiced with this class of work, both for the welding and the pipe material itself. Welding of this type is expensive and time-consuming. Results can be profitable only if the quality of workmanship and material standards are maintained at the highest level.

Radioactive lines are best embedded in concrete, in earth or in other massive material from the standpoint of minimizing their radiation

hazard. Therefore, such lines must be carefully planned and arranged to serve the need for waste handling by being (1) adequately sloped and sized for proper drainage, (2) sufficiently shielded, and (3) simply arranged to give the most direct path to the waste collection point to minimize possible hold-up volumes.

Cell Area

Cell areas must be provided with necessary piping services that are suitable for uses inside the cell. This involves the problems of inside handling by remote manipulation. Simple means of connection and disconnection are essential features for inside cell services. Couplers having simple release and engaging mechanisms fulfill this need in small sizes (up to ½-in. IPS). Above this size the required work will overtax hand-powered manipulators, rendering them nearly useless. Valved couplers in sizes above ⅜-in. IPS also require an excessive amount of work. The location of outlets in the cell must be arranged for easy reach with the manipulators, with ample space for tubing and hoses.

Control valves for inside services should be

TABLE 10.2

TYPE OF INSTALLATION	LIGHTLY CORROSIVE AND/OR RADIOACTIVE WASTES		HIGH CORROSIVE AND/OR RADIOACTIVE WASTES	
	Accessible	*Inaccessible**	*Accessible*	*Inaccessible**
1. Temporary laboratory	*a.* Extra heavy CI (B&S) *b.* PVC (welded)	*a.* Extra heavy CI pipe (B&S) *b.* High silicon iron (B&S) pipe or VC pipe (B&S)	*a.* High silicon iron (B&S) *b.* PVC (welded) or lead pipe	*a.* Welded stainless steel pipe *b.* High silicon iron (B&S) pipe
2. Semi-permanent laboratory facility or service areas. (2 to 8 years use)	*a.* PVC (welded) *b.* High silicon iron (B&S) pipe	*a.* High silicon iron (B&S) pipe *b.* VC pipe B&S *c.* Welded stainless steel	*a.* High silicon iron (B&S) pipe *b.* Welded stainless steel pipe	*a.* Welded stainless steel pipe
3. Permanent laboratory facilities and cell areas† (life expectancy over 8 yrs)	*a.* High silicon iron (B&S) *b.* Light wall stainless steel pipe	*a.* High silicon iron pipe‡ *b.* Welded stainless steel pipe‡	*a.* Welded stainless steel pipe‡	*a.* Welded stainless steel pipe‡

* Not readily replaceable such as being in wall chases, but not embedded in concrete or other permanent encasement.

† Under continuous use any facility may require major replacement of some drain piping. Therefore the word permanent is used to imply a facility in an overall permanent type building. This means allowances must be planned and provided for the replacement of deteriorated piping.

‡ When lines are embedded in concrete, or encased where it is permanently inaccessible, heavy wall seamless stainless steel pipe is used having the least number of welds as required to install.

located on the front operating face of the cell within convenient reach of the operator, preferably in such a way that he may see through the cell window while adjusting the manual valve. Service valves inside the cell with remote operators or extension stems to the outside are generally not very practical, since repair, replacement or adjustment can cause serious delays and troubles for which there is no easy, inexpensive solution. Service lines into cells must be kept simple to be effective. Those entering the cell from outside control valves are embedded in the shielding wall, usually having offsets to minimize streaming of radiation through the shield. Lines should slope into the cells, if possible, to prevent backup in a disconnected line. If the cell is being lined, as is advisable for most gamma and alpha-gamma handling, service lines should be thoroughly sealed at the liner. For metal liners this may be done by careful welding or by the use of bulkhead fittings.

Drains leaving a cell generally are classed as radioactive hot drains if the wastes entering the drain are exposed to the atmosphere of the cell interior or to any radioactive matter. Completely closed systems of cooling water, steam condensate, etc. may be classed as process wastes if kept isolated from contaminated matter. Hot drains are arranged for gravity flow, without traps. This reduces the retention of radioactive and corrosive wastes. These drains without traps must be supplied with a closing device, such as a sealing plug, that can be remotely handled to seal the passage of air inleakage. Drain lines inside cell walls and floors become completely inaccessible and therefore necessarily require the design features mentioned above.

A waste system providing for radioactive and/or chemical wastes must have a point of collection that is separate from other waste systems. If there is the slightest chance of radioactive contamination the system should be provided with adequate monitoring devices and means of control when wastes exceed the allowed tolerances of radioactivity. These can be obtained from the Atomic Energy Commission or the state or local laws having jurisdiction. Depending on the quantity and characteristics of the contaminants involved, various needs for detention, processing

and confining may be required. Such facilities can be very involved and expensive; investigation of all wastes (regardless of quantity) and their ultimate disposal must be carefully considered in the primary stages of planning and design of hot laboratories, service areas and cells. The locality has a major bearing on type of disposal systems that may be employed.

Service Area

Those areas adjacent to cells where equipment may be handled, especially areas to the rear of cells, must be provided with a system of floor drains capable of handling effluent from the entire floor area when it is washed down. Normally these drains are classed as process wastes and as such are provided with trapped inlets. A means of manually diverting this process waste to the radioactive hot drain can be used to hold up any known radioactive wastes without continual collection of large volumes into the hot waste system.

Miscellaneous Piped Services

Change rooms require piped services involving hot and cold potable water, process and sanitary drains. A conventional arrangement for a change room would mean a radioactively clean side and a potentially radioactively dirty side. All floor drains and hot side lavatories, sinks and showers would be piped as chemical waste subject to light contamination. Sanitary fixtures, water closets and urinals should be routed to a sanitary sewer.

Safety showers are required throughout the laboratory and service areas. These should be carefully located to best serve an emergency where chemicals are used, handled or stored. Various styles are common for indoor uses—pullchain, lever or platform-actuated. A preference should be given to the style, if any, that may be in popular use in the locality. The safety shower location should be well marked and provided with a green flashing light.

Fire protection piping is frequently required in hot laboratory spaces just as in conventional construction. The method and material employed must be suited to each particular case and hazard involved to meet the necessary codes and conditions of building construction.

HEATING, VENTILATION AND AIR CONDITIONING

An up-to-date and complete hot laboratory must be provided with air-conditioned spaces. In service spaces this is not mandatory, but it is advantageous. Because of high rates of ventilation and high-peaked internal gains, heating, ventilation, and air-conditioning facilities will represent a considerably greater part of design and construction costs than in conventional commercial establishments. Where problems of radioactive contamination and radiation exist, unique relationships and somewhat different philosophies are required. Many of these features are critical in respect to the design and arrangement of other portions of the over-all laboratory and hence they will require decision in the early stages of planning.

Hot-laboratory work usually entails the extensive use of precision equipment, i.e., electronic, optical, etc. These instruments are adversely affected by changes in temperature and humidity. Experimentation over long periods of time (months and even years) requires equipment accuracy and calibration to remain virtually constant. By control of temperature and humidity to reasonable limits two of the principal variables are minimized. Much of the maintenance and "down time" on vital equipment is removed. If the humidity level is maintained sufficiently low, deterioration through surface corrosion is more easily controlled. These are some of the reasons a modern hot laboratory needs good control of temperature and humidity.

The exact level of temperature is not vital to the equipment (if held constant) inasmuch as it can be calibrated at any reasonable point; therefore, the level is normally taken as that which offers a comfortable year-round temperature range for the persons occupying the space. A range of 72–75°F and a wet-bulb temperature of approximately 60°F (effective temperature of approximately 68°F) would be near average for a laboratory having moderate activity. Such temperatures will not meet the approval of all individuals and may be varied to suit a particular locality or group. Spaces having persons at rest will require a high effective temperature, though the dew point should be limited to approximately 52°F maximum.

In hot laboratories handling appreciable quantities of radioactive materials, greater than normal safety measures should be included to insure the safety of the surrounding areas. Normal measures should provide for items such as: zoning to control personnel activity, precise operating and maintenance procedures, protection from fires and explosion, emergency power sources and stand-by equipment, training personnel, etc. Greater than normal safety measures include such features as: insured confinement by multiple containers, more complete radiation detection, better filtration or retention of waste streams, control of airborne matter by means of sufficient negative pressures to retain or route undesirable effluent, and criticality controls. The thorough training of technique and procedure for those who operate and maintain the facility are essential preparatory steps for safe operation. The designer must bear these needs in mind in all phases of design effort.

Initial planning must establish the design criteria and the requirements for both temperature and humidity. If only conventional heating and ventilation are deemed necessary, this feature should be decided at the outset. A later change in criteria or design will mean additional space requirements and a re-evaluation of furnishings and experimental equipment.

Where standard test conditions must be supplied in a laboratory space for test purposes, definite design requirements are thereby established. Constant conditions can most easily and often more economically be achieved with specially prepared cubicles. These can be temporary or permanent structures, from a few cubic feet to full room sizes.

By definition, air-conditioning, without further qualification, includes both temperature and humidity control. The final results to be achieved will dictate the refinement of controls and type of equipment required to do the job properly. It is this feature of "how accurate the results are expected to be" that reflects the complexity of the system. This requirement is not limited to the controls alone but the items of equipment as well. The equipment must be able to respond to the demands of the controls throughout the full design range. Too many systems are based upon full load conditions alone, without sufficient regard for partial load demands, which are by far the most common. The greatest variations occur when loads are not a maximum; the percentage of change is greater at partial conditions.

To be serviceable every space must be at least heated and ventilated. Though year-round air-conditioning is much preferred for a fully complete laboratory, there are occasions when mechanical means of cooling cannot be justified because of its cost. Temporary installations may fall in this category, as well as laboratories located in northerly climates, where summers are mild and short.

Service areas are seldom provided with more than a complete heating and ventilation system, regardless of locale. This means that adjacent areas must be separated from service areas by well fitting doors to protect air-conditioned spaces and the control of air movement. For areas that are subject to air-borne radioactive contamination a positive means of air control should be provided. Equipment selection must be made carefully to fit all uses of the space even under contaminated conditions. Areas directly serving cells, for example, must be provided with suitable filters and controls to cope with the many conditions of the cells, open or closed. The movement of air must always be into the cell openings, never outward to adjoining spaces.

Laboratory ventilation becomes of paramount importance when radioactive materials are involved. As an average rule the rates of fresh air ventilation are higher for hot laboratories. Any radioactive substance that can become air-borne by natural evaporation or evolution of dust and fumes, or that can be physically suspended in the air becomes a hazard that must be controlled and confined by the system of ventilation. The system must never further disperse the contaminants. The arrangement of laboratory equipment should always permit air to flow through the spaces from clean areas to areas more likely to become contaminated. This rule applies equally well to ventilation of the entire building. For example, air should move from office areas and corridors to laboratory areas, then to hot service areas and cells. Air from a "hotter" area should

never be reused in a "colder" area to help prevent air-borne cross-contamination. This philosophy results in the higher fresh air rates of ventilation as tabulated in the following paragraph.

Listed below are representative rates of ventilation for hot laboratories, service areas and cells, and conventional types of systems employed.

TABLE 10.2a

TYPE SPACE	TYPE SYSTEM	*Rate of Ventilation* AIR CHANGES	% FRESH AIR
Hot laboratory	Year round filtered ventilation with temperature and humidity control	8 to 15 chgs/hr	33 to 100%
Service area for labs	Year round filtered ventilation with temperature and humidity control	12 to 20 chgs/hr	33 to 100%
Cell area	Full time filtered ventilation with indirect temperature control	2 to 60 chgs/hr	—
Service areas for cells	Year round filtered winter temperature control	12 to 30 chgs/hr	50 to 100%

Spaces normally benefited from air-conditioning are those where precision instruments and personnel are employed. Though internal heat gains in modern laboratories fluctuate over a wider range than conventional commercial spaces, the principles involved are identical. Sensitive controls responsive to small variations are essential to achieve uniform conditions. This close control demands the use of quality equipment and a program of good maintenance. In a majority of equipment and control arrangements there is a cooling demand of considerable magnitude whenever the laboratory is in use.

Controls and equipment for laboratory spaces should be capable of maintaining a set temperature, within the range of design, with maximum variations not to exceed $\pm 1°F$ where the load on the space is above 70% of the design maximum. Variations should not exceed $\pm 2°F$ between 30 and 70% of design loads. Variations in relative humidity should not exceed 2% using conventional equipment. Where very exacting conditions are required, consideration should be given to isolated cubicles so that ordinary handicaps, such as personnel doors and solar load variations, do not influence the problem. Systems employing reheat are used to accomplish the above limits of control.

Cell Area Ventilation

To use a gamma cell facility as illustrated in Figure 10.26 as an example of how all types of areas are combined in a composite arrangement we have the following:

(*a*) Operating area: The area on the operating side of the cells may be equated to a laboratory space, an area of improbable but not impossible air-borne contamination. An operating area of this type should be air-conditioned for the benefit of the equipment as well as the personnel. This area is arranged to have a slightly higher relative air pressure than adjoining service areas, thus minimizing the possibility of cross contamination of air-borne material. This is done by using a higher rate of make-up air than the deliberately routed exhaust air.

(*b*) Service area: That space at the rear of the cells becomes an area of probable air-borne contamination. This probably would occur while equipment is being handled in and out of the cells, during filter changing, or in a major accident. Winter heating and humidification, along with year-round filtered ventilation of this area,

Figure 10.26   Pattern of normal air flow.

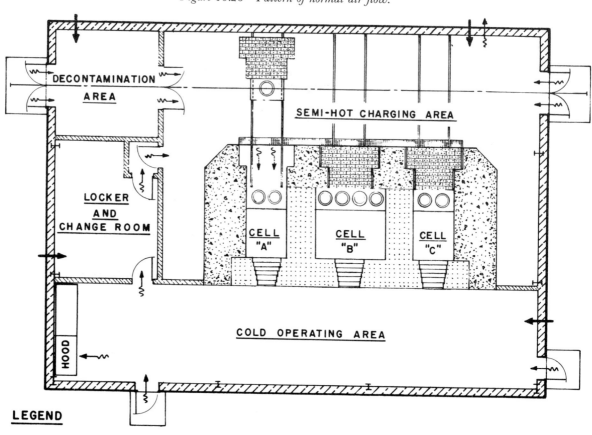

is essential. It should be understood that all the exhaust from this area, except that which may escape into the cells, must be adequately filtered before release to the atmosphere.

Service areas are kept at a relative pressure less than the operating area but greater than the cell spaces. Additionally, the service areas should be slightly negative to outside conditions. Any sizable opening to the outside must be provided with an air lock to preserve the air balance. Normally, all openings to other areas should be closed.

(c) Cell spaces: Under conditions of contamination by gamma radiation or by any air-borne particles, each cell should be so arranged and operated as to be independent of the adjoining cells. Intercell transfer systems make this a difficult objective to achieve. Cells should be constructed to have a very minimum of unrestricted openings. It is desirable to operate with relative negative pressures inside cells from -0.2 in. wg to -2.5 in. wg. Large quantites of inleakage into cells becomes impractical when openings are excessive, because all the air being exhausted from

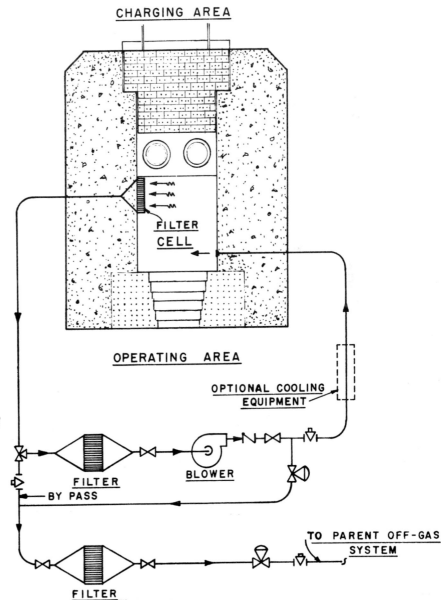

Figure 10.27 Schematic view of individual cell ventilation system.

the cells must be adequately filtered before release to the atmosphere. Refer to Figure 10.27 for one scheme of individual cell ventilation.

Since the inside spaces of cells definitely will become radioactively contaminated, proper facilities must be included to cope with the expected problem of confinement, collection and clean-up. Prefiltering the exhaust air while it is inside the cell is strongly recommended. This can greatly reduce the problem of high radiation background due to filters and ducts and reduce the frequency of filter changes outside the shielded cell. The inside "prefiltering" takes advantage of the existing shielding, confinement and remote-handling devices normally present and the inside clean-up facilities usually provided in cells.

AIR HANDLING AND CLEANING

In laboratory spaces air handling will in most instances become a part of the air-conditioning system and the means of exhaust. Air handling is specifically a term depicting the controlled movement of the air within a space. Cell and service areas require this "controlled movement" of air to even a greater degree of refinement and reliability. Air cleaning, too, follows these same tendencies, i.e. more refinement and reliability as the actual or probable level of air-borne activity increases.

Laboratory Areas

In planning the ventilation system for a hot laboratory area, the designer must consider the problem first as though it were a problem of air movement alone. The question should be asked concerning the layout of adjacent areas that interconnect with the space under consideration, "Which path will the air take under all conceivable uses of the space?" The answer to this question must always depend on the cardinal rule, "Air movement must be from clean areas to dirty areas, or from cold to hot in the sense of its probable air-borne activity."

When recirculation of air is a minor portion of the total air being handled, the chance of spreading air-borne contamination and fumes is least, but little recirculation represents high percentages of make-up air. In an arrangement of multiple laboratory rooms, or spaces, definite advantages are gained by having individual air-handling equipment for each space, without any return of air common to other spaces. Such an arrangement lends itself to individual room control as previously discussed. Figure 10.28 illustrates this arrangement. Recirculation will require adequate filtration of radioactive particulate.

In moderate climates the tendency in design is to eliminate recirculation and reduce the air handled to that quantity required for adequate ventilation, or necessary to meet the needs for air-conditioning, whichever is the limiting quantity.

Cell and Service Areas

As cell volume is relatively small compared to service areas and laboratories, ventilation is accomplished by smaller total quantities of air. However, when specific and controlled conditions of temperature and humidity must be considered in designing a system of cell air handling, the problem becomes complex. Due to the intense lighting normally encountered in cells there must be a system of mechanical cooling to maintain reasonable temperatures.

When standard conditions are required within cell spaces, further complications are encountered in controlling humidity and reliably maintaining internal negative pressure in cells. In utilizing air from the surrounding spaces to accomplish this need, the quantity increases flow to excessive amounts. It must be remembered that all the air introduced into the cell spaces must be controlled and cleaned. Recirculation of air is most feasible when the cell and the air-handling equipment are under a safe negative pressure. This permits having a cell space that is virtually free of inleakage and under an adequate negative pressure at all times. The latter will vary widely in different circumstances, but has a nominal range of -0.2 in. wg to -2.5 in. wg. There are many limitations in achieving an anticipated level, such as glove openings, manipulator openings, service plugs, untrapped hot drains and unsealed cracks. The strength of booting and sealing materials can impose a limit.

It becomes readily apparent that openings must be held to a minimum to keep inleakage within reason. When large charging doors or apertures in cells are open, a safe inward movement of air is not within reason when the system is designed to best suit closed conditions.

Distribution of movement is not uniform through a bare opening. The movement of materials and personnel through the opening flushes air from inside to outside. This cannot happen without the detrimental effects of spreading airborne contamination, as well as adherence of particles to footgear, clothing, tools, etc. One means of alleviating this is to provide an air barrier in the large opening to act as a restriction. An area that provides an air lock, and a means of primary decontamination, offers far more advantages than a single barrier. The problem of decontamination is paramount in any operation where personnel, materials and equipment are transferred from the contaminated cell spaces.

Washing down the closed cell eliminates most of the loose particulate before the cell is opened. This liquid waste is conveyed down the hot drain. In such an arrangement any internal filters must be protected from the moisture or be suited to such conditions. As a normal rule the filters are replaced remotely after an initial washdown and before a final washdown prior to opening the cell. This helps to minimize the amount of contamination within the cell that may become air-borne

and that will add to the background of radioactivity to which persons entering the cell might be exposed.

Classes of Air Cleaning

Laboratory Areas. The source of make-up air for all areas can be one central arrangement of equipment. Then each laboratory, or section of laboratory, should be supplied with a device for handling and cleaning any recirculated air that may be used within the area. Filters for this recirculated air are desirable to collect local dust and help improve the general quality of the air within the spaces.

These filters and the air-handling equipment may become contaminated on occasions of accidental releases of air-borne activity. Attention should be given to location of the equipment, ease of maintaining the filters and type of filter. In the majority of cases a disposable filter would best suit this application. The equipment should be located in a service space immediately adjoining the laboratory spaces.

Hoods and equipment exhausts are also involved in the problem of air cleaning in laboratories. Where radioactive materials and only mildly corrosive chemical fumes occur, hoods should be supplied with a suitable filter in the exhaust. After passing the proper filter, the ex-

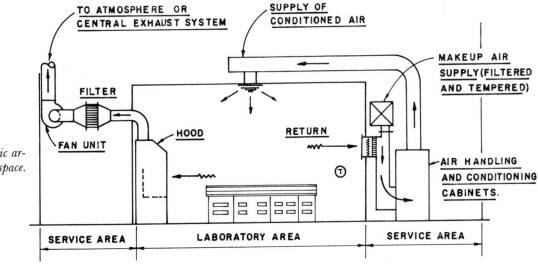

Figure 10.28 Schematic arrangement of laboratory space.

haust may be conveyed to the atmosphere. A system of monitoring may be required downstream from these filters as a safety device. In a large laboratory a common means of filtering and monitoring can be utilized; however, the local filter has definite advantages, such as providing a barrier from an adjoining hood which may be more or less contaminated, more localized confinement of contamination, and less shutdown time for maintenance reasons. To control the air movement better, the hood exhausts are used continuously.

Cell Areas. Like the laboratory, the cell area requires air cleaning, but in an even more exacting manner. All air entering the cell will eventually become the air to be exhausted and therefore must be properly cleaned. The atmosphere expected to be generated within the cell, including air-borne particles, determines how the exhaust must be treated. If it is non-corrosive, non-toxic and contains only contaminated particles, then mechanical filters may be employed to remove virtually all the particulate matter as large as 0.3 micron (also a large percentage down to 0.10 micron). However, if corrosive and radioactive gases are involved, the problem of cleaning is far more complex. The evolution of such gases should be confined as much as possible to allow more convenient handling. The smaller and hence more concentrated the volume of gases, the easier and more economical it is to clean them. This is a use of the service previously described as "off gas"; it affords safer confinement and removal. Radioactive gases must be cleaned by chemical means such as wet scrubbing (absorption).

Filtering Needs, Installation and Disposal

Filters play a principal part in any air-handling and cleaning system. Choosing the best-suited filtering arrangement is as basic and important as choosing the type of system of which it will be a part.

Filtering requirements for make-up air to the building spaces are conventional, as long as there is no reasonable chance of their becoming contaminated. Electrostatic precipitation may be employed to advantage on air entering the building.

An example of the handling of intake air (make-up), where a high degree of refinement is required, is as follows (in the direction of air flow):

(1) Fixed weather louver (admitting the outside air).

(2) Cleanable insect screen.

(3) One 2-in. throwaway glass fiber filter (or two 1-in.) or as an alternate a 2-in. cleanable filter.

(4) Electrostatic precipitators.

(5) Permanent filters with renewable glass fiber media. Units must be capable of withstanding high humidity due to washdown of precipitators.

For exhaust air where contamination is imminent, such as that leaving cell spaces, filtering needs must be established by a series of questions for which answers must be determined.

(1) What type (s) of contamination is to be encountered?

(2) What is the range of particle size that must be retained on the filters; by what efficiency?

(3) Are there any radioactive gases; if so, must they be collected?

(4) Is the atmosphere corrosive in nature; is it moist or dry?

(5) What shielding is required?

The quantity of air being considered has a bearing on how filtering is accomplished, but in principle the problem is the same, regardless of quantity. The presence of alpha contamination requires very close confinement and careful handling of filters and the interior surfaces of equipment. Little shielding is needed for alpha particles alone. On the other hand, when gamma or alpha-gamma radiation is encountered, containment and massive shielding are necessary. Filters and air-handling equipment act as traps for particulate matter. This is especially true for filters. Hence, the trapped radiation can become a serious problem if proper shielding is not provided. Primary filters inside the cell space, where shielding and remote-handling facilities are provided for other uses, offer good shielded confinement, ready maintenance with least hazard to personnel and usually minimum investment. As cell space is too limited to house all filtering equipment with control by remote manipulation, only the primary filters are placed inside, the remaining equipment being in less expensive surroundings.

FIRE PROTECTION AND SAFETY REQUIREMENTS

Specific fire protection requirements will vary for each installation depending upon the type of building, its location and its uses. However, there are a few requirements common to all hot laboratory facilities: (1) filters that are the most fire-resistant as well as of sufficient capacity, (2) first aid equipment for fire prevention, and (3) adequate systems of detection and alarms.

Filters become one of the most difficult fire hazards to overcome effectively. Careful planning is needed to combat possible filter fires and provide confinement of radioactive contamination as a result of a fire.

Safety requirements include convenient arrangement of equipment, safe handling methods and enforcement of good housekeeping rules. Safety showers, protective equipment and radiation monitors are other devices needed where chemicals and radioactive materials are handled and used. Hazardous areas, equipment and services should be clearly marked. Even water supplies that are not potable should be labeled "Not for Human Consumption."

SPECIAL EQUIPMENT

In hot-laboratory work one is always encountering new and specialized equipment and processes. It becomes the mechanical designer's problem to meet the needs for such equipment and processes and make the hot laboratory as effective as possible for those who use it. There is no substitute for simplicity in hot-laboratory facilities. Versatility is achieved by simple and convenient arrangement of equipment.

d. HOT CELL FIXTURES

FRANK RING, JR.
Oak Ridge National Laboratory
Oak Ridge, Tennessee

Since the hot cell is basically a shielded enclosure around the work to be performed, some form of remote operation is required to bridge the radiation barrier provided by the shielding walls and thus, extend human arm movements and forces from outside to inside the cell enclosure. Through-wall and intercell material handling devices are also required for handling of materials and equipment in and out of the cell enclosure. It is the purpose of this chapter to discuss hot cell fixtures in these categories. Various types of doors have been discussed in a previous section covering general cell design features.

MANIPULATORS

Several types of general-purpose manipulators to accomplish this extension of arm and hand movements have been developed and are in current use. These manipulators may be classed as electric and mechanical. The electric-operated types require only wire connections for transmission through the barrier walls. The mechanical types require either wall or ceiling penetrations. The size and optimum locations of these penetrations must be determined in advance and incorporated in the design of the cell structure. Present-day general-purpose manipulators are unfortunately limited to extending finger tong action only.

Wall Penetration Mechanical Manipulators

The mechanical type of manipulator described herein is essentially light-duty, that is, in the range of 3 to 10 lb rated lift capacity.

Ball Socket Manipulator. This is one of the simplest types of mechanical wall penetration manipulators. It is particularly adapted to shielding walls 3 to 6 in. thick and its scope of in-cell coverage is limited to a volumed space in the form of a cone. Figure 10.29 illustrates this form of manipulator. It consists of a set of tongs on one end of a 3 to 5 ft. long stainless steel tube. The clamping or tong action is controlled by a cable fastened to the squeeze handle and extending to the tong configuration. The tong tube extends through a ball-socket arrangement located in the shielding wall. The ball and socket are usually constructed of lead to provide effective heavy mass shielding at least equal to that of the shielding wall.

The socket housing should either be cast into the shielding wall or inserted into a preformed opening.

Motions along polar coordinates are obtained by swinging the tube handle in any direction and by sliding the tong tube in and out of the ball in the wall unit. Tong rotation can be obtained by twisting the master end of the long tube. The slave or "hot" end of this type of manipulator should be covered with a pleated boot to keep contamination from being drawn to the master side of the barrier wall when the tong is moved inward and outward or when the ball is rotated.

Cylinder Disc-Type Manipulator. The cylinder disc-type manipulator pictured in Figure 10.30 is somewhat similar to the ball-socket type described above in its motions, limitations and insertion. It has been used in shielding walls up to 12 in. thick. The cylinder-disc arrangement offers less resistance of movement, especially in the larger sizes, as both the cylinder and disc are mounted on antifriction bearings. The tong shown also features a wrist-swing motion to add to its versatility.

Model 8 ANL Master-Slave Manipulator. One of the most widely used and most versatile manipulators is the Model 8 ANL Master-Slave Manipulator shown in Figure 10.31. This manipulator with its seven degrees of freedom faithfully reproduces shoulder to finger tong movements. It also features "shoulder canting" to increase its range of operation. It has been used in cells having walls 2 to 5 ft. thick. This manipulator requires a 10-in. inside diameter tube cast in the front or operating wall when booting is used, or an 8-in. inside diameter tube when no booting

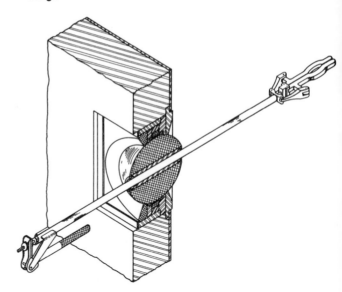

Figure 10.29   Section through shielding wall showing ball socket manipulator.

Figure 10.30   Cylinder disk type manipulator.

is used. These tubes are located at an elevation 10 ft. up from the operating floor level. The manipulator also requires a 24-in. vertical clearance above its horizontal centerline at the master end. It is usually used in pairs, the horizontal centerlines being 30 in. apart. A pair of manipulators is installed at the viewing window described in the section dealing with the structural aspects of hot laboratories. Sufficient space out from the operating cell wall must be provided in the hot laboratory building for removing and replacing these manipulators. This space is of the order

of 13 ft., depending on the length of the through-tube member.

Cell Roof Penetration Type

Figure 10.32 shows a line drawing of a Model 4 ANL Master-Slave Manipulator. It is essentially a large pantograph and its operating characteristics are similar to the Model 8 ANL Master-Slave Manipulator. It is also used in pairs and the manipulators are placed 24 in. apart. It requires a 66-in. mounting height above the work table surface in the cell, a penetration hole

Figure 10.31   Model 8 ANL master-slave manipulator.

in the cell roof for entry of the slave end into the cell, and a 51-in. vertical clearance above the centerline of the main horizontal member. When radiation beaming through the hole in the cell roof can be tolerated, this type is quite satisfactory.

Electric Rectilinear Types

The electric rectilinear types are similar to bridge cranes. Tracks are fastened to the front and rear walls or set on ledges on the front and rear walls to provide support for the movements of the bridge. The height of the rails depends on the construction of the particular manipulator; it is a compromise between under-rail clearance for the work to be done and stability of the vertical extended manipulator arm. This type of manipulator can be constructed and installed to have 100% coverage of the horizontal plane. Its capacity rating is somewhat higher, with considerable sacrifice in dexterity. Such manipulators with straight lifts in the range of 300 to 2000 lb are available. Two of these are shown in Figures 10.33 and 10.34.

Figure 10.33   Electric rectolinear type of manipulator.

Figure 10.32   Master-slave manipulator.

Figure 10.34   Electric rectolinear type of manipulator.

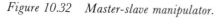

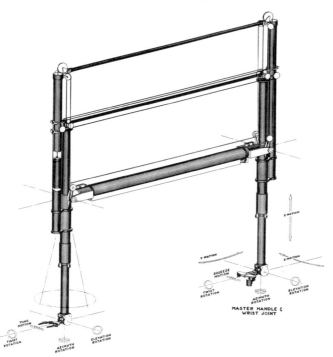

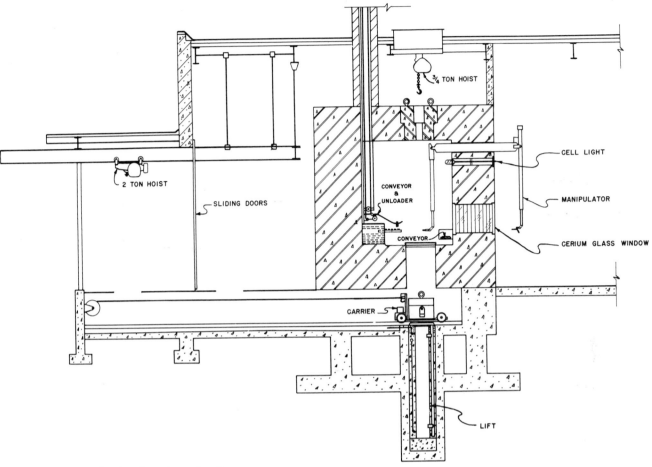

3/4 TON HOIST

2 TON HOIST

SLIDING DOORS

CONVEYOR & UNLOADER

CONVEYOR

CARRIER

CELL LIGHT

MANIPULATOR

CERIUM GLASS WINDOW

LIFT

Figure 10.35 Section through work cell.

INTERCELL TRANSFER DEVICES

When two or more cells are constructed in line, some means of transferring the radioactive materials from one cell to another should be provided. Belt or slat conveyors and drawers are used for this purpose.

Conveyors

Conveyors are employed when there are more than two cells in line. Sufficiently large openings must be designed in the walls between cells to accommodate the conveyor and the articles to be conveyed. The conveyor is usually placed so that it runs directly in front of the cell window and just below the lower edge, so that the conveyor structure does not interfere with vision through the window. It is well to arrange to have the drive of the conveyor outside of the cell wall, the final drive shaft extending through the wall. This is done to provide easy access to the conveyor drive for maintenance. Each cell window position should be provided with control buttons and indicating lights. The conveyor should be constructed of stainless steel throughout to prevent rusting and permit cleaning with acid solution. Figures 10.35 and 10.36 show a typical slat type intercell conveyor installation.

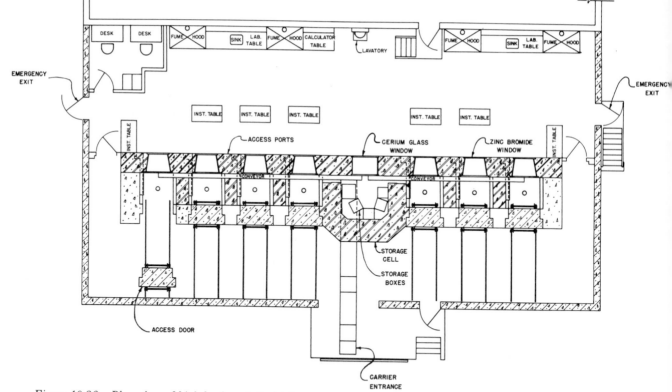

Figure 10.36   Plan view of high level analytical laboratory.

Figure 10.37   Equipment transfer drawer.

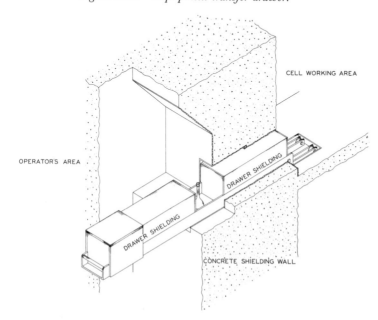

Drawers

Transfer drawers are used for both storing and transferring materials from cell to cell. These drawers are constructed with shielding at each end and a carrying compartment in the center. The drawer opening in the wall is usually constructed with a "blister" of lead around the drawer tunnel so that the material can be confined within effective shielding when the drawer is midway between cells. The drawer rides on rails and wheels similar to a supported filing cabinet drawer, and it is propelled by a hand wheel at the operating face of the cell bank. Less elaborate transfer drawers may be installed in the barrier walls between cells and propelled by pushing and pulling with the adjacent cell manipulator tongs. When the intercell barrier walls are quite thin, a system of double doors and shelf arrangement can be used and operated with manipulators.

It is advisable to construct these transfer devices of stainless steel and design them to provide flush surfaces when closed and a minimum of joint crevices where contamination might lodge. This is mandatory for all hot cell construction and the associated equipment items.

Wall Transfer Devices

Drawers are primarily used to transfer tools, small equipment and "cold" materials into the cell enclosure. One of the lowest-cost designs is a long drawer on rollers with concrete ends to provide shielding equal to that of the cell wall and a cavity to hold the article to be transferred. Figure 10.37 illustrates the basic construction. Drawers for 3 ft thick walls seem to be about the limit of practicability; beyond this the drawers become too massive, with the attendant difficulty in starting the rolling action due to inertia.

Wall transfer devices have also been developed for introducing radioactive materials from shielded carriers. With this type of transfer device the carrier is set on a shelf and its drawer is pushed from the carrier through a matching shielded wall hole arrangement into the cell.

Carriers are frequently opened and unloaded within the cell structure. The entry of the carrier into the cell is brought about by three methods: a rear access door may be used; the carrier may be lowered into the cell through a roof plug opening; or the carrier may be brought in by an underfloor tunnel. Figures 10.35 and 10.36 illustrate the layout of a tunnel and conveyor type entry.

e. ELECTRICAL ASPECTS OF HOT LABORATORIES

H. K. WALKER

Oak Ridge National Laboratory
Oak Ridge, Tennessee

High among important engineering considerations for the development of a practical, useful, and diversified single or multiple hot-cell installation is the design of the electric lighting and power distribution for the hot-cell interiors and for the operating and charging areas. When the hot cell contains unshielded radioactive materials, its interior is accessible to the operator only through the remotely operated equipment and the visual means placed at his disposal. The cell operations are carried on under conditions of extreme handicap in comparison to the operating conditions of the normal open laboratory. Under these unfavorable conditions, proper lighting and provisions for remotely controlled electric power become extremely important.

It is the intent of this section to bring to the attention of the prospective hot-cell designer those considerations of lighting and electrical design which are essential to hot-cell and hot-laboratory design.

LIGHTING WITHIN HOT CELLS

The lighting problems within hot cells are, as elsewhere, related to visual needs. Secondary considerations such as eye appeal and general appearance command little attention, since the high-intensity lamp is not within the line of sight of the operator.

The lighting fixture whose characteristics, lumen output, and resulting foot-candle illumination are necessary for optimum performance of hot-cell tasks should be selected after first determining both the nature of the work to be performed within the hot cell and the structural makeup and characteristics of the materials used in cell construction. Contrasts of lighting become less of a problem in the relative confinement of hot-cell interiors, since the extremely high illumination requirements will in most cases be highly effective within the entire cell area.

Before selection of the desired type of illumination a review of the various characteristics of available lamps most suited to the application is in order.

The Sodium Vapor Lamp

The sodium-vapor lamp produces an amber light that is rather easy on the eyes. The monochromatic nature of the light permits needle-sharp focus, free from the color fringes produced by illumination from a mixed spectrum. Its light is concentrated within a narrow wave band, and is close to the peak in eye sensitivity.

Its efficient conversion of energy to highly

visible light lowers operating costs. It is estimated that approximately 100 foot-candles of sodium vapor illumination give vision equal to 500 foot-candles of incandescent illumination. For a project which demands the ultimate in clarity and detail, this lamp is no doubt ideal.

The start-up time of a sodium-vapor lamp is approximately 12-15 minutes to full output; however, considerable illumination is produced within 8-10 minutes. The average restart time is approximately 10 minutes, after a cooling period of approximately 5 minutes. The rated life is 4000 hours on intermittent basis and 8000 hours on a continuous basis.

Since no known commercial sodium-lamp fixture has been specifically manufactured for a hot cell installation, the required parts must be purchased (socket, lamp, flasks, transformers, and certain other miscellaneous parts of a standard fixture designed for highway) and the fixture designed to satisfy the criteria of the cell, such as directions of mounting, space allocation, wet or dry locations, accessibility, etc. Design must be based on either a horizontal or a base-up position.

Standard parts which are basic to a design usually include the following:

Sodium Lamp, type NA-9, 10,000 initial lumens, 4 pin base Flask, #70G

Standard connecting cable with plug

Standard lamp and flask holder

Assembled standard panel with High PF transformer.

The transformer can be mounted at any distance from the lamp, provided the maximum drop in voltage between the transformer panel and lamp socket does not exceed 0.5 volt.

The over-all dimensions of the outer flask are 16 in. long and $4\frac{7}{16}$ in. wide. The space requirements of this type of lamp may present a serious problem within the confines of a small hot cell having manipulators and other operating mechanisms. The lamp and fixture may be partially recessed into the front interior wall to reduce its protrusion into the working area.

Mercury Fluorescent Lamp

Mercury fluorescent lamp installations within hot cells have had an increasing rate of acceptance in recent years. This lamp has reasonably long life and it is a relatively compact source of high-intensity illumination. The mercury fluorescent lamp produces a white light which is approximately of the same quality as that obtained with a mixture of equal wattages of mercury and incandescent lamps. This latter combination has long been desirable in much of industry, but it is high in cost as well as space-consuming when mounted in a cluster of separate mercury and incandescent lamps under one fixture canopy.

Because of the abnormally high initial lumen output (20,000), the mercury fluorescent lamp is particularly adaptable to use within cells which employ thick, high density radiation-shielding windows which have a relatively low efficiency of light transmission. During the first 100 hours of operation, the lamp lumen drop is 5 to 10 per cent. For the remaining life of the lamp (which would be 5900 hours for intermittent service), the lumen drop is rather gradual to a minimum of 12,000* lumens.

The mercury fluorescent lamp produces a line spectrum having strong lines in the ultraviolet and visable regions and some in the infrared. Much energy is produced in the four important lines and in their side bands within the visible spectrum, i.e., violet, blue, yellow-green, and orange yellow. Although it does not keep within as narrow a band as the sodium lamp, its advantage for cell lighting is due to its limited spectrum band, which introduces some color; its unlimited mounting directions; its rapid starting time of 4 minutes to full output, and restrike of 4 minutes; its 20,000 lumen output; its much smaller dimensions; its rated life of 6000 hours; and its lower cost and simplicity of installation. It has been referred to as a "color-corrected" mercury lamp. Although it does not meet the demands for highly accurate color discrimination or for needle-sharp focus and clarity, it is a well balanced and a highly acceptable compromise lamp.

In a recent cell installation, six 400-watt JH1 mercury fluorescent lamps installed within a white-painted hot cell containing 576 cu ft and having a 3 ft thick lead glass viewing window produced 600 foot-candle readings 0-4 feet from the inside of the window rearward and on a plane

---

* General Electric Bulletin 1.2-438-1

with the bottom of the window, and 300 foot-candles 7 feet rearward from the window on the same plane. The viewing at this window was considered to be excellent.

Some facts supplied by the manufacturer and deemed to be highly important when considering design and application of mercury fluorescent lamps are as follows: After usage of 70 per cent of lamp life (4200 hours), the lamp still provides approximately 88 per cent of its initial light. For those installations where operations are critical and where low voltage is frequently experienced, a single lamp on a single-lamp ballast can stand about 10 per cent drop in voltage without going out. When two lamps are used on a two-lamp ballast, the lag lamp may go out at about a 10 per cent drop; however, the lead lamp will not go out until the voltage drop is of the order of 40 per cent.* An actual interruption of service will cause the loss of both lamps and a restart time of 4 to 6 minutes will be required. Stroboscopic effect is reduced by the use of two-lamp ballasts or by adding filament lighting.

Design Considerations

Because of the high intensity of sodium and mercury fluorescent lamps, they must be located outside the line-of-sight of the operator, preferably on the wall immediately above and on each side of the viewing window. Because it is usually necessary to locate numerous operational items in addition to mechanical services near the window on the inner wall, lighting fixture space often becomes a difficult problem. Without proper location and application, the efficiency and diversified operations of the lamps are seriously impaired. Of secondary importance is the need to eliminate any shadowing within the critical work areas due to bulky mechanical devices. The intensity or level of lighting required is somewhat dependent on the contrast to be achieved.

Lamps can be mounted in a vertical or horizontal position, thus utilizing the shorter dimension to minimize the required space. Complete freedom of movement for manipulators or other operating devices must take precedence unless conditions permit some acceptable compromise.

* Ibid

In most cases, protective rods should be installed to prevent breakage of the lamps should the manipulator's scope of maneuver bring it within the space occupied by the lamps.

Observation of fine detail through a window whose thickness is 3 to 5 feet requires the use of monochromatic lighting, especially when the area under observation is within 10 feet of the window.

When it is expected that personnel will not be permitted to enter the hot cell for long periods of time due to continuing high levels of radioactivity within the hot cell enclosure, it is recommended that either of the two following schemes be used to provide against reduced illumination due to lamp failures.

(1) Provide spare lamps and circuits as stand-by lighting.

(2) Provide plug-type lighting fixtures which will permit replacement of lamps without entering the cells.

Plug-type lighting fixtures consist of a sodium, mercury fluorescent, or incandescent lamp mounted on the end of a plug which extends through the cell wall. The plug consists of a pipe or tube filled with concrete and/or lead. The conductor's wireway—whether mineral-insulated, copper-clad, or conduit—must be cast with a full diameter or more offset within the plug to prevent a direct radiation path toward the outer cell face. Items to be considered when designing plug-type lighting fixtures are as follows:

(1) The hot cell wall thickness established by operating radiation levels.

(2) The location of the fixture—whether within or above the operator's height.

(3) The amount of shielding reduction permitted at various locations on the hot cell operating face.

(4) The methods of inserting the fixture, since some single-section plugs are quite heavy.

(5) Whether the hot cell is to be classified as explosion-proof. Should this be the case, the plug fixture must be confined within an enclosure which will provide maximum safety commensurate with the volatility of materials used within the cell while maintaining the required illumination levels. Such fixtures must be air-cooled within their confined enclosure, and electrical

interlock must be provided to ensure air supply before the lamps can be energized.

Various open type plug fixtures for typical operating conditions are shown in Figures 10.38 through 10.40. A plug fixture for an explosion-proof hot cell is shown in Figure 10.41.

Incandescent fixtures should always be installed within the hot cells for general illumination for personnel when working within the cell, since both sodium and mercury fluorescent illumination are uncomfortable and damaging to eyesight because of their extreme brilliance.

LIGHTING FOR OTHER AREAS
Operating Areas

The four important considerations for the illumination of the operating areas are elimination of glare, uniform distribution, color control, and illumination intensity of 50–60 foot-candles. Diffusion-type fixtures tend to eliminate glare and provide uniform distribution of light.

Should fluorescent fixtures be the choice, con-

tinuous row patterns mounted parallel to the face of the hot cell have been found to be highly acceptable. Louvers should be provided on the fixtures.

A mixture of an equal number of daylight or cool white lamps with soft white lamps will produce good illumination with some color, thus providing a condition conducive to pleasant working. It should be noted that soft white lamps are much lower in lumen output than are many other fluorescent tubes and will require a somewhat greater number of fixtures to provide the desired 50–60 foot-candles of illumination at working surfaces.

Uniform lighting permits flexibility of general laboratory equipment arrangement. If it is not feasible to attain complete uniformity, extreme brightness differences should be eliminated. Walls should be light-colored.

Although incandescent lighting is generally a more simple and lower cost installation, operating costs are quite high. Fluorescent lighting is most desirable from an operational standpoint, since

Figure 10.38 Sleeve and plug light fixture.

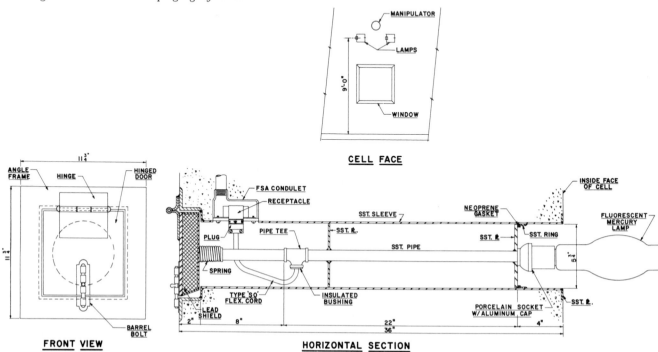

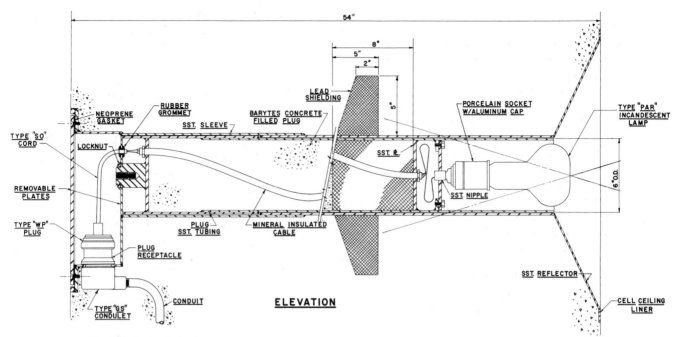

Figure 10.39   Sleeve and plug light fixture.

Figure 10.40   Sleeve and plug light fixture.

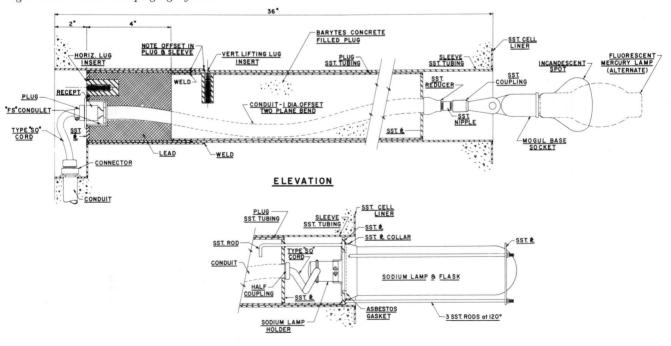

wattage is much less on a comparable basis. Although the quality and general appearance of filament lighting can be quite satisfactory, the heat produced for illumination values above 40 foot-candles is much higher than for fluorescent lamps. This would have some bearing on increased air-conditioning requirements.

In order to provide more effective visual conditions at the hot cell windows, the lighting fixtures should be wired alternately so that the lighting level may be reduced to any level of illumination desired. For those times when complete elimination of main lighting is desired, a separate lighting circuit of several incandescent lamps should be provided to facilitate personnel movement within the operating area.

Work or Charging Areas

Illumination of the work areas behind the hot cells is generally accomplished with filament lamps, structural details governing their locations. Usually 30–40 foot-candles are the maximum illumination level required.

Hazardous Areas

Apart from design innovations and features similar to those shown in Figure 10.41 for a mercury fluorescent or sodium lamp installation in an explosion-proof hot cell, the usual code requirements for such areas should govern both lighting and power design within hot cells or in the operating or charging area.

POWER DISTRIBUTION

Within Hot Cells

The following items of design criteria should be fully explored before final layouts are prepared for power distribution within hot cells.

(1) The number of grouped or separately

Figure 10.41   Sleeve and plug light fixture.

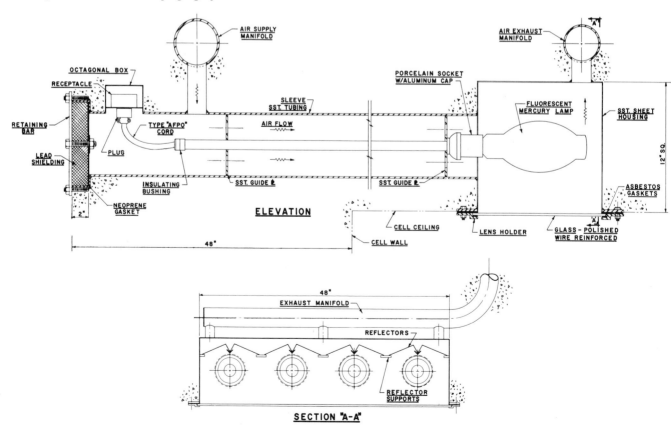

switched items of equipment to be served.

(2) The most practical location of the receptacles to the equipment to be served. Operational function of specific processing equipment will usually govern such locations. In most installations, the receptacle locations must be such that the manipulator can uncover the receptacles, insert, and remove the plugs.

(3) The general nature of operations to be conducted within the hot cell, whether volatile, wet, dry or dusty. Most hot cells must be flushed during cleaning or decontamination. Even though it is often found that flushing is necessary only on the lower portion of the walls and floor, it is recommended that hot cells which are designed to be flushed in any manner be provided with receptacles having covers, either of the spring door or screw cap type. A strictly dry cell may be provided with standard open receptacles.

(4) Should the hot cell be lined with stainless steel, it is desirable that the number of service entrances through cell liners be as few as possible. For this reason the maximum number of electric circuits entering the cell should be grouped within the minimum number of conduits. If possible, carry all services through one raceway to an inner junction box from which general distribution can be made. Provide spare conduits for future services as required.

(5) Whether receptacles are grouped within limited areas or are required at various locations and elevations, the number of raceway and receptacle boxes around the walls should be minimized.

Raceways within any hot cell should not be welded or attached directly to the cell liner, for this will form a shelf which may collect contaminated dust that will be difficult to eliminate. Stainless steel brackets should be provided, and the raceways attached to them with straps of the same material.

Within the Operating Area

It has been found that a generous number of 115- and 230-volt receptacles grouped at equipment such as laboratory benches and hoods, and other 115-volt receptacles spaced approximately 12 feet apart along all walls will prove to be quite adequate. At least one 440-volt, 3-phase receptacle is usually required for operating a small furnace or perhaps an equipment item having a motor of that voltage.

REMOTE CONTROLS AT HOT CELL WINDOWS

It should be quite obvious that grouped controls for operating the mechanisms within the hot cell must be mounted at a convenient height, immediate to, and preferably on the right side of the window. Should the location of other apparatus be more paramount in that general area, it may be necessary to mount such groups of controls on a portable table which could be located very near the cell face and to the operator's right side. Needless to say, should several separate groups of controls be required on the same panel, the order of operating sequence must determine the layout pattern.

MATERIALS FOR HOT CELLS AREA

A basic fundamental of design engineering is to specify both operating devices and materials which will, as far as possible, ensure prolonged and satisfactory operation under such adverse conditions as determined by the scientific planning personnel. Prolonged operations within limited access areas demand that materials be utilized which provide for uninterrupted operations and that the economics of maintenance be minimized.

Radiation effects in regards to insulation flexibility and to insulation resistance are two dominant questions of concern.

The following insulation materials were submitted to be tested under radiation at the Oak Ridge National Laboratory. Estimated gamma radiation level was 10^6 roentgens per hour.

(1) "Silastic" 80—Dow Corning
(2) "Silastic" 80—Dow Corning (with glass braid)
(3) Neoprene—Sheath from SJO Cord
(4) Natural rubber
(5) Polyethylene
(6) Type TW—Anaconda "Densheath"

"Teflon" was not tested because it is already

known to crumble badly under radiation.

Table 10.3 shows the results in regard to flexibility changes under progressive amounts of radiation.

Since Type TW appeared to withstand radiation better than any other sample of building wire insulation, a radiation check for a comparison of stability was made on various color pigments of TW wire, the results of which are shown in Table 10.4. These results were considered very

TABLE 10.3

PHYSICAL EFFECTS OF RADIATION ON CONDUCTOR INSULATION
(FLEXIBILITY)

(Radiation Estimated at 10^6 R Gamma per Hr.—total equivalent)

Radiation Time	1 HR.	3 HR.	22 HR.	46 HR.	116 HR.	242 HR.	REMARKS
(1) Silastic 80 (Dow Corning)	Flex. no change	No change	Brittle—breaks under moderate bend	Very brittle			Discarded after 46 hours
	Color slightly darker	Progressively darker	Brown	Very dark			
(2) Natural rubber	Flex. no change	No change	Slightly stiffer	Stiffer—recovers from sharp bend	Very stiff breaks on moderate bend		Discarded after 116 hours
	Color no change	No change	No change	Slightly darker	Darker		
(3) Polyethelene	Flex. no change	No change	Slightly stiffer	Stiffer—still somewhat springy	Brittle—breaks on moderate bend		Discarded after 116 hrs. better than 2 or 5
	Color no change	No change	Slightly darker	Darker	Yellow		
(4) Type TW	Flex. no change	No change	Slightly stiffer	Stiffer	Considerably stiffer—does not crack on moderate bend	Stiffer sometimes breaks on mod. bend	Best sample
	Color no change	No change	No change	No change	Darkened to dark blue color	Very dark	
(5) Neoprene jacket	Flex. no change	No change	No change	Somewhat stiffer	Very stiff breaks easily on mod. bend		Discarded after 116 hours
	Color no change	No change	No change	No change	No change		
(6) Silastic 80 (with copper) left in and white glass braid.	Flex. no change	No change	No change	No change will not fray	Glass flexible but frays easier	Glass flexible frays badly	Best for this type insulation
	Color no change	Glass slightly darker	Darker, but satisfactory	Glass turning yellow	Glass very yellow	Glass deep yellow	

good for all test samples throughout 154 hrs. of radiation. Similar results have been obtained by others.*

Table 10.5 shows the effects of radiation on the insulation resistance of type TW. Approximately

---
* *Electronic Equipment,* "How Nuclear Radiation Affects Engineering Performance," Sullivan, Burros, and Brocklehurst, p. 61.

30 feet of #14 TW Rome conductor was inserted in copper braid shielding which was tightened up on the wire as much as possible.

Radiation equivalent was 10^6 roentgens per hour. Readings were taken with a megohmeter at about 14 volts. The resistance was measured through 332 exposure hours. A further test was

TABLE 10.4

PHYSICAL EFFECTS OF RADIATION ON TYPE TW CONDUCTOR INSULATIONS
—ALL COLORS

(Radiation Estimated at 10^6 R Gamma Per Hr.—total equivalent)

RADIATION TIME		70 HR.	106 HR.	154 HR.
(1) Anaconda white #8	Flex.	Stiffer—no break on moderate bend	No change	Stiffer—no break on moderate bend
	Color	Grayish yellow	No change	Gray
(2) Anaconda black #10	Flex.	Stiffer—no break on moderate bend	No change	Stiffer—breaks on three moderate bends
	Color	No change	No change	
(3) General green #12	Flex.	Stiffer—no break on moderate bend	No change	No change
	Color	No change	Blue—Green	Darker blue—green
(4) General black #14	Flex.	Stiffer—no break on moderate bend	No change	Very good condition Slightly good
	Color	No change	No change	No change
(5) Rome white #10	Flex.	Stiffer—no break on moderate bend	Stiffer—No break on moderate bend	No change—good condition
	Color	Slightly yellow	Yellowish—gray	Gray green
(6) Rome red #10	Flex.	Slightly stiff—no break on moderate bend	Stiffer—no break on moderate bend	No change
	Color	No change	Darker red	Very dark
(7) Collyer rose #12	Flex.	Stiffer—no break on moderate bend	No change	No change
	Color	Fading color	Gray	Dark brown
(8) Circle yellow #14	Flex.	Slightly stiff—no break on moderate bend	Stiffer—no break	Very stiff—breaks on moderate bend
	Color	Fading color	Grey	Dark grey
(9) Hatfield black #14	Flex.	Stiffer—no break on moderate bend	No change	Very stiff—no break on moderate bend
	Color	No change	No change	No change

made of Rome Red #14 under similar conditions and approximately the same results were obtained.

It is therefore well established by the foregoing tests that type TW conductor, having polyvinyl chloride insulation, withstands radiation better than most other types of insulations used on building wire.

Stainless Steel and Aluminum

The interiors of most hot cells are either lined with stainless steel or made of painted concrete. For those cells having stainless steel liners, the same type of material as that of the liner should be specified for all pipe or tubing, junction boxes, and outlet boxes which penetrate the liner, for such material must be welded to the liner.

It is highly recommended that all other electrical raceways and boxes be stainless steel and of the same type as that of the liner. Should stainless steel conduit fittings not be found as standard stock items, it is recommended that copper-free, high-aluminum content fittings be utilized.

TELEVISION

Several points must be borne in mind should operations be carried on wholly or partially via television. Since the best view possible with commercially available closed-circuit television equipment is inferior to that of even a moderately

TABLE 10.5

EFFECT OF RADIATION ON INSULATION RESISTANCE OF ROME WHITE TYPE #14 CONDUCTOR

(Radiation 10^6 R/Hr. Megohmeter—14 volts)

EXPOSURE HRS.	INSULATION RESISTANCE	REMARKS
0	4×10^{10}	Before starting radiation
20 min.	1.5×10^9	
35 min.	1×10^9	
18 hrs.	5×10^8	
24 hrs.	2.8×10^8	
47 hrs.	2.4×10^8	
70 hrs.	2.3×10^8	
118 hrs.	3.5×10^8	Increase (?)
132 hrs.	1.15×10^9	Reactor Down
152 hrs.	2.9×10^8	O.K. at 700V D. C. Meggar
176 hrs.	3.5×10^8	Increase (?)
200 hrs.	3.5×10^8	Increase (?)
224 hrs.	3.0×10^8	O.K. at 700V D.C. Meggar
248 hrs.	2.2×10^8	O.K. at 700V D.C. Meggar
262 hrs.	6×10^8	Reactor Down
284 hrs.	2.2×10^8	
332 hrs.	2.2×10^8	Withstood 1000V D.C. Meggar

good periscope*, and if no other optical methods of viewing are possible, a very high illumination level must be provided in most cases, and in such positions as to provide the proper pattern to satisfy the inherent characteristics of TV operation, i.e., camera and receiver reproduction. Even with the best illumination possible, the image has little perceptible depth and low resolution. However, television has been successfully used for monitoring hot operations at great distances.

* *A Manual of Remote Viewing*, Argonne National Laboratory, p. 17.

PART 3: HOSPITAL RESEARCH LABORATORIES

DONALD L. SNOW AND HENRY J. THAILER
National Institutes of Health
Bethesda, Maryland

Laboratories for specialized diagnostic procedures and for a variety of clinical research programs are fast becoming important elements in the architectural design of many hospitals.

Clinical research laboratories may be operated by those hospital departments which are organized around representative disciplines of the clinical science specialties (see box), or by clinics identified with such categoric diseases as arthritis or heart disease.

There are several characteristics to clinical research laboratories which distinguish them both from laboratories concerned solely with investigations in the basic medical sciences (see box) and from those clinical pathology service laboratories associated with hospitals.

Clinical Sciences

Anesthesiology, Internal Medicine, Obstetrics and Gynecology, Ophthalmology, Otolaryngology, Pediatrics, Psychiatry and Neurology, Radiology, and Surgery

Basic Medical Sciences

Anatomy, Physiology, Biochemistry (Physiological Chemistry), Microbiology (viz. Virology and Bacteriology), Pharmacology, Pathology (viz. Cytopathology, Histopathology), and Biophysics

Clinical research laboratories conduct research procedures which are, in many cases, identical with those carried out in basic medical science laboratories. However, they differ from basic medical science laboratories, for example, in that they employ research animals to a far lesser degree. The materials tested in clinical research laboratories generally are those derived from patients, although materials of animal origin are used in several patient diagnostic tests.

Clinical research laboratory tests are more likely to involve a variety of processes and equipment not normally found in clinical pathology service laboratories, although research is an accepted function among many laboratories in this latter group. Further, another criterion of the hospital research laboratory is that it is normally situated within the physical confines of the hospital. However, it is evident that in the more extensive hospital research programs, "best" locations for the clinical research laboratories or diagnostic research areas to which patients are brought are necessarily compromises between the convenience with respect to patient care areas and hospital service departments on one hand and supportive facilities for basic medical science procedures on the other.

Supportive facilities for basic medical science procedures cover a considerable range of functions. They may include quarters for laboratory animals, glassware cleaning and preparation areas, low-temperature laboratory-cold storage rooms, instrument and electronics development, calibration and repair shops, chromatography,

Kjeldahl, ultracentrifuge, electron microscope or other special laboratory procedure areas, radioactivity counting and radioisotope storage rooms, and chemical stores and other storage space. Sterilizers, stills and other water processing equipment, and the space they occupy also can be included within the definition of supportive facilities.

Other important support facilities include those for data-processing equipment and for library, seminar, medical illustration and photographic functions.

SPACE ALLOCATIONS

The amount of net or gross space which should be assigned each staff member is a question frequently raised in planning hospital research facilities. Analysis of a limited number of present and proposed facilities for clinical research and their staffing patterns show wide deviations. However, "rule-of-thumb" figures of 200 sq ft and 300 sq ft for each laboratory employee on a net and gross area basis,* respectively, are sometimes employed in the preliminary planning stages for the basic medical science type of laboratories. It is apparent that reasonably generous allowances of area per employee should be made initially in anticipation of building population increases with expansion of research programs.

In areas exclusively devoted to diagnostic research, more space will be required than the above figures would indicate since beds, stretchers and various bulky equipment used in clinical procedures must be brought in and shifted about.

GENERAL PLANNING AND DESIGN CONSIDERATIONS

Special requirements for laboratory instrumentation also may dictate the general location of laboratory areas within hospitals and clinics.

---

* *Net Area Definition:* The net area of a (floor) (building) includes that portion between the walls which is actually put to work use. It excludes toilets, corridors, elevator shafts, vertical ventilating ducts, mechanical space and the like.[1]

Gross Area Definition: The gross area of a (floor) (building) is the entire area of the floor(s) based on the outside dimensions of the building. It includes the outside walls and such areas as toilets, corridors, vertical ventilating ducts, storerooms, machine shops, elevator shafts, and the like.[1]

For example, the trend for more sensitive pickup and recording of physiological events associated with patients require correspondingly greater care in locating areas for special diagnostic instruments.

Patient Care and Related Requirements

Under some conditions, to secure generous ratios of new laboratory to existing patient care space, an adjoining laboratory wing or building may be designed with corridors which connect at those floors where patients must be moved to special diagnostic research facilities. Door openings of ample width must be planned for areas to which patients must be moved on wheeled stretchers.

As mentioned, an equally important consideration is that certain clinical research functions may need to be located convenient to other hospital service departments. For example, local conditions may make it desirable to carry out the cardiology department's catheterization procedures adjacent to or even physically within the diagnostic X-ray department.

Another valid design objective should be to help minimize any feelings of apprehension on the part of the patients when moved to unfamiliar research environments. Thus, special diagnostic or clinical testing facilities may be justifiably located adjacent to patient care areas, even at some cost in increased distance from the bulk of the department's basic science laboratories. Within the diagnostic research area, every opportunity should be exploited to provide a familiar decor for the patient. For aesthetic reasons, prudent planning suggests that associated animal rooms and animal procedures areas be located remote from possible patient and public hearing and view. However, there is no one location of choice. Suitable animal quarters in hospital-type structures can be provided in a variety of locations, such as the ends of halls where they can be screened by corridor bulkhead doors, or, alternatively, in separate but connected structures. There are advantages—and disadvantages—to each of these locations. The particular location selected will determine, for example, the required degree and direction of imbalance in the ventilation system design, and whether to use vestibules

and other structural features to help exclude animal odors which can drift into clinical and patient care areas.

To restrict casual traffic and promote general safety, hazardous agent laboratories, such as those which handle radioisotopes and pathogenic materials, may be located at the ends of corridors where there is normally no public traffic, or in "cul-de-sac" corridor arrangements which can be blocked off if more positive controls are required.

Proper illumination is important in the study of certain disease conditions in diagnostic areas where interpretations of skin color changes are involved. If fluorescent lighting systems are used, they should be planned to maintain a balance between the cool white and warm white fluorescent tubes (blue and red bands of visible spectrum), and there should be assurance that the laboratory's fluorescent tube replacement program will continue to maintain the original color balance in these diagnostic areas.

A light intensity of 50 foot-candles for examining room and other clinical research space illumination, supplemented with local lighting at a level of 100 foot-candles, represents the current best judgment for lighting levels in these areas.[2]

Standard vs. Special Laboratory Designs

Designs for hospital laboratories which involve the basic medical sciences have many features in common among them, but differences in research processes and equipment preclude their being standardized completely.

One general procedure in laboratory design, to which the layouts of biomedical research laboratories are generally amenable, is to utilize a limited number of laboratory furniture items and from these develop a few "basic" groupings of laboratory furniture for related research functions. A trend which is highly important to recognize is the growing number of research apparatus now being marketed which require only floor space and electric power and, less frequently, water and drain. Scientific equipment manufacturers are increasingly unitizing such equipment as chromatography, electrophoresis, and scintillation counting systems, and incorporating them into free-standing, bench-height cabinets, or in relay racks. The need to reserve a substantial amount of free-floor space for placing this growing volume of equipment, including freezers and incubators, cannot be too strongly emphasized.

Instrumentation Requirements

Special requirements for instrumentation associated with clinical research often sharply reduce the number of locations where certain research procedures can be conducted in existing hospital or adjoining laboratory structures, and even in new structures.

Sound pressure levels in a broad range of frequencies, and intermittent noise peaks must be considered in selecting an optimum site for audiometry rooms or for interview-recording facilities used in behavioral studies. Locations close to elevators and corridors with moderate-to-dense foot and cart traffic may present serious problems with structure-borne noise for a variety of scientific apparatus.

Building vibration, particularly in the frequency range of $\frac{1}{10}$ to 20 cycles per second (cps) can interfere with the operation of galvanometers, electrometers and microscopes. It is important to note, however, that recent developments in electro-balances have to some extent minimized the need for vibration-free space. Structurally-transmitted frequencies of up to approximately 1000 cps may interfere with audiometric and other sensitive equipment. Vibration, corresponding to the natural or harmonic frequencies of the speeds of exhaust fans, pumps, and other mechanical equipment, can be transmitted over long vertical distances through a multistory building. Usually, basement locations for rotating or oscillating mechanical equipment are selected to minimize machinery-induced vibration. Compromises in locating exhaust blower and motor sets will be necessary when chemical fumes must be exhausted at the rooftop. Each of these types of equipment should be isolated from the building structure with vibration damping or decoupling mounts selected for the natural frequency and mass of the equipment. All rigid connections between motors, blowers and pumps connected to ducts and electric conduits must be eliminated. In addition, specially designed instrument tables may be needed for decoupling at either the high or low ends of the scale of interfering frequencies.

Highly specialized apparatus, such as ballistocardiography tables may need to be located where there is a minimum ambient vibration interference from the hospital building.[3] Generally, basement areas are most desirable for this critical equipment. In any case, the locations of vibration-sensitive equipment, including such facilities as anechoic rooms, must be carefully chosen. For example, street traffic and local microseisms can substantially contribute to vibration in a building. Where instrument performance may be critical, and if alternate building sites can be considered, it will be desirable to make comparative vibration surveys before selecting a final location. With proper initial surveying, massive rigid vibration "grounds" can be provided for in the building design. These "grounds" are isolated from the building but serve as anchors for sensitive pieces of equipment. The use of consultants in this specialized field of vibration control is strongly recommended prior to designing a structure which will contain instrumentation whose performance is critically sensitive to vibration.

Voltage transients and electrostatic and electromagnetic interference with medical instrumentation can pose some of the most vexing problems to proper instrument operation. Electroencephalographic recording procedures can be adversely affected by local electrostatic and electromagnetic fields. While shielded rooms are sometimes used, they are not necessarily mandatory for the successful operation of this equipment. This is particularly true if the electroencephalograph room is located some distance away from high-power radio frequency equipment, electric motors (including those in elevator penthouses), high amperage A. C. feeders and X-ray equipment. In laboratories or clinical areas where such equipment is installed, the possibility for interference caused by local electrostatic fields must be anticipated. Both custom-built shielded rooms or prefabricated, demountable shielded rooms can be successfully used to overcome these conditions. Since the improper construction of a built-in shielded room can nullify its proper operation, adherence to specific construction details and continued inspection during its construction is highly important. To assure maximum effectiveness of the shielding, it is recommended that close visual inspection be carried out during all stages of construction of the room. Attenuation performance tests for the room can be made in accordance with military standard specifications.[3a]

Pipes and conduits passing into the room should be electrically bonded to the shield. A protective, non-conductive section should be fitted in the pipe or conduit external to the shielded room to prevent grounding of the shield at multiple points and to prevent the penetrating piping and conduits from radiating electromagnetic energy into the room. Another desirable detail is to confine all services entering the room to a single section of one wall. The shield should be electrically isolated from the structural slab by a non-conducting membrane to prevent electrolytic action and minimize possible "ground loops."

Effective electrical grounding for shielded rooms and various instruments used in medical research is also essential. Neither the neutral "ground" common to 4-wire electrical systems, nor the sheathing or armored electrical cable or conduit can be considered as true grounds. Grounds should be single conductors of solid or braided copper cables which extend into the permanent water table surrounding the building. "Ground loops," formed by connecting the grounding cable to the reference ground at more than one point should be avoided. The need for dependable grounding of various instruments associated with medical research is growing and grounds are now being viewed as an essential utility in many medical research structures.

Instrumentation problems may also be encountered with transient voltage peaks. It is recommended that the voltage fluctuations of the local power supply at the building site be investigated prior to designing the electrical distribution system for the research facility. Where the primary power source has an excessive voltage fluctuation, a means of voltage regulation may be necessary in the general distribution system within the building. Possible alternating current wave shape distortion should be considered before selecting the particular type of voltage regulating equipment. In addition, separate main feeders may be needed for sensitive instruments. This will avoid their being supplied by any lines subject to voltage drops due to connected heavy, intermittent loads, such as elevator motors, pumps, centrifuges, and other equipment having high-starting torques. As a local measure where voltage fluctuations cannot be readily controlled by the above procedures, scientific instruments can be equipped with individual voltage regulators.

SUPPORTING FACILITIES

Animal Location

No position has developed regarding the relative merits of centralized facilities for laboratory animals as opposed to placing animal rooms adjacent to the laboratories with which they are associated. Unless there is a fixed institutional policy to the contrary, small animals (mice, rats and guinea pigs) can be successfully housed in locations close to small groups of investigators to promote efficiency in studies. Considerations of cleanliness, odors, and insect control tend to lead to the selection of a central quarters for larger animals. One advantage to the centralized arrangement is that it is easier to provide for special facilities, such as exercise runs for dogs on long-term studies.

Odors are frequently associated with fixed cage facilities for dogs, monkeys and chimpanzees. Hence, the location of an animal room with fixed-in-place cages in hospital or hospital-connected structures presents a special problem. Movable racks and cages which can be brought to a central cleaning area can be more thoroughly cleaned than fixed-in-place equipment and, consequently, odors are usually not as much of a problem.

Glass Cleaning and Preparation

Analytical and physiological chemistry procedures use a substantial amount of calibrated and optically matched glassware items. It is not always feasible to release this special glassware from the laboratory for cleaning. The usual practice is to clean it in a sink in the laboratory. Sinks 15 to 18 inches in depth, and with extra cold water outlets for jet rinsers and pipette rinsers, and provisions for distilled or demineralized rinse water, and knee- or pedal-operated controls will normally meet most glassware washing needs within the small laboratory. Efficient mechanical glassware washing units, approximately the size of household dishwashers, are finding increased use in the individual laboratory or groups of associated laboratories.

A glass cleaning facility for a group of laboratories is useful where there is a sufficient volume of glassware to justify assigning the necessary space and personnel. As a minimum, such a facility will require a two- or three-compartment sink equipped with provisions for a distilled or demineralized water rinse. Ample drainboard space on either side of the sink unit is recommended and a motor-driven brush machine may be found desirable. Other equipment in the room may include glassware drying racks or drying ovens. Where warranted by the volume of soiled glassware, mechanized batch or conveyor type machines that have been specially designed for the washing of laboratory glassware are now available. Glass cleaning areas designed to handle larger units of research than those of department-

size are particularly feasible where financing central-type operations is not a problem.

The processing of glassware for bacteriological research requires additional space for media preparation and for the sterilization and the plugging, wrapping, and filling of a variety of glassware. These functions may be performed in the laboratory, or in conjunction with a central glass cleaning department.

Glassware used in tissue culture presents more critical cleaning requirements. Acid cleaning equipment may be required, but is not always necessary, especially with the effective performance of the newer glasswashing machines which have high nozzle pressures and glassware hold-down grids. These machines provide several cycles of rinsing, including a final demineralized or distilled water rinse. They can be furnished in a variety of sizes and designs for both batch and continuous flow or conveyor belt operation. Figure 10.42 shows a partial view of the machines installed in one of the central glass cleaning facilities at the National Institutes of Health.

Figure 10.42 View of glass cleaning facility.

Instrument Repair and Fabrication

Metal-working equipment and glassblowing and electronic equipment test benches and other shop facilities are important adjuncts to medical research programs. Depending on program needs, local shops for repairs and minor fabrication may be established or more completely outfitted central instrument design and fabrication shops may be required.

Special Equipment Rooms

Some heat and fume-producing equipment, such as batteries of macro-Kjeldahl units, may be too large to place in standard size chemical fume hoods. If a large quantity of this equipment is involved, consideration should be given to placing it in well-ventilated rooms which will not be constantly occupied. Excessive heat or fume-producing equipment may need to be located inside hoods or canopies of special design.

Low-Temperature Laboratories and Incubator Rooms. Combination low-temperature laboratories maintained at approximately 35°F, with an allowable temperature range of ±1°F, and adjoining frozen storage compartment set at 0° to 5°F, are useful for dialysis, column chromatography, centrifuging and other procedures used in separating heat-labile biological materials. Because of their specialized character, these rooms are frequently designed for joint use by a number of investigators.

Cold rooms may be built in place, or may be constructed of prefabricated, demountable wall, ceiling, and floor panels. A schematic plan of one type of demountable-panel, low-temperature laboratory and cold storage room used at the National Institutes of Health is shown in Figure 10.43. Sink and bench facilities in the low-temperature laboratory section and storage shelving in the rear frozen storage compartment will vary with individual needs. Evaporator units which mount flush with the ceiling so as not to protrude into the occupied zone and automatic defrost equipment for the evaporator coils are desirable design features. Care must be taken to prevent evaporator unit drain lines from clogging, and to insure that the utility lines in the front laboratory section will not freeze.

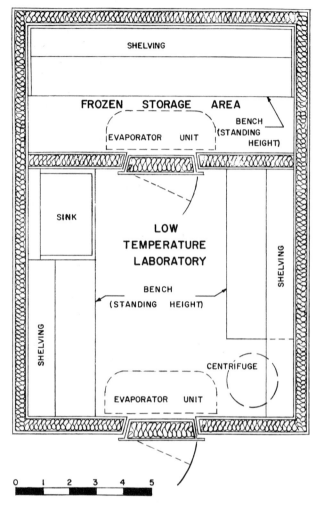

Figure 10.43   Plan of combined low-temperature laboratory and cold storage room.

Since mold growths in low-temperature rooms can become a problem, the rooms should be designed for easy cleaning. Some provisions for either general or local exhaust ventilation should be included to safeguard personnel. Heat economizers can be successfully used to temper the room makeup air and minimize refrigeration compressor requirements.

Incubator rooms for 37°C operation find widespread application. Prefabricated incubator rooms constructed in sections which bolt together have proved quite successful. As temperature gradients will develop within a room of large dimensions, the room air circulating system should be carefully designed. Where the room will be used for holding tissue culture flasks, all shelving must be carefully leveled to insure that liquid nutrient media will evenly cover the bottoms of the flasks.

Water Processing Equipment and Distribution Systems. Distilled water intended for clinical use must be pyrogen-free and it should have a specific resistance of 1,000,000 ohms or greater (less than 0.1 parts per million (ppm.) of sodium chloride (NaCl). Stills which reduce foaming in their evaporator chambers and prevent water solids carryover by a combination of especially-designed baffles and additional height in the chambers are used for this purpose. Central distribution systems for pyrogen-free water are not yet available, although they are under development. Equipment for producing and storing sterile, pyrogen-free water is usually located in the hospital's sterile supply department where it can be continuously checked.

Medical laboratories use distilled or deionized (demineralized) water both for solution preparation and glassware rinsing. Where water of several million ohms specific resistance is required, specially designed, small capacity, all-quartz stills are frequently used. The demand for water of such high quality is limited. Recent experience indicates that water having a specific resistance of 500,000 ohms (0.6 ppm. NaCl) will meet the majority of the needs of biomedical research laboratories for solution preparation and rinsing purposes.

As continuous inspection of stills is usually not practical, such features as automatic flushing of solids in evaporator pans and conductivity controls to divert low quality water to drain are recommended.

Sterilizer Rooms and Equipment. Since steam sterilizers contribute substantially to laboratory internal heat loads, their placement in normally non-occupied rooms is recommended. Where convenience factors dictate their location within the laboratory, well-insulated cabinet-type sterilizers should be considered to reduce sensible heat loads. Automatic cycling and steam pressure regulating valves which can be set for precise temperature control are useful features to specify for steam sterilizers used in biomedical research.

CLINICAL DIAGNOSTIC RESEARCH UNITS

Some test procedures used in clinical research require special facilities for proper patient observation or diagnosis. Each facility may consist of from one to several rooms designed to exploit one or more related diagnostic procedures. Other basic medical science laboratories may be required in conjunction with the diagnostic or clinical laboratories.

Four types of clinical laboratory facilities are described in the following sections. These are designed for: (1) radioisotope uptake measurements; (2) diagnostic virology; (3) cardiovascular and cardiopulmonary investigations; and (4) energy metabolism studies for sustained periods.

Figures 10.44–10.46 described in detail, also illustrate features of several research units in actual operation. Two of the illustrations, Figures 10.44 and 10.45 are based on prototype units but have been modified to show how adjoining modular laboratories may be adapted to incorporate their related elements. It should be noted that the direction of the utility feed in Figure 10.44 has been assumed as originating at the outside wall. Utilities fed from the corridor would have altered the physical arrangement of the rooms shown.

Radioisotope Uptake Measurement Facilities

Where radioisotopes are used for clinical diagnosis or treatment, space for any or all of the following functions must be provided: radiochemistry patient uptake measurements, radioisotope assay and counting, instrument calibration and minor repairs, and radiotherapy. Radiochemical laboratories are discussed in this section only as they relate to particular needs of clinical practice. The design of teletherapy installations, which employ radioisotopes of cobalt and cesium as gamma radiation sources, is a specialized subject and is discussed by Taylor *et al.*[4] An excellent list of publications on radioisotope applications and facilities used in medicine is available from the Atomic Energy Commission.[5]

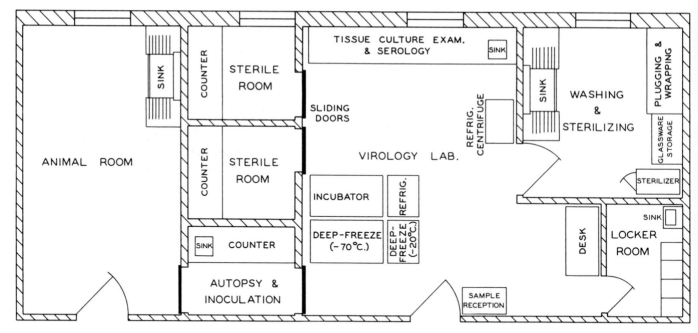

Figure 10.44   Diagnostic virology laboratory suite.

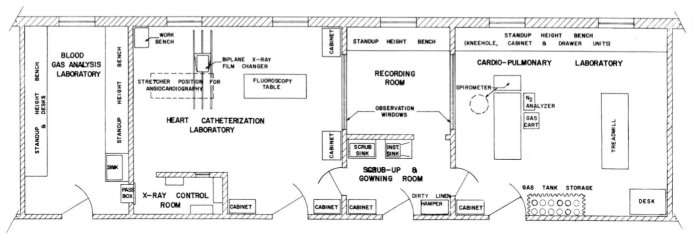

Figure 10.45   Cardiovascular and cardiopulmonary research unit.

Clinical investigations using radioisotopes will most frequently employ the following: gold-198, iodine-131, phosphorus-32, sodium-24, and carbon-14. Except for carbon-14, the medical use of radioisotopes is generally confined to materials with a relatively short physical half-life. Levels of radioactivity for individual diagnostic procedures will rarely exceed 10 millicuries and, generally, will fall in the range of 1 millicurie or less.

To minimize handling responsibilities, and to permit the efficient utilization of specially trained personnel in this field, the functions of storage, assay and dilution of concentrated solutions of radioisotopes shipped in may be brought together in a common facility within the hospital. This facility may be located in the area occupied by the hospital's Radiology Department, particularly where it is under this department's administrative control. Patient uptake and therapy studies will normally be conducted directly within the physical facilities of each hospital department using radioisotopes in research. The smaller hospital or research unit may find it more suitable to integrate both the radioisotope preparation and investigative functions in one central facility.

New developments in equipment have helped to simplify laboratory design. For example, scintillation detection equipment with anticoincidence circuits is widely used for counting low activity samples in clinical studies and has greatly reduced the problem of radiation background interference with *in vitro* work.

With patient uptake and other *in vivo* measurements, minimal radiation backgrounds depend on

the proper design and location of the patient-uptake measurement area. Separate rooms for uptake measurements and for radiochemistry will help minimize radiation background. Some basis for sizing these facilities can be developed from information that a 14′ x 17′ uptake measurement room and a 12′ x 17′ radiochemical laboratory will handle about 60 patients per month, with a daily maximum of 10 patients. This data is predicated on not more than two or three of these patients receiving gold-198. Further, an average of 30 minutes required for each patient is assumed.[6]

Uptake Measurement Room: The patient radioisotope uptake measurement room should provide space for the uptake measurement-examination table, scanning tube stand, and radiation counting equipment. The latter may be placed on a laboratory bench or built into a free-standing, movable relay rack. Within the same room, space should be set aside for the technician's desk. Additionally, space may be required for a stenographer's desk and file and chair space for a patient's attendant. Cubicle curtains can be used to screen the patient from unauthorized observers and provide the patient with the necessary privacy.

To promote aseptic techniques, the room should be equipped with a clinical sink fitted with knee- or foot-operated controls. Storage space for linens should be provided.

Low, and even more importantly, constant radiation background are factors to be considered in locating this room. Hence, the uptake room should also be located away from the immediate vicinity of X-ray, high energy accelerators, and storage areas for gamma-emitting radioisotopes. Individual composition floor tiles are recommended for ease in removal in event there is a spillage of radioactive materials.[6] Special care should be taken to insure a continuous film of adhesive coating under these tiles.

Radiochemical Laboratory. Low radioactivity levels, combined with the use of lead bricks for shielding temporary setups, and lead pots (pigs) for storing concentrated solutions of radioisotopes, will generally obviate the need for expensive built-in-place radiation shielding for radiochemical laboratories in medical research areas.

Figure 10.46   Plan of environmental chamber for metabolism studies.

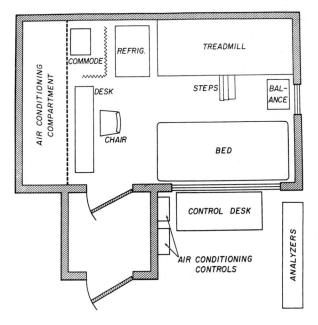

Figure 10.46a   Clinical Center of the National Institutes of Health.

As in the uptake measurement room, the primary design needs require relatively low and constant radiation backgrounds. The selection of composition floor tiles is also recommended here. The use of a non-pervious bench top material is not required. Bench tops can be protected against contamination by using metal or plastic trays to confine solutions spilled from containers. An integral backsplash on the rear of the bench top is recommended as a design feature.

Separate plumbing lines or retention tanks are not necessary for the disposal of laboratory or clinical radioactive wastes from the average size hospital. In small clinics conducting research, the disposal procedures for solutions of phosphorus-32 and iodine-131 should be based on the dilution procedures recommended by the National Bureau of Standards.[7]

Diagnostic Virology Unit

The suite of four modules (see Figure 10.44) contains the basic functional areas and illustrates several considerations in planning a self-contained diagnostic virology unit.

The four modules contain space for inoculated animals and provide for animal and egg inoculation procedures and such functions as incubation, microscopy, glassware cleaning and sterilizing, record-keeping, and personnel clothing change. It is assumed that the bulk of the nutrient media and standard cell lines required are secured from an outside source.

Where the diagnostic unit will handle agents of maximum pathogenicity, several desirable design objectives illustrated in Figure 10.44 should be considered. These include: (1) restriction of access to the animal room; (2) provision for a locker room; (3) location of the sterilizing and washing room adjacent to the laboratory; and (4) segregation of infected and uninfected materials handling procedures in separate sterile rooms. Not included in the plan is a photomicrography area.

A desirable feature in the locker room would be a full-length mirror for tick and other insect checks, and insect-proofing construction details are particularly recommended in the animal room. Laboratory furniture can be of standard construction, with a large sink and integral drainboards suggested for the animal room. Stainless steel counters with seamless construction are desirable for maximum cleanliness in the autopsy and inoculation rooms and the washing and sterilizing room. A Formica-type bench top material will adequately meet the needs for most work surfaces in the virology laboratory. Backsplashes that are molded integral with the counter top will assist in cleaning.

Special equipment may include a counter top transfer hood or safety hood in the inoculation room and in the sterile rooms. Depending on the type of work to be done, the hood may be designed to accommodate one or two persons. For maximum personnel safety, suggested features for the hood are glove ports, a separate exhaust system leading to the exterior of the building, and an exhaust-air filtering or incinerating unit. Also important are such items as a floor built integral with the hood and a bare-tube ultraviolet lamp installation in the hood interior.

To accommodate tissue culture roller drums, test tubes, flasks, or petri dishes and embryonated eggs, one large-sized incubator should be located in the virology laboratory. One $-70°C$ deep-freeze chest for stock viruses and a $-20°C$ freezer unit for labile media and sera are required. A refrigerator for stock nutrient media should also be provided. Cabinet and drawer units under the bench tops can vary with individual requirements. A similar diagnostic unit of this approximate size handles a monthly average of from six to eight patients and will process about 160 specimens for virus isolation and about 150 serum samples for serologic studies.[8]

Cardiovascular and Cardiopulmonary Research Unit

One type of an integrated clinical facility for cardiac research will include space for heart catheterization, pulmonary studies, instrumentation, blood gas-analysis, and combined surgical scrub and gowning procedures. Because of their completely different physical space requirements, each of these functions should be located in separate but related areas. Figure 10.45 illustrates one scheme for coordinating the major elements of this type of research facility.

Cardiac Catheterization Laboratory. The basic items of fixed equipment employed in the heart catheterization procedures consist of the fluoroscopic table, biplane X-ray film changer, a two-tube X-ray unit equipped with two power supply packs, and a minor surgical light.

If the entire research facility can be located adjacent to the X-ray department, the biplane film changer and X-ray unit can be readily serviced by this department. Regardless of where the department is located, it is good practice to place both the fluoroscopic and X-ray equipment within the same room so as to avoid any hazards which patients with attached catheters may encounter when being transported to the X-ray department.

Since heart catheterization techniques involve surgical procedures, the same care in designing architectural and mechanical features which promote aseptic techniques in an operating room should be extended to the design of the heart catheterization laboratory. For example, a gowning and scrub anteroom should be provided. The scrub room should contain a surgeon's washup sink equipped with knee- or foot-actuated controls, and foot-operated soap dispensers should be provided. A cabinet for sterile gowns and a dirty linen hamper are also required. Every effort should be made to avoid storing equipment and materials, other than sterile supplies, within the catheterization room. Materials for wall, floor, and ceiling surfaces should be selected for their cleanability. A filtered, non-recirculated fresh air supply, with an hourly air change rate of at least 12 room-air volumes, and diffusers which minimize air turbulence are recommended.

It is desirable to install a minor surgical light above the fluoroscopic table. A similar light is also required at the biplane X-ray film changer. One ceiling track-mounted surgical light may be installed to serve both locations. An electronic image intensifier may be used to reduce the amount of radiation dosage during fluoroscopy. Using the image-intensifier eliminates the need for light-proof shades, but windows and doors and other sources of outside light should be equipped with shades for subdued lighting.

A section of the heart catheterization room should be reserved for the X-ray control station and program selector equipment. The use of X-ray equipment requires that walls and floors in the rooms be examined as to their shielding needs. The X-ray shielding design standards of the National Bureau of Standards Handbooks[9, 10] may be consulted here. X-ray film developing facilities should be convenient to this laboratory.

Space must be provided for anesthesia personnel and the placement of their equipment at the head of the fluoroscopic table and between the biplane film changer table and the fluoroscopic table. The top of the fluoroscopic table may be arranged to move the patient into position above the biplane film changer to avoid transferring the patient from one table to another. Ample floor space should be reserved for such portable equipment as a power syringe (for catheter dye injection), dye machine, recording oscillograph and surgical instrument tables. Cabinets raised off the floor should be provided for the storage of sterile linens and surgical instruments.

Cardiopulmonary Laboratory. The pulmonary studies laboratory should be designed to serve both bedfast and ambulatory patients. Ample floor space is needed to maneuver a full-size hospital bed and to accommodate such equipment as a treadmill and bicycle exerciser. Where the research program requires a treadmill, if possible, it should be recessed in the floor to reduce the patient fall hazard and to assist in patient handling. The treadmill should have a variable speed drive and variable angle of inclination. Maximum belt speeds generally need not exceed 10 miles per hour. Maximum treadmill bed tilt should be approximately 15 per cent.

Gas sample bags, spirometers, gas analyzers, polygraphs and other equipment will require ample floor space and adjacent laboratory bench space. A curtained storage area for equipment not in use is recommended.

Blood Gas-Analysis Laboratory. The blood gas-analysis laboratory serves both the heart catheterization laboratory and the pulmonary studies laboratory, but it is more important that it be located convenient to the catheterization laboratory. A lightproof passbox located between the catheterization laboratory and the blood gas-analysis laboratory will enable blood samples to be passed directly to the laboratory for immediate

analysis. The same passbox can be used for passing exposed X-ray film and other materials so as to minimize personnel entries into the catheterization room. Storage cabinets, sinks, and other equipment normally found in a chemical laboratory should be provided. A hood will be required if gaseous radioisotopes are to be stored.

Scrub-up and Gowning Room. A scrub-up and gowning room should be located between the catheterization and cardiopulmonary laboratories. In addition to a surgical scrub sink, a small sink for surgical instrument washing will be needed.

Recording Room: A recording room can be located directly to the rear of the scrub-up and gowning room. This position for the room will make possible the common use of highly specialized electronic instrumentation for both laboratories.

Fixed sash should be installed in the two observation windows shown in Figure 10.45. A speaking tube or other communications arrangement is also necessary. Cable pass-through ports should be located below both windows. A passbox for handling records between the rooms may also be found desirable.

Metabolism Studies Unit

A tightly sealed, controlled environment chamber is basic to metabolism studies using indirect calorimetry methods. Both a schematic plan and exterior view of the National Institutes of Health Metabolic Chamber are shown in Figures 10.46 and 10.47.

This type of environmental chamber is designed to permit a subject to live in it for several or more days at a time and during that period carry out all normal activities, as well as exercise on a treadmill.

To control air infiltration or exfiltration, an airtight, metal wall construction of the chamber is required. Continuous welding of all interior seams and joints and continuous, inflatable gasketing for door seals are desirable details for an airtight chamber. The chamber includes an anteroom to permit limited access to the interior of the chamber with a minimum of heat loss or gain. The habitable portion of the chamber has approximate inside floor dimensions of 9 x 13 feet and has an 8-foot ceiling. Temperatures can be maintained between 5° and 49°C. Humidity control can range between 10 to 95 per cent over most of this temperature range.[11]

Indirect calorimetry is accomplished by continuously analyzing the carbon dioxide and oxygen content of the air expired by the subject undergoing a variety of activities. A lightweight plastic collection helmet or hood worn by the subject collects air exhaled during the period of test. The carbon dioxide and oxygen content of the fresh air in the chamber are intermittently monitored.

Heat loss and gain to the chamber is minimized in other ways. The treadmill motor and drive mechanism is located outside. The driveshaft passes through an airtight seal into the chamber. A water-cooled treadmill bedplate removes the heat of friction developed as the subject exercises on it.

The chamber, less its vestibule, occupies space approximately the size of a 12 x 20 foot laboratory module. A repair shop, which also contains the air conditioning compressors and treadmill drive components, occupies another module of space. Two additional modules are required for instrumentation and other needs associated with the chamber.

This special chamber is associated with special nursing facilities, details of which have been described elsewhere.[12] The nursing facilities make possible the complete collection of urine and stool specimens for metabolic balance studies. Additionally, metabolic kitchen facilities are required for the precise control of patient dietary intakes.

REFERENCES

1. Based on definitions from Health Research Facilities Branch, Division of Research Grants, National Institutes of Health, Public Health Service, Washington, D. C.
2. Based on data from Public Health Service patient bedroom lighting study now in progress and Report No. 1, IES Committee on Recommendations for Quality and Quantity of Illumination. *Illuminating Engineering*, 422–435, August 1958.
3. Smith, J. E., Lederer, L. G., and Mandes, J. C.:

Figure 10.47   Gas analysis instrumentation for indirect calorimetry shown at right and view looking into metabolic chamber.

Evaluation of the calibrated displacement velocity, and acceleration ballistocardiograph in angina pectoris. *Am. Heart J.* 49:3, 344–359, March 1955.

3a. Military Standard Attenuation Measurements for Enclosures, Electromagnetic Shielding, for Electronic Test Purposes, Method of (MIL-SID-285 25 June 1956), Superintendent of Documents, U. S. Government Printing Office, Washington 25, D. C.
4. Taylor, W. R., Mills, W. A., and Terrill, J. G., Jr.: Design of teletherapy units. Architectural Record. 216, 220, 227, 229, 231, Nov. 1957.
5. "Special Sources of Information on Isotopes," TID-4563 (Rev.), United States Atomic Energy Commission, Office of Industrial Development, Washington 25, D. C.
6. Ingraham, S. C., Taylor, W. R.: Radioisotope facilities in the general hospital. *Hospitals* 26: 74–78, December 1952.
7. "Recommendations for Waste Disposal of Phosphorus-32 and Iodine-131 for Medical Users," U. S. Department of Commerce, National Bureau of Standards Handbook 49, Supt. of Documents, Government Printing Office, Washington 25, D. C.
8. Utz, J. P., Parrott, R. H., and Kasel, J. A.: Diagnostic virus laboratory for clinical service.

J. Am. Med. Assoc. 163: 350–352, February 2, 1957.
9. "X-ray Protection Design," National Bureau of Standards Handbook 50, Superintendent of Documents, Government Printing Office, Washington 25, D. C. (20 cents)
10. "X-ray Protection," National Bureau of Standards Handbook 60, Supt. of Documents, Gov-

ernment Printing Office, Washington 25, D. C. (20 cents)
11. Metabolic Chamber, *Public Health Reports.* 72:12, December 1957.
12. Ceglarek, M. M., Bryant, B. E., Whedon, G. D.: A Manual for Metabolic Balance Studies. Public Health Service Publication No. 607, Supt. of Documents, Government Printing Office, Washington 25, D. C. (20 cents)

PART 4: ANIMAL QUARTERS AND EQUIPMENT

DIVISION OF RESEARCH SERVICES

National Institutes of Health
Bethesda, Maryland

Decisions concerning the size and arrangement of animal facilities are usually based on the type, size, and number of animals to be housed and on the complexity and requirements of the research. Obviously the health, comfort, and safety of both animals and personnel are major considerations. Rapid changes in programs and emphasis demand that these facilities be flexible, easily adaptable, and geared to possible future expansion. Orderly planning and design are particularly important in this area of laboratory construction. Problems posed by odors, refuse, insects, and escaped animals require special handling, especially where offices, laboratories, and animal quarters are in the same building. For these reasons, and to assure the production of uniform, healthy laboratory animals needed for research, sanitation is vitally essential in design as well as in practice.

GENERAL CONSIDERATIONS FOR ANIMAL QUARTERS

Location

In spite of the tendency to construct multi-storied structures to house laboratory animals, the optimum location of animal quarters is on the ground level. Although real estate costs for ground level construction are greater, they are often offset by subsequent savings in the labor and time required to transport animals, equipment, feed, bedding, and refuse.

Multi-level structures present numerous other problems of transportation and maintenance. Duplicate facilities must be installed to prevent interruptions in the event of mechanical failure of elevators, escalators, or dumbwaiters. The necessity for heavy foundations for upper stories and for vertical transportation and ventilation systems increases building costs substantially.

Where possible, construction of a separate, specially designed building is preferable to adaptation of an existing one. However, the housing of experimental animals in hospital or research buildings is an accepted practice, especially if the animals are in or adjacent to laboratories or in a centralized animal-holding section. Many investigators prefer to have animals housed near their laboratories, particularly for short-term studies in which the animals must be observed or treated frequently. In hospitals, it is advisable to locate animal quarters as far as possible from patient areas to eliminate animal sounds and odors.

Arrangement and Design

Good management of animal quarters provides separate rooms for each distinct function. For effective prevention of epidemics and intercurrent infections, separate rooms should be maintained for experimental, breeding, and quarantined animals. Species in use in different experiments, especially in infectious disease research, should also be in separate rooms.

Small rooms or closets near the animal rooms should be designated for the storage of cleaning equipment, disinfectants, and other materials in constant use. It is essential to assign a spacious area for clean food and bedding, taking care that these facilities are fire-, rodent- and vermin-proof, and easy to clean. Finally, an area should be provided for caging equipment not in use, rather than using valuable animal-room space for this purpose.

In large or specialized animal operations, separate but adjacent surgical and recovery suites are desirable additions (see Figure 10.48). These suites can serve a dual purpose and are especially useful for animal bathing and preparation. Today's animal surgeries are incorporating details common to hospital surgeries, such as ceiling-mounted operating lights. X-ray facilities convenient to the surgical suites have been found useful. A treatment room, a pharmacy, and diagnostic laboratory are also essential to a well-rounded facility.

In determining ideal sizes for animal rooms, the function of the room and the maintenance requirements of the species to be housed are primary considerations. Approximate sizes in the following areas are suggested.

Experimental. A room measuring 15 x 20 ft is satisfactory for most experimental areas, although larger rooms are often used to house several species for different studies.

Breeding. The maximum room size for a breeding colony should not exceed 30 x 30 ft and may be less where strains are maintained in small numbers. Ideally each strain of a species should be housed separately. In any case, not more than three strains of one species should occupy a small room.

Quarantine. Quarantined animals can best be observed in small groups, a practice which also minimizes the possibility of intercurrent infection. For this purpose, a small room measuring approximately 10 by 20 ft is adequate.

Flexibility in animal rooms can be achieved by dividing available space with movable partitions. In this way, a large area can be converted into several small rooms to meet changing program requirements.

The arrangement of rooms is a matter for careful consideration. Facilities should be designed to eliminate contacts and crossovers between clean and dirty (refuse) areas. It should not be necessary to pass through one animal room to get to another; therefore, rooms should open onto a corridor or central area. Separation of clean and refuse areas can be effected by locating a clean corridor on one side of a bank of rooms and a refuse corridor on the other (see Figure 10.49). Thus clean caging material, food, bedding, and personnel travel through the clean corridor into the animal rooms. Cans of refuse, trash, and soiled caging material move from the animal rooms into the refuse corridors.

INTERIOR FINISHING OF ANIMAL FACILITIES

Floors

Several commercial firms manufacture floor-surfacing compounds (for use in combination with cement) that are said to have vermin-repellent and/or germicidal properties. Although effective, these compounds are somewhat unattractive and their effect is nullified by painting. Proprietary cement-floor hardening and sealing compounds may be used to minimize dust and facilitate cleaning operations. Water-sealing compounds are also available, but the permanence of these compounds should be thoroughly inves-

Figure 10.48   View of an operating suite in the animal hospital.

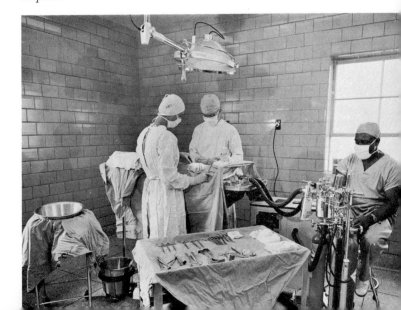

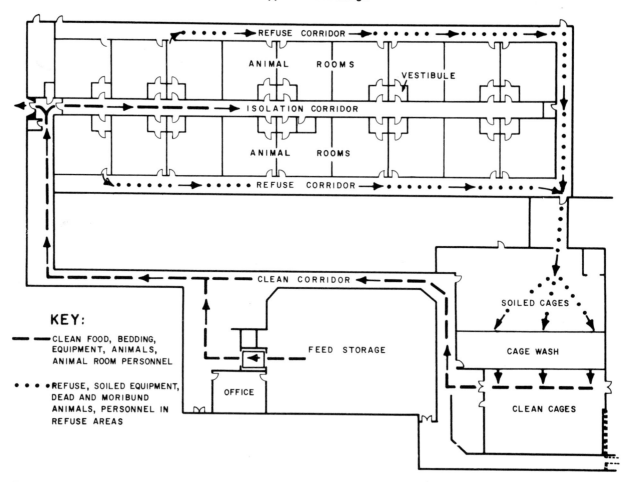

Figure 10.49   Animal facility illustrating separation of clean and refuse areas.

tigated before purchase. It is suggested that a waterproof diaphragm be laid under floor surfacing and extend at least 6 in. up the wall. Other materials used successfully for surfacing floors include concrete, tile, and aggregate compositions. For obvious reasons, wood and similar porous materials should not be used. Painted floor surfaces require frequent renewal and are easily marred.

The use of floor drains in animal rooms is largely a matter of choice and depends on the floor-surfacing material, the type of caging, and the species of animal. Floor drains are considered essential in colony type rooms and dog kennels, as considerable soil can be anticipated in these areas. Cleaning problems are simplified if easily

removable bucket-type drains are installed. A blind plate and gasket may be placed over the drain when not in use.

When drains are permanently built into animal quarters, the slope of the floor should be such that excess water can be squeegeed to the drain. Extreme slopes should be avoided, especially where removable cage stands are used. For maximum convenience, floors should be at the same level as those in the adjoining corridor. Floor sills at doorways are unnecessary.

Curbs

To prevent damage by moving vehicles and equipment, curbs can be installed at the bases of permanent walls. In the same manner, bumper rails may be used at the base of movable partitions. A recommended size for curbings is 6 in. in height, projecting about 4 in. into the room. These devices are also useful in preventing damage to electrical wall fixtures and temperature controls. For additional protection, replaceable shock-absorbent bumpers can be attached to movable equipment.

Walls

If no interior wall-finishing material is used, the exterior walls and load-bearing walls should be constructed of a smooth, moisture-resistant material. These criteria also apply where interior surfaces are bonded to the exterior wall.

Interior wall surfaces should be resistant to mechanical shock from cage racks and should have a nonabsorptive finish. Walls resistant to damage, yet easy to clean, may be composed of a wide variety of materials. Many types and sizes of interlocking sheetings are now available. These are easily applied and sealed with recommended adhesives.

A glazed tile wainscot or wall is advocated for its easily cleaned surface. Care must be taken, however, to protect tiles from damage by installing protective devices. The tile wainscot should extend from the floor to a height corresponding to the tallest cage rack. The wall above the wainscot may be finished with plaster painted with high-gloss enamel or other washable surface.

Prefabricated metal panels, finished with baked-on enamel, can be assembled on the building site. If these are used, care should be taken to seal all joints to prevent waste from accumulating in cracks and to minimize vermin infestation.

Screened vestibules and partitions erected within animal rooms should be designed to facilitate cleaning and to minimize insect and rodent harborage. Crevices can be avoided if partitions are constructed of chain link fencing or welded wire mesh and are set clear of the floor, wall, and ceiling by at least an inch. Cleaning is easier if metal pipe is used to frame these partitions.

Doors and Windows

The doors to animal rooms, especially in structures of mixed occupancy, should be equipped with door closers and self-sealing automatic door wipes. Vestibules equipped with inner and outer electrically interlocked doors are an effective precaution against animal escape. A metal door, mounted on at least four butt hinges, with a clear plate-glass window is highly recommended.

Doorknobs and lock cylinders are often damaged by contact with passing vehicles and portable cage stands. This problem can be minimized by installing recessed hardware, swinging "D" rings, or other devices. In heavy traffic areas, doors operated by photoelectric mechanisms such as electric eyes are convenient; they prevent damage to doors and door frames, but often require adjustment. Satisfactory control is obtained from pressure pads that actuate electrical equipment, or from hydraulic or pneumatic devices operated by pull chains or push buttons.

Doorways should be a minimum of 3½ ft wide by 7 ft high. It is essential that crevices between door frames and walls or partitions be caulked. For safety, doors should open into rooms, especially where there is heavy traffic in corridors. A single wide door is usually easier to operate than double doors.

Although it is strongly recommended that all animal rooms have controlled climatic conditions, it is considered desirable to install windows where possible, since some employees require an outside view for psychological reasons. Small-paned windows permanently fixed into the masonry are most satisfactory. Animal-room windows can be plate glass, wire-reinforced, anti-glare, or glass block.

Ceilings

A suspended ceiling that conceals all ductwork and piping is an effective means of reducing dust accumulation. The preferred ceiling material is stainless steel. However, plastic-coated panels or plaster ceilings have also proved satisfactory. Plaster should be securely bonded to metal lath and may be coated with a vinyl plastic or similar material.

Painting

The selection of paint for laboratory animal quarters is governed by the material to which the paint will be applied. To avoid cracking, masonry paint should be of a consistency and composition to penetrate and form a firm bond with surfaces. Plastic-coated panels are frequently impregnated with color at the time of manufacture and may be repainted when desired. Color is intended primarily to improve appearance, but room size and light reflection must be considered when colors are selected. Light colors, combinations of colors, or a wall of a different color often lend spaciousness and increases an employee's acceptance of his surroundings.

LIGHTING AND OUTLETS

Excellent illumination is provided by continuous bands of daylight-type fluorescent tubing, flush-mounted and covered with clear glass plates.

Double convenience outlets located at two or more diagonally opposite positions facilitate the use of portable electrical equipment. Cover plates for outlets not in use are essential. These plates should be sealed with a gasket, gasket-forming material, or caulking compound. For protection against moving equipment, switches and outlets may be recessed. To guard against electrical service disruptions, the number of rooms controlled by an individual circuit breaker should be limited.

PLUMBING

The most durable sink units are constructed of stainless steel, particularly those alloys containing nickel. Stainless sinks are easily cleaned and soil is readily detected. They are seldom, if ever, damaged and may be easily and permanently repaired by welding or silver soldering. Damaged stone sinks can be repaired with litharge or glycerine, but these corrections are not permanent.

Sinks are a necessity in animal rooms for washing special equipment, filling water containers, and washing hands. Even where hoses are not used for room cleaning, it is useful to have two sinks, diagonally opposite each other, in a large animal room.

Drainboards and cabinet space beneath sinks are rarely functional. Too often, they serve as collection spaces for unused equipment, are not cleaned frequently, and become breeding places

for vermin. Traps beneath sinks should have a threaded plug in the bottom of the "U" for removing glass particles and other insoluble debris.

The sink backsplash should be set either flush to or away from the wall by a least 4 inches. If the sink is butted against the wall, crevices should be sealed with a nonhardening caulking compound. It is advisable to select sink fixtures that have easily replaceable washers.

Faucets should be equipped with anti-syphoning devices and threaded for hose connections. Both hot and cold water faucets, controlled by hand and/or knee operation, are suggested. Valves should be located on all water lines to assure continuing service during repairs. Control of faucets by foot pedals has some merit, but breakdowns are frequent and debris may collect between the pedals and the floor. Aerating devices are not necessary for faucets.

Where hoses are used for cleaning purposes, hot and cold water faucets are generally affixed directly to walls. These faucets should be equipped with anti-syphoning devices and protected from damage. If steam is available, conveniently located outlets and hoses will permit occasional steam cleaning of rooms and permanent cages.

Permanent or semi-permanent watering devices affixed to cages are rarely practical and are not readily sanitized. If the water supply fails, these devices are useless. Automatic type fount valves may be used, but they are easily rendered inoperative by spring failure or by minute particles of bedding or food that lodge in the mechanism.

Fixed cage stands or permanent shelvings are often furnished with permanent watering devices that require additional plumbing facilities. Modern animal husbandry practices, however, incline toward mobile cage stands, in which case removable watering devices are most satisfactory.

Precautions should be taken to ensure that fixtures are carefully fitted. Failure to seal pipe openings in floors, walls, or partitions and spaces left between sinks and partitions, result in breeding places for insects and stray rodents.

HEATING AND VENTILATION

Year-around systems for controlling air, temperature, and humidity must be carefully considered in planning animal rooms. It is important that each have its own ventilation control system and that the air pressure in these rooms be higher than that in the adjoining corridors. Separate ventilation systems without recirculating air should be provided for breeding, experimental, and quarantine rooms, and for areas enclosing farm animals.

Fresh air introduced into animal rooms through perforated ductwork prevents drafts that encourage respiratory infections. Insulated wall panels are also a valuable aid in controlling temperatures.

Many investigations concerning the heat output of various species and the airflow required for acceptable odor levels and comfort have been published.[1,2,3] These data are extremely valuable in designing air-conditioning systems for animal quarters.

The extent to which the heat output of animals varies with activity is illustrated by Table 10.6[4].

Table 10.7[5] can be used to determine the odor-free air requirements of common species of laboratory animals.

Opinions concerning optimum temperatures for maintaining various laboratory animals are exceedingly varied. The importance of temperature control is emphasized by numerous publication describing the effect of enviromental temperature on the health and behavior of animals.[6-11] See Table 10.8.

Some humidity control is essential for experimental and breeding animals. To some extent, the amount of moisture in an animal room can be controlled by the frequency of air change, but this method sometimes makes odor control difficult. Relative humidities in the lower ranges frequently produce a condition in rats known as ringtail.[24]

TABLE 10.6
Heat Gain in Btu per Hour

ANIMAL	QUIET	ACTIVE	SENSIBLE
Rat	2.25	6.00	3.00
Mouse	0.50	1.32	0.66

NOTE: The animals studied concentrated 95% of their daily activity from 6 p.m. to 2 a.m. and were comparatively quiet for the remainder of the day.

TABLE 10.7
AVERAGE ODOR-FREE AIR REQUIREMENTS
(For Dilution of Odors to Threshold Concentrations in Animal Laboratories)
(*Average conditions per animal*)

ANIMAL	WEIGHT	HEAT GENERATION (BTU/HR.)	GROSS SPACE (CU FT)	ODOR-FREE AIR (CFM)
White mice	21 g	0.6	1.0	0.10
Rats	200 g	3.6	3.5	0.75
Rats	400 g	5.5	4.0	1.5
Guinea pigs	410 g	5.7	6.0	1.5
Rabbits	2.6 kg	19.0	10.0	2.0
Cats	3.0 kg	25.0	35.0	8.0
Monkeys	3.2 kg	25.0	100.0	20.0
Dogs	14.0 kg	80.0	150.0	50.0
Hen	2.1 kg	19.0	8.0	2.0
Cock	2.8 kg	24.0	8.0	2.0

NOTES:
(1) Btu values for animals in muscular repose 24 hours after feeding.
(2) Weights of dogs, which incidentally are the worst odor offenders, are subject to wide variation.
(3) Odor-free air volumes are average and suitable for use in design. Experience indicates, however, that the contemplated occupancy in proposed laboratories is often optimistically low and, therefore, allowance for more crowded occupancy is advisable.
(4) In all cases, 20% of the odor-free air should be displacement air from outdoors.

TABLE 10.8
RECOMMENDED
ANIMAL ROOM TEMPERATURE

ANIMAL	SUGGESTED TEMPERATURE (°F)		NIH PREFERENCE (°F)
Rats	50–70	Gordon[12]	73–77
	65–70	Worden & McGaughey[13]	
	65–75	Farris[14]	
Mice	70–80	Strong[15]	73–77
	65–75	Tuffery[16]	
Hamsters	68–80	Hindle & Magalhaes[17]	70–72
	70–80	Poiley[18]	
Guinea pigs	70–80	Ibsen[19]	72–74
	60–65	Paterson[20]	
Monkeys	75	Eckstein & Zuckerman[21]	76–79
Cats	70–72	Dawson[22]	75–77
	70–75	Scott[23]	
Rabbits			70–72

CAGING AND OTHER EQUIPMENT FOR ANIMAL QUARTERS

Design, Construction, and Location of Cages

Although most animal cages are designed to meet the needs of an individual species, flexibility is achieved by purchasing cages that can be used for two or more types of animals. An example of this versatility is the general-purpose cage used by the Animal Production Section at the National Institutes of Health (see Figure 10.50). This cage has been used successfully for rabbits, guinea pigs, rats, mice, hamsters, small monkeys, baby chicks, and several species of small wild rodents. In the same manner, a versatile dog cage comfortably accommodates monkeys, cats, small chimpanzees, and full-grown chickens and ducks.

Cages are best constructed of stainless steel. This material is long-lived, extremely durable, and has been in use long enough to demonstrate good corrosion resistance to animal excreta and urine. Although the initial cost is greater than for galvanized cages, the expense is offset by the elimination of periodic replacements. Fabrication that incorporates continuous-seam welding eliminates crevices caused by overlapping sheets in spot welding and adds to strength and durability.

Galvanized sheet metal has been used in caging for many years, but must be repeatedly coated

with zinc to prevent rusting. Because of its copper content, Monel metal has been found to corrode and pit when exposed to animal urines. Transparent acrylic plastic and "Plexiglass" cages have been used in some animal quarters. Some of these materials, however, are somewhat fragile and will not withstand temperatures above 145° F. Opaque plastics, such as polypropylene, show better resistance to impact and high temperatures.

One of the newest materials used in cage manufacture is plastic-impregnated glass fiber. It is heat-resistant at normal steam sterilizing temperatures and, to a great extent, resistant to shock. However, rodents confined in these cages have been known to gnaw holes in the material.

While the present tendency is toward portable caging equipment for laboratory animals, there are some installations where fixed cages are used for economy. In most facilities, however, permanent cages lack the versatility required by changing programs and tend to create excessive sanitation problems.

Movable cage racks mounted on casters should be no more than 5 ft long, 6 ft high, and 2 ft deep. Racks of this size are easily maneuverable and can be serviced by a person of average height. Portable cages and racks can be easily cleaned in automatic washing equipment. They may also be removed temporarily for thorough cleaning of the animal room. Animal facilities are more versatile if cages can be interchanged and several cage sizes used in the same room. Ideally, cage stands or racks should be designed to hold more than one type of cage.

It should be pointed out that permanent cages may be practical for certain uses, such as for holding dogs, cats, and primates in surgical suites. Where built-in cages are used, they must be provided for in the building plans. Fabrication materials include slate and metal.

In some laboratories, wire cages are suspended above paper rolls which collect urine and feces. For general use, however, these cages create excessive sanitation problems and are believed to be uncomfortable for the animals.

Cage Washing and Sterilizing

To assure the maintenance of healthy laboratory animals, thorough cleaning of caging

Figure 10.50   General purpose cage for small animals.

equipment is extremely important. The type of machine or device selected for this purpose is determined by the number and kinds of cages that must be serviced.

Machines that utilize an alkaline detergent spray wash, followed by one or more rinses, are effective in removing soils from caging equipment. In principle these machines are similar to those used for mechanical dishwashing. Fan pattern nozzles are usually positioned to direct powerful streams of wash water, at nozzle pressures of at least 25 psi, onto the cages from many angles. For more effective spray coverage, the cages are also mechanically rotated, oscillated, or moved by conveyer. In some machines, the cages remain stationary and the nozzle headers rotate or oscillate.

Satisfactory water temperatures for cage washing range from 140° to 180° F. Satisfactory wash-rinse cycles are from one to three minutes in duration and frequently last for 15 minutes or longer. The resulting cleaning-pasteurizing process reduces the need for cage sterilization to special situations.

Figure 10.51 shows a conveyer type machine for washing small and medium-size cages. The accompanying rotary table type machine washes stands and large cages on casters. Wash solution tanks, rinse tanks, and pumps are located in a pit below the room floor. Stainless steel construction was used in this installation to minimize corrosion and other maintenance problems. The ventilation hood at the end of this conveyer type machine and the insulated panels on the housing and tanks help to contain the heat load.

An oscillating nozzle type of machine for washing cages and stands is illustrated in Figure 10.52. Although wash spray coverage is generally more effective in the rotary table system, the oscillating nozzle type is usually cheaper and requires less space than a rotary table type of the same load size. Figure 10.53 shows a small rotary table type cage washing machine constructed of stainless steel. The design includes a vertical immersion type of centrifugal pump which reduces leakage from packing glands. An electrically controlled dispenser automatically maintains the preset concentration of detergent in the wash solution.

Figure 10.51 Conveyor and rotary table type washing machines for cleaning animal cages.

Figure 10.52 Oscillating nozzle type machine for washing cages and stands.

Figure 10.53 Small rotary table type cage washing machine.

For small research facilities, manual washing methods augmented by steam-detergent or compressed air-detergent spray-gun devices may be successfully used. Figure 10.54 shows a spray booth in a central cleaning room equipped with a gas-fired steam generator with a detergent tank, hoses, and a spray gun. Glazed tile walls with quarry tile floor and coving help keep this facility sanitary and easy to clean.

Additional Equipment

In so-called "germ-free" or "specific pathogen-free" animal colonies, specialized equipment must be added for sterilizing food, bedding, and air and for conveying these products to the animal enclosures.

It may at times be necessary for an institution to manufacture its own pelleted rations. In this case, it is advisable to maintain adequate storage space for raw materials and finished product and to set up a testing laboratory.

To eliminate the need for returning refilled water bottles to the cage of origin, an automatic bottle washing, sterilizing, and filling machine can be acquired. Filled bottles leave this type of machine capped with a disposable cover. Rubber stoppers and tubes, processed in a similar ma-

chine, are returned to the animal room in sealed containers for positioning on the bottles. It is also possible to sanitize and fill animal food holders in automatic machinery.

Transportation of Equipment

In large installations or where animal quarters are located on different levels, the movement of caging equipment creates a serious problem. Generally, movement is expedited if more than one unit of equipment is transported at a time. Where the building design includes two or more parallel corridors, one can be designated for freight and cage transportation.

Vertical. Movement from one level to another can be accomplished by elevators, escalators, or dumbwaiters. The method of choice should include duplicate equipment to compensate for mechanical breakdowns. Manually operated dumbwaiters can be installed for temporary use during power failures.

Horizontal. Time and labor are conserved if caging equipment is designed so that individual units can be connected in trains and towed by an electric tractor. Other methods include the installation of an overhead monorail, below-floor monorail, an endless chain below the floor equipped with hooks or electromagnets, or a moving belt. For sanitary purposes, the overhead monorail is preferable.

Figure 10.54   Spray booth and steam generator for cleaning caging equipment in a small laboratory facility.

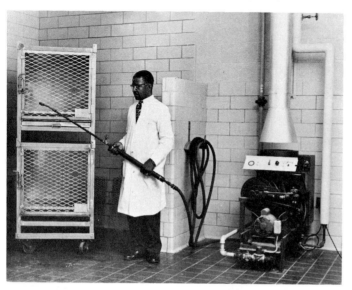

REFERENCES

1. Benedict, F. G. and MacLeod, G.: The heat production of the albino rat. I. Technique, activity control, and the influence of fasting. *J. Nutrit.,* 1:343–366 (March 1929).
2. Benedict, F. G. and MacLeod, G.: The heat production of the albino rat. II. Influence of environmental temperature, age, and sex: comparison with the basal metabolism of man. *Ibid.,* 1:367–398, May 1929.
3. Stoecker, W. F.: "Refrigeration and air conditioning." New York, McGraw-Hill Book Co., Inc., 1958.
4. Ruddy, J. M.: Air conditioning rodent quarters. *Heating and Ventilating,* 49:95 (March 1952).
5. Munkelt, F. H.: Air purification and deodorization by the use of activated carbon. *Refrig. Eng.,* 56:6 (Sept. 1948).

6. Chen, K. K., Anderson, R. C., Steldt, F. A., and Mills, C. A.: Environmental temperature and drug action in mice. *J. Pharm. Exp. Ther.*, **79**: 127–132 (Oct. 1943).

7. Fuller, R. H., Brown, E., and Mills, C. A.: Environmental temperatures and spontaneous tumors in mice. *Cancer Res.*, **1**: 130–133 (1941).

8. Hellmer, L. A.: The effect of temperature on the behavior of the white rat. *Am. J. Psychol.*, **56**: 408–421 (1943).

9. Mills, C. A. and Schmidt, L. H.: Environmental temperatures and resistance to infection, *Am. J. Trop. M. Hyg.*, **22**: 655–660 (Nov. 1942).

10. Mills, C. A.: Environmental temperatures and thiamin requirements. *Am. J. Physiol.*, **133**: 525–531 (July 1941).

11. Mills, C. A.: Influence of environmental temperatures on warm-blooded animals. *Ann. N. York Acad. Sci.*, **46**: 97–105 (June 1945).

12. Gordon, W. S.: Quoted in Worden, A. N. and Lane-Petter, W. (ed.): *The UFAW Handbook on the Care and Management of Laboratory Animals.* London, Universities Federation for Animal Welfare, 1957, p. 344.

13. Worden, A. N. and McGaughey, C. A.: The Norway rat. In Worden, A. N. (ed): *The UFAW Handbook on the Care and Management of Laboratory Animals,* Baltimore, Williams and Wilkins Co., 1947, p. 111.

14. Farris, E. J.: The rat as an experimental animal. In Farris, E. J. (ed.): *The Care and Breeding of Laboratory Animals.* New York, John Wiley and Sons, Inc., 1950, P. 44.

15. Strong, L. C.: The care of experimental mice. *Ibid.*, p. 81.

16. Tuffery, A. A.: The mouse. In Worden, A. N. and Lane-Petter, W. (ed.): *The UFAW Handbook on the Care and Management of Laboratory Animals,* London, Universities Federation for Animal Welfare, 1957, p. 244.

17. Hindle, E. and Magalhaes, H.: The golden hamster. *Ibid.*, p. 326.

18. Poiley, S. M.: Breeding and care of the Syrian hamster. In Farris, E. J. (ed.): *The Care and Breeding of Laboratory Animals,* New York, John Wiley and Sons, Inc., 1950, p. 124.

19. Ibsen, H. C.: The guinea pig. *Ibid.*, p. 97.

20. Paterson, J. S.: The guinea pig. In Worden, A. N. and Lane-Petter, W. (ed.): *The UFAW Handbook on the Care and Management of Laboratory Animals,* London, Universities Federation for Animal Welfare, 1957, p. 207.

21. Eckstein, P. and Zuckerman, S.: Monkeys. *Ibid.,* p. 665.

22. Dawson, A. B.: The domestic cat. In Farris, E. J. (ed.): *The Care and Breeding of Laboratory Animals.* New York, John Wiley and Sons, Inc., 1950, p. 204.

23. Scott, P. P., Da Silva, A. C., and Lloyd-Jacob, M. A.: The cat. In Worden, A. N. and Lane-Petter, W. (ed.): *The UFAW Handbook on the Care and Management of Laboratory Animals,* London, Universities Federation for Animal Welfare, 1957, p. 484.

24. Flynn, R. J.: Studies on the etiology of ring-tail. *Proc. Animal Care Panel.* Nov. 1958. Unpublished.

PART 5: HIGH-PRESSURE LABORATORY FACILITIES

E. J. BRADBURY

Battelle Memorial Institute
Columbus, Ohio

Significant advances have been made in recent years in the diversity of uses and in the range of pressure applications. Pressure technology is employed under several atmospheres of pressure at ambient or lower temperatures in organic intermediate synthesis and in the production of synthetic minerals under pressures greater than 1,500,000 psi and temperatures above 5000°F.[33] Specialized studies using shock-wave pressure techniques have produced transient pressures around 15,000,000 psi. Recent advances in superpressure techniques have been summarized by Simon.[41]

The extreme complexity and broad field of pressure utilization in research today precludes complete coverage in a general laboratory publication. Considerable emphasis was placed on the chemical process pressure laboratories in "Laboratory Design" (1951). Since much of the information presented by Dr. Savage is still valid, the present report on high-pressure laboratories will expand the scope of this section and present information on current facilities and techniques. Problems involved in the planning of pressure laboratory facilities will be reviewed and general recommendations presented where possible. The scope of this work, however, will prevent detailed presentation, so frequent reference will be made to additional source material.

Regardless of the ultimate use to which a given pressure laboratory will be placed, pressure facilities have several features in common:

(1) The inherent hazards, which must be evaluated and intelligently handled.

(2) The need for properly trained personnel to keep the calculated risk as low as possible.

(3) A need for specialized pressure equipment and facilities.

(4) A need for tools for maintaining facilities in safe working condition.

In addition to considering factors which will influence the specific construction, layout, and equipment for the contemplated pressure facility, provision must be made for the conventional laboratory services, such as air, water, electricity, drainage, ventilation, and possibly gas.

LABORATORY LOCATION AND BARRICADE CONSTRUCTION

Recommended location and barricade construction depend on the estimated degree of hazard of the work contemplated for the laboratory. In general, the higher the kinetic energy of the system, the more isolated the facilities and the more extensive the protection should be. High-pressure gas and/or exothermic reactions present the greatest hazard, and barricades should be provided accordingly. Hydraulic systems normally do not possess the hazard of a gas system. Considerable energy can be present, however, if the system is large or if the test temperature is above the boiling temperature of the fluid. Thus, in the event of equipment failure, flash vaporization occurs, with blast and hot vapor danger. Hydraulic systems in which the kinetic energy is limited may be handled in less isolated locations and with less barricading.

The philosophy of protection varies widely for these applications. Some laboratories use no protection other than the factor of safety designed into the equipment. Other research organizations install protective barricading and safety features for all pressure applications. There are at present no well-established methods for the derivation of satisfactory minimal barricade protection, since the service requirements cannot be accurately predicted. A number of methods have been developed for calculation of barricading based upon system energy, wall loading, or missile penetration.[23, 31, 32] In order to provide completely reliable protection, barrier designs should be based on the estimated maximum hazard of the system.

There is a great diversity of barricade construction among the various pressure laboratories. However, since the type of research determines to a great extent the most satisfactory and convenient barricade for a given application, the selection must rest with the design engineer after consideration of the specific requirements.

Barricades employed in the more hazardous and high kinetic energy applications must be designed to withstand four types of loading:

(1) Small, high-velocity fragments such as tubing, nuts or other small fittings.[17] These generally have a high degree of penetrability and will pass through unreinforced, steel-plate barricades.

(2) Large missiles such as a reactor head moving at a low velocity compared to the small fragments. These require a barrier capable of absorbing the impact without damage to the barricade. Reinforced concrete walls are often spalled by such an impact and the flying chunk of concrete becomes a hazard in the operating area. This is prevented in many laboratories by the installation of an antispall plate on the operating side of the barricade.

(3) The shock wave of a detonation within the equipment, which results in a heavy, directionalized, high-intensity loading.

(4) The blast effect from a ruptured pressure vessel or space explosion. Wall loading due to this factor is generally minimized by the inclusion of a blast relief wall in the protective barricade design. A minimum of 5 sq ft of venting area per 100 cu ft of volume is recommended by Stephens, *et al.*[43] for cubicles housing pressure equipment.

Similar venting ratios are suggested by the work of Hartmann, *et al.*[18] from their study of dust explosions.

Blast and missile barriers currently used in pressure laboratory applications may range from the safety factor of the equipment to several feet of heavily reinforced concrete. Safety records, however, consistently point to the advisability of making barricades a primary safety feature of laboratories engaged in research involving pressure. Several excellent discussions of various barricading systems have been published.[10, 11a, 28, 37]

Satisfactory protection is obtained from a metal shield around three sides of the reactors to protect personnel from blast and flying fragments. Metal thickness may vary from ⅜ to ¾ in. depending upon the reactor size and anticipated hazard. However, the trend in work involving pressure reactions and high-hazard processes continues to be toward an isolated location using a heavy-walled, totally enclosed cubicle with a blast-relief wall facing a hill, revetment, or large open space. This is a more expensive installation,

but service limitations are higher, and more hazardous materials and work can be handled safely.

Both B. F. Goodrich and Union Carbide and Chemicals Company's barricades, reported in the 1951 edition of "Laboratory Design"[10], have given satisfactory service without significant modification. The latter system was followed in the construction of new pressure laboratory facilities (Figures 10.55 and 10.56) at the National Carbon Company, Parma, Ohio. B. F. Goodrich's original pressure laboratory building (20 x 50 ft) was lengthened, and two more bunkers of the same construction and size incorporated in the 33 ft addition. These cells are about 8 ft 6 in. wide and 10 ft long. Three sides of the cells are reinforced concrete walls 1 ft thick, the fourth wall acting as blast relief. A laboratory and office area 12 x 33 ft also was added to the building on the side opposite the bunker openings. This provides facilities for chemical laboratory operations and office facilities for technical personnel working within the building.

Figure 10.55   Floor plan and cell design.

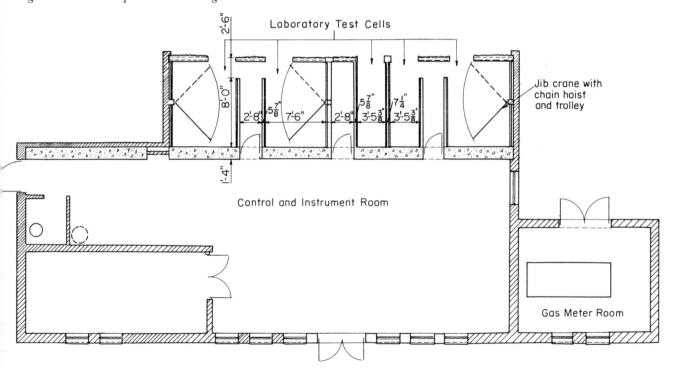

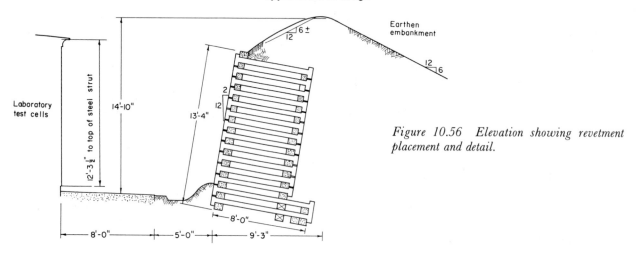

Figure 10.56   Elevation showing revetment placement and detail.

In addition to the expansion of the original facility, a new building 50 x 43 ft was constructed. This has four bunkers similar in construction to those in the original building. Laboratory and desk space, locker room, and a service area were incorporated in this structure.

A similarly reinforced concrete barricade construction was used by The Dow Chemical Company, Texas Division. Cubicles at this installation are 3 ft 8 in. x 5 ft 10 in. Barrier sidewalls and ceiling are reinforced concrete 8 in. thick. The operating face of the cell is reinforced concrete 12 in. thick. Figures 10.57 and 10.58 show details of these facilities.

Figure 10.57   Pressure laboratory floor plan.

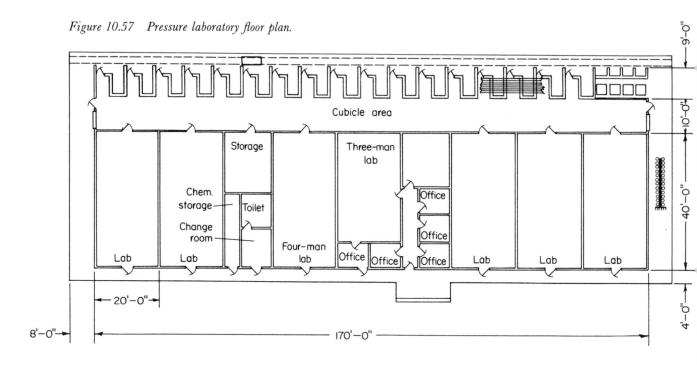

A similar laboratory arrangement was used by Linde Company in their Tonawanda Pressure Laboratory. Operations are planned to function about a control corridor with test cells on one side and laboratory, shop, and offices on the other. The main wall, separating the cells and control area, consists of 18-in. heavily reinforced concrete backed up by a ¼-in. steel plate 6 in. inside the corridor for spall protection. Cells are 8 ft deep, from 6 to 14 ft in width and 10 ft high. Unistrut channels are embedded in the floor and control wall for mounting equipment. Two ½-in. steel plates are welded to the inside of a 10 WF column (Figure 10.59) and the space filled with sand to give a resilient energy-absorbing side wall. The blast wall (1 sq ft per 10 cu ft) faces the revetment shown in Figure 10.60. The earth mound, 9 ft from the cell wall, is faced with concrete cribbing and 2 in. tongue-and-groove soft planking to stop flying fragments.

Figure 10.59   Interior of pressure cell.

Figure 10.60   View of Blast wall and revetment.

Figure 10.58   Cubicle detail.

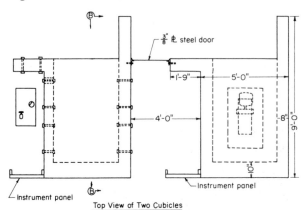

Top View of Two Cubicles

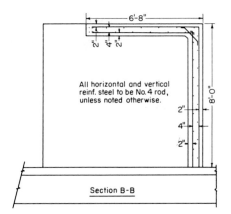

All horizontal and vertical reinf. steel to be No. 4 rod, unless noted otherwise.

Section B-B

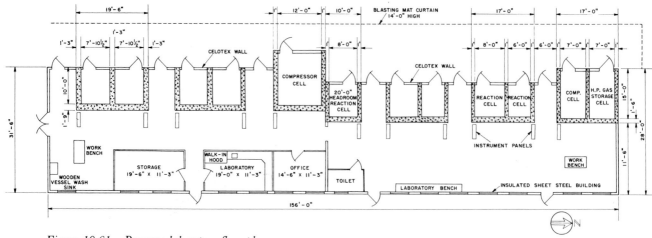

Figure 10.61   Pressure laboratory floor plan.

The recently constructed Standard Oil Company (Indiana) Pressure Laboratory[20] consists of 12 reinforced concrete cells (Figure 10.61) arranged along the long side of a rectangular building with the weak "Celotex" side facing a swampy lake area. The construction of an adjacent building necessitated hanging a blasting mat curtain (Figure 10.62) along this side about 10 ft from the blast wall. The operating and office areas are housed in a "Celotex" insulated sheet metal building. Heating and ventilating is by two forced air fans of sufficient capacity to change the air every five minutes. Each cell is also equipped with a blower giving a complete air change every minute. All cells have a 12 ft head room except one which has a 20 ft ceiling. The cell roofs are reinforced concrete 1 ft thick.

In contrast to the solid construction of the reinforced concrete cubicles, Harwood Engineering uses a wooden, earth-covered bunker shown in Figure 10.63. The unanchored construction of this bunker permits it to give to absorb the energy released in an explosion. These cells were constructed by stacking wooden railroad ties over and around a steel framework and covering the entire assembly with dirt. Such construction is rapid and inexpensive. Operation, however, requires complete remote control, since a thick covering of earth is required to give adequate protection.

Figure 10.62   View of blast wall and fragment net.

It has been suggested that the mass of the totally enclosed concrete cubicles gives a psychological lift to the worker. An accepted advantage of the totally enclosed cubicle is that standard electrical equipment can be used in the control area and control laboratory providing complete isolation is practiced and satisfactory positive ventilation is maintained. However, it is advisable to use vapor or explosion-proof lights and fixtures at points of high hazard within the cubicle. This lessens the likelihood of a space explosion within the cubicle in the event of equipment failure. However, a possible source for space explosion ignition is always present whenever electrical resistance units are used for heating. Oil or "Dowtherm" heated units may be used to lessen this hazard.

Considerable reference has been made to the construction of safety barricades for chemical processing studies. These have been based on the principle of a strong, blast-resistant, box-like structure. However, an innovation has been added to the totally enclosed reaction cubicle by The Dow Chemical Company, which merits discussion. This design (Figure 10.64) makes use of permanently mounted blast-resistant walls and ceiling for an extremely small reaction space. A frangible wall is provided in the rear of the cubicle for blast relief. The front of the cubicle consists of a steel panel anchored securely to a skid upon which is mounted the reactor. The skid and panel are easily handled by a lift truck (Figure 10.65), so the loaded skid can be slid into the cubicle and the panel securely bolted at the top. This allows the skid and front panel to function as a ballistic pendulum to absorb kinetic energy in the event of an explosion. This cubicle is reported by Miller[26] to have the following advantages:

(1) Improved built-in safety features make it impossible for operators to expose themselves to the reactor during the course of the reaction.

(2) Ease of construction and maintenance. The portability of the skid permits the entire unit to be moved to the shop for servicing and the free access to all sides of the equipment greatly facilitates maintenance.

(3) Ease of charging and discharging the reactor is improved by the portability of the unit which permits it to be moved to the laboratory for servicing.

(4) Improved flexibility of the reaction units are derived by making the unit so it will fit any reaction cubicle, or transferred to a storage area when not in use.

(5) Better utilization of high-pressure equipment and instruments is obtained since the same instruments can be used for any reaction in any cubicle.

The principle of the ballistic pendulum for absorbing kinetic energy generally is used more widely in enclosing hydraulic systems than in

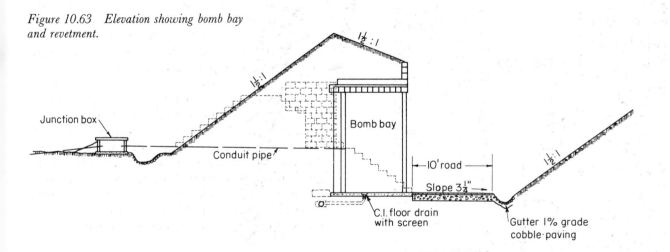

Figure 10.63 Elevation showing bomb bay and revetment.

Figure 10.64   View showing cubicle and blast relief wall.

Figure 10.65   Magnadash unit and skid in position for installation in reaction cell.

barricading chemical process equipment. In the former application, adequate protection is obtained by installing safety shields to arrest flying fragments without the necessity of providing blast protection. A comprehensive analysis of the application of the ballistic pendulum protection was conducted by O. L. Anderson, Bell Telephone Laboratories and D. H. Newhall, Harwood Engineering Company.[1] They concluded that barricading with the ballistic pendulum mounting is more effective than with rigidly mounted barriers. The Bell Telephone Laboratory pressure cells consist of a series of box-like spaces rigidly constructed from a suitable metal framing material, as shown in Figure 10.66. The front panel is permanently and rigidly mounted to provide personnel protection. Equipment and controls are mounted on the top plate of the cell to facilitate easy removal by hoisting the assembly out of the cell. Cells are separated by a suspended plate on the sides and back to absorb energy of rupture and deflect fragments. Where it is necessary to allow pressure equipment to protrude above the top plate of the cell, the unit is covered with a heavy metal cap which surrounds it and is free to shift upward to absorb energy released by rupture of the unit.

Current practice in the shock-wave research at the Poulter Laboratory, Stanford Research Institute, employs a different approach to safety. The use of explosives for production of extremely high pressures precludes a reaction or test of prolonged duration such as is normal in synthesis or physical studies under pressure. Tests are made in an isolated test area, using open-air or sand-pit detonations. Since blast effects from detonations require protection against high-energy shock waves and fragments, the protective structures for housing test personnel and equipment are heavy-walled bunkers made of thick sections of reinforced concrete faced with metal or other types of construction suitable for use in ordnance work. While heavy timber and sod-covered bunkers are inexpensive and quickly installed, the thickness of the earth-timber barrier required to give satisfactory protection for extremely high-energy systems results in cumbersome structures. Current ordnance publications appear to favor reinforced concrete for personnel protection.

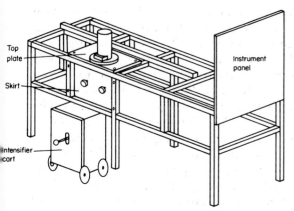

Isometric View of Pressure Cubicles and Control Facilities

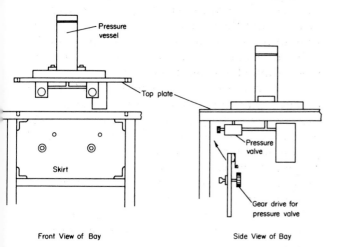

Front View of Bay   Side View of Bay

Figure 10.66   Pressure cubicles.

Precautions must be taken during the construction of the safety wall for any high-hazard pressure work to provide adequate reinforcement against shock-wave destruction. Studies have shown that the major destructive effect of shock waves comes from failure of the barricade in tension at a plane within the wall parallel to the face of the wall. This phenomenon has been discussed at length.[31, 40] Severity of the destruction of the barricade may be lessened by several expedients. Reinforcing metal may be installed within the barricade in a web arrangement such that optimum reinforcement of the tensile strength of the wall is provided. The metal configuration, known

as the Warren truss (Figure 10.67) is recommended for reinforcing bomb-resistant structures.[31] Another expedient is to construct the wall in several thicknesses to give a series of explosion-resistant barriers similar to the sandwich type of barrier construction.

Regardless of the ultimate use to which a protective structure will be placed, several general points of construction apply:

(1) The design should be adequate to provide satisfactory protection for the maximum possible hazard.

(2) Steel-plate barricade walls should be designed with either welded seams or lap construction to avoid the use of bolts or rivets under tension. Accidents involving bolted or riveted

Figure 10.67   Warren truss reinforcing in bomb resistant structures.

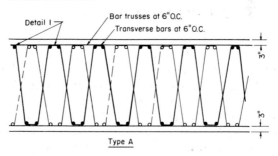

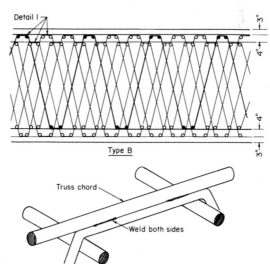

barricades have indicated that failure of the joining member can produce missiles on the operating side of the barrier.

(3) Steel or sandwich panels should be anchored to members that are an integral part of the building rather than expansion bolts in the floor to prevent overturning of the barricade by a major blast.

(4) Revetments or embankments facing the blast wall should be graded to reduce the rebound of shock wave into the reaction area.

(5) Revetments should be faced with a material, blast mat or wood, capable of retaining flying missiles.

(6) Installation of either automatic or manually operated fire extinguishers is advisable where the possibility exists for fire following equipment failure. Carbon dioxide is generally preferred to foam or water.

SAFETY PROGRAM AND LABORATORY FACILITIES

Adequate barricades should be considered the primary protection against laboratory mishaps and personnel injury. However, any accident involving pressure equipment is undesirable, since it frequently involves prolonged down time and loss of expensive equipment. Consequently, the following factors are also extremely vital to the safe operation and utility of the laboratory:

(1) Personnel, properly trained and qualified;

(2) Safety regulations, realistic and operative;

(3) Safety devices on all pressure units;

(4) Laboratory tools, adequate for maintenance and operation of laboratory facilities;

(5) Periodic inspection of pressure equipment and accessories;

(6) Ventilation, adequate to prevent accumulation of gas or vapors.

Personnel

Next to adequate barricades for protection against the completely unforeseen accidents (a runaway reaction, fatigue failure of a fitting, and improper sequencing of operations), properly trained personnel are the best insurance against accidents. Here, the protection lies in the ability of laboratory personnel to anticipate either a troublesome reaction or possible equipment difficulty and to provide a remedy before the situation gets out of hand. The laboratory supervisor should have a basic knowledge of the temperature-stress relationship of the laboratory units, and of the allowable limits of temperature operation of the equipment. Where chemical studies are involved, a knowledge of the corrosive effects of the reagents on the equipment is necessary. A broad knowledge of the properties of the pressure equipment and complete information on the projected work will permit the laboratory head to evaluate the hazard of the contemplated work and to proceed safely. Proper background will often prevent costly mistakes. However, where the field of operation is unexplored, discretion dictates that the system be kept as small as possible to minimize the potential hazard and the safety of installation be made adequate to provide shrapnel and blast protection.

Aside from the broad technical background required of the supervisory personnel, mechanical proficiency is the primary skill involved in the use of pressure facilities. The operator should possess good mechanical aptitude to permit him properly to prepare, install, test, and run equipment under nominal supervision. Mechanical aptitude and alertness on the part of the operator will facilitate the discovery of malfunctioning of equipment in time for corrective measures to be taken.

Safety Regulations

Safety rules and instructions should be aimed at protecting the operator from inadvertently making either a costly or a dangerous mistake. Normally, laboratory rules vary considerably with the type of work being conducted. However, these rules always represent a compilation of common sense directives designed to alert laboratory personnel to unsafe practices. *The responsibility for providing adequate training and an understanding of hazards involved in operating procedures must rest with the technically trained personnel.* No one should be permitted to operate a pressure unit until the laboratory engineer is satisfied that the worker is familiar with the function of the control equipment, knows what steps to take in the event of an emergency, and will not panic.

Thus, a primary rule of pressure laboratory safety is, "No one operates pressure laboratory equipment until his competence has been established."

Safety Devices

No pressure unit should be installed for operation without adequate and properly located safety devices, such as rupture or relief valve assemblies. At least three firms (Baker and Company, Black, Sivalls and Bryson, and Frangible Discs, Inc.) manufacture safety discs for sale. Two types of assemblies, the shear plate[38] and the rupture disc,[29, 30, 44] are used for pressure vessel protection. Most commercial units are of the burst type. Such commercial rupture assemblies are currently available for service up to 100,000 psi (Figure 10.68). Fail-safe rupture or relief protection should be integral with the bomb or as close to it as possible. While rapid, more positive pressure relief is obtained by making the safety device integral with the reactor, proper allowance then must be made for the capacity and stress behavior of the disc at operating temperature. For this reason, rupture disc manufacturers routinely request operating temperature data before recommending a unit.

It should be emphasized that rupture assemblies will not protect the unit against detonation shock waves or against pressure from overheating when the wall material is weakened at a rate faster than the rupture disc. Thus, rupture disc protection does not eliminate the need for adequate barricades.

All pumps, compressors, and flow systems should be protected with safety assemblies, both upstream and downstream to the unit. The rating of the pop-valve or rupture assembly should be specified to protect the weakest member of the immediate system. This is especially important where several weights of pressure tubing are used in a system, where a high-pressure unit feeds into a high-temperature reactor, or where a pressure booster is fed from a light-weight closed system. Proper installation of the safety units thus protects the weak points of the system against a dangerous build-up of pressure due to leaking valves or accidental opening of the wrong valve.

It is preferable to mount all pressure equipment, tubing, and accessories behind protective panels. This offers complete protection in the event of any failure. This, however, has several disadvantages and consequently is sometimes disregarded. Mounting valves behind barricades requires either remote operation by means of gears, reach rods, or power-driven units. When manual operation is used, the remote manipulation sometimes robs the operator of the feel of the valve, and destructive tightening results. A spring clutch may be used to prevent this on either manual or power-driven valves.

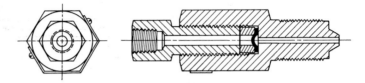

Figure 10.68   100,000 PSI rupture disc assembly, Black, Sivalls and Bryson.

Frequently, valve manifolds are mounted outside the barricades on the less hazardous operations and reliance placed on the high factor of safety of the valves and tubing and upon relief protection at the reactor. However, it is advisable to mount gages, rupture assemblies, and other accessories which are the potential points of failure in the cell. Bullet-proof glass portholes may be installed in the operating face of the cell to provide visibility, or remote-reading instruments may be used. These units and tubing should be firmly anchored to prevent whip in case of failure. Flow systems which are potentially highly exothermic should be protected by surge check valves to prevent pressure surges from the reactor from back-flowing into feed streams. Temperature controllers should be equipped with overheat and thermocouple break protection. The additional cost of this extra easily pays for itself by saving a single unit from destructive overheating.

Laboratory Tools

Proper tools are invaluable in maintaining a high degree of versatility and safety in the pressure laboratory. Laboratory equipment should include bomb-handling facilities, such as a portable hoist, bomb dolly or monorail hoist which eliminates the need for manual handling of the larger pressure units. Shop facilities should be available for reconditioning equipment. It is not imperative that these facilities be an integral part of the pressure laboratory, but many organizations have found it expedient to provide such facilities in conjunction with the laboratory. Power tools are extremely convenient in the maintenance and reconditioning of equipment, providing laboratory personnel qualified to operate them are available. Tools which have proved valuable for maintaining pressure facilities include a lathe, drill press, power drill, power hacksaw, and bench grinder.

It appears advisable to isolate shop facilities from both the pressure control area and the chemical or physical laboratory facilities (Figure 10.69). This will prevent dust and oil vapors from grinding and reconditioning operations from getting into the reaction or the control units. Isolation of the chemical laboratory from other facilities is also advisable to prevent attack of valuable equipment by corrosive chemicals fre-

quently employed in the laboratory. Where corrosive, noxious, or toxic materials are employed in pressure studies, it is imperative that bomb-handling facilities be installed in a fume hood or that adequate ventilation be provided to safeguard personnel opening or working with the equipment.

Inspection

A realistic program of inspection and preventive maintenance pays dividends in greater operating safety and more reliable equipment. Periodic inspection of pressure equipment should be made to determine whether signs of corrosion or erosion are present and whether any fatigue or creep has occurred. During this inspection, it is well to clean out threads and replace worn thrust bolts or other worn or damaged parts. Initial examination of the equipment with X-ray to determine whether pot holes or slag inclusions are present is valuable, but subsequent examinations may omit this inspection. Crystal structure or phase changes which produce weakening are difficult to detect, although ultrasonic or fluorescent penetrant techniques will reveal many flaws. As a safeguard, many laboratories recommend periodic hydrostatic tests of the equipment at 1.5 to 2.0 times the working pressure. Diameter measurements are taken prior to the test, during the test, and after the pressure has been released and the unit allowed to return to equilibrium. These measurements are filed and periodically the unit is retested and the test dimensions compared with the original values. Hydrostatic testing is normally considered a relatively safe procedure. Nevertheless, it is advisable to pressure-test behind barricades and to fill the unit under test with a noncompressible metal plug to minimize the stored energy in the event the unit is so weakened that failure does occur.

Gauges and control equipment should be periodically inspected and calibrated to insure the validity of results and to prevent inadvertent operation under unsafe conditions. All reconditioned pressure equipment should be leak tested using an inert gas prior to use. It is advisable to maintain a complete file of pressure equipment showing the material of construction and service life. This file can be extremely valuable to the

Figure 10.69   Pressure laboratory floor plan.

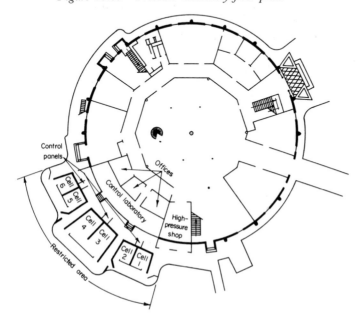

engineer in determining whether the equipment is suitable for a given task.

Ventilation

The current trend in ventilation of pressure facilities involving noxious or toxic gases and chemical processing is toward positive pressure within the operating area and vent fans within the reaction area. Make-up air is introduced into the control area through ceiling pans or outlet panels. Ventilation systems which depend upon air infiltration around windows and doors are seldom efficient or safe, especially where highly hazardous, flammable, or toxic materials are used. Ventilating practices disclosed during this survey varied from 12 to 30 changes per hour in the laboratory buildings and up to a change every minute in the cells. However, the rate of air turnover required is greatly dependent upon the construction of the laboratory and the nature of the work conducted.

Thus, a laboratory in which cubicles consist of three-sided shields facing a blast or conventional wall will require a more rapid replacement of air to prevent fumes, gases, or vapors from working back into the operating area than one in which the reaction area is sealed from the operating area both by cubicle construction and a positive-pressure air barrier. Also, the requirements will vary considerably depending on the noxious and toxic character of the materials involved.

PRESSURE EQUIPMENT*

The rapidity of the expansion of this field is reflected in the steadily increasing number of companies[2] that now manufacture basic or auxiliary equipment. Pressure units vary in design and construction depending somewhat upon the specific function required. However, with the exception of shock-wave facilities, there are functional similarities in pressure equipment. It is beyond the scope of this report to discuss equipment in detail. Comings[11b] gives an excellent discussion of the theory and details of construction of pressure equipment, and Perry[36a] presents a good equipment review.

* Specific manufacturers items are given as examples. Other equally suitable products may be available.

Research under pressure requires means of obtaining, equipment for holding, and devices for measuring and controlling the pressure and other parameters of the system. The first function is served by a compressor (mechanical, thermal, or hydraulic), a high pressure pump, or a booster intensification system. Mechanical compression is used by the Chicago Pneumatic, Hofer, Norwalk, and Rix compressors. Standard units are available for service up to 25,000 psi. The addition of a booster permits the Hofer to go to 90,000 psi. Hart produces a line of high-pressure equipment which includes a Michael's mercury piston gas compressor (Figure 10.70) and a thermal

Figure 10.70   Mercury piston compressor.

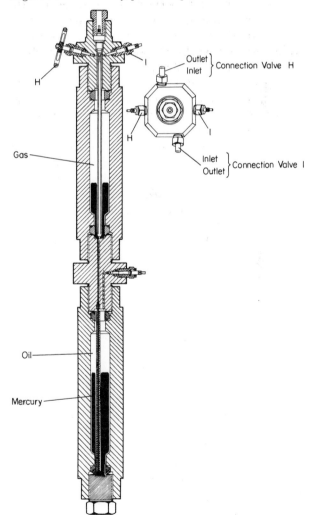

compressor for service to 60,000 and 15,000 psi, respectively. These units produce compressed gases without contamination or loss of material and are suitable for experiments where small quantities of pure gases are required. An automatic, single-stage, hydraulically operated compressor is produced by Burckhardt for service to 60,000 psi. La Croix has commercially available equipment capable of producing pressures to 140,000 psi. The company will custom-produce complete units capable of operation up to 700,000 psi.

Pumps for pressure service are available in a wide range of designs and capacities. Harwood Engineering can supply extreme-pressure intensifiers and equipment operable to 350,000 psi. Pumps for pressure service* are produced with capacities ranging from 2 cc/hour to 1800 gal/hour. Extremely small flow rates are available with the Ruska Hypodermic Pump which operates against 25,000 psi.

Autoclaves and reactors are commercially produced in many sizes, types, closures, and capacities. The design of the modern autoclave is complex in that many factors of construction and service must be considered. Consequently, it is normally advisable to place this problem with a reputable equipment manufacturer. Still, it is of considerable importance for the engineer to be familiar with design information to use in periodic checks on the equipment.

A detailed discussion of the theory of design and the production of thick-walled cylinders including the various methods of wall reinforcing is presented by Comings.[11c] Data are tabulated to show the elastic breakdown behavior of test cylinders of different alloys and to show the deviation between calculated and observed values. The discussion in Perry[36b] is less detailed, but design formulae, manner of failure, effect of temperature, and methods for improving wall stress distribution are covered. Performance characteristics of bombs fabricated of various alloys using several different design formulae are reported by Voorhees[46] and Faupel.[13, 14]

The arbitrary pressure test of 1.5 to 2.0 times the operating pressure will give a quick, qualita-

* See list of manufacturers at end of this section: 1, 5, 11–13, 16–18, 21, 23.

tive check on the equipment. Quantitative information on the operating characteristics of a pressure vessel must be obtained by hydraulically pressuring the unit and measuring the deformation to determine the pressure at which the unit begins to exceed the elastic limit. Correlation of the measured with the calculated deformation is used to show the loading at which the operating behavior departs from elastic strain. Lame's formula (maximum principal stress) is used by some laboratories for this purpose, although any formula which validly relates the stress to the strain for a given unit may be used. Observed and calculated deformations are plotted as a function of pressure. The point of departure of the experimental from the calculated curve indicates the maximum pressure to which the vessel can be loaded without exceeding the elastic limit of the metal. Strain may be followed either by a dial gage or a strain gage cemented to the bomb wall. These tests are normally made at ambient temperatures; however, when the pressure vessel is operated at elevated temperatures, a reduction must be made in the allowable operating pressure to compensate for the creep and weakening of the vessel at elevated temperature.

Proper selection of closure design and material of construction is highly important to the utility and life of the pressure vessel. Screw or compression-gasket closures are often used for the lower and moderate pressure ranges because critical machining is not required and the units are easily reconditioned. The limiting factor with this type of closure is the internal pressure at which the loading on the head is sufficient to relieve the compression on the gasket. Closures for the operating ranges in which the compression-type gasket is unsuitable make use of some form of self-sealing design. These may be roughly classified into an axially loaded seal, such as the Bridgman, or radial seal including lens ring, delta ring, or Vickers-Anderson. A comprehensive review of closures, operating ranges, and desirable features is given in Comings[11d] and in an article by Meigs.[25]

Five important factors must be considered in the selection of a material of construction and the design of a pressure vessel:

(1) Working pressure;

(2) Working temperature;

(3) Size of the vessel;

(4) Corrosivity of the process;

(5) Nature of the stresses involved.

The first three factors are closely interrelated. The design must employ a material which has proper strength-temperature characteristics to produce a pressure vessel of the desired size and operating characteristics. The effect of the process materials on the strength characteristics of the reactor walls must be anticipated. Several damaging effects may be encountered if improper selection of metal is made:

(1) Embrittlement;

(2) Corrosion in its various forms;

(3) Stress-cracking.

Any one of these produces weakening of the pressure unit and increases the hazards of operation. Both Comings and Perry discuss the behavior and suitability of different alloys with respect to service conditions. Lastly, consideration must be given to the ability of the metal to resist creep and work-hardening.

In many laboratories, the trend is toward the use of a stabilized, stainless steel unit.[22, 24] These are generally resistant to attack, easy to clean, and have good strength at high and low temperatures.

Although pumps, compressors, and reactors constitute the major items required in pressure research, proper tubing, valves, fittings, safety devices, and accessories are of equal importance. Valves and fittings have been developed for service as high as 350,000 psi. Complete lines of accessory equipment are available in several pressure ranges up to 100,000 psi. Interchange of the different ranges are nominally prevented by various coupling devices. Precautions must be taken to prevent the installation of low-range equipment in an assembly specified for use at pressures higher than the rating of the accessories.

Care should be taken in the selection and design of accessory equipment to make certain that safety shoulders are provided on all shafts and stems to prevent the part from becoming a projectile in event of failure. Packing gland nuts should be equipped with a locking device to prevent the nut from being loosened by vibration. Bleed holes should be drilled in pressure fittings

to vent leaks so that pressure does not build up under the thrust nut. All fittings should be stamped to show the material of construction and the allowable design operating pressure.

Accessory equipment commercially available includes pressure cells, dead-weight testers, manual and motor control valves, filters, check and surge valves, optical and PVT cells. Fairly complete lines of pressure equipment are available from several companies.* Other companies, such as Conax, Hoke, and Parr, are primarily producers of specialty items. Conax makes a broad line of thermocouple assemblies and pressure sealing glands for high-pressure and high-temperature work. Hoke produces compressed gas tank adapters, valves, and pressure regulators for use with compressed gases. Parr specializes in small laboratory units for low to moderate pressure reactions and combustion studies.

INSTRUMENTATION

Equipment required for pressure studies generally include pressure and temperature monitoring and control devices, and possibly apparatus for determining specific physical changes. A comprehensive instrumentation discussion is beyond the scope of this report. However, several articles[6, 7, 11b, 12, 19] discuss various methods of measuring and controlling pressure dependent reactions.

Three primary methods of handling instrumentation were noted in the laboratories surveyed. These consist of:

(1) A central control panel;

(2) Control panels at each cubicle;

(3) Portable control units.

Normally, if a central panel is used, wires are run to each cubicle and terminated at the panel in a plug. Thus, the control units can be connected into the cell desired by means of a flexible jumper. Central operation can best be used provided electric or pneumatic valves and transmitting units are employed.

If manual manipulation of the control valves is used, operation normally is conducted at the cubicle face (Figure 10.71). Reach rods are fre-

* See list of manufacturers at end of this section: 2, 3, 11, 12, 15, 21, 23.

quently used to operate valves mounted within the cubicle, although occasionally the valve manifold is mounted outside the cell. In either case, the instrument panel is usually located convenient to the operating area. Several positions have been used:

(1) As an extension of the cell face, Figure 10.57

(2) Parallel to, and in front of the cell face

(3) At a right or oblique angle to the front of the cell face (Figures 10.61, 10.69, and 10.71).

Fixed mountings, such as those just described, require a fairly high instrumentation inventory or frequent shifting of the units as different pressure units are needed. An alternative method which has given extremely flexible service in several laboratories is the use of a portable control unit. This is designed for mobility and equipped to permit it to be plugged into the cubicle circuits. This system has shown a high degree of utility for experimental work where needs are constantly changing.

Satisfactory temperature control for electrically heated laboratory units can be obtained with any of several commercially available units. Either anticipatory control or balanced heat input can be used to give good temperature stability for most purposes. However, in the case of exothermic reactions, the mass of the reactor may prevent rapid abstraction of heat and frequently internal cooling is required to prevent overheating.

Instrumentation used in detonation studies differs greatly from that used in hydrostatic or chemical systems. Several methods are used to obtain quantitative information on shock-wave characteristics:

(1) High-speed photography using a smear or sweep camera

(2) X-ray flash photography

(3) Electronic timing of the shock wave with a high-speed oscillograph.

These and several qualitative methods are compared by Taylor.[45] Additional detail on instrumentation for shock-wave research is given in several recent articles.[9, 27, 34, 47, 48]

SPECIALIZED EQUIPMENT AND TECHNIQUES

In addition to stock pressure equipment available from numerous manufacturers, many designs for specialty units have been reported. Midget reactors and valves which permit operation at high pressures with small batch sizes are available from several companies. These are especially valuable when the reaction involves a high energy system or an exceedingly costly reactant.

Studies using radioactive chemicals introduce the need for adequate radiation shielding. A unit designed for radiochemical studies at elevated temperature and pressure is reported by Calkins, et al.[8]

Unique reactors worth mention are the resonant agitation system of Bjorkman,[5] which was reported to give efficient mixing. Reciprocating engines and turboprop motors have been used as unconventional high-temperature, high-pressure reactors.[3]

Fitch, et al.[15] report the design of an apparatus for optical studies to 200,000 atmospheres. The effect of superpressures on glass is discussed by Bridgman and Simon.[7] An electrical lead for superpressure service is presented by Simon.[42]

Modification of Bridgman's electrical plug with insulated cones can be used satisfactorily from D.C. to 9,000 megacycles. Details are presented for the use of this unit in the radio-frequency region[21] and in the microwave region.[49] Beryllium-copper has been shown to be satisfactory for bomb construction for service to 20,000

Figure 10.71   View of cell control facilities.

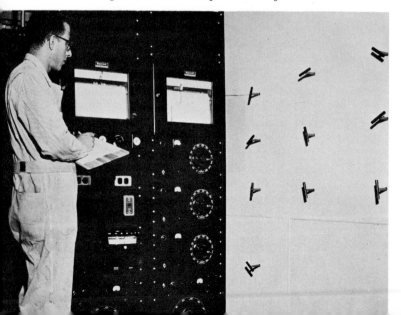

atmospheres at temperatures below 150°C.[4] The non-magnetic property of the metal permits magnetic measurements under high pressure. An apparatus for measuring linear compressibility of solids under 4,000 kg/cm² and temperatures to 260°C was reported by Reitzel.[39]

Leaks in high-pressure systems may be detected by a halogen leak detector. The application of this device to pressure work is reported by Paul[35] to be a very sensitive and convenient method.

REFERENCES

1. Anderson, O. L., and Newhall, D. H., "Some Safety Problems Associated With High Pressure Equipment," Private communication.
2. Anon., "Equipment, What's Available and How to Select It," *Ind. Eng. Chem.,* **48,** 827 (1956).
3. Anon., "New Reactors Spur Fuel Research," *Chem. Week,* p. 83 (February 8, 1958).
4. Benedek, G. B., and Purcell, E. M., "Nuclear Magnetic Resonance in Liquids Under High Pressure," *J. Chem. Phys.,* **22,** 2003 (1954).
5. Bjorkman, Anders, "Shaking of High Pressure Vessels According to the Resonance Principle," *Ind. Eng. Chem.,* **44,** 2459 (1952).
6. Bridgman, P. W., "Recent Work in the Field of High Pressures," *Rev. of Mod. Phys.,* **18,** 1 (1946).
7. Bridgman, P. W., and Simon, I., "Effects of Very High Pressures on Glass," *J. Applied Physics,* **24,** 405 (1953).
8. Calkins, G. D., Whitney, J. E., and Lusk, E. C., "Equipment for Corrosion and Heat-Treatment Studies of Radioactive Materials," ASTM Bulletin 224, September, 1957.
9. Christian, R. H., and Yarger, F. L., "Equation of State of Gases by Shock Wave Measurements. I. Experimental Method and the Hugoniot of Argon," *J. Chem. Phys.,* **23,** 2042 (1955).
10. Coleman, H. S., "Laboratory Design," p. 241, Reinhold, New York (1951).
11. Comings, E. W., "High Pressure Technology," McGraw-Hill (1956): (a) p. 65, (b) p. 75, (c) p. 160, (d) p. 156.
12. Darling, H. E., and Newhall, D. H., "A High-Pressure Wire Gage Using Gold-Chrome Wire," *Trans. ASME,* **75,** 311 (April, 1953).
13. Faupel, J. H., "Yield and Bursting Characteristics of Heavy Wall Cylinders," *Trans. ASME,* **78,** 1031 (1956).
14. Faupel, J. H., and Furbeck, A. R., "Influence of Residual Stress on Behavior of Thick-Wall Closed End Cylinders," *Trans. ASME,* **75,** 345 (1953).
15. Fitch, R. A., Slykhouse, F. E., and Drickamer, H. G., "Apparatus for Optical Studies to Very High Pressures," *J. Optical Soc. Am.,* **47,** 1015 (1957).
16. Freeman, A. R., "Gaskets for High Pressure Vessels," *Mech. Eng.,* **74,** 969 (1952).
17. Greenlee, K. W., "Butadiene-Crotonaldehyde Explosion," *Chem. Eng. News,* **26,** 1955 (1948).
18. Hartmann, Irving, and Nagy, John, "Venting Dust Explosions," *Ind. Eng. Chem.,* **49,** 1734 (1957).
19. Johnson, D. P., and Newhall, D. H., "The Piston Gage as a Precise Pressure Measuring Instrument," *Trans. ASME,* **75,** 301 (April, 1953).
20. Kuentzel, Dr. W. E., "Standard Oil Co., Ind., High Pressure Research Facilities at Whiting Laboratories," Private communication.
21. Kushida, T., Benedek, G. B., and Bloembergen, N., "Dependence of the Pure Quadripole Resonance Frequency on Pressure and Temperature," *Phys. Rev.,* **104,** 1364 (1956).
22. Lobo, P. A., and Sliepcevich, C. M., "High Temperature, High Pressure Chemical Reactors," *Research and Engineering,* p. 32 (October, 1956).
23. Loving, F. A., "Barricading Hazardous Reactions," *Ind. Eng. Chem.,* **49,** 1744 (1957).
24. McFee, W. E., "Know Stainless Steels When Selecting for Equipment," *Ind. Eng. Chem.,* **48,** 1964 (1956).
25. Meigs, D., "Closures for High Pressure Vessels," *Trans. Am. Inst. Chem. Eng.,* **39,** 769 (1943).
26. Miller, J. F., "Unit-Type Batch Reaction Cubicles," *Ind. Eng. Chem.,* **48,** 846 (1956).
27. Minshall, F. Stanley, "Properties of Elastic and Plastic Waves Determined by Pin Contactors and Crystals," *J. Appl. Phys.,* **26,** 463–469 (1955).
28. Moll, Godfrey J., "Laboratory Barricading of High Pressure and Extra Hazardous Reactions," National Safety Congress (October 24, 1957).
29. Murphy, T. S., Jr., "Determining Needed Relieving Capacity for Rupture Diaphragms," *Chem. Eng.,* **51,** No. 12, p. 99 (1944).
30. Murphy, T. S., Jr., "Rupture Diaphragms," *Chem. Eng.,* **51,** No. 11, p. 108 (1944).
31. Navdocks TP-TE-3, "Basic Structural Engineering," Dept. of Yards and Docks, Washington 25, D. C., 15 May 1954.
32. Newmark, Nathan M., "An Engineering Approach to Blast Resistant Design," University of Illinois, Engineering Experiment Station Re-

print Series 56.

33. *New York Times,* February 16, 1955.

34. Park, D. C., Evans, W. M., and James, H. J., "The Propagation of Shock Waves in Steel and Lead," *Proc. Phys. Soc.,* **60**, 1–8 (1948).

35. Paul, W., and Warschauer, D., "High Pressure Leak Detector," *Rev. Sci. Inst.,* **26**, 731 (1955).

36. Perry, J. H., "Chemical Engineers' Handbook," Third Edition, McGraw-Hill Book Co., Inc. (1950): (a) p. 1258, (b) p. 1237.

37. Porter, R. L., Lobo, P. A., and Sliepcevich, C. M., "Design and Construction of Barricades," *Ind. Eng. Chem.,* **48**, 841 (1956).

38. Prescott, G. R., "Rupture Disc Design, Evaluation and Bursting Tests," *Trans. ASME,* **75**, 355 (1953).

39. Reitzel, J., Simon, I., and Walker, J. A., "New Method for Measuring Linear Compressibility of Solids," *Rev. Sci. Inst.,* **28**, No. 10, 828 (1957).

40. Rinehart, J. S., "Fracturing Under Explosive Loading," AIChE Convention, Chicago, Illinois, December 8–11, 1957.

41. Simon, Ivan, "Research Techniques in Very High Pressures," *Research and Engineering,* July-August (1955).

42. Simon, Ivan, "Electrical Lead for High Pressure Apparatus," *Rev. Sci. Inst.,* **28**, 963 (1957).

43. Stephens, H. R., and Walker, K. E., "Safety in Small Scale High Pressure Experiments," ACS Meeting, Miami, Florida, April, 1957.

44. Stewart, P. B., and Fox, R. T., Jr., "Aluminum Foil Rupture Discs Offer Low Cost Protection," *Chem. Eng. Prog.,* **52**, 115 (1956).

45. Taylor, James, "Detonation in Condensed Explosives," Clarendon Press, Oxford, p. 24 (1952).

46. Voorhees, H. R., Sliepcevich, C. M., and Freeman, J. W., "Thick-Walled Pressure Vessels," *Ind. Eng. Chem.,* **48**, 872 (1956).

47. Walsh, J. M., and Christian, R. H., "Equation of State of Metals From Shock Wave Measurements," *Phys. Rev.,* **97**, 1544 (1955).

48. Walsh, J. M., and Rice, M. H., "Dynamic Compression of Liquids From Measurements on Strong Shock Waves," *J. Chem. Phys.,* **26**, 815 (1957).

49. Walsh, W. M., Jr., and Bloembergen, N., "Paramagnetic Resonance of Nickel Fluosilicate Under High Hydrostatic Pressure," *Phys. Rev.,* **107**, 904 (1957).

LIST OF MANUFACTURERS

1. Aldrich Pump Company, Allentown, Pennsylvania.
2. American Instrument Company, Inc., Silver Spring, Maryland.
3. Autoclave Engineers, Inc., Erie, Pennsylvania.
4. Baker and Company, Inc., Newark 5, New Jersey.
5. John Bean Division, Food Machinery and Chemical Corporation, Lansing 4, Michigan.
6. Black, Sivalls and Bryson, Inc., Kansas City, Missouri.
7. Burckhardt Engineering Works, Dornacherstrasse 192, Basle 2, Switzerland.
8. Chicago Pneumatic, 8 East 44th Street, New York, New York.
9. Frangible Discs, Inc. Pennsgrove, New Jersey.
10. W. C. 't Hart & Zn, Rotterdam, Holland (American Sales, Girard Associates, Chambersburg, Pennsylvania.)
11. Harwood Engineering Company, Walpole, Massachusetts.
12. High Pressure Equipment Company, Erie, Pennsylvania.
13. Hills-McCanna Company, Chicago, Illinois.
14. Andreas Hofer Ltd., Mülheim-Ruhr (American Sales and Service Autoclave Engineers, Erie, Pennsylvania).
15. Inferno Company, Shreveport, Louisiana.
16. A. F. LaCroix, 10 Boulevard, Malesherbes, Paris, France.
17. Lapp Insulator Company, LeRay, New York.
18. Milton Roy Company, Philadelphia 18, Pennsylvania.
19. Norwalk Company, Inc., South Norwalk, Connecticut.
20. Parr Instrument Company, Moline, Illinois.
21. Pressure Products Industries, Hatboro, Pennsylvania.
22. The Rix Company, Inc., San Francisco, California.
23. Ruska Instrument Company, Houston 6, Texas.

PART 6: CONTROLLED HUMIDITY AND TEMPERATURE ROOMS

GENE GADDIS

Minneapolis-Honeywell Regulator Company
Minneapolis, Minnesota

We have all experienced the wide range of atmospheric conditions which can prevail in an unconditioned indoor area. For example, the temperature in a room can vary from 70° to 100°F in the summer, depending on outside conditions. The relative humidity can be over 90% on a summer day and under 10% in the winter when space heating only is provided. It is significant that different materials respond to narrow bands of both temperature and relative humidity; for example, wood changes dimensions and weight depending on the relative humidity of the surrounding air. On the other hand, liquid bromine requires a temperature of 19°F or lower to maintain its properties. These are only a few of numerous situations requiring controlled temperature and humidity. When laboratory work must be performed at predetermined values of temperature and relative humidity, special consideration must be given the design of the room from this point of view.

If it is necessary to conduct simultaneous tests requiring different combinations of temperature and relative humidity, there should be an independently controlled room for each combination. To the extent that tests requiring different values and combinations of temperature and relative humidity can be scheduled in sequence, a single room designed for the entire range of conditions to be encountered may be most expedient. The narrower the range, the easier it is to design a system to ensure smooth, reliable control at all times.

It is outside the scope of this chapter to provide detailed design data; these are available from consulting engineers and manufacturers of the type of materials and equipment employed. On the other hand, it is our purpose to outline a reliable guide for planning the general layout of the room or rooms and the associated equipment.

It must be recognized that high-quality engineering design and construction is a necessity if close temperature and humidity control is to be obtained on a reliable basis. The first cost is higher, but it is less expensive than correction and maintenance of a poorly designed system.

TYPES OF ROOMS

When designing a constant-temperature room, one should carefully anticipate its range of uses. The author chooses to classify all possible applications under the following six categories for the purpose of clarifying the discussion of the basic concepts of controlled room design. Naturally, the sixth category is the most popular in practice as it provides for combining the features of two or more of the other five.

Normal Ambient-temperature Rooms—Type A

Under this classification, it is presumed that no consideration is given to humidity. The value of relative humidity which exists in the space will be the natural result of space temperature, nature of the space load, and the absolute humidity of the incoming air.

The temperature will be controlled within specified tolerances. Minimum investment is required for equipment and for wall, floor, and ceiling construction, because the heat transfer into or out of the laboratory will be small. This is possible when laboratory work can be planned at a specified temperature within 10°F of the normal ambient temperature surrounding the constant-temperature room. For air-conditioned buildings, space temperature is nominally 65 to 80°F, just outside the controlled laboratory. For nonair-conditioned buildings, the range of 65 to 80°F applies during the heating season. During the summer season, tests are necessarily limited to several hours duration and conducted at a constant controlled temperature, selected within the range of the surrounding air temperature, 70 and 100°F.

High-temperature Rooms—Type B

If Type A rooms are used, any tests at temperatures above normal must be planned during the summer when the air surrounding the room can be adjusted (in the case of an air-conditioned building) or happens to be in the desired temperature range (in nonair-conditioned building). In the later case, a further limitation is that the duration of each test must be held to a few hours to prevent uncontrolled changes in surrounding conditions.

Frequently, such limitations are not acceptable, and temperatures over 100°F and up to 150°F are needed. High-temperature rooms must then be specified. This classification covers the range of 70 to 150°F and, as in the above type, presumes that no concern is given to the value of relative humidity. These values will tend to be lower, the higher the controlled laboratory temperature.

Essential differences exist between Types A and B rooms. The latter require larger-capacity heating equipment and less cooling capacity. The importance of cooling equipment must not be underestimated even in high-temperature rooms, because in some cases the process being studied may give off more heat than required to maintain the desired temperature level. In such instances, cooling rather than heating may be needed. Another difference is that good insulation must be provided for the walls, ceiling and floor, because significant temperature differences will exist between inside and outside the space. Properly engineered insulation will "pay off" not only in dollars saved in initial cost, but also in reduced operating costs.

Low-temperature Rooms—Type C

This classification covers the range of temperatures nominally from 0 to 70°F. As may be concluded from the discussion of high-temperature rooms, it would be erroneous to assume that all Type C applications require cooling equipment. Certain processes operating well below 70°F may absorb heat from its surroundings to the extent that heat rather than cooling must be provided

by the air-conditioning equipment serving the laboratory.

As in Type B rooms, full consideration must be given proper insulation of walls, ceiling, and floor to reduce heat transfer caused by the appreciable temperature differences which exist between inside and outside the enclosure.

As in the above two classifications, no concern is given here to regulating the humidity. Again, we "take what we get," because this class of room is selected only when the value of relative humidity (high or low) has no bearing on the process being studied.

One new problem, however, arises: with lower temperatures within the laboratory, the likelihood of wall, ceiling, and floor reaching the dew point of the surrounding air is greater. This possibility must be anticipated and suitable vapor barriers installed.

High-humidity Rooms—Type D

In the high-humidity room category, relative humidities up to 100% are sometimes required. Since no effort is made to regulate the temperature, thermal insulation deserves no special consideration. As adding humidity to a space is usually accomplished by heating water or releasing steam, space temperatures above ambient are common. In these applications, it is desirable to employ an effective vapor barrier on the side of the laboratory walls, floor, and ceiling which has the higher vapor pressure,* to minimize loss of water vapor.

Low-humidity Rooms—Type E

In low-humidity rooms, the first cost of dehumidifying equipment as well as operating cost dictates the need of vapor barriers to prevent water vapor transfer through the walls, ceiling, and floor. The requirement for a vapor seal here may differ, however, from that for Type D rooms in that a vapor pressure is usually low. If so, the vapor flow is from the outside to the inside, and the vapor barrier must be on the *outer* surfaces.

This class of room precludes any requirement for holding prescribed dry bulb temperatures. It is practical, however, to anticipate whether

---

* This can be determined by a psychrometric chart.

lower than normal* or higher than normal temperatures are more desirable. For example, if space temperature *below* normal was considered more desirable for the anticipated usage of the room, one might well consider refrigeration type of dehumidification, which is practical for dew point temperatures down to 35°F. For those applications where *higher* than normal space temperatures are permitted, increasing temperature alone may satisfy the relative humidity requirements. If not, chemical dehumidification should be considered because inherently the air is heated while drying. Chemical dehumidification should be given special consideration for dew point temperatures below 35°F, where freezing becomes a problem with other types of systems.

Multi-purpose Rooms—Type F

Frequently more than one of the above five types of use is required to meet the need of a given laboratory. Whether we are considering a single room, or a group of rooms planned to provide simultaneous testing under different kinds of atmospheres, each individual room will naturally be set up to serve its specially assigned function, or following combination of simultaneous functions:

(1) Normal temperature and high humidity
(2) Normal temperature and low humidity
(3) High temperature and high humidity
(4) High temperature and low humidity
(5) Low temperature and high humidity
(6) Low temperature and low humidity

When the number of desired functions (5 or less) and/or number of needed combinations (6

* 70–75°F are considered normal temperatures.

or less), can be scheduled for sequence performance, fewer rooms will suffice.

All the above naturally leads us to the concept of the "king" of all rooms, an "All-Purpose Room," capable of providing any one of the five above-described functions as well as any desired combination. This will provide a normal temperature range from 0 to 150°F and relative humidities from 5 to 95%. Only under the most unusual circumstances will wider operating ranges be needed, and if so, similar principles apply.

ROOM DESIGN

Location

Care exercised in the proper location of the laboratory will be reflected in lower initial cost of room construction and equipment, lower operating expense and improved quality of performance. Factors to consider are:

(1) Use of inside partitions and ceilings to avoid effects of extreme outdoor conditions of sun, wind, and temperature.

(2) Locations appreciably removed from exterior walls and ceilings for the above reasons.

(3) Arrangement permitting accessibility to plumbing, venting facilities and related services.

(4) Arrangement permitting proximity to refrigeration, heating, and other equipment serving the rooms.

Thermal Insulation

Selection of the specific type and amount of insulation for walls, ceilings and floors to be used should be made by the consulting engineer. It will depend upon the maximum temperature difference contemplated between the inside and outside surface.

Wall Insulation. Walls may be insulated either by thermal fill or by reflective type of insulation. Figure 10.72 illustrates the conventional fill type insulation. The several layers of "batt" type insulation is preferred over the loose fill-type because it insures against settling and resulting loss of insulating effect.

Although the heat transmission coefficient is not as good, 8 in. gypsum or magnesia blocks make a satisfactory and economical wall material.

Figure 10.72   Basic fill type insulated wall.

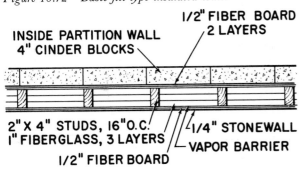

INSIDE PARTITION WALL
4" CINDER BLOCKS

1/2" FIBER BOARD
2 LAYERS

2" X 4" STUDS, 16"O.C.
1" FIBERGLASS, 3 LAYERS
1/2" FIBER BOARD

1/4" STONEWALL
VAPOR BARRIER

This is particularly applicable for Type A rooms, having relatively small heat losses. Conventional plasters on both inner and outer surfaces provides a durable and finished surface. If a still harder surface is required for physical protection, the room can be lined with ¼ in. "Transite" or ¼ in. stone sheets.

Figure 10.73 shows another method of providing fill type insulation. "Staggering" the studs as shown gives improved performance. It costs more but the insulation value is increased by minimizing the heat conducted through the studs. This refinement is usually justified economically only for those applications where temperature differences between inside and outside the space approach or exceed 50° F.

The above solid or fill type thermal insulations are reasonably easy to install and do an excellent job of retarding heat flow. In practice they have one serious limitation; they all have an appreciable mass and specific heat. This is of no consequence for tests of long duration or even for short tests if repeated tests are conducted at approximately the same temperature level. If the different tests are to be performed at different temperature levels, a minimum of 3 or 4 hours must elapse between tests to permit walls, floors and ceiling to come to thermal equilibrium before the new tests get under way.

The second type of wall insulation, the reflective type, is used where it is desirable to schedule successive tests conducted at appreciably different temperature levels. See Figure 10.74. This construction offers low mass and low specific heat permitting change from one temperature level to another appreciably different in a matter of a few minutes compared to several hours.

Ceiling Insulation. The problems of ceiling insulations are relatively simple. Since 6 to 12 in. depth is maximum, no concern is given to settling, with resulting change of coefficients. "Blown in" type loose spun glass fill has minimum mass. It is usually favored over the multi-layer reflective insulation because of comparative simplicity of installation. Figure 10.75 shows an installation of ceiling insulation combined with recessed fluorescent lamps.

Floor Insulation. The proper construction of floors presents a more difficult problem because

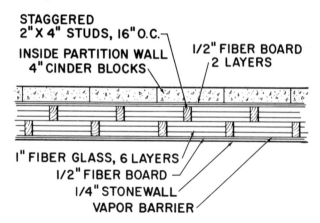

Figure 10.73   Insulated wall, special construction.

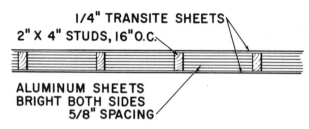

Figure 10.74   Wall construction employing reflective insulation for low mass.

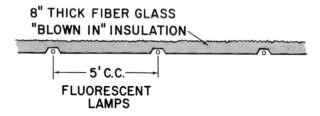

Figure 10.75   Typical ceiling insulation.

compromises must be reached between need for low mass *vs.* sufficient strength to support the physical loads imposed upon them. There are two types of construction to consider.

In the first, four inch cork built up in two 2 in. layers on top of the regular building floor. The surface is covered with asphalt tile to present a suitable surface for traffic.

The second uses "wood sleeper" construction. Basically, this method involves placing 2 x 2 or 2 x 4 in. wood sleepers on top of the regular building floor. The resulting 2 or 4 in. of deep space is filled with fiber glass insulation and covered with ¾ in. plywood. Sheet-galvanized iron over-all effectively serves as an inner surface vapor seal if properly lapped and joints soldered. The galvanized iron must be surfaced with a special thin "safety walk" covering, usually glued on, to provide suitable traction.

Moisture Barriers

As discussed earlier, the addition of an effective vapor barrier deserves special attention for room types C, D, E, and F. In Type C (low-temperature rooms) and Type E (low-humidity rooms), the flow of water vapor will usually be from outside to inside. If so, the vapor seal should be applied to the outside surface. This prevents the moisture from entering the insulation where it could condense or even freeze, and not only reduce the effectiveness of the insulation but in addition cause deterioration of the wall.

In Type D (high-humidity rooms) the flow of water vapor will usually be from the inside to the outside. Applying the same reasoning as above, it follows that the vapor seal in this case must be applied to the inside surface of the walls, floor, and ceiling.

Many effective vapor barriers are on the market. The least expensive forms usually consist of a combination special asphalt-treated paper. However, the small additional cost of aluminum foil makes it especially attractive for this service, as it has the added feature of its reflective insulation effect.

It must be pointed out that special care should be exercised in the application of moisture barriers or their effectiveness can be materially reduced. The sheets should be overlapped and sealed and free of cracks or tears.

It is significant to note that the reflective-type insulation pictured in Figure 10.74 inherently provides its own vapor barrier.

It must be recognized that several varieties of Type F (multi-purpose rooms) have the unique characteristic that when operated as high-humidity rooms for example, they will require

installation of the vapor barrier on the inside surfaces, but if operated as a low-humidity room, they will require the vapor barrier to be installed on the outside surfaces. The only solution to this situation is that the vapor barrier be applied to both the inside and outside of walls, ceilings, and floors. This conclusion dictates that extra special attention be given to assure absence of leaks so that water vapor cannot condense between the outer and inner surfaces.

Special Considerations

Temperature Tolerance Less Than ½%. When temperature is to be controlled to this precision unusual steps should be considered, as illustrated in Figure 10.76. Here a room is built within a room. The outer room is controlled to within a few degrees of the required temperature of the inner room. If the load changes can be kept small, the "control factor" is now so small that extremely close temperature can be held.

Air Locks. Notice the two entrance doors of the room in Figure 10.76 form an "air lock," such that as one enters the controlled space, one door is always shut, ensuring minimum leakage of air from the space. *Any* room can be equipped with such an air lock commonly arranged as in Figure 10.77 if personnel must enter or leave the space during the progress of a test. It may be desirable to install a fan in the air lock arranged

Figure 10.76   A controlled room within a controlled room for precision results.

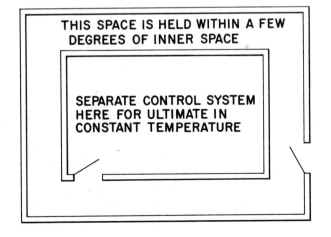

THIS SPACE IS HELD WITHIN A FEW DEGREES OF INNER SPACE

SEPARATE CONTROL SYSTEM HERE FOR ULTIMATE IN CONSTANT TEMPERATURE

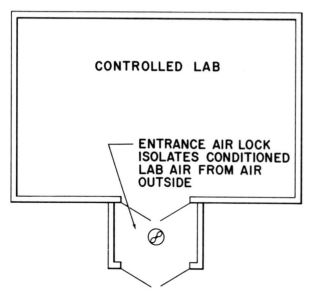

CONTROLLED LAB

ENTRANCE AIR LOCK
ISOLATES CONDITIONED
LAB AIR FROM AIR
OUTSIDE

Figure 10.77   Air lock for controlled laboratories.

to develop a pressure in the air lock higher than on the outside to ensure against "incoming air" when the exterior door is opened.

Vibration and Noise. Should the process within the controlled area be in any way affected by vibration or noise, the existing conditions should be investigated and proper consideration should be given to these factors in the room design. Similar precaution must be taken should the process within the room have an objectionable effect on the surroundings.

AIR-CONDITIONING SYSTEMS

Ventilation Requirements

Mechanical ventilation is universally required for constant-temperature humidity chambers. The rate of ventilation, however, can vary between quite wide limits from one air change per half minute to one air change per 15 minutes. Higher flow rates may be considered where there are closer tolerances on temperature than $\pm1°F$ and on humidity than $\pm1\%$ or where there are fluctuating heating, cooling, or humidity loads.

The total air to be handled is made up of two parts: that returned from the space and re-used (return air), and that brought in from outdoors (outdoor air). The percentage of outdoor air employed will depend on the nature of the air conditioning load being served. If large quantities of objectionable odors or other forms of pollution are given off by the process, 100% outdoor air may be required. On the other hand, operating costs can be materially reduced to the extent that the once-conditioned air can be re-used. In fact, 100% return air is sometimes recommended. This may be true when no unfavorable gases are given off and when the condition of the outside air is such that it would add to the air-conditioning load.

Air Distribution

It is important to exercise care in selecting the type of humidifier and heating and cooling coil to ensure that supply air has a uniform temperature and a uniform moisture content at this point in the duct for any load condition. Extra special attention must be given this factor if a steam-heating coil is used, because its inherent tendency is to be hot on the supply end and cold at the return (trap) end, particularly at small loads. *Coils and humidifiers must be as small as possible and still large enough to match the largest load imposed upon them.* Then by proper duct design and insulation, this uniform condition of the air can be maintained to the point of discharge through the supply grilles.

Once the air has been properly conditioned to meet the needs of the space, a big job still lies ahead in distributing the air uniformly to the area. Outlets must be so arranged that every segment of the room receives its just share of the total quantity of air. Furthermore, to be acceptable, the air current within the space must usually be held to 40 to 50 fpm.

It must be appreciated that the greater the rate of air flow, the greater the care that should be exercised in admitting the air to the space, to ensure even distribution without setting up high-velocity air currents.

The perforated bottom of the distribution ducts shown in Figure 10.78 provides an excellent means of discharging air into the space at high flow rates. An alternate method is that of employing discharge heads each with four discharge

Figure 10.78   Perforated ceiling air discharge.

Figure 10.79   Ceiling air discharge units.

grilles as illustrated in Figure 10.79. Each grille is equipped with a means of individually adjusting each of its many vertical vanes for uniform lateral distribution, as well as a means of adjusting the angle of the vertical discharge pattern. This affords the greatest flexibility of room configuration. If the system is designed for sufficiently high discharge velocities, one has the option of using the bottom of the discharge heads for a return grille to permit centralizing of the duct work. Otherwise, return grilles are best located at strategic points near the floor line distributed around the periphery of the room.

Classification of Systems

The nature of air-conditioning systems is such that they inherently fall under similar categories as those for the different room types listed earlier.

Heating. Steam coils, hot water coils and electric grids provide three common means of heating air for conditioned rooms. Of these, steam coils show a lower operating cost than do electric grids except in special geographical areas; they respond more quickly to a call for heat and are easier to protect from freezing than in the case with hot water. At the same time they are harder to maintain between close temperature limits, particularly at low load conditions when the valve disc is operating closest to its seat. This results not only from the high temperature of steam—215°F but also from its high heat of vaporiza-

tion—1,000 Btu/lb. Precision built valves are required for acceptable performance or else the system must be set up so that the valve never closes. Such "extra" heat must be counterbalanced by refrigeration, which increases operating costs.

Hot water coils use steam in the generation of hot water. Since steam is easy to transmit from the location of its generator to the air-conditioning system, it can be easily employed to heat water to the approximate maximum temperature required. The hot water in turn can serve a hot water coil in the duct. The water can also be effectively heated directly from a hot water boiler if "central steam" is not readily available.

There are at least two advantages in using hot water coils. With them, air temperatures at any level between 70 and 210°F are easy to control. Their operating costs are usually lower than electric grids. On the other hand, they do not respond rapidly to quick load changes and they must be given protection from freezing when exposed to sub-freezing.

Electric grids have a low initial cost and show a fast response to rapid load changes. They do have high operating costs except where electric power is cheap.

Cooling. Although a wide variety of cooling systems are available for air-conditioning, only those types most commonly applicable to constant temperature-humidity rooms will be considered. These are outdoor air and chilled water.

When the temperature of outdoor air is below that of the conditioned space (and when its relative humidity is acceptable), it can be effectively used as a cooling agent, and obviously is the lowest cost of all forms of cooling. To utilize this "free" medium, all that is required is a set of automatically controlled dampers designed to permit admitting the desired volume.

The other most commonly used source of cooling is chilled water mechanically circulated through heat transfer coils. Chilled water may come either from well water when available at a temperature as low as 45°F or be water which is cooled artificially. Theoretically when well water exists below the temperature of the space to be conditioned, it qualifies as a cooling agent. In practice, however, unless the temperature is at least 10°F lower than the space temperature and/or below the dew point of the space, its use may not be economical.

By far the majority of installations depend upon artificially cooling the water to be circulated through the cooling coils through which the air to be cooled is passed. Figure 10.80 illustrates a typical basic system. The temperature of the water leaving the chiller is controlled by regulating the flow of refrigerant to the chiller. This is set for the lowest cooling water temperature to be demanded by the space. A three-way modulating by-pass valve on the cooling coil automatically reduces the average temperature of the coil as required to match the load.

If the cooling system must provide temperatures 35°F or lower, liquids with freezing points suitably low must be substituted for water in the circulating system. Fluids commonly employed for these low-temperature applications are methyl alcohol, proper concentrations of brine, and properly proportioned mixtures of ethylene glycol with water.

It is also possible for the compressor in this basic system to serve directly as a cooling coil in a duct and thus eliminate the intermediate water chiller. This is recommended only if modulating control* is applied.

---

* Modulating control is a means by which cooling (or heating) is continuous (not intermittently "on" and "off"), the quantity of cooling (or heating) being continuously adjusted to match the load.

Moisture Removal or Dehumidification. Moisture is removed from air either by cooling coils or by chemical dehumidifying agents.

The most common manner of removing moisture from air is to lower its temperature below the dew point, which is the temperature at which the air is completely saturated. The extent to which the air is cooled below its dew point is a measure of the amount of water which will be removed. For example, suppose that air exists in the chamber at 70°F and 60% relative humidity. This condition is represented on the psychrometric chart Figure 10.81, by point A, which discloses that the air contains 66 grains of water per pound of dry air, with a dew point temperature of 55½°F. If the desired condition is 40% relative humidity at the same temperature of 70°F, the chart reveals that the moisture content must be reduced to 44 grains per pound. This reduction of 22 grains per pound can be accomplished by first cooling the air along the line *AB* to point *B* its dew point, then continue to cool it to 45°F, along line *BC* to point *C*, the dew point corresponding to the desired 44 grains per pound. In so doing, the desired 22 grains per pound has been removed in the form of water. In order to achieve the desired end result at point *D*, the air must be re-heated to the desired 70°F temperature along line *CD* to point *D*.

Under certain conditions it is necessary to use chemical dehumidifiers. Suppose in the above example, the desired condition was point *E*, 20% relative humidity instead of 40% at 70°F. It is not so significant that another 22 grains per pound of dry air must be removed to reach the required dew point of 28°F; the critical factor is that this temperature is below the freezing point. It does not require a great deal of imagination to realize that if cooling coils were to be used here, the water condensing from the air onto the surface of the coil would freeze and immediately begin to reduce the effective area for the flow of air, until the coil would ultimately cut off the air flow completely. A different approach must then be employed for required dew points below 35°F. For these situations, chemical dehumidification is suggested. The air to be dehumidified passes through continuously reactivated silica gel which removes the water, delivering

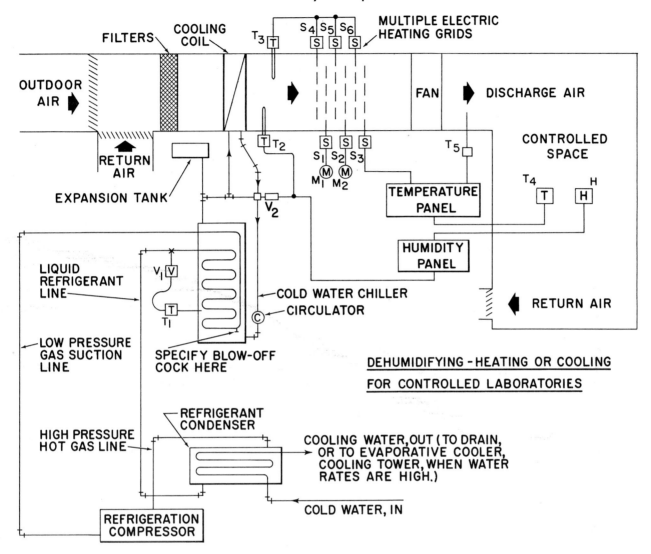

Figure 10.80 Dehumidifying-heating or cooling for controlled laboratories.

suitably dried air to the space. The temperature of the dry air, however, is elevated above the inlet air, to the extent of the latent heat of vaporization of the water removed. This means that usually a cooling coil is required at the discharge of the drier to reduce the dry bulb temperature as required.

Although chemical dehumidification can be applied actually to any drying problem in this area of operation, it is most commonly used for low dew point requirements.

Moisture Addition or Humidification. Adding humidity to the air is a simpler problem than that of removing it. However, several precautions are in order.

Mechanical atomization-type humidifiers, such as those employing pressure nozzles, or water jets impinging on "targets," demand specially clean soft water equivalent to distilled water, not only to prevent water impurities from being disseminated throughout the space in the form of fine dust. Except for the smallest humidity load, this

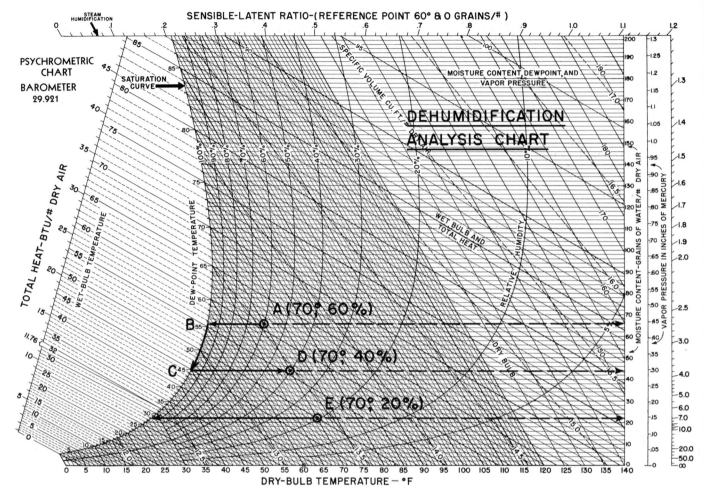

Figure 10.81   Dehumidification analysis chart.

restriction usually precludes the use of this form of humidification.

Thermal vaporizing types are somewhat more acceptable. They consist of a pan of water with immersed electric heaters or steam coils which boil the water. A disadvantage here is the small time delay in bringing the water to the boiling point; care must also be taken to provide reasonably soft water to minimize service on the float chamber mechanism.

Steam jet humidifiers which are short lengths of pipe with holes drilled in a row along the tops are most popular for they respond rapidly to the demand for moisture and need relatively little

service. They do require a clean source of steam to prevent unpleasant odors. Careful sizing of the automatic control valve is a critical necessity here.

Multi-purpose Systems. As indicated under discussion previously, it is most common experience that a single room will require two or more of the above air-conditioning functions. For example, where one is dehumidifying by refrigeration, reheat is usually always needed. Similarly, when dehumidifying chemically, dry bulb after-cooling is usually necessary.

Besides such examples calling for combination of simultaneous functions, all the above duties may possibly be required of a single room over a period of time. The design of the over-all system will be influenced accordingly.

CONTROL OF TEMPERATURE AND HUMIDITY

Fundamentals of Control

In laboratory work, a frequently specified tolerance on the desired temperature to be maintained is $\pm 2°F$ to $\pm\frac{1}{4}°F$. On relative humidity control, the tolerance usually runs in the range of $\pm 2\%$ to $\pm\frac{1}{2}\%$. Good commercial-grade control equipment can give $\pm\frac{1}{2}°F$ and $\pm 1\%$ relative humidity, *but only when the very best practices are followed under favorable conditions,* including slow rates of load change. Otherwise, industrial equipment should be recommended.

If, in the case of a heating application, a tolerance of $\pm 1°F$ were specified and if the heating coil employed had only enough maximum capacity to raise the temperature of the space $2°F$, there would be no problem; the valve could open wide and the tolerance could not be exceeded. Unfortunately, in practice, the capacity of the heating equipment must be many times greater than that required to raise the space through tolerance on the temperature or humidity. Other things being equal, the difficulty of control is directly proportional to the ratio of equipment capacity (in terms of space temperature or humidity change) and the tolerance permitted on the condition. For the purpose of this discussion, the author chooses to call this ratio, "control factor" equals c/v in which c is the capacity of equipment in °F temperature rise or relative humidity rise, which is under the command of the automatic controller. This represents the number °F or per cent relative humidity the equipment can change the space condition if turned full "on;" v is the variation permitted in temperature or humidity in °F or per cent relative humidity respectively.*

This suggests the underlying principle that, for the best and most economical control, *the automatic controller must have command of the smallest possible quantity of heat, or humidity,* as the case may

* Although in practice, the selection of equipment cannot usually be resolved into such a simple formula, it is introduced here to illustrate an important principle.

be. In applying this principle, all heating, cooling, humidifying and dehumidifying *equipment must be accurately sized*—no larger than actually required to meet the greatest load. Let us examine several cases:

Case A. Temperature in the laboratory will be held at $86°F \pm \frac{1}{2}°F$, while the temperature surrounding the room, from which the "fresh air" is taken, will be $70°F$, representing a heat loss of 1,200 Btu/hr. The nature of the process being tested is such that full heat and no heat are alternately required. The control factor here is

$$\frac{86 - 70}{+\frac{1}{2} \text{ to } -\frac{1}{2}} = \frac{16}{1} = 16.$$

Assuming that the heating valve is correctly sized, this control factor of 16 cannot be reduced, as the full capacity to maintain the $86°F$ space condition must be under the command of the automatic thermostat to control the heat input according to the cycling load condition.

Case B. Suppose in the above example the load variation was only 300 instead of 1,200 Btu/hr which is equivalent to $4°F$ temperature rise instead of $16°F$. If the capacity of valve and coil were unchanged, the control factor would remain the same at 16. However, if we can arrange to set the basic heat input manually at 900 Btu, to just handle the minimum load and thus reduce the capacity of the automatic valve to 300 Btu/hr, we have reduced our control factor to

$$\frac{4}{1} = 4.$$

A typical way to accomplish this, in practice, is with two heating coils having the correct total heating capacity, one manually and the other automatically controlled, or by a single coil served by a properly sized manual valve and automatic valve piped in parallel.

Case C. Assume that the conditions mentioned above were not foreseen to permit the installation of means to reduce the control factor below 16. A control factor below the general area of 10 or 12 would be a clue that commercial controls may be satisfactory. A control factor (such as in our example) above 10 or 12 indicates the possible need of features found only in industrial type control. In either event *a thorough analysis of the system* *characteristics* (including capacitance, capacity, lags, and pick-up rates*) *by your control engineer is required* to establish the final selection of control equipment. It must be noted that although the cost is higher, industrial type controls offer more flexibility and greater simplicity in design of equipment layout and completely automatic controls, superceding the need to set the basic rate manually.

Typically Controlled Systems

It is beyond the scope of this treatise to cover all possible applications. It is the intent, however, to treat all the basic principles involved, so that a reader can combine them as best serves his specific purpose. The following applications are illustrative of different types which find widespread application.

The first application involves both humidifying and heating (See Figure 10.82) using in one case commercial control and in the other industrial central equipment.

In this, the outside air and return air dampers are manually set to meet the requirements as previously discussed under the ventilation requirements of air-conditioned systems. After being properly proportioned, the mixed air passes

---

* The control problem can frequently be materially simplified by employing a separate valve and coil (or other controlled heat exchanger) for fast pick-up service when this feature is specified.

Figure 10.82   Humidifying-heating for controlled laboratories.

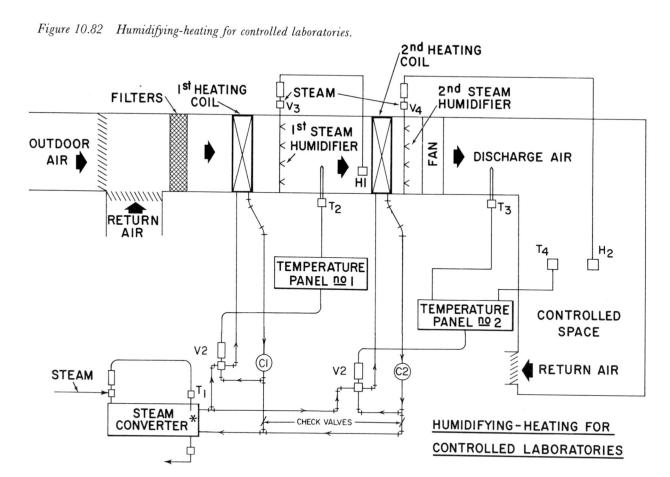

* HOT WATER BOILER MAY BE SUBSTITUTED

through a filter bank which normally will consist of one or two banks of glass spun or equivalent, 2 in. thick filters or for more exacting standards of air purifications, Electronic Air Cleaners may be used.

From the filters, the air passes through the first heating coil which is arranged to handle the basic minimum load as measured by T2 controlling the three-way mixing valve V1 through temperature panel #1. The humidity controller H1 is set to insure that the basic minimum relative humidity is being supplied; this controls valve V3, feeding its steam humidifier.

The air from the first heating coil and humidifier then passes through the second heating coil which is served by the 3-way mixing valve V2 which provides the refined regulation of space temperature as measured by T4, assisted by T3 in the discharge air.

Both heating coils are supplied with hot water by a steam converter or hot water boiler. In either case, this hot water is supplied at the lowest temperature which will just match the heaviest demand, by setting T1, the temperature controller measuring converter water temperature and controlling the steam inlet valve.

After passing through this final heating coil, the precise addition of moisture is given by valve V4 which serves the second humidifier and is controlled by the space humidity controller H2.

By employing industrial control equipment, similar good results can be obtained with a single hot water coil and a single modulating humidifier. In special applications requiring humidity measurement in a duct, "wet and dry bulb" control may prove expedient. This measures both wet and dry bulb temperatures, which defines a given relative humidity.

The second application to be described involves dehumidifying and heating or cooling (see Figure 10.80).

Here again dampers to proportion and mix outside and return air and filters of spun glass or electronic type to purify it are used as described in the first application.

The air now passes through a chilled water cooling coil whose principal purpose is to cool the air as required below its dew point. Sufficient water will thus be condensed out of the

air to satisfy relative humidity controller H. Modulating control should always be specified for constant humidity room applications.

The modulating controller T2 is a high limit temperature controller serving as an "auxiliary" to the temperature control system. Unless a precision-type control valve V2 is employed, the temperature level can be "upset" when the humidity controller "just opens" or "just closes" the valve. This limited range of a commercial control valve can be satisfactorily eliminated by setting T2 at such a value as to slightly load the coil at all times, never allowing the valve to reach the critical closed position. This solution actually calls for slightly higher operating cost due to running the compressor at times when dehumidification is not demanded. Nevertheless, this is accepted practice where the small amount of over-dehumidifying occurs infrequently and is not objectionable to the process. Otherwise, the extra cost of industrial control components will be justified.

The temperature of the water supplied by the chiller must be as high as possible and still satisfy the greatest demand of the humidity controller for dehumidification. This is sometimes accomplished by T1 controlling the solenoid refrigerant valve, but preferably by employing modulating control on the refrigerating machine.

The principal additional components of the dehumidification system include the humidity control panel which links the humidistat with the valve it controls, the circulator C which insures constant circulation of the chilled water through the chiller, the refrigeration compressor, the source of energy for the refrigeration cycle, and the refrigerant condenser which removes the latent heat of vaporization from the refrigerant, usually Freon F12 and thus converts the hot high pressure gas to a liquid.

Alternately a direct expansion coil can be successfully substituted for the chilled water coil, and served directly by the liquid refrigerant from the condenser. In this case, the modulating humidity panel resets a back pressure throttling valve in the "suction" line to the compressor, so set that when no dehumidification is needed, the coil temperature will just handle the minimum temperature requirement. A call for maximum dehumidification will produce the required reduced coil temperature. Applications of this type are usually limited to refrigeration load changes from 100% to 40 or 20% minimum, depending on type of equipment selected.

The final step in this second application is that supplying the minimum quantity of heat required when the humidistat is satisfied (when dehumidification is not required). This is manually set by switches M1 and M2. Electric heating grids are used.

The space thermostat T4, operating through its control panel operates S3 adjusted to the smallest valve which will still satisfy all demands of the thermostat at zero dehumidification load. If the load changes are extremely small, such that S3 handles less than 5% of total load, the control action may be two-position (i.e., on or off), under certain special circumstances. However, modulating control would give superior performance here because it avoids possible unfavorable interaction from mixing modulating with two-position control. The heat can be modulated by positioning a variac serving the electric grid.

Note that the heating capacity of S3 operated by the space thermostat has sufficient capacity only when the humidistat H has the cooling valve closed to the minimum value established by T2. The "reheating" load, caused by H subcooling the air to dehumidify it, is measured by T3 which turns on S4, S5 and S6 as required.

When industrial control equipment is used, the cooling coil valve can be operated to full closed position from a single modulating space humidity controller, eliminating T2 and the wasteful overlapping with heating. In addition a single space stat can successfully serve to modulate a single bank of electric heating grids.

The third and final application is that involving dehumidifying and cooling. (See Figure 10.83.) The system given in detail uses commercial controls. Mixing of outdoor and return air and filtering of the mixed air is handled as described in the first and second applications.

In this case the humidity controller H operates through a panel to regulate the amount of dehumidification by controlling the face and by-pass dampers of the chemical dehumidifier. As the need for dehumidification increases, more air is permitted to pass through the dehumidifier and less through the "by-pass." In this application the manual damper D is set to provide the basic minimum amount of dehumidification which will be needed at all times. M1 will then position to handle only the variation in dehumidification requirement.

The temperature of the air leaving the first cooling coil is measured by thermostat T1; this regulates the valve V1 to reduce the air temperature to match the minimum load of the space. Similarly thermostat T2 measures the final space temperature and assisted by T3 measuring the discharge air temperature, controls valve V2 serving the second cooling coil.

This system is especially recommended for relative humidities as low as 5% and for those applications where dew points below 35°F are required.

If industrial controls are used in place of the commercial type, a single cooling coil controlled by a single space thermostat could be used.

Indicating and Recording

It is usually not sufficient to provide a well-designed room, equipped with proper air conditioning equipment and control system. It is also important that the operator know the exact relative humidity and temperature at any time during the test and to have a record of these values for analysis and reference after the test is concluded. Appropriate indicating and recording equipment are available and can be combined with the design and installation of the automatic controls.

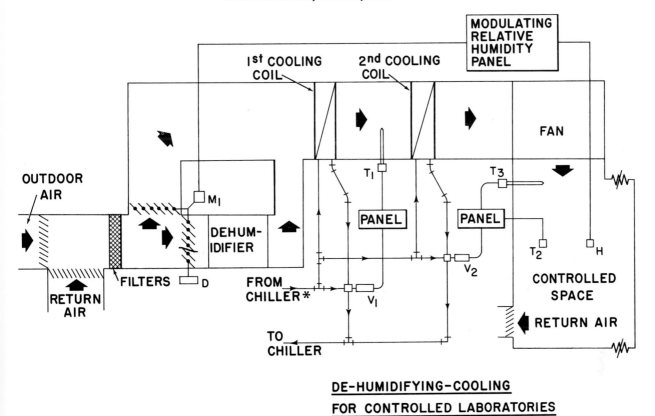

DE-HUMIDIFYING-COOLING

FOR CONTROLLED LABORATORIES

Figure 10.83   Dehumidifying-cooling for controlled laboratories.   * For chiller arrangement see Figure 10.80.

Laboratories for the Academic Functions

CHAPTER XI

University and College Laboratories

M. G. MELLON

Purdue University
Lafayette, Indiana

Academic laboratories are designed primarily for instructional purposes, often for both undergraduate and graduate students. All the larger ones have more or less extensive facilities for research programs, and occasionally this type of work is the major activity. In many aspects they resemble industrial laboratories, although the latter are designed almost entirely for routine testing and analysis, research, development, and often studies on a pilot plant scale.

This section is devoted to college laboratories. The nature and kind of facilities vary enormously in the hundreds of institutions in this country, from the largest and finest laboratories in large universities to a few rooms allotted to chemistry in the small college which has only a modest building for two or more sciences.

Primarily, this diversity arises because of the different problems faced in large and small institutions. In the former, for example, facilities may be needed for several thousand students in the course in general chemistry alone, whereas the small college may need to provide for no more than fifty. Secondarily, it may be a matter of funds. Many a small college operates as it does only because of lack of money to provide more nearly adequate and better facilities.

Because the problem varies so much from place to place, no effort has been made to describe *the* laboratory. What satisfies one individual may not appeal to another. It has seemed best, therefore, to consider in a general way (1) the kinds and nature of facilities most likely to be needed, and (2) the problem of arranging these facilities in a building for their most efficient use.

PERSONAL RESPONSIBILITY

Too much emphasis cannot be placed on the desirability of having some individual, or very small committee, given the responsibility for supervising the planning, and then watching construction to see that the specific details are included in the way intended. Many defects in buildings are probably attributable to failure to work enough on the plans and specifications, and/or to follow the construction closely. There is no perfect building, as there is no perfect book, but lots of hard work based on an understanding of the problem will reduce oversights both of omission and commission, and otherwise improve the product.

The planner(s) of the facilities, and the department(s) concerned with the building, should assume responsibility for telling the architect what is wanted and the preferred location of each item for its intended service. Few architects have had much experience with chemistry buildings, especially with what is needed for special purposes. For example, the planner should be prepared to describe the requirements of a special laboratory for all kinds of research work in electrochemistry, if this is needed, and to try, as far as possible, to locate this laboratory where it is wanted. Above all, no one should assume that "George" will do it.

Inspection during construction should not be neglected. Even with the best of intentions, foremen and workmen make mistakes because of oversight or misunderstanding of the plans or specifications. Large institutions will probably have their own inspectors, one for each kind of work, such as general construction, plumbing, heating and ventilating, and electrical installations. Their responsibility is to see that the materials and workmanship are acceptable. The planner should assume some responsibility for inspection, especially to see that the various services and facilities are suitably installed. Better than anyone else, if he really understands his plans, the departmental representative knows what should be where. Almost daily inspection is suggested for a large building. Occasionally some new idea, still possible of achievement at this stage, will come to mind. Ordinarily any significant changes or criticisms will have to be made through the chief inspector rather than a foreman or workman.

SERVICES NEEDED

Any chemical laboratory designed for experimental work must have a variety of services, such as water, gas, and electricity. The experimental work may be in lectures, in undergraduate and graduate class laboratories and research work, or in pilot plant operation. For the planner this means determining, as far as possible, what services are wanted, in what amounts, where they are desired, and in what arrangement. For example, it is the responsibility of someone, if he wants it, to ask for a 220 volt d.c. line delivering 60 amperes at a particular place in a given room. All such items must be incorporated in the plans and specifications, and inspection is necessary to see that they appear as desired. Such items are primarily engineering, and are discussed in detail elsewhere. The objective here is to remind the planner of their existence. If the work to be done must not be interrupted, it may be necessary to have spare installations of some equipment, such as an air compressor or a fan for radioactive gases.

Water

The ordinary or tap water usually is that of the community in which the institution is located. Probably the chief thing to question is whether the supply line is large enough for the over-all requirements, and from it any branch lines for specific purposes. Thus, a pipe for a desk top may not be of sufficient diameter to deliver enough water so that all the students at the desk can use their suction pumps at the same time. In nearly all laboratories the tap water is too impure to use for many purposes. Treatment with a still and/or a deionizer is necessary. An installation for the specific situation is required, and the product must be stored, and delivered where wanted.

Gas

Gas for burners, blast lamps, furnaces, and other equipment is still widely used. A Bunsen burner is almost a symbol of a chemical laboratory. Ordinarily natural or artificial gas is used, but a suitable substitute may be liquid propane.

Air

Air under some pressure is used for a variety of purposes. Various kinds of compressors and distribution systems are available. The pressure, the approximate amount desired, and the outlet locations must be known.

Steam

In addition to providing heat in most laboratories, steam is used for a number of chemical

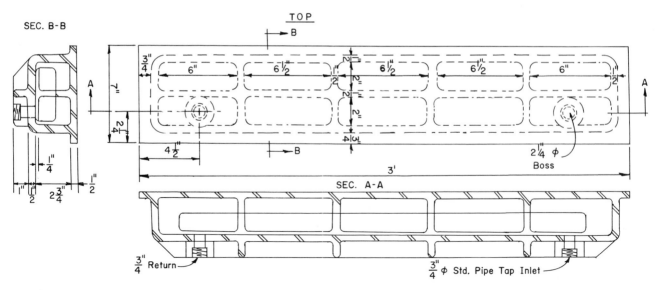

Figure 11.1   Steam hot plate.

purposes. Examples are steam baths, steam cones, steam hot plates, and steam distillations. Usually low pressure steam (6 to 10 psi) is used for such purposes, except for the hot plates. The hot plate shown in Figure 11.1 operates at about 40 lbs. pressure. Steam from a power plant may not be usable for a particular purpose. Thus, if it carries nitrogenous material, it cannot be used for making Kjeldahl nitrogen distillations.

Oxygen and Other Gases

Although oxygen does not have many uses, some laboratories have it piped to each research laboratory where glass working is likely to be needed. If it is so distributed, a distributing center will be required where cylinders may be stored and connected to the line. Certain other gases are increasing in use in the laboratory. Facilities may be needed for distribution of one or more of these chemicals, such as nitrogen. The use of a central hydrogen sulfide system is decreasing.

Suction

Much experimental work requires reduced pressure. The most common means is an aspirator water pump, which serves for simple operations such as filtering precipitates or organic preparations. The operation of many pumps requires an adequate water supply. Because of lack of water, or of personal preference, many laboratories use a central vacuum pump with piping to individual laboratories. This arrangement is exasperating when one has to search for the valve left open by a thoughtless student. In research work, especially when lower pressures are necessary, individual, electrically operated pumps are best.

Ventilation and Air Conditioning

The ventilation system, especially the hoods, are probably the most characteristic thing about a chemical laboratory. Because so many such systems have not worked satisfactorily, unfortunately the most vivid memories of chemistry for many students are the unremoved odors of chemicals. Not only are many odors unpleasant, but many are dangerous and very toxic. Small concentrations of hydrogen cyanide or hydrogen sulfide, for example, are lethal. Radiochemistry has brought new hazards which require very special installations. The whole ventilation system must be adequate for whatever is to be done in different parts of a laboratory.

If any or all of a building is to be air-conditioned, the ventilation problem is more difficult.

The system must be adequately designed for the load. Inadequate or poorly working installations are an abomination. This item is very important for inside rooms and those requiring certain temperatures and humidities.

Electricity

An adequate electrical supply is indispensable in a modern laboratory. This involves having both alternating and direct current, in sufficient capacity for what is to be done. The architect will provide for general lighting. Any special situations for chemical work must be called to his attention.

The main responsibility of the planner is to check the requirements of every room for everything which ought to be included in the whole installation. In a large building designed for a wide variety of work, this is one of the more difficult planning problems. Will alternating current of 220 volts be needed, and, if so, in what amounts? Will generators be needed for direct current? If so, what should be the voltage(s) delivered? Is a generator with compound winding necessary to maintain a reasonably constant voltage? Is a battery system required for constant, low-voltage current? If so, how many cells? What equipment, such as furnaces, will need heavy capacity lines? Answers to all such questions are necessary.

In addition, where and how are all, or part, of these to be made available? In general, laboratories for freshman chemistry need least, and laboratories for graduate research need most in variety of electrical facilities. To have complete electrical flexibility for research, all areas designed for this work should have all services available for each student. If this cannot be afforded, a workable compromise must be decided.

As an example, in one modern laboratory each graduate student has the following electrical possibilities at his laboratory desk: Two lines for 110 V a.c., each fused for 12 amp. and having two duplex outlets, and one plug panel box with two circuits for the other kinds of current. The latter include a.c., single-phase at 110 or 220 V, and three-phase at 220 V, and d.c. at 1.5 to 30 V from Edison storage batteries or at 110 or 220 V from motor generators. If desired, current

may be taken directly from the university power house. Selection of any such possibility is made at appropriately placed plug panels in the corridors on each floor. Extra trunk lines provide for connecting, through the numbered circuits, any room to any other room containing plug panel boxes.

KINDS OF ROOMS

Every building of more than one or two rooms has many different kinds of facilities. Examples are laboratories, lecture rooms, classrooms, offices, library, storeroom(s), and shop(s). Anyone planning a new building must decide ultimately which of such possibilities are to be included and the services needed in each. Then comes the problem of location.

A viewpoint as long-range as possible should be sought, with the help of those who are to use the facilities. Because of the rapid changes in science, one university president stated that no such building can be planned for efficient service for more than twenty-five years in the future. Although the writer heard this statement made, it is not necessarily true. However, it is a warning to try to achieve as much flexibility as possible. Can a classroom, for example, be converted to a research laboratory, and, if so, without too much expense?

In considering any specific facility, such as a departmental library, at least three questions arise: (1) what would be ideal? (2) what would be reasonably satisfactory for the intended use? and (3) what should be avoided, if possible?

Because of diversity of viewpoints, it seems pointless to try to describe an ideal anything. Thus, what one professor wants in a lecture room, another does not. Consequently, the writer has chosen to comment on what seem to him desirable features observed in one or more of many buildings visited during the past twenty-five years. It is his belief that many mistakes could have been avoided if the planner had been provided with a list of the more important points to consider in deciding what is desirable in a given kind of room, such as a library.

Although a complete listing of all kinds of facilities for all kinds of purposes has not been attempted, it is believed that those selected will concern many planners. Any kinds not included should be considered in the same way.

Lecture Room(s)

A room which will accommodate more people than the conventional class or recitation room is generally referred to as a lecture room. There is, of course, no difference between a large recitation room and a small lecture room. Usually lecture rooms hold at least 50 and not more than 500.

The characteristics of such rooms vary widely around the country. Partly this may be due to wishes of the planners and often, no doubt, to architectural compromises or necessity. Occasionally the latter have led to interesting innovations.

As space precludes going into these variations in detail, this discussion is limited to a fairly large room, that is, one holding 300 to 350 on one floor. Usually smaller rooms differ chiefly in having fewer facilities.

Capacity and Number. Determination of the number of such rooms needed is important. No architect can decide this point. The decision must be based on a careful study of the probable requirements, both present and immediate future. Sizes of the various kinds of classes, meetings per week, and sectioning of very large groups are of most concern. In large institutions, with many large classes in both undergraduate and graduate work, several sizes of rooms will be needed. Conditions vary widely, but the following are suggested as not excessive: One holding 300 to 500; two holding 150 to 200; two holding 100; and one holding 50.

Proportions. The proportions of such rooms are of some importance. If too wide, those sitting at the sides of the front rows have difficulty seeing the blackboard or beaded projection screen clearly, since the angle is too great. In rooms which are too long those in the back rows may not be able to see lecture experiments unless they are done on a large scale or projected on a screen. Also amplification may be necessary, at least for some speakers. In general, a room should be somewhat longer than its width, a ratio between 5:4 and 5:3 being a reasonable value.

Seats. Styles and kinds of seats are discussed elsewhere. Spacing of seats should provide as much capacity as feasible, but not be so close that access is difficult. A reasonable spacing for easy movement is 26 x 38 inches. There should be sufficient aisles so that no seat is farther than the fifth space from an aisle.

Grouping of seats in odd numbers per row gives efficiency for placing students in alternate seats for tests. Thus, 10 people can be seated in a 5-7-5 combination, but only the same number in a 6-8-6 combination.

If lecture attendance is to be checked, consideration should be given to numbering the seats. Numbers should be large enough and properly positioned for easy reading. On wood backs the number may be stamped both on the front and the back. Some easily usable system should be adopted so that vacant seats are readily noted. The accompanying chart represents usable schemes (Figure 11.2).

A foot-rail underneath the back of the seat itself is convenient for those sitting in the row just behind.

Slope of Floor. In general, rooms accommodating many more than 50 people should not have a flat floor, because of difficulty of seeing the lecture table and blackboard from rows toward the back. The slope to use is a matter of argument. The rise can be too much or too little. If the lecture table rests on the floor, the first row or two of seats may also be on the floor. Then the third row may be up three inches. Each succeeding row should be higher, but in slightly parabolic rather than regular succession. Sight lines drawn to scale to a point on the lecture table help to decide what will be satisfactory.

Balcony. Whether or not to include a balcony in a large room is debatable. Many buildings have them. The arrangement does increase the capacity, which architecturally may not otherwise be possible, and it brings more people closer to the lecture table to see demonstrations better. Some lecturers believe that no one should be more than 50 to 60 feet from the center of the table unless special, large-scale experiments are performed.

To include a balcony requires more over-all height for the room. This may not be readily feasible. If it is included, the slope of the main floor should be kept to a minimum for good vision; otherwise the balcony will be high and its slope steep to give good sight-lines for observers. It is uncomfortable for a lecturer to look up to the back rows of seats in a high balcony.

Blackboard. Some instructors prefer several relatively short boards, about 10 to 12 feet long, mounted one behind the other, which can be pushed up or down. Sometimes a hood or preparation room is immediately back of such a board. Other instructors prefer a single fixed board, 25 to 30 feet long. The chalk rail should be at the height of the lecture table, usually about 36 inches. The board should be 42 to 48 inches wide. A rail at the top is convenient for hanging charts and similar displays. Joints should be kept to a minimum in a long board.

Although the name implies a black surface, many boards are green. Partly the choice is a matter of preference, although the writer was able to demonstrate to one manufacturer that writing on a black surface could be seen 20 feet farther than that on a green surface. In this case, the black surface is preferable for visibility in a long room. Materials available are discussed elsewhere.

Lighting. Several general aspects of lighting are important in a well-equipped lecture room. First is the question whether the room is to be theater-type construction, that is, without windows. Such rooms are simpler to construct, and they need no darkening device to cover windows. Many years of experience with both kinds of rooms have convinced the writer of the merit of windowless rooms.

It is an architectural question whether to use indirect general lighting. One solution is to have both direct and indirect installations. Thus, one lecture room has tungsten lights on two circuits. One is for spot lights directly above the lecture table to serve as pilot lights and to illuminate displays and experiments, and the other is for the main battery of lights recessed in the ceiling. The latter are under rheostat or dimmer control so that the level of illumination may be varied from full to very low light. One use is to darken the room for showing pictures and yet have enough light for students to take notes.

The other lights in this room are long rows of

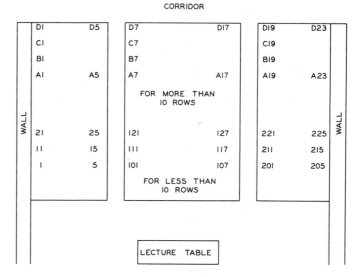

Figure 11.2   Numbering lecture room seats.

fluorescent tubes concealed in the coves of the ceiling. For some occasions this lighting effect is desirable.

It is very convenient to have the main light switch coordinated with that of the projection lantern so that turning off the room lights turns on the lantern light, and vice versa.

Certainly in a large room, and preferably in all classrooms, the blackboard should be specially lighted. This can be done by means of spot lights suitably mounted, but it seems preferable to mount a line of fluorescent tubes just above the board. The light is not quite as good as with spot lights, but there is one important advantage. If the board is long, the lights can be on with the projection screen down and thus leave space on either side of the screen for the lecturer to write on the board without putting up the screen and turning on the room lights. The reflector (a satisfactory commercial product is "Daybright") should extend down just enough to cut off direct view of the light tubes by those seated in the front row.

Electrical Controls. There should be duplicate electrical control switches on the lecture table and in the projection booth for all lights and mechanical features, such as the projection screen. In addition, at one entrance door for each corridor and at the door(s) from the preparation room(s), there should be a switch to a pilot light or the spot lights for the lecture table.

Projection Booth. At least one lecture room, and preferably more in a large institution, should have a projection booth for showing pictures. There should be provision for equipment for all the usual kinds of pictures, such as television, sound movies, and different kinds of slides. All the electrical controls at the lecture table should be duplicated here. There should be an electric signal device from the table to the booth. In addition, telephone communication between lecturer and booth operator may be desirable in a large room.

The architects should suggest a location, size, and suitable arrangement for the projection room. It should be on the main floor of a room having a balcony.

A permanent opening may be left in the front wall at a suitable location for the projectors. To protect them heavy wire screen of about 2 x 2 inch mesh may be used. Pictures will project very satisfactorily through this screen.

Projection Screen. Preferably the projection screen should be electrically controlled, both from the lecture table and the projection room. The size will depend upon the room. Various kinds of material are used. Many lecturers prefer a glass-bead surface.

Mounting is also important. For most viewing, and also for the convenience of the lecturer, the bottom of the unrolled curtain should be at about the height of the lecture table. This will cover part of a long blackboard. If the board is lighted along the top, the curtain must clear the lighting fixture in descending.

Displays. In addition to the rail above the blackboard for charts, some boards have a narrow cork-board strip on which items may be fastened with thumb tacks. This is hardly possible if the board is lighted by a row of fluorescent tubes, for they should be close to the top of the board in order to illuminate the bottom.

Other facilities may be desired inside the room, such as corkback boards on which to mount various items. Usually such rooms have tables or charts, such as the periodic table of the chemical elements and the EMF series of the elements.

Sometimes these are painted on the wall, but more often they are on curtains which can be rolled up.

A few institutions have the periodic table arranged to illuminate each element separately, all at once, or in any desired combination. The installation may be permanent or portable.

Outside of the entrance(s) to the room there should be adequately lighted bulletin boards with glass doors for the various announcements that need to be posted concerning lectures and other events scheduled for the room. Included would be displays to arouse interest in chemistry.

Public Address System. If a room seats 200 or more, a public address system may be needed. To a large degree the need depends upon the acoustical properties of the room and characteristics of the speaker. The architect is responsible for the acoustics. No doubt it is best in any case to assume that a system will be needed and include necessary conduits and outlets. Then installation is easy if and when needed. The speaker may serve both for sound movies and a lecturer. Only first quality products should be used. Permanent installation of the speaker is preferable.

Provision for Wraps. Without taking considerable space for a separate cloak room, it is not very feasible to provide facilities for wraps for the occupants of a room seating several hundred people. However, it does seem desirable to provide something. Figure 11.3 illustrates an inexpensive steel rack which has proved servicable. One rack 4 ft 6 in. x 2 ft 0 in., and 6 ft 0 in. high, contains 36 hooks and two levels above for hats and books. Usually several of these can be placed in the back of a room. They serve very well also in laboratories and recitation rooms.

Lecture Table(s). The size of lecture tables varies, of course, with room size and with what is to be done, but one hears no complaint of any being too large. In large rooms for many sections of general chemistry the table should be 24 to 30 ft long. For smaller rooms 12 to 18 ft is suitable. A height of 36 to 38 in. and a width of 36 to 42 in. is usual.

Tables may be fixed or partly movable. A movable section should be carefully designed for weight and ease of handling. In order to avoid excessive weight, a length of 6 ft is about

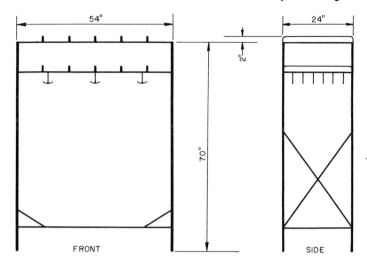

Figure 11.3   Coat rack

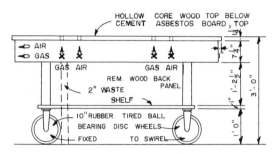

Figure 11.4   Portable section of lecture table.

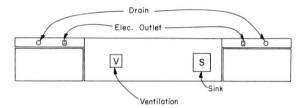

Figure 11.5   Top view of lecture table with two portable end sections.

enough. Stone tops are heavy. The wheels of the truck should have ball bearings and not be too small. The tires may be *hard* rubber. A few buildings have steel rails in the floor for flanged steel wheels, but this limits flexibility of movement. It does bring the movable section easily into position. Figure 11.4 shows a design for a free-moving, movable section.

For a table 24 ft or more in length it is probably best to have a movable section at each end, with a fixed section in the center. Figure 11.5 shows such an arrangement.

For smaller rooms the same center section, with or without one of the movable sections, will serve.

Services on the table should be adequate for any demonstrations contemplated. These items include at least the following: water (distilled and ordinary), steam (with mixer for hot water), aspirator for reduced pressure, gas, exhaust for noxious fumes (down-draft hood), and electric current. If possible, these should be mounted so that the entire table top may be clear. Both a.c. and d.c. (whatever is available from a plug panel in the preparation room) should be included.

It seems best to have the lecture table placed on the floor rather than up one or more steps on a platform. If a platform is used, vision to the top of the table is not good from the first row or two of seats. In fact, in one lecture room the first three rows are never assigned because the table was elevated about 30 in. so that the experiments could be seen from the back rows. Perhaps just as important is the problem of bringing special items and equipment to the table. If it is on the floor, there is no problem. Anything that can be transported to the room can easily be put in the desired position at or on the table.

There should be a 36 to 45-in. clearance between the chalk rail of the blackboard and the edge of the table top.

Access to Room. At this point Figure 11.23 (p. 308) may be referred to in mentioning the problem of traffic flow to and from lecture rooms. This is important when sections of several hundred students are scheduled in a room for successive periods. If possible, the chief entrance doors should be at the back of the room. This is especially advantageous to prevent people entering the room from passing in front of the lecturer after he starts to talk. The door(s) near the table may be closed to make late-comers go to the back. Until the lecture starts these doors provide access from this part of the building. Then at the end of the lecture period they can again be opened to facilitate rapid clearing of the room.

The corridor or foyer at the main entrance doors should be wide enough to facilitate the interchange of large classes.

Lecture Preparation Room. Any lecture room in which many experimental demonstrations are to be done should have an adjacent preparation room. Two desirable locations, if architecturally possible, are shown in the part plans of Figures 11.24 (p. 310) and 11.31 (p. 316).

In Figure 11.31 the preparation is done immediately behind the lecturer. If the blackboard slides up, it is possible to arrange for transfer of items under the board when it is raised. Secondary entrances are from the side corridors as shown. Primary entrances are from the back corridor. In this arrangement at Princeton University, the room occupies the position where the two arms of the cross-plan cross each other. The lecture room is one of the four half arms. The other three are large laboratories. In this way the preparation room serves also as general storeroom.

In Figure 11.24 the preparation room is at either side, or there may be one at each side. In the latter arrangement, at Purdue University, four lecture rooms seating 463, 170, 170, 77, are grouped together, with the storeroom just across the back corridor.

Within the preparation room(s) there should be provision for storage of the special equipment, chemicals, and apparatus necessary for the required demonstrations. Adequate and fully serviced working space is necessary for experimenting, cleaning apparatus, and incidental operations. There should be some office space for the chief demonstrator.

Floor space is needed for several trucks to transport items to the lecture table. These will be principally the movable sections of the table, if it has this form. Doors and space must be planned to handle these.

Class or Recitation Rooms

Rooms for small classes or recitations are usually distinguished from lecture rooms in being smaller and in having fewer facilities for experimental demonstrations and for projection of pictures.

A capacity for 25 students is a reasonable average for rooms designed for recitations. Many instructors insist on no more than 30, but there is increasing pressure to accommodate more. From 500 to 600 sq ft of floor space is adequate. Preferably the room should not be far from square. Satisfactory sizes are in the neighborhood of 20 x 26 x 24 ft for 25 to 30 students.

Blackboard space is a problem. Materials are discussed elsewhere, along with chalk rails, lighting, and facilities for charts and other displays. In order to get as many students as possible to the board at one time in recitation rooms, many instructors like to have boards on three walls. If the fourth wall is not taken up by windows, still more space is available.

Especially in northern climates space should be provided for wraps. If space is too limited for other facilities, one solution is illustrated in Figure 11.6. The boards, split into sections 6 to 8 ft long and suspended with weights like a window, are pulled down for use. When these are raised, space is accessible for hats on the shelf and for coats on the hooks underneath the shelf.

Few instructors will use any demonstration facilities in a recitation. However, to make simple experiments possible, it seems worthwhile to pro-

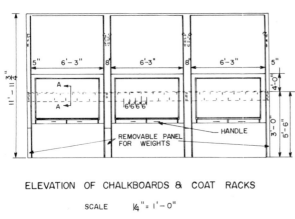

ELEVATION OF CHALKBOARDS & COAT RACKS

SCALE ¼" = 1'-0"

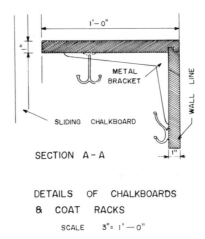

DETAILS OF CHALKBOARDS
& COAT RACKS

SCALE 3" = 1'—0"

Figure 11.6   Sliding chalkboard in front of coat racks.

vide at least gas, water, and a 110 V a.c. electric line. A small desk, about 3 x 6 ft, is suitable. Some drawers should be included for chalk, paper, and other supplies. There should be an a.c. outlet at the back of the room for a projector.

Pedestal and some other types of seats are fastened to the floor, but ordinary tablet arm chairs may not be. If not fixed, usually it is preferable to fasten 3 to 5 such chairs together, suitably spaced, in a row by means of wood strips.

Offices

Provision of adequate office space for the permanent teaching and research staffs contributes both to efficiency and morale. Nearly everyone needs some space for books, files, and various items connected with his work. Teachers need space, and often more privacy, for interviewing students. Only a large department will be considered, as its problem is more difficult. A small department will simply have less of the same kind of facilities.

General Offices. Probably no two large departments handle the office problem in the same way. Usually, in any specific case, things have simply developed without any definite long-term plan. Requirements differ widely. An institution doing little beyond undergraduate teaching has a much lighter office load than one with the same number of undergraduates and in addition many graduate students and post-doctoral fellows. Graduate programs, especially those involving frequent reports to sponsors of fellowships, require personnel and consequently space and facilities.

The space required for a general office must be calculated in terms of what is to be done in it, and the number of people involved. Dimensions on the plans shown will give some idea for the individual parts.

Figure 11.7 illustrates one arrangement which provides for the following personnel: head of department, private secretary, receptionist, executive assistant, and 6 stenographers. There is a wash bowl in the stenographers' room. In addition to individual rooms for the people mentioned, the following space is included in the plan: conference room, toilet, vault, storage closet, mail room for junior staff, mail boxes for senior staff, and mail chute outlet from upper floors. The architecture just happened to make this arrangement possible.

Large enrollments in particular kinds of courses, such as general chemistry and organic chemistry, seem to justify separate subgeneral offices. Figure 11.8 illustrates one possibility for an organic staff occupying an entire floor of a large building. There are separate offices for 4 instructors and an outside office for 3 or 4 stenographers and general records.

The office space and accompanying facilities

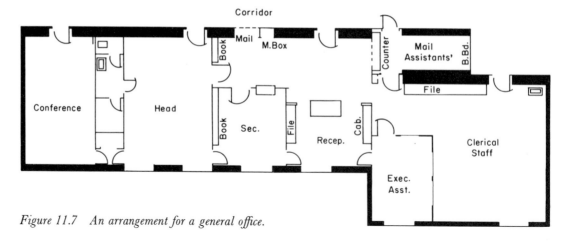

Figure 11.7   An arrangement for a general office.

needed for handling large enrollments in general chemistry depend upon the method of administering the work. The planner must rely upon those in this area for advice on what is wanted.

If needed, group offices can be designed for other areas, such as chemical engineering and biochemistry. Individual offices are the usual practice in analytical, inorganic, and physical chemistry.

A subgeneral office is necessary for the storeroom of a large department, especially one with a large graduate program. Ordinarily it is best incorporated as part of the storeroom itself. Administrative systems differ, but estimates of prices have to be obtained, material ordered, shipments checked, invoices maintained, and student accounts kept. Many catalogs are required and endless records accumulate. All these activities require space and facilities.

What is best in a given building depends upon the local situation and the storeroom system used. Some institutions maintain extensive general stores; if so, the chemistry department maintains one of the substore centers. In this case less space is needed in the chemistry building.

Individual Offices. Small offices for the permanent staff may provide for single or multiple occupancy. Most instructors prefer one to themselves, although occasionally two or four seem able to endure each other, or possibly even to like

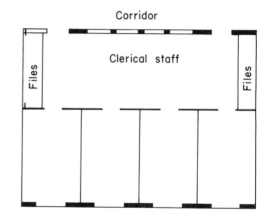

Figure 11.8   A group of divisional offices.

the sociability possible; but conferences with students are difficult and the environment is hardly conducive to scholarly work, such as writing a book.

For an individual office 100 sq ft is about a minimum (9 x 11 or 10 x 10 ft); 150 sq ft is adequate (10 x 15 or 12 x 12 ft); and 200 is semi-luxurious (12 x 20 or 14 x 18 ft) to most instructors. The dimensions given are only suggestive, but long, narrow offices, such as 8 x 25 ft are psychologically objectionable and furniture does not fit in well.

Lighting, ventilation, and electrical outlets should be adequate. Usually there are no built-in cases. If there is an adjoining private research laboratory, it is desirable to have a door between the two rooms.

A combined office and research laboratory is feasible for a young instructor, or for a professor who has no graduate students. If such use is contemplated for a room approximately 10 x 22 to 12 x 24 ft, it should be equipped on both sides for regular laboratory use. If T-slots are mounted in the walls, all service lines and any shelves may be hung here. The lines should have unions midway in the room. Then 6 ft portable research desks sit against the wall. For combined use one or both desk units on one side, together with pipes if desired, are removed. By replacing them the room is ready for regular research load.

Junior Staff Offices. It is desirable to have some space set aside for members of the junior staff, and especially those who conduct recitation classes or have charge of laboratory sections. Some study is possible, but there is most need for a place to interview students about their work. As there are more student problems in large courses in general chemistry than elsewhere, the space problem is greatest here. Unfortunately, few institutions with large enrollments have been able to do much in this direction. Anything that can be spared for this use is of value.

Junior Staff Social Room. In a department having a large group of graduate students it seems worth while to set aside a room for them for general use. It provides a place for small groups to congregate, to play an occasional game of bridge, or to read a magazine for a few minutes. A room of 600 to 800 square feet is suitable. The furnishings may be simple—a few small tables, chairs, and magazine rack. A small adjacent kitchenette extends the social possibilities. A "Coke" machine is inevitable, of course.

Conference Rooms

In large departments handling many graduate students at least two rooms are desirable for a number of conference uses. One should be considerably larger than the other.

If there is space, the larger room may have some 700 to 800 sq ft, a good dimension being 24 x 32 ft. On one end there should be a blackboard (about 10 ft) and a projection curtain of suitable size to pull down. If the room can be paneled, or otherwise finished better than most chemistry buildings are, the board and curtain may be recessed enough to be covered with draw curtains when not in use. In the wall opposite the curtain there should be an electrical outlet for a lantern for showing slides.

Adjacent to this room, and connected with it, it is convenient to have a small apartment-type kitchen. The size of this room determines what it will hold, but two useful units are one containing stove, sink, and small refrigerator, and one consisting of a counter with drawers underneath and cabinet shelves above. If there is space in this room, extras, such as folding chairs, may be stored here.

This combination serves many purposes. Examples are departmental meetings, seminars, colloquia, meetings of school heads or large committees which may last a half day or more, registration of graduate students, and social meetings, such as tea for a visiting speaker or entertainment of groups of students.

It is fitting in such a room to have a large table, such as 4 x 16 ft, with glass top, and as good chairs as can be afforded.

The smaller room may serve rather different purposes. Three common ones are for meetings of small committees, for oral examinations of graduate students, and for industrial interviewers of graduate students. A convenient size is 12 x 15 ft. There should be a blackboard the length of the room. Furnishings should include a center table and chairs. If feasible, this room should be adjacent to a secretary, who can help an interviewer keep a group of students moving in and out of the room.

Shops

University administrators have to decide whether to maintain both general and departmental shops. Assuming both, usually only the central shop will have large and very specialized equipment which would be used infrequently in a departmental shop.

The type of work carried on in a departmental shop usually involves repair and construction of apparatus and equipment used in the laboratory. This has come to include work with wood, metals, glass, electrical parts, optical pieces, thermal materials, and others. Space and equipment for such work varies from a small table in a corner, with a few tools, to the most elaborately furnished shop, manned by professional operators.

The need for one or more shops in a chemistry building is related to the research program maintained. A small department, devoted completely to undergraduate teaching, generally needs little beyond a small space to repair apparatus and perhaps to construct an occasional simple piece of equipment for lecture demonstration or laboratory use. An exception is the small college where the chemistry faculty are actively engaged in research and where the students may participate in independent study or honors research. In contrast, a large department having many graduate students working on very diverse programs will need considerable work done on widely differing equipment.

Obviously, one cannot recommend *the* shop for such different situations. The planner should consider the likely needs for the program contemplated in the building. Visits to see the facilities of similar institutions are very helpful. Only more or less general suggestions are offered here, but it is assumed that the shop needs are fairly large.

Wherever there is considerable work of some variety, the question of subdivision of activity arises. Until a real need seems to justify splitting up the facilities, one general shop is all that can be expected. In it all work, of whatever kind, is done. As some specialization has been assumed for this discussion, several kinds of shops are mentioned.

General Shop. Even where subdivision of work seems best, perhaps the major load will remain rather general. Mechanical and electrical repairs of equipment, and the design and making of many items of wood and metal can be done here. Unless other services are available, this work will include many items connected with operating the building itself.

The space, equipment, and storage needed for supplies depend upon the nature and size of the program. Many large departments have an office for the supervisor and space for 3 to 5 men in the shop. Most shops are too small.

If possible, the shop should be located for easy access to a freight elevator in order to get material and equipment to and from the shop. If it is too close to class or lecture rooms, shop noise may be objectionable.

For a wide variety of work, power and other special equipment such as the following, are needed: (1) *Metal working*—vises; anvil; threading machine; shears; bending machines for sheets and angles; emery wheels; hack saw; milling machine; lathes (small and large); drill presses (small and large); welding equipment. (2) *Wood working*—rip saw; cross-cut saw; band saw; jig saw; planer; shaper. If much painting has to be done, it is desirable to do the work in a separate room. Much of the time there is too much dust in the air of a general shop for good painting work. (3) *Glass working*—blow torch and table; annealing oven; lathe; cutting tool (for tubing); cutting table (for sheets).

Storage of supplies and parts requires appropriate bins, drawers, and supports. For metals this includes suitable sizes, lengths, and types of sheets, rods, tubes, pipes and fittings, angles, wire, bolts, screws, nails, and electrical parts.

Wood supplies include common sizes of boards, bill stock, and plywood sheets.

For both wood and metal there should be easy access from unloading platform to storage space so that 20-foot pieces may be handled.

Special Shops. In general, it is most efficient to have all kinds of shop facilities closely coordinated. If all cannot be together, they should be as close as possible. Some equipment and supplies are common. In making new apparatus some parts may be metal, some wood, some glass, and some electrical.

1. GLASS WORKING. The most common special shop is for glass working. Facilities are considered only for professional work. To support the research program of a large group of graduate students the amount of glass working is likely to warrant one or more professional workers. If so, quarters should be set apart from this activity. The space needed depends upon the number of workers, the amount of equipment, and the storage space needed for glass supplies and completed items awaiting call.

If there is a course on glass working, a room

should be available for instructional purposes and for students to make their assigned pieces. Service lines for gas, air, and oxygen can be hung on "Uni-strut" verticals in rows about 10 ft on center.

For each student worker a portable table about 2 ft 3 in. x 4 ft 0 in. is suitable. Figure 11.9 is a suggestion. The open drawer space is used by the student when he brings his assigned (locked) drawer from the drawer cabinet on one wall. There should be a blackboard for the instructor, adequate ventilation, space to exhibit sample products, and a bulletin board. Ordinarily students will obtain their supplies from the store room.

2. OPTICS AND ELECTRONICS SHOP. Another special type of shop is for the design, building, and maintenance of all kinds of the relatively new electronic and optical apparatus. This includes many kinds of devices incorporating transistors, vacuum tubes, photocells, and a variety of items for radiochemistry. Many of these pieces of apparatus include some optical parts. It is because of the nature of such things that the work is best done in a separate section of the main shop or in a separate shop.

3. STUDENT SHOP. Some departments of chemistry find it advisable to maintain a student shop in which some work, especially simple metal and wood working, can be done. Often it is difficult

Figure 11.9   A student table for glass working.

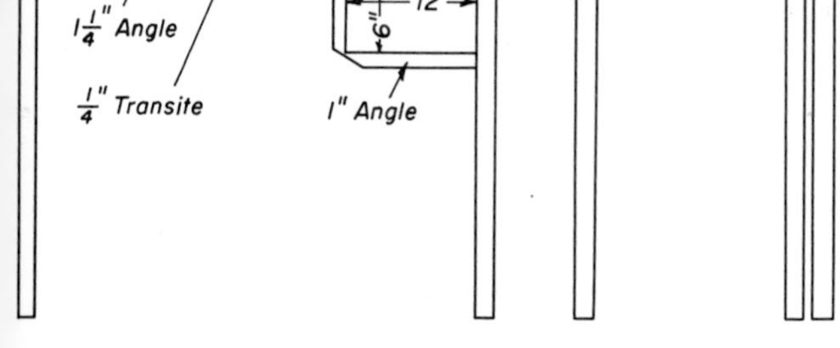

to keep tools and supplies where so many have access to the room.

Stock Room(s)

A chemical laboratory could hardly function without some kind of system for receiving and distributing chemicals, and other supplies, and equipment. Also, there may be more or less outgoing shipments, such as returned items and equipment sent out for repair.

Probably no two large universities have the same administrative setup for handling this business. In some an elaborate central stores keeps the main stocks, to which requests go from a chemistry department as needed to replenish the small stock maintained there. At the other extreme, the department may operate practically on its own. If so, its operations alone may be rather large.

Most large departments are probably somewhere between these extremes. In this discussion a midway arrangement will be assumed. That is, everything except standard items, such as "Pyrex" ware and certain common chemicals kept in central stores, will be ordered from manufacturers or supply houses and be delivered to the chemistry building. Ordering, receiving, storing, dispensing, and accounting of these items are then part of the operations of the storeroom.

Storeroom systems developed for doing what is necessary differ considerably. Planning a building has little relation to how the financial details are operated, except to enable them to be done as economically as possible. The primary concern is to have rooms and their connected facilities serve staff and students efficiently.

Because the magnitude of the operations, and the methods of conducting them, vary so much, little specific advice can be given on appropriate sizes for various parts of a system. The planner will probably have to rely heavily on advice from the storeroom supervisor concerned, particularly if he has had long experience with the requirements of the local situation.

Ordering. Maintaining supplies for large undergraduate classes and obtaining all the many diverse items needed for many graduate students doing individual research work is no small part of the storeroom office assignment. Primarily the building needs are for office space for people, many catalogs, and records of several kinds. Much letter writing is required.

Receiving and Checking. Thousands of items are received in the course of a year. They range in size from something barely visible to research equipment weighing several tons. A semi-trailer truck may bring a load of acid or of varied items.

In the latter case an unloading platform is needed up to which the truck can be backed. If feasible, at least the back end of the truck should be under cover for working in bad weather. Trucks vary in bed height, but 34 to 36 in. is workable for the platform. If possible, there should be at least two overhead-type doors, as there may be more than one truck.

Following unloading, many items have to be unpacked and checked as soon as practical. It is convenient to be able to have a chute near the platform into which small boxes may be placed to slide down to an unpacking and checking room. If possible, the freight elevator should be close to the platform, preferably so that it can be stopped at the platform level for direct transfer of items, which do not or cannot go through the checking room. Large shipments of acid, for example, can be taken at once to the acid room for storage. How much of this immediate transfer is necessary depends, of course, upon how much space can be reserved for the unloading dock.

The unpacking room needs a table, perhaps 4 x 12 ft, on which to place the small items for checking. At some institutions all bottles of chemicals, expect a few like acids, are dated before shelving, as some chemicals are unstable. There should be adequate shelving nearby on which to place various items, chiefly equipment, which must be held temporarily for one reason or another. As soon as possible all acceptable items will be put in storage or transferred to the appropriate location for research or teaching.

Distribution and Storage. Where to put what is always a problem. There are all kinds of chemicals, glassware, many kinds of equipment, special instruments, and office supplies and records. Both convenience of operation and suitability of facilities are to be considered.

Office supplies and records belong to the storeroom office. If individual student accounts are maintained, a separate section will be needed, preferably with a corridor window counter to which students come.

Large stocks of acids are usually stored in a separate room, with adequate ventilation, as some corrosive fumes are inevitable. There should be a large sink and a work table. For shelves many seem to prefer material such as soapstone supported by brick or 4-in. concrete blocks.

Chemicals having any fire or explosion hazards should have a special storage place. Some buildings have a fireproof room, equipped with an automatic fire-extinguishing system and a door or window which will blow open to the outside in case of an explosion inside the room. The shelving must be fireproof. There may be state or local regulations on keeping more than relatively small amounts of certain chemicals, such as acetone and diethyl ether in the building. If so, the main stock must be stored elsewhere in an approved place.

Nearly everybody now uses adjustable steel shelving for storing the small bottles and boxes of many kinds of chemicals. The shelving should be easily adjustable and have good quality finish. Many other supplies are stored in steel bins, drawers, and other arrangements, as for glass tubing.

Some supplies, such as boxes of glassware, are conveniently stored in bulk in the original containers, usually in a basement or attic. Aisles of wooden supports may be made for items that are standard and are used in considerable quantities.

A vault may be needed for items which are likely to be taken, such as ethanol, or which may be especially valuable, such as platinum. In the latter case protection from fire is a consideration.

Special instruments, particularly electrical and optical equipment, may be used in quantity and by different people in different places. If so, a room for their reconditioning and storage away from corrosive gases may be desirable.

Dispensing. Storeroom men tend toward centralization to facilitate keeping the system efficient. This is likely to mean one dispensing room, probably on the first floor, with the main storage in the basement. Such an arrangement usually is impractical in a multi-story building. For example, if the organic undergraduate laboratories are on the fourth floor, hundreds of students should not have to go up and down stairs to the first floor for supplies. This can be avoided, of course, by having enough dumbwaiters from each floor to the storeroom.

If a dispensing room can be maintained on each floor having heavy and varied demands, the kinds of supplies in most demand on a given floor should be stocked there. Each floor cannot be expected to stock every kind of chemical and general equipment. A freight elevator should go through each dispensing room, and also an automatic dumbwaiter. By means of a storeroom intercommunication system, the attendant in a room not having a given item can call one which does and have the item sent on the dumbwaiter. If one floor is devoted entirely to organic chemistry, for example, ordinarily the main stock of organic chemicals will be kept in the dispensing room on that floor, and only a few of the most common and widely used compounds on the other floors.

Each dispensing room should have a laboratory desk with a large sink and a hood. Usually there should be some provision for storing chemicals which give off objectionable fumes.

Throughout the storeroom system small trucks of several different designs are handy. A special insulated truck is useful to transport a supply of cracked ice to locations using considerable at certain times.

Library

Occasionally a university will not have departmental libraries, but if possible nearly every chemistry department has one. The space needed depends primarily upon the number of bound volumes in the collection, the number of current periodicals to have available, and the average number of users to be accommodated at one time.

Catalogs of concerns making library furniture give bases for calculating estimated needs. Shelves will hold about 8 volumes per linear foot. Reading room tables, if to be used on both sides, should be 4 ft wide, with 3 linear ft allowed per reader. Present large buildings have 6000 to 8000 sq ft of library floor space. None of them is large enough to hold the rapidly expanding publications and to serve the increasing enrollments.

Common needs in a departmental library are space for the following items: stacks for bound volumes, shelves for other books, tables for general reading, display racks for current periodicals, office for the librarian, service desk, card files, coat racks, room for incidental work by the library staff, and a private toilet for them.

If possible architecturally, the library should be on one floor. Next best is a separate stack room with several stack levels. The building must be designed for the latter arrangement, if advantage is to be taken of standard stack heights. Two stories of an average building will take three stack levels.

Three considerations are important in locating the library: (1) a central, quiet location is desirable; (2) unless unavoidable, the library should not be under a laboratory; and (3) if a separate outside entrance is possible, the library may be kept open while the rest of the building is closed.

An early decision must be made between (1) a general open arrangement of the library space, in which there is little segregation of kinds of publications, and (2) separate spaces for stacks, general reading room, current periodicals, reference sets, and possibly others. There are administrative problems with either arrangement.

If certain kinds of publications are to have restricted use, for example to staff and graduate students, a separate stack room is needed. An adequate number of carrels or study alcoves, located appropriately through the stack area, provide quietness for work and facilitate using bound periodicals. Where there are several levels of stacks there should be an automatic elevator at least large enough to hold a book truck. One or more acoustically treated alcoves will be useful for typing.

The storage of patents, bulletins, manufacturers' technical publications, and photoreproductions (films, photostats, microprint cards) should be considered. Space and a dark nook may be needed for reading film copies.

A work or service room is desirable for unpacking, packing, and servicing library materials. There should be a work counter and shelves. A wash room and toilet should be close.

Furniture and shelving are important. Many standard types are illustrated in catalogs of manufacturers and suppliers. Needed are tables, chairs, wall cases, and often certain incidental items in a reading room, and display racks and reading furniture for current periodicals.

Provision for handling reference sets, such as abstracting journals and the great multi-volume treatises, is a special problem. In using them often one has to go from volume to volume, and it is highly desirable to be able to do this with as little getting up and sitting down as possible. The writer prefers a long table, about 34 in. wide with shelves fastened at the back holding three rows of books. There should be sufficient width at the front to work from opened books. It is easy from one's seat to reach and return volumes to the shelf (Figure 11.10). (Incidentally, the bound volumes of *Chemical Abstracts* and the various decennial indexes as of 1960 take up 63 feet of shelf space.)

A check should be made with the architect that all spaces are adequately lighted for their prospective uses.

Air conditioning is very desirable in a library.

There should be some kind of facilities for displays, such as cases outside and bulletin boards inside.

Research Laboratories

Universities have almost the greatest diversity possible in the rooms devoted to research and in the service facilities therein. Because opinion on what should be provided varies so widely, only fairly general observations are presented. It is assumed that the rooms are to be designed for research, rather than being a screened-off portion of an undergraduate laboratory.

Size. The first point of argument is the size to make a research laboratory. Some administrators believe that greatest efficiency is achieved in a room accommodating 8 to 12 workers, who might or might not all work in the same area of chemistry. In contrast, many believe that small rooms accommodating 2 or 4 workers are preferable, particularly if there is reason for some isolation of work or workers.

If the floor plans are based upon a suitable module width such as 10 to 12 ft, flexibility in room size is easily possible. It is necessary only to plan the partitions, and any service lines associ-

ated with them, so that a partition may be put in or removed easily and economically. One possibility is to use commercially available partitions which are easily assembled. They are expensive.

If cement block construction is used for inside walls, the partitions may be constructed of 4-in. blocks, with two laid end to end between vertical aluminum T-slots set 33½ in. on centers. Or the T-slots may be fastened to vertical 4-in. channel irons. The channels support the blocks, if a wall be desired, or hold the T-slots if blocks are not used. Figure 11.11 illustrates these methods of using this type of construction. In either case, service lines are supported by the T-slots.

If module construction is used, flues should be spaced so that there can be a hood in each small room, if desired. Also all service line connections must be spaced for possible incorporation in small rooms.

Services. An important decision concerns the kinds of research laboratories that are to be provided, and the service facilities to be included in each room. In a few types of work special provisions must be made, such as radiochemistry and nuclear chemistry. This possibility is discussed elsewhere. The requirements needed for any such special rooms should be carefully checked and then incorporated in the plans and specifications.

In planning for research in the usual fields of

Figure 11.10   A table for reference sets.

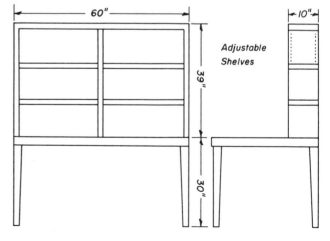

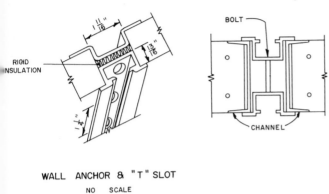

WALL ANCHOR & "T" SLOT

NO SCALE

Figure 11.11   Aluminum T-slots in concrete block wall and in channel irons.

chemistry, such as analytical, biological, inorganic, organic, and physical, a long-range view indicates that it is wise to equip all rooms so that work can be carried on in any of these areas. It will add some to the cost, but no one can predict for long the direction research will take. Such provision affords maximum flexibility of use.

All the following common service lines and facilities would be included: gas, compressed air, oxygen, ordinary water, distilled water, water aspirators for suction, low pressure steam (6–10 lbs), higher pressure steam (40 lbs), if to be used for hot plates in hoods, steam-water mixer, alternating current (110 V), and plug panel box for 220 V alternating current or direct current from storage batteries or d.c. generators. All these service lines should be installed for ease of removal, if desired. In a four-man laboratory probably one outlet each for distilled water and oxygen is sufficient.

If the over-all planning for distribution of service lines has been far-sighted, it should be fairly easy to bring to a given room a line for some service other than those mentioned. Usually this means space in, and accessibility of, pipe shafts.

Arrangement. Rooms smaller than 10 x 22 ft are cramped for two people. A better size is 12 x 24 ft. This assumes that the desks are against the walls. If they are back to back in the center, the room should be about 2 ft wider to give a reasonable aisle on each side.

One possible arrangement is shown in Figure 11.12. Two 12 x 24 ft rooms are shown, but there could be more indefinitely. The following specific points may be noted: (1) There is a narrow door or thin crash panel, between rooms A and B for emergency exit from one room to the other in case of accident or fire; (2) the shower-heads and floor drains are at the doors; (3) the sink arrangement is designed for a maximum occupancy of one Ph.D. student on the left side, and two M.S. students on the right side with a sink between them; (4) all service lines and reagent shelves are carried on T-slots in the walls; (5) the desk units, D, are portable so that one or all in a room are easily removed to provide for other items, such as distillation columns; (6) the T-slots run from floor to ceiling; (7) replacement of one desk unit with a writing desk makes a combined office-laboratory for a young instructor; (8) removal of the blocks in the wall between A and B gives a 4 to 6-man laboratory; (9) there is room at the end of the desks for steel coat lockers; (10) a writing drawer for the student is part of the 6-foot desk.

If more hood space is needed, and if the room is long enough (at least 24 ft), the hood may be turned lengthwise along the partition. (Figure 11.13.) However, this prevents direct venting of the back into a flue, and omission of partition walls is hardly feasible.

Figure 11.12   (Left) Two or four man research laboratory.

Figure 11.13   (Right) Modified arrangement for a two man laboratory.

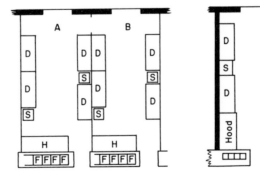

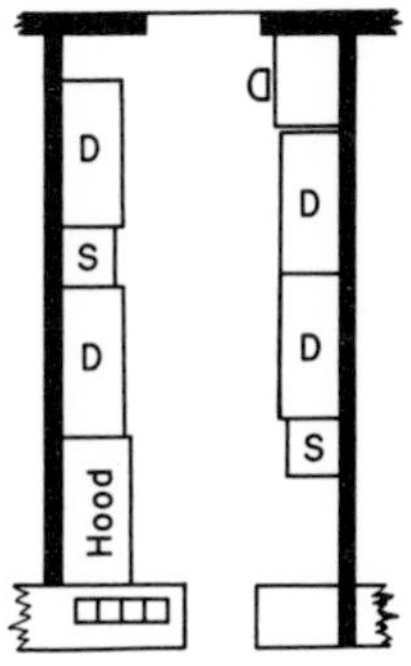

The portable 6 ft research desk is shown in Figure 11.14. In addition to being portable, its merits are (1) writing-desk drawer, interchangeable for an ordinary drawer, (2) narrow and wide shallow drawers, (3) deep drawer, (4) low and high cupboards.

Instructional Laboratories

In contrast to relatively small laboratories used for research work, all departments having undergraduate laboratory sections require much larger rooms. The needs range from space for several thousand in general chemistry to classes of 25 to 100 first-year graduate students.

As consideration is given elsewhere to such facilities for specific kinds of chemistry, only general items are discussed here.

As in most other matters, the first problem of the planner is to determine, as far as possible, just what is wanted and needed. Then comes the question of how this may be done efficiently and economically.

First in importance is the number of students to be accommodated. Unless a static enrollment is assumed, reasonable predictions for future increases must be made. In view of present trends in enrollment, along with many administrators' reluctance to set limits, future requirements seem very uncertain. Most serious study of the possibilities of using a given student working space more hours per day may help greatly. Many undergraduate laboratories are occupied only a fraction of the working hours of the week. Primarily this depends upon individual locker design, and secondarily upon scheduling. Instructional personnel are involved, of course.

Second in importance is the number of students per laboratory section. What is best is decidedly a matter of personal opinion. Some instructors want no more than 20 to 25 per section. At the other extreme one laboratory in this country was designed for more than 260.

Third in importance is standardization or uniformity in dimensions of student working area on the desk top. The main objective here is to be able to convert a laboratory for one kind of chemistry to one for a different kind. Certainly for analytical, biological, and organic chemistry the

Figure 11.14   A six-foot portable desk for research laboratories.

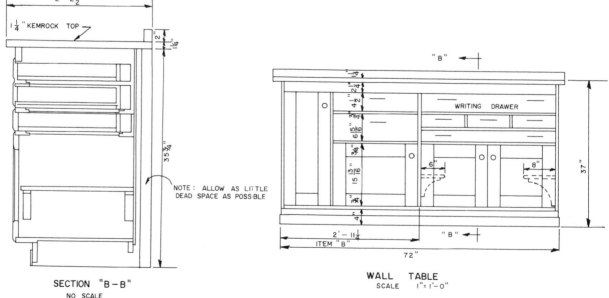

SECTION "B-B"
NO SCALE

WALL   TABLE
SCALE   1"= 1'-0"

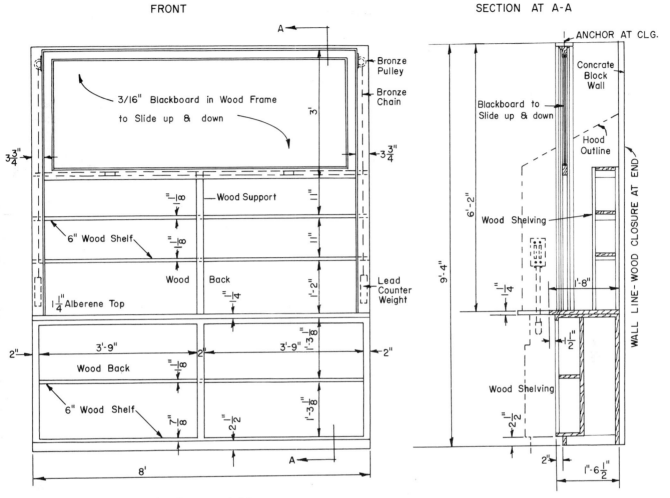

Figure 11.15   Blackboard and reagent shelving.

same design of desk can serve. Possibly a different one will be better for physical, although with thought perhaps the same service line openings will serve. General chemistry is less likely to fit in, as most instructors feel that less linear feet per student are required on the desk top.

All such rooms should have a distilled water outlet, an emergency shower and floor drain, and doors near each end. Hangers for wraps are needed in bad weather.

Ventilation should be adequate for the work intended. Usually side shelves are needed for general reagents and there should be one or more small blackboards for announcements, and student conferences. Some instructors like a small raised desk, with blackboard, at one end for occasional demonstrations.

A possible combination of hoods, side shelves, and blackboard is shown in Figure 11.15 (see also Figure 11.16). The blackboard is mounted in front of the reagents by sash cord and pulleys. Then it may be pulled down for writing. When raised, announcements on it are easily visible across the laboratory. Also one may be locked down to keep one set of reagents from another class using the same laboratory.

Although methods of teaching courses differ widely, there is usually need for more or less space adjacent to a student laboratory for items such as special apparatus, preparation and storage of stocks of special reagents used in the courses, analyzed samples, and others. Often teaching assistants look after this kind of work. In some institutions at least part of it operates through the storeroom system. Some analytical instructors want space and equipment for preparing primary standards and analyzed samples. Also they need at least a screened-off corner in the laboratory for keeping these samples and standards in form for dispensing, and for handling records.

Laboratory Desks. Quite apart from any particular design of laboratory desks for specific purposes, there are a number of fairly general questions which have to be decided by the planner. These are items for which there is no one answer. Often merely personal preferences are involved; but for some purposes, or in a particular situation, one design may be better than another. In any such cases plans and specifications must indicate that particular kinds of materials and/or designs are to be used.

There is not space to enter into an extended discussion of all the merits of the various possibilities. Rather, attention is directed to various items, with occasional comments. Again the planner should see typical installations, preferably after considerable use, and if possible talk with those who have used them.

Arrangement of desks is mentioned in connection with floor plans. In large laboratories it is primarily a question of island vs. peninsula setting. In a small rectangular research laboratory, it is a question of putting the desks, one on each side, with a center aisle, or of putting them back to back in the center.

The kind of material for the tops of desks remains a debatable question. The ideal economical material for all purposes has not been found. Wood, suitably handled (drying, working, fastening, acid-proofing), soap stone ("Alberene"), synthetic or treated stone ("Kemrock," "Scioto Stone"), tile, pressed asbestos ("Transite") and others all have merits, and also limitations. Any of them will serve well with adequate care, and none will withstand misuse indefinitely. Attack

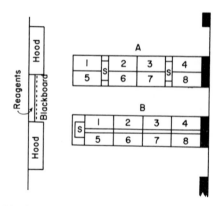

Figure 11.16   Locker arrangement for cross and end sinks.

may be fairly rapid with some chemicals.

Wood or metal base for desks is an open question. The president of one furniture company told the writer that he recommends steel for industry and wood for colleges, because wood withstands student mistreatment better. Tailor-made wooden desks are probably easier and cheaper to obtain than steel, but movable parts in them change dimensions with the weather. Some people have had trouble with acid fumes attacking some steel desks, but this may have been because of poor enameling.

Locking desks in large student laboratories causes administrative difficulties. Integral combination locks cannot be lost, but neither can

Figure 11.17   Sliding seat-in desk.

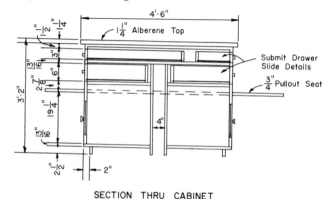

they be rotated at the end of semesters. Changing combinations is not feasible. All key locks are subject to loss of the keys or students forgetting to bring them. Integral key locks cannot be changed. Padlocks come either with a key or a combination. With either type, interchange of locks at the end of school sessions is easy. Combination locks have no key to lose or forget. A master-keyed system, whatever it is, is convenient for the instructor and for storeroom servicing of lockers.

Figure 11.16 shows two methods of arranging sinks in a long peninsula type desk designed for working space for four students per side per section. Arrangement B has the traditional end sink and center trough. All students have to go to the end sink to wash large items. Usually such a sink is along an aisle, so sufficient width should be allowed for congestion around the sink. Every experienced instructor knows the difficulty of preventing students from throwing debris in the trough, and of keeping the community sink presentable.

Arrangement A shows two cross sinks placed so that four students, two on each side, use each one; thus, every student works next to a sink. In this case the service lines should be distributed so that any leaking valves drain into a sink. Adequate sizes of cross sinks are 10 x 38 x 10 in. deep for general chemistry and 14 x 38 x 10 in. deep for other courses.

Most instructors prefer a center reagent shelf running lengthwise of the desk top. In addition to providing a place for certain generally used reagents, such a shelf serves for holding certain items used in the laboratory exercises. Perhaps the most general use is to support the service lines along the desk.

Some instructors do not like reagent shelves. If there are none, the main architectural problem is to get service lines and outlets to the student's working space.

Some instructors want stools in the aisle for students, but others consider any kind of seats a general nuisance. Stools are often in the way. If they are to be used, the aisle between desks should be at least 5 ft 6 in. wide. A usable sliding seat is shown in Figure 11.17. As it slides into the desk out of the way when not needed, extra aisle width is unnecessary. It is cheap, and spartan enough so that a student is unlikely to go to sleep on it.

Every manufacturer and jobber of laboratory furniture carries what they call standard types of desks. The one which characterizes a chemical laboratory consists of a drawer at the top 6 to 8 in. deep, with a cupboard underneath. In spite of its very wide distribution, few designs could be less convenient for many purposes. In most kinds of work there is need of some space for small items, such as stoppers, machines, and spatulas, and for items 20 to 30 in. long, such as burets, condensers, and long thermometers. Narrow and wide drawers respectively, meet these needs. Such drawers should be 1½ to 2½ in. deep.

If standard desks can be purchased, no doubt this will be most economical. Over many years, however, manufacturers seem to have been curiously slow to provide desks designed for specific kinds of work. In a large building, which will serve thousands of students over many years, the possibility of tailor-made desks should be investigated.

Duplicating Room

Most large departments do considerable duplicating work. Perhaps the most common example is the preparation of many copies of examination questions by mimeographing them from a stencil. A half-dozen other processes have come into more or less use in the last decade. Nearly every departmental office makes some use of such facilities.

Whenever the volume of work justifies it, the equipment should be in a separate place. Shelves are needed for supplies. There is noise from mimeographing machines, and some odors with certain processes. A wash bowl in the room is convenient.

Mail Room

Departments having several hundred graduate students, and a corresponding permanent staff, have much mail to handle. Only distribution is considered here. The most desirable arrangement is to have the mail delivered to the central office where a clerk can sort and distribute it.

For the permanent staff a standard post office box installation is convenient, especially if it can be located in a corridor wall. With the open ends of the boxes on the inside and the locked ends on the outside, there is ready access from inside and individuals can get their mail outside if the office is locked. Suitable sizes of boxes should be selected.

Outgoing mail may be conveniently collected in a box suitably located for teaching and clerical staff to use. Preferably this will be somewhere in the general office. Where feasible, a mail chute enables those on higher floors to drop letters into the collection box.

A separate room for junior staff and graduate students is preferable. Wooden boxes about 4 x 8 and 10 in. deep serve most needs. They should have holders for the names. An adjacent bulletin board provides for notices to this group. A small waist-high counter is convenient for writing notes and for handling the mail to be distributed.

Preferably this room should have an outside door which can be closed until the mail is distributed.

First Aid Room

In some buildings a special room is set aside for first aid. It serves for the more serious cases. Perhaps the most use is for girls fainting in freshmen laboratories. Equipment should include at least a cot, chair, wash bowl, first aid kit, and blanket.

Because of the possibility of accidents in chemical laboratories there should be provisions generally available for first aid. This will include a standard kit in each large laboratory. In addition,

there should be at least one in the corridor on each floor, preferably in the same location on the different floors, so that this spot will be known to everyone. A steel locker in the wall makes a good installation in the corridor.

Animal Room(s)

Animals of various kinds are needed for certain kinds of experimental work in biological chemistry. Ordinarily these should be housed separately, if possible. If this kind of work is extensive, a particular part or wing of a building may be devoted to it, or even a separate animal building may be needed. Here a small separate animal section is assumed. The size needed will depend upon the number of animals to be housed. Many mice can be kept in a small cubage, but one dog needs relatively much space. Also the kinds and number of cages or enclosures depend upon the kind of animals. Outside runways may be needed for dogs.

In addition to places to keep the animals, space is necessary for storage of foodstuffs, drugs, and some other material. A kitchen for preparing foods, a wash room, and an operating room may be needed. The whole area should be air-conditioned. Figure 11.18 is one suggestion for a small area.

Balance Room(s)

As the mass of a substance undergoing chemical transformation is so important, determination by means of a balance is fundamental. Usually equal-arm, or analytical balances are implied

Figure 11.18   Small animal rooms.

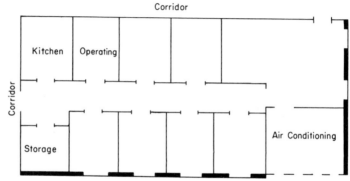

when a room for balances is mentioned. Anyway, if a special room is needed, it is probably best to isolate them from injurious fumes of a working laboratory, or to have them where other conditions of use will be less disturbing than elsewhere.

The space needed depends upon the length of shelf allotted to each balance and the number to be accommodated. From 30 to 36 in. per balance is suitable. If possible, not more than two students per laboratory section should be assigned to the old-style balance. More can be accommodated on the new semiautomatic, one-pan instruments.

As a matter of convenience in use, such a room should be as close as possible to where the substances are prepared for weighing. In many analytical laboratories, the room will be adjacent to the main working area or across a corridor.

Two suggestions for incorporating balances in a protected enclosure within the over-all area of the working room are shown in Figure 11.19. Arrangement I shows a wide room divided through the center by a windowless room, the balance area having glazed partitions. In arrangement II the balances (A, B, C, D) are on the wall end of peninsula-type desks. In this case each balance is enclosed by a large, second case.

Figure 11.19   Two suggestions for locating balances within the working area of a laboratory.

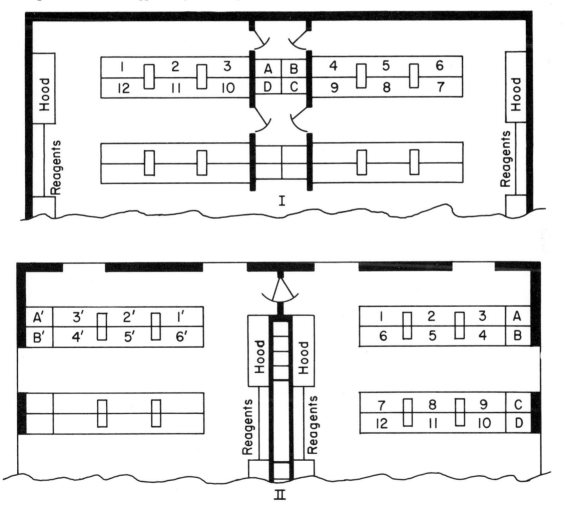

This outer case and the center enclosure in arrangement I, should be under enough positive air pressure to keep corrosive gases away from the balances. The balance shelf should be 30 in. high. In either arrangement students 1, 2, 3 use balance A, students 4, 5, 6 use balance B, and so on. The lighting should be adequate and properly directed.

Because of vibration in some buildings, there may be the problem of mounting the balance to reduce the disturbance to a tolerable level.

Research Service Rooms

Where the graduate research program justifies installation and maintaining such facilities, special areas may be set apart for equipment to provide certain kinds of routine test and analytical data needed on a fairly large scale. These data might be of a wide variety, but perhaps the most commonly needed are microanalyses and absorption spectra. This applies especially where there is an extensive program in organic chemistry.

Room for Microanalysis. Perhaps the chief special needs usually requested for this kind of laboratory are air-conditioning and freedom of vibration for the balances. Some analysts like specially designed desks on which to assemble the equipment for elemental and group determinations.

Room for Absorption Spectroscopy. Absorption spectra have become almost a must in much organic and biochemical research. The ultraviolet, visual, and infrared regions of the spectrum are most used, but the x-ray and microwave regions are becoming more important.

A room for this kind of work should have the services needed for using the various kinds of instruments. Freedom from corrosive fumes is necessary, and air-conditioning should be supplied if the equipment includes infrared instruments.

Distillation Room. Some buildings contain a separate room for making distillations, usually in connection with organic preparative and/or separative work. The main items needed are T-slots or "Uni-strut" verticals for mounting service lines and equipment, with adequate floor drains to catch any liquids lost accidentally. There should be a raised edge on the area underneath

the stills to keep liquids from spreading over the floor. If there is need for vertical space of two or more stories to erect a tall still, provision must be made for it, unless there is enough room elsewhere, as in a vertical pipe shaft.

Kjeldahl Digestion, Distillation, and Titration Room(s). If Kjeldahl determinations of nitrogen on a macroscale are done in sufficient number, as in some biochemical work, separate rooms may be desired. Usually one is for digestion, one for distillation, and one for titration.

Certain manufacturers specializing in Kjeldahl equipment have very compact units, such as a bank of 12 digesters or stills. For such installations service facilities and space required should be checked from the manufacturers' literature. Special care should be taken to have the ventilation flue and fan for the digestion room suitable and adequate for the fumes of sulfur dioxide. Some installations are "Duriron."

Computation Room. Some kinds of research work, especially physical chemistry, require extensive calculations. For simple calculating machines, tables and electrical connections suffice. If large, complicated computers are involved, space and other requirements should be checked. In the latter case, the space should be air-conditioned.

Halogenation Room. In case of extensive work with chlorine, fluorine, or hydrogen fluoride, it may be desirable, or even necessary, to isolate the work on account of the corrosive properties of these gases. It is likely to be particularly bad if the gas is generated inside the building. Small leaks are very difficult to eliminate completely. Special attention must be given to have adequate ventilation, and the materials for the system should be selected for these gases.

Special Temperature Room(s). For certain kinds of work, especially organic and biological chemistry, there must be facilities for maintaining chemicals and/or equipment at some reasonably constant temperature above or below the usual room temperature.

Modern refrigerators and *cold boxes* serve for many such purposes. In case these are not large enough, or equipment and space are needed to do some work inside, usually a separate room of appropriate size is set aside and equipped for this purpose. Standard construction for refrigeration or heating can be used, along with the necessary equipment and controls. The requirements must be known. Thus, biochemists may need several such rooms, each for a different temperature, and special facilities may be needed inside.

Provision for very low or high temperatures, for example in physical chemistry, will seldom involve the building itself. Special research equipment and services are needed. All the planner needs to do is to have rooms and service facilities, or the possibilities for them, as flexible as possible.

Dark Room(s). If there is only one dark room, probably the planner should assume that a medium size room, say about 10 x 12 ft, and that facilities for ordinary photographic work, will suffice. Out of long experience photographic concerns, such as the Eastman Kodak Company, have prepared plans for this kind of room. Unless some special situation has to be met, it is easiest to obtain such plans and use them.

For various kinds of specialized work, such as emission spectroscopy and x-ray diffraction, someone may want a dark room designed for his work and located convenient to his equipment. Such individuals should assume responsibility for proposing something to meet their needs. Two small dark rooms are shown in Figure 11.20.

High-pressure Rooms. Chemical reactions are often carried out under much higher pressures than that of the atmosphere; this is especially true in organic chemistry. Hydrogenation, for example, may be done under pressures of several thousand atmospheres. These conditions are intentional. In contrast, other systems, again usually organic, are not put under pressure, but unexpectedly they may suddenly explode. For these

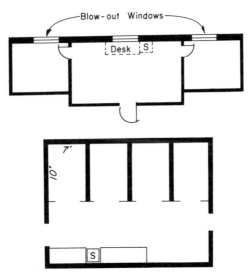

Figure 11.21 Possible arrangement for rooms for hydrogenation and for explosive reactions.

and any similar situations rooms are needed in which such work is safe.

For hydrogenation the metal equipment is designed for the pressures to be used. Any accidents which occur may likely be caused by carelessness in use and to defective material. When they do occur, pieces of metal may be thrown with great force.

In comparison to this kind of work, some chemical reactions start with or produce substances which are either potentially or actually explosives. Perhaps under careful control there will be no violent reaction or explosion, but too sudden rise of temperature will set it off. The materials may not be known to be explosive, but no chances are to be taken.

High-pressure laboratories require various facilities and service lines. Many industrial laboratories have special areas designed for this kind of work. (See Chapter 10, Part 5.) Ideas keep changing on what is best in terms of economy, safety, and convenience.

Figure 11.21 is merely suggestive of one possible arrangement for a room for hydrogenation and one for carrying out reactions which may explode. More important, of course, are the structural details of the cubicles.

Figure 11.20 Two suggestions for small special dark rooms.

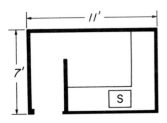
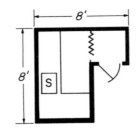

Maintenance Room(s). Chemical laboratories, especially those with large student populations, require much janitorial service. A room is needed as a headquarters for supplies and extra equipment. In addition, there should be on each floor at least one small room in which to keep a truck for collection of waste material, brooms, mops, and some supplies, such as light bulbs and toilet paper. This may also have a janitors' floor sink and hot and cold water. It may be feasible to make this room a part of the space allotted to a toilet room.

Modern chemical laboratories are fairly complicated buildings, particularly in service facilities for heating (including more and more air conditioning), ventilation, plumbing, electricity (both a.c. and d.c.), refrigeration, and disposal of waste solids. The maintenance of all these services in good working order is an assignment of some magnitude. For example, in how many buildings do all the faucets and stopcocks work?

To whatever extent maintenance is to be done by the staff of the chemistry building, provision must be made for personnel and equipment. It may be part of the work of the general shop, as simple electrical and plumbing work often is. Occasionally a separate shop is set apart, as for a plumber or a ventilation engineer.

Other Special Rooms. Depending upon the nature and administration of different kinds of chemical work, various other kinds of special rooms may be desired. Examples are sample preparation, sample storage, preparation of reagents, and storage of special but routine laboratory equipment. All such requirements must be known.

ARCHITECTURAL ITEMS

The general architectural problems relating to chemical laboratories are discussed in other sections. Here the objective is to emphasize certain items of particular concern to those working in academic institutions.

Specific Items

There are a number of specific architectural items which are of concern in designing chemical laboratories for educational use. Details of most of these are discussed elsewhere. The present objective is primarily to remind the planner to keep such items in mind, and to make suggestions of some possibilities.

Lighting. Primarily, lighting is the architect's problem. He is in a position to know what should be done in general situations, such as offices, corridors, and small classrooms. Also he knows the relative merits of fluorescent and incandescent tungsten sources for general-purpose installations. Finally, he should provide for adequate emergency exit lighting in case of failure of the main power line.

The planner should ask for the amount and kind(s) of lighting needed for any special purposes. Examples have been cited.

There has not been agreement on the position of lights for a long laboratory desk. In many buildings the arrangement is lengthwise of the desk over the center. The present trend, at least with lines of fluorescent tubes, is to install them at right angles to the axis of the desk. This cross arrangement is used also for small research rooms with dimensions such as 10 x 24 ft.

Number of Floors. Like various other aspects of buildings, the question of the relative merits of single and multi-story structures can generate serious debate. Each has important advantages. The multi-story type is much more common. If a single story is contemplated, examples in large institutions should be studied carefully, as at Yale, Ohio State and North Carolina. Interesting examples of such industrial and government laboratories are discussed elsewhere. It is difficult to get all the desired facilities of a large university department coordinated into an efficient working unit in a single-story building.

If two or more stories are to be used, again careful study is needed to have each working unit as suitably placed as possible. The number of stories depends upon the estimated needs and the size of the plot available. There may be legal limitations, or too many stories may detract from a roof line which harmonizes with surrounding buildings.

There are many four-story buildings, and this is a maximum without adequate passenger elevator service. Columbia University, of course, has long had much higher buildings because of lack of land. In such a case, careful attention should be given to adequate elevator service for people and supplies. No doubt the feasibility of escalators should be considered.

Windows. Windows are largely a problem of the architect. He and the administration will no doubt decide first whether there are to be any. It is unlikely, however, that a windowless building will be built on a college campus if all the present buildings for similar purposes have windows.

If there are to be no windows, buildings of this type should be visited. Inside planning is easier without windows; but if one is shut off from the exterior world, the ventilation system must work. It should be kept in mind that many ventilating installations have not been nearly 100% successful.

If there are to be windows, their type and size probably will be determined by the general style of the building. However, the planner should understand what is being selected, as some people have been very disappointed in the functioning of the windows chosen by the architect. The planner should have a part in deciding on the location of windows. Exterior appearance of the building should be as attractive as possible with the funds available, but the architect should not ruin the interior in order to achieve a particular effect outside. There are many buildings in which it was impossible to have particular laboratory desk arrangements because of the windows.

Although seldom given this opportunity, ideally the planner should prepare at least rough floor plans showing the arrangement of the desks desired. If it can be afforded, "island" location of long laboratory desks is preferable, in that there is a passageway entirely around them. However, this is least economical of floor space. If this arrangement is used, the position of windows is not much of a problem.

To achieve efficiency, the "peninsula" arrangement is best. One end of a desk then is placed against the wall. If this is on the outside between two windows, it determines the window spacing. The distance from the center of one desk top to the center of the next one becomes a unit for planning the building. A minimum center to center distance is 9 ft, 4 ft 6 in. for aisle, and 4 ft 6 in. for width of desk top. Six to 12 in. more is better for the aisle, and some instructors prefer a little more width on the desks.

Ventilation and Air Conditioning. Provision of desired air conditions in a chemistry building is an engineering problem for which the architect is responsible. The planner must be clear on what is wanted and needed for specific situations. Ventilation, air-conditioning, and temperature control may all be involved. Simple air-conditioning of a lecture room is a very different problem from that in a room devoted to the generation and use of fluorine and/or hydrofluoric acid, for example.

Hoods of different kinds for various purposes are discussed elsewhere. They are indispensable for much chemical work and the planner must advise on the specific needs.

The best cooperation possible between planner, prospective user(s), and the architect is needed. The writer has heard more adverse criticisms of ventilation and air-conditioning than of any other feature of chemistry buildings. As handling gases is apparently a difficult engineering feat, anything of this kind needs special attention.

Acoustics. Acoustical treatment of various areas is important unless the construction materials and/or the general situation in an area keep the noise level low. Many lecture rooms, classrooms, corridors, stair wells, and offices are objectionable without some treatment. This is an engineering problem, but the planner should check with the architect to be sure what is needed has been done. There is increased use of certain structural materials on walls and ceilings which provide the desired effects.

Toilets. The only problem here for the planner is what is needed and desired for the prospective population of the building. Typical questions are: (1) What is the relative proportion of men and women for the general toilets? (2) Should there be a special toilet room, with lounge and vanity, for the female clerical staff? (3) Are there to be any private toilets, as off the office of the head of the department or off the headquarters of the librarian? (4) Is a special toilet to be set aside for the male staff of the shop(s) and storeroom(s)?

Doors. In a large building there are many doors of various sizes. In general, the architect decides upon what is appropriate in size, material, hardware, and direction of swing. If there is any question of interference with something to be in a given room, the planner should check the swing.

Attention should be paid to the width of doors to offices and laboratories. Offices and all small research laboratories ordinarily should have doors at least 36 in. wide. It is usually best to have an opening of 5 ft, with double doors, in all larger rooms. This provides for handling large equipment and also for the passage of students in large laboratory sections. Preferably all rooms accommodating 30 or more students in a section should have two separate doors, one of which may be 3 ft.

Doors out of large laboratories must swing out for hurried exit in case of fire or accidents. They may have double-acting hinges. When fully opened they should turn back against the corridor wall to avoid partial blocking of the corridor.

Single doors on small rooms which open only part way outward into a corridor are a traffic hazard when large groups of students are hurrying to class (or more likely out to the "sweet shop"). If the door swings in, there is danger in case of explosion or fire. In a building having a very thick wall for flues and service lines, these doors may be hung on an inside corner and swing out.

Locking System for Doors. A large building, with many small rooms and offices, will have several hundred doors to be locked. Usually some system of master keying is desired.

The outside doors should be considered separately. All those opening into the corridors will have the same key, and it probably will not be on the inside master key system. Doors of rooms opening directly to the outside, such as the shop and the storeroom, should not be keyed with the other outside doors.

Each inside door may have a different key. A grand master key is very convenient to one who wants more or less frequent access to many rooms. If desired, individual rooms, such as the head's private office or a laboratory for secret research work, may have a lock not operated by the master key. In addition to the grand master key, it may be convenient to have submaster keys for certain groups of rooms. Thus, the rooms assigned to analytical chemistry would have a submaster

key for their doors, and probably each analytical instructor would have this key.

Safety. Promotion of safety can hardly be overemphasized in chemical laboratories. Lack of precautions and meager facilities for safety are well known in college buildings. First aid kits and a first aid room are discussed elsewhere. The items in mind here are facilities for putting out fires, washing off chemicals, such as acids, and wrapping up anyone burned.

General fire-fighting facilities will probably be required by state law. These will be specified by the architect, and will include both fire hose and carbon dioxide cylinders. In addition, there should be at least one small carbon dioxide cylinder readily available in every laboratory where there is any possibility of fire. Fire blankets should be available at well-marked locations, perhaps one in a corridor on each floor and one in each large laboratory where there might be need for such protection.

Shower heads are almost a must in a laboratory having any possibility of fire and explosions. There should be one in at least each of the following locations: main laboratories, research laboratories, and toilets. They should be located, as far as possible, in a uniform position in the various kinds of rooms. Everyone should note where such things are, for the need nearly always arises in an emergency. There should be some uniform method of releasing the shower, such as chain hanging where it can be grabbed quickly. Unless there is a floor drain somewhere underneath the shower head, release of the water may produce a minor flood.

Elevators. The writer was once told that any professor able "to profess" was able to walk up stairs, and that consequently no passenger elevator would be approved. Nevertheless, he has observed that many able-bodied men make much use of an elevator in a building having a basement, four laboratory floors, and an attic.

A size of 4 x 6 ft or better 5 x 8 ft is satisfactory, unless there are many people to accommodate. One of even the larger size would not be adequate if it is open to all the senior, junior, and service staffs. If only one of small size is possible, it may be controlled on the outside with a key, and keys can be issued as desired. There should be punch-button controls inside the car. The system for designating floors inside and outside should correspond to the numbering system for the floors. Thus, B, 1, 2, 3, 4 and A would indicate the basement, "100", "200", "300", "400", and attic floors, respectively. If it is architecturally feasible, the location of this elevator should be as nearly central as possible.

The indispensability of a freight elevator and an automatic dumbwaiter has been mentioned in connection with the storeroom. This elevator will probably have to serve the shop staff also. It should open into the storeroom area on one side, and preferably on a corridor on the opposite side. Many items have to be moved, both within and without the storeroom. This elevator should be of reasonable size and capacity for handling fairly large and heavy items. A size such as 8 x 8 ft or 7 x 10 ft is very useful. The capacity should be at least 2500 lbs.

The dumbwaiter in the storeroom serves for small items. A size 30 x 30 in. and 36 in. high is convenient.

Telephone Systems. The provisions for communication should be studied in terms of efficient operation of a large building. There is always the problem of talking with people outside; but, in addition, talking with, or signaling in some way to those inside is usually necessary or desirable.

EXTERNAL SYSTEM. The external system will involve standard telephones for communication both inside and outside of the building. There will be three questions to decide: (1) Who is to have telephones, and where in each case should the outlet be located? (2) What special provision, if any, should be made in the office of the head of the department? (3) Will individual lines, each from the university or city switchboard, or several trunk lines and a building PBX distribution system be preferable for the given situation?

The department head has to decide who should have phones. Involved are locations such as the following: central office, secretary, receptionist, executive assistant, individual professors, library, storeroom, and shop(s). By means of special outlets, provision may be included also for temporary use of a portable phone in particular places, such as a conference room.

A head may wish to have special provisions in

his office. Thus, on a long-distance call, he may want one or more others to listen in or to take part in the conversation. Also he may have a private line and a telephone with switches to enable him to hold one line temporarily while he talks on another. Local telephone engineers can advise on various possibilities.

Whether to install an individual line to each telephone, with some extensions, or to have several trunk lines and a PBX system in the central office is a debatable question. There seems to be no ideal system. With individual lines each telephone may always be called, night or day. There is no one, as in a central office, who can listen to the conversation. However, if an instructor, for example, happens not to hear the ring, there is no one to make a note of the call. With a PBX installation, all calls come in to the board, which will probably be operated by a receptionist. If she does not locate the one called, she can make a note for return of the call, or later transmit the information desired. When her office closes, there is then no means of connecting an incoming call to the individual wanted. The best that can be done is to leave the trunk lines connected to a "night-call" setting. Here again telephone engineers should be consulted on the possibilities.

In a large building it is well to have at least one outside telephone in a booth on a corridor for student use. This should preferably be a pay telephone.

INTERNAL SYSTEM(S). Various situations make one or more internal systems of communication desirable in a large building. Here attention is directed chiefly to the nature of the problems. Architects and communication specialists know what can be done to meet the needs.

Often it is suddenly necessary or desirable to communicate with someone of the service staff who is in the building, but whose location at the moment is unknown. For such a purpose a call system is needed. One useful installation consists of voice-powered house telephones with a separate 110 V signal buzzer. The telephones should be in strategic locations around the building probably in corridors, where the buzz can be heard and the call answered. Individuals such as the following are likely to be wanted: janitor, supervisor of the general shop, and the ventilation supervisor.

This kind of communication is necessary between rooms on different floors of a storeroom system. By calling, something may be sent from one floor to another on an automatic elevator.

Mention has been made of the possibility of telephone communication from lecture table to projection booth in a large room.

Another possibility is a buzzer system from the central storeroom office to individual research laboratories to let an individual know that something is ready or that he is wanted in the shop.

Lockers. Almost no one attempts to meet the needs of large numbers of students with lockers, either in locker rooms or in the corridor walls. However, it is worth while, if possible, to include some lockers where occasional space in the corridor has not been utilized otherwise. They are especially useful for graduate students who spend much time in the building but have not been assigned laboratory working space. A convenient size is 18 x 18 in., 5 ft high. Where the work of graduate students, or others, necessitates work clothes, it is desirable to have banks of lockers associated with a toilet room.

Directories. Strangers and the occasional visitor to a building find useful both floor numbers and directories. Directional arrows familiar in hotels would help in some buildings. Fairly large numerals mounted in locations such as near stairways and at the elevator will show the number of the floor. A directory should be close to each entrance door. It should carry the names and room numbers of the senior staff and any others likely to be sought often. If possible, the case should carry small copies of the floor plans. Another helpful idea is to mount at appropriate places a floor plan for the floor involved with the location of mounting encircled in red.

Names, Signs, and Numbers for Rooms. Names and signs suitably located on doors and in corridors are an aid in finding rooms and offices in a large building. They are most helpful to strangers and those who visit the area infrequently.

Included here are name plates for (1) the kind of work in all the chief laboratories, such as physical chemistry, (2) lecture and recitation rooms, (3) storerooms, (4) shops, (5) library, (6) general office, (7) men's and women's toilet rooms, (8) preparation rooms, and (9) any others which people may want to find. Individual offices may have the name of the occupant. In corridors an occasional directional sign to an area or certain room numbers may be helpful.

There are various possibilities for designating such items. The more elaborate ones are metal, with glass sides on which the name is stamped and a light inside for illumination. Much more economical are plastic sheets, about $3/32$ in. thick, which can be cut to the desired size. A machine made for this purpose enables one to cut quickly the desired letters, numerals, or other characters. In one form the whole surface is black. When this is cut through, the characters show in white. Various letter sizes are available.

A consistent system for numbering rooms is of some importance. There are at least three items to consider. First, there has to be a starting point and a direction to start. The main entrance seems a logical place to begin. Whether one then goes clockwise or the reverse is a matter of preference. Starting on a corridor from this point there is then the question of whether to use even numbers on one side and odd numbers on the other, or to go generally forward, back and forth across the corridor, with increasing numbers. Which is the better probably depends upon the building.

The second item concerns the adoption of a system which will indicate the floor on which a room is located. Many buildings are confusing on this point. Someone decides that the basement, ground, and main floors must be so designated, for example by B4, G6, and M8. Then come the first, second, and any higher. A system more practical in use seems to be basement, first, second, and on to the top. In the latter case the basement rooms would be assigned numbers under 100, first floor rooms "100" numbers, second floor rooms "200" numbers, and other floors in succession.

The third item concerns consistency in numbering from floor to floor. For architectural simplicity and efficiency certain kinds of rooms will probably be in the same location on each floor. Toilets and large laboratories are examples. Service and other staffs find it advantageous to have rooms in the same location on each floor bear the same final digits. Suppose, for example, that all large rooms on a corner bear the digits 50. Then the numbers 50, 150, 250, 350, 450 indicate at once this corner room in the basement, first, second, third, and fourth floor, respectively. Users of a building learn this rapidly.

Waste Disposal. Unless such material is dangerous to dispose of through the sewer system, most chemicals, in the amount involved in the usual laboratory, may be washed away in the waste line. Metallic alkali elements should not be thrown into the sink, nor should a cyanide plating solution be emptied into the sewer. Radioactive wastes are a special problem. In the discussion of plumbing, attention is given to suitable materials for waste lines.

Solid wastes are a problem in every chemical laboratory. Paper, some chemicals, glass, and other materials accumulate. Most undergraduate and graduate laboratories have waste receptacles in the room into which to throw such materials for collection by a janitor. A galvanized can, about 24 in. in diameter and 30 in. high, on a low truck, is convenient for collection.

What to do with the waste at this stage is the main problem. Often much of it is paper, along with some other combustible matter. If so, the total volume to be hauled away may be greatly reduced by burning in an incinerator. If an incinerator is to be included in a building, the location should be such that material may be put into it from a corridor. Then removal of unburnable debris to a truck for final disposal should be made as convenient as possible. Collection is likely to be done at night by a service staff. If a building is on a hillside, it may be possible to have a hopper chute open from the incinerator directly into a truck underneath.

In buildings of more than one story the cans of waste may be collected on all floors and taken down on the elevator to a central platform to be trucked away. Or there may be a waste chute into which the waste can be dumped on each floor. Such a chute should be lined with firebrick and open through the roof, as occasionally the combustible waste may ignite. For this reason both the chute doors and the collection room must be fireproof.

Exhibits. Chemists and chemical engineers have much to show which relates to their work. Included are (1) many naturally occurring substances and raw materials which are handled as such or processed in some way, (2) endless individual compounds, (3) a great array of synthetic products, (4) new apparatus and equipment, and (5) models, flow sheets, pictures, and other illustrative material. If visual education has all the merits its proponents claim, few subjects other than chemistry have so much to offer in this direction.

To take advantage of this possibility, three things are required: (1) materials for the exhibits; (2) people to prepare and maintain them in good condition; and (3) money to provide the space and facilities. Only the facilities are of concern here. If exhibits are to be included in a building, several questions arise: (1) how much space is needed? (2) where are the facilities to be? and (3) what facilities are needed?

The space needed depends, of course, entirely upon what and how much is to be exhibited. The planner will have to decide. It is very helpful to see what others have done in a given space. Presumably since exhibits are to be seen, they should be located as far as possible where those likely to be interested can find them. There is involved an element of advertising. Items of most general interest are best located where most people come and go. Generally this is near the entrances to the building and the main lecture room. Exhibits relating to some particular kind of work, are better placed where this work centers. Thus, library exhibits belong in or near the library.

The facilities needed depend upon one's idea of how exhibits should be handled. The great museums in large cities are excellent examples of superb displays presented in this way. Some chemical exhibits have been arranged in a separate museum room. In general, reports do not indicate that these rooms have been very successful. Perhaps they did not have enough maintenance attention. Care should be taken to select cases appropriate to the intended exhibits.

The alternative to a room set apart for a museum collection, and/or other exhibits, is incidental cases, usually located in or along the walls in main corridors. Unless the walls are quite thick, wall cases lack sufficient depth for some exhibits. If the walls carry supporting columns, flues, and service lines, cases have to be fitted in wherever space is available.

A variety of suitable wall cases may be purchased. They should have inside lighting, adjustable shelves, and glass doors with locks. If they are to be made, a convenient size is 4 ft wide, 6 ft high and 12 to 24 in. deep. A special case was designed by the writer for an exhibit of the elements of the periodic table (see Figure 11.22).

Initial success of any exhibit depends upon its nature and location. Subsequent success will depend heavily on the continued attention given by the exhibitor.

Schedule Holders. It is useful to have at the entrance(s) of all lecture rooms, recitation rooms, and laboratories a schedule card showing when the room is scheduled to be occupied and by which course or group. A printed form schedule card 3 x 5 in., or better 4 x 6 in., should be filled in at the beginning of each semester. There should be a metal holder on the wall or door into which the card can be slipped. The clerical staff should keep it up-to-date.

Bulletin Boards. Bulletin boards serve a variety of purposes—announcements, assignments, items of interest, lists of grades, reports, and other items to be posted. Except for some special purpose, such boards are usually quite thin. Any mounted in corridors should have a glass door. The back should permit the use of thumb tacks to hold papers. Unless the general lighting is good, there should be an individual light. If this is inside the case, there must be adequate depth. Sizes vary with the purpose contemplated, 30 x 30 in. to 36 x 42 in. being normal. Whether they should, or can, be inside or outside a given area depends upon the situation. If a laboratory is kept locked except when in use while the material posted should be visible, the mounting should be in the corridor.

Needs for bulletin boards depend upon the building and its uses. Certainly the following rooms need them: all main laboratories, lecture rooms, dispensing room windows, general offices, and library.

General Items

Most important in any laboratory are adequate facilities, both in kind and number, to

Figure 11.22   A display case.

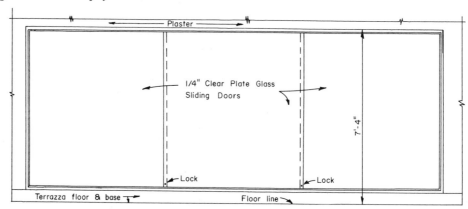

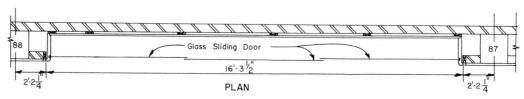

carry on the work contemplated. Next in importance is their location for maximum convenience and efficiency. To achieve this objective the planner may encounter more difficulties than in working out the details of the desired facilities. Thus, with sufficient thought, one may settle on the most important items required for an efficient lecture room; but it is a quite different problem to incorporate the room in the over-all floor plans in a location which will best serve all the staff and students using it.

Efficient arrangement of a large building is likely to present serious problems, particularly if there are many different kinds of facilities, including laboratories for a variety of undergraduate and graduate classes, and space for research for graduates, post-graduates, and permanent staff. The problem is a kind of puzzle to solve, but there is likely to be no *one* solution which all concerned will agree is most acceptable. The planner should strive for a broad and detached viewpoint in giving careful consideration to all relevant items.

Selection of a final plan will almost inevitably necessitate many compromises, both among the permanent staff and between the planner and the architect. For example, one cannot have the individual offices of a half-dozen professors arranged around a central office and at the same time have these small offices adjacent to the main laboratories which each professor is to supervise. A choice must be made, although someone may not like it.

In the following subdivisions there is brief mention of some of the problems of arrangement which seem important. Their nature and difficulty depend very much upon local situations, and upon the size, complexity, and ultimate purpose of the building.

In order to illustrate arrangements selected for certain situations, a few floor plans are included at the end of this section. The question of location of a number of facilities, such as elevators, has been covered previously. Consequently, the discussion here is directed toward the broader problem of locating the various kinds of rooms.

General Construction. In general, the problems of construction belong to the architect and engineer. If the change seems justified, however, the use of a different design, and perhaps different materials, may enable one to locate a special facility in a particular place. Here again, the planner must present what is wanted, and agree to any compromises only when they are necessary.

Traffic Flow. The general floor plan or layout of a building is important from the viewpoint of traffic flow, both external and internal. This is especially true where there are surges of traffic, as at the beginning and end of several large laboratory sections and at the time of interchange of large, consecutive lecture sections.

Usually the administrators decide where a building is to be located on a campus. The planner should consider the possibility of traffic problems, if given an opportunity to express a preference.

The architecture of the building is involved here, too, to the extent that location and sizes of entrance doors are important.

Traffic to and from the building involves entrances. What is preferable in a given situation, if there is opportunity for a choice, must be decided on the basis of probable student and service traffic. The following questions are typical: (1) How can trucks reach the building for the storeroom, shop, and general services? (2) What directions will heavy student traffic take to and from the building?

Figure 11.23 shows the plan adopted in one institution. The following specific points may be noted: (1) there are five principal entrances for general traffic, A, B, C, D, E, with total of seven double doors; (2) F is a double door from the service drive into the shop; (3) G and H are overhead doors at the unloading dock of the storeroom, H being directly in front of a freight elevator stopping at the level of the dock; (4) I is a single back door for service men; (5) doors A, B, D, E, lead down a few steps to the first floor, off whose corridors open lecture rooms 1 (front only), 2, 3, 4, and their interconnecting two preparation rooms; (6) the stairs at door A, B, D, E, and the two side stairs at the triple-door entrance C, go up to the second floor main entrances to lecture room 1; (7) the center stairs in entrance C go down to the first floor and lecture rooms 2, 3, and 4.

Internal traffic flow is evident also in Figure

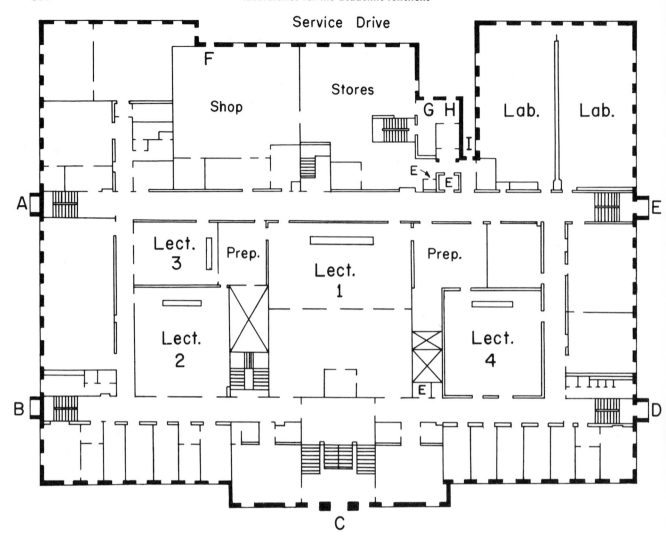

Figure 11.23 Floor plan showing relation of entrances, lecture rooms, preparation rooms, elevators, shops and stores on first floor.

11.23. Shop and storerooms are are at the back, reasonably close to the large laboratories, which have the largest number of students. Small research laboratories are at the front. In addition to the stairways at entrances A, B, D, E, there are two others on the long corridors. The freight elevators are at the back and the passenger elevator at the front.

General Layout. Difficult decisions are involved, and compromises are inevitable, in allotting certain locations in a building to partic-

ular kinds of work. Although no allocation ideal for everyone can be achieved, serious efforts should be given to deciding where to put what. Local situations should always be taken into account; but excluding these occasional possibilities, there are certain broad principles of allocation. An important consideration is whether the building is to house one or more departments. If it is one, this will be chemistry. If more than one, the other(s) may be some other science(s), or one or more kinds of engineering.

CHEMISTRY ONLY. Staff offices, at least in a large department are seldom segregated much, unless by divisions. Usually, the general office is preferred near the main entrance for ready accessibility for visitors, those coming from without the building, and others. Unless other members of the department serve the head in some administrative capacity, there is little reason for them to be in or adjacent to the general office. Often there is some segregation by divisions, particularly if a common outer office with a secretary or two can be located there to look after the business of the division. Figure 11.8 (p. 284) shows one such plan.

Many instructors like to have their offices relatively close to the large laboratories which they supervise. Others seem to want to be as far removed as possible. If single offices are to be distributed more or less around a building, the architectural plan may lend itself to setting aside such space here and there in a reasonably convenient location.

Lecture rooms, especially the large ones, present a nearly unique problem. Lecturers prefer them centrally located within the building for ready accessibility from offices and laboratories. Students coming from outside the building to lectures would no doubt prefer to enter the room directly from the exterior. There would be at least one entrance, of course, from the building, as at the University of West Virginia. A variation is at the University of California at Los Angeles.

Main lecture rooms should not be under laboratories having service lines for liquids, as sooner or later there will be leaks or accidents above. There are two general possibilities for avoiding this situation. The room may be put on the top floor; but this may mean a noncentral location, and it is certain to be undesirable if there are three or four floors, and there will be heavy traffic on the stairways during interchange of large sections.

If the lecture room is within the building, the preferable location is near the ground level entrances. With closed court construction, the top of the room(s) may be the bottom of the court. Also, it may be feasible to put above the room(s) some room such as the library. For a large room, this may mean heavy beams to carry the load

above. In no case should the planner agree to any columns in the lecture room to support such loads.

The library, too, should be located as centrally as possible, and there should be no laboratories above it if they have any service lines carrying liquids, for one leak in an acid drain may ruin an irreplaceable periodical set. If there is heavy usage by people from outside the building, a location on a fourth floor is inconvenient for them unless elevator service is available.

Many instructors feel that laboratories for general chemistry should be as near ground level entrances as possible. This keeps to a minimum the confusion and noise of the large numbers of students in such classes. Physical chemists, however, usually want the ground level laboratories, because they feel such rooms may be less subject to vibration. It may be desirable, too, to be just above basement rooms where it is preferable or necessary to put heavy equipment and apparatus. Few buildings are designed to carry the loads of some modern equipment on upper floors.

There is rather general belief that work producing the most dangerous or otherwise objectionable fumes, such as inorganic qualitative analysis or organic chemistry, should be on the top floor nearest the exhaust outlets of the ventilation system. However, if the system is really efficient, this is not a major point.

The ground floor, with separate outside entrance, is first choice for the shop. Second choice is the basement, with deep areaways for the windows and a straightaway outside entrance through which to bring long supplies, such as steel and lumber.

The storeroom needs direct access to the outside, at least for receiving and shipping.

CHEMISTRY AND SOMETHING ELSE. There are two situations in which chemistry will occupy only part of a building. In small institutions often the other part will be allotted to physics, biology, geology, mathematics, or some combination of these.

Although the decision may depend upon the nature of the building, usually the division of space will be horizontal, chemistry being given one or more floors. Then the chief question is which floor(s) should be given to chemistry. If it is on the top floor, there is least liability for objectionable fumes in other departments underneath. The flues will be shortest and so least expensive. The opposite holds for service lines. There is most liability for leaks to floors below.

In large institutions subdivision of floor space may be horizontal by interests, but probably it will be vertical. This often works out in the architecture of the building. The building at Northwestern University is a fine example: the six wings are allotted, not quite equally, among chemistry, physics, and four subdivisions of engineering.

Selected Floor Plans. There are practically as many floor plans as there are buildings. Although examination of them will show that most of the variations are in details, a few quite distinctive practices have been followed. Several of these are discussed briefly, with some comments on what seems to be advantages and disadvantages of each. It will be assumed that sufficient ground space is available in each case. Probably in the majority of practical situations this will not be the case; if so, one must adjust to the area available.

RECTANGULAR FORM. A large percentage of present buildings are essentially rectangular. They are structurally simple, and, from an engineering viewpoint, they probably present the fewest difficulties for the installation of all the various services. Altogether, this means economy, but in various respects they are not easy to plan to achieve various desirable features.

The simplest, common form is shown in Figure 11.24. The basic module is 10 x 22 ft, except on the corners, where it is 12 x 22 ft. This is about a minimum. The corridor, between two rows of columns, bisects the building. The following items in this design may be noted: (1) the corridor walls are thick enough to contain the hood flues; (2) the four flues shown for each hood are for hoods in this position on four floors; (3) possibility is shown for subdividing for offices, 2-man and 4-man research laboratories, recitation and lecture rooms, and a general laboratory.

Sometimes it is difficult to subdivide the two halves satisfactorily. If they are wide enough for large undergraduate laboratories, they are too wide for offices and other small rooms. In one such building the offices are 8 x 28 ft. A variation of this plan, shown in Figure 11.25, has a single row of central columns. These form one side of

Figure 11.24   Section of simple rectangular floor plan.

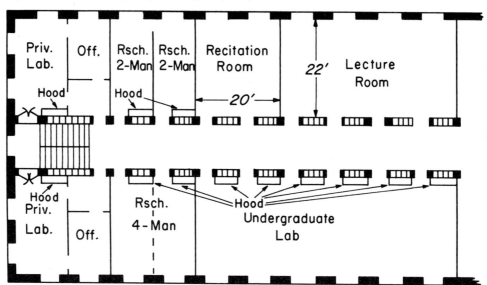

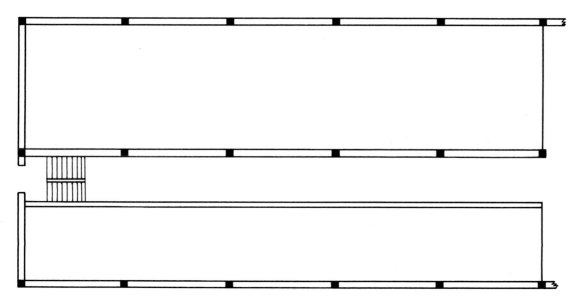

Figure 11.25   Column placement on 24' x 28' centers with off-center corridor.

Figure 11.26   Modified rectangular floor plan.

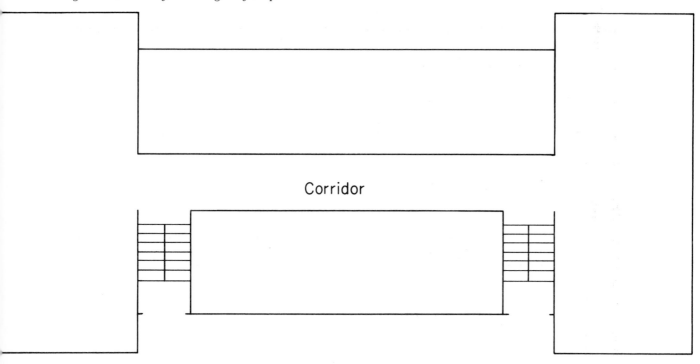

Corridor

the off-center corridor. There is one deep and one shallow side for subdivision.

Figure 11.26 illustrates a different variation. It might be considered one type of capital "I" or "H". The ends provide for large rooms and the center for small ones. One objection to such large laboratory rooms is the single entrance in case of accident or fire.

The two stairways, if leading from entrances, form a U-type main corridor. This arrangement may be used, of course, in the plain rectangular form of building (Figure 11.24) and thus leave the two ends for large rooms.

Figure 11.27 shows still another variation which has appeared since air-conditioning has become fairly common. It is essentially a three-corridor plan, the one in the center being given over entirely to services, such as plumbing, electricity, and ventilation. The two outside rows of rooms are not deep and may be subdivided for purposes needing relatively small areas. The two inside rooms provide for larger rooms. They have no windows and must be air-conditioned.

HOLLOW RECTANGLE OR SQUARE FORM. A few buildings were originally designed as hollow squares or rectangles, or have acquired this form through efforts to add to a building perhaps not planned for expansion. Figure 11.28 shows an outline for such a building. Such plans are likely to have a corridor cutting through some large laboratory; or, if not, there are no rooms deep enough for large undergraduate sections. In some cases the court area on the first floor is used for the main lecture room, storeroom, and shop (along with other space inside the corridors).

MULTIPLE WING FORMS. There are several interesting variations of wing forms. They differ chiefly in the central unit(s) which connect the wings.

Figure 11.27   Rectangular form with small rooms on outside and large ones on inside.

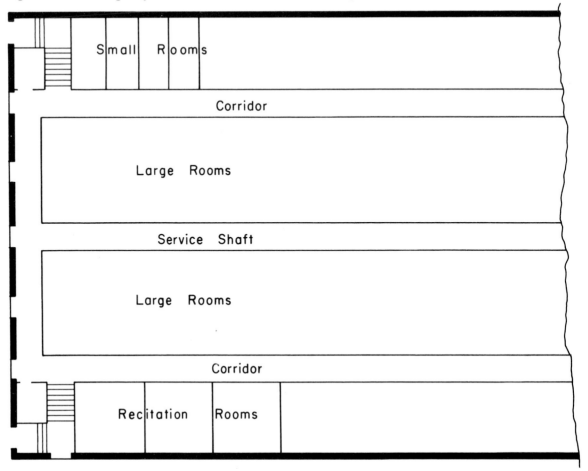

1. *H-Form.* The essence of the H-form is shown in Figure 11.29. Two cross arms (four wings) are shown, along with the possibility of adding another cross arm at the back. Further additions are possible. Although attractive for future expansion this form is not easily subdivided, especially for small rooms. An example is at Michigan State University.

2. *Cross Form.* If horizontal expansion is impossible, or not to be made possible, the cross form has distinct merit. Figure 11.30 shows the outline of the design of the Frick Laboratory at Princeton University. Three wings are around a central storeroom, which serves also as the prep-aration room for the main lecture room. Small laboratories and offices are between two of these wings and the front section, which is devoted to intermediate and research laboratories, the library, offices, and classrooms.

3. *Double Block-E Form* (Open-court). This arrangement may be considered a variation of the H-form. It differs chiefly in two aspects: (1) the section connecting the wings is broader in order to accommodate items such as storeroom(s), lecture room, and library; and (2) they occupy an area having no possibility for expansion. Two examples are the State University of Iowa and Northwestern University. The latter is the more recent. One floor is illustrated in Figure 11.31. In such a plan one kind of chemistry may occupy

Figure 11.28   Hollow rectangular floor plan.

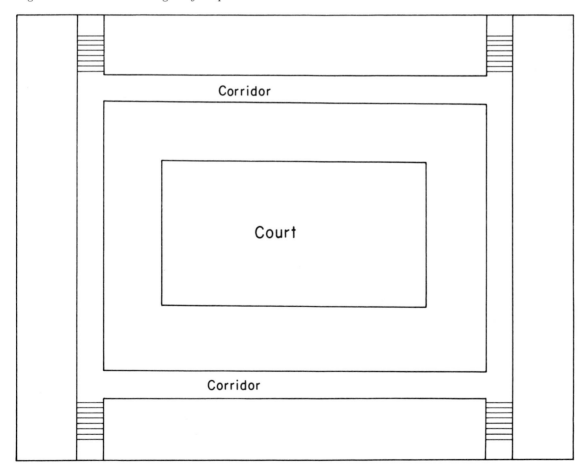

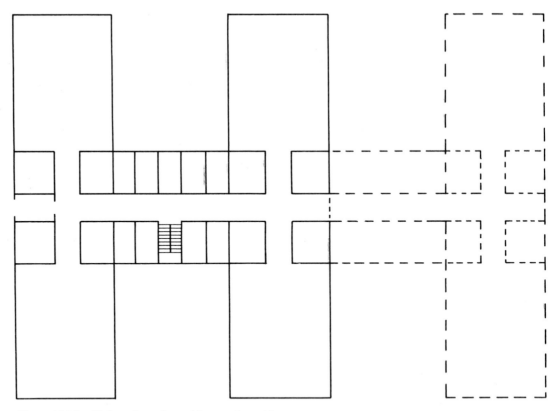

Figure 11.29   H-form floor plan with central corridor.

one wing (or more) and, as at Northwestern, some other science or division of engineering another wing.

4. *Open-closed Court Form.* The original plans for the chemistry building at Purdue University are essentially a combination of the front of the Baker Laboratory of Cornell University (closed courts) and one-half of the laboratory at the State University of Iowa (open courts). Figure 11.32 shows the general arrangement for the top floor, designed entirely for organic chemistry.

Like other plans it has defects. Some points of merit are the following: (1) each of the large laboratories on the back may be used as a unit or divided for large undergraduate courses; (2) two recitation rooms and a lecture room seating 100 are on the floor; (3) the two end laboratories may be used as shown or divided for special work; (4) small rooms for research and offices are on the front; (5) practically all laboratories and offices have outside light.

Possibility of Expansion. Many college buildings are fine examples of lack of planning for possible future needs as the result of increased enrollments or expanded programs. Sometimes, by choice or necessity, the site available allows for no horizontal expansion. This should be avoided in an expanding institution, if possible. Sometimes, by careful planning, provision may be made to add one or more stories; but service facilities, especially ventilation systems, make this difficult.

If horizontal expansion is planned, the general method and possibilities must be worked out. Where can the elevator(s), storeroom, and other services of this nature be located in what is to be built to serve present needs and at the same time serve reasonably well in an enlarged structure?

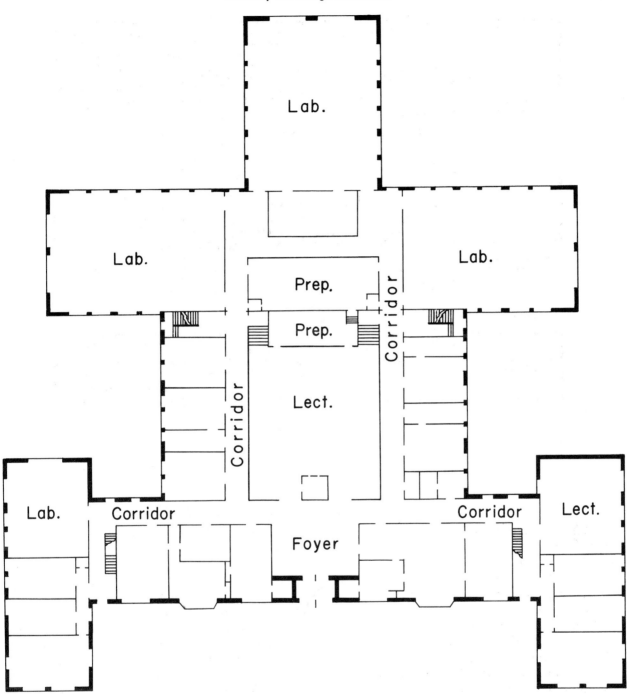

Figure 11.30   Cross form of floor plan.

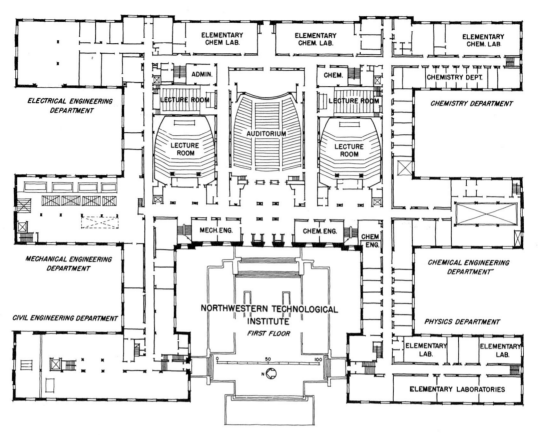

Figure 11.31   Electrotype of main floor of Northwestern building.

Such things cannot easily be moved. What items can be located temporarily and later moved? In these cases, what services should be brought to the floor line at first for later use, or what needs to be done to make this easily possible later? Long-range planning for flexibility is required.

Three examples of such planning are the possible extension of unit hollow squares at Cornell, unit "H's" at Michigan State, and unit wings at the State University of Iowa.

Examples of Floor Plans. The writer's most valuable help came from visits to many laboratories over a period of years. It is an invaluable aid to see what others have done and how they did it. Ideas come from talking with those who have planned buildings, especially if they point out items which might well be done differently in a new building. Valuable, too, is an oppor-

tunity to talk with the maintenance men who take care of plumbing, ventilating, and other service installations. Such men know what does not work well and usually they are willing to talk about it.

Next to inspecting a building is to have a description of it. Two decades and more ago a number of booklets were published, a fine example being the one distributed at the dedication of the Baker Laboratory at Cornell University. In addition to description of many items, including pictures, floor plans, and other architectural details are included. Such plans, especially if labeled, give one a good idea of the general arrangement.

Through the architect of a building it may be possible to obtain a set of working drawings. Probably most valuable to the planner, unless trained in engineering, are the drawings for the floor plans and the equipment. These show all dimensions, where the columns are located, and various other interesting details.

Lack of space permitted the inclusion in this chapter of only a few floor plans of the hundreds possible; these were selected to show considerable variation in a number of items.

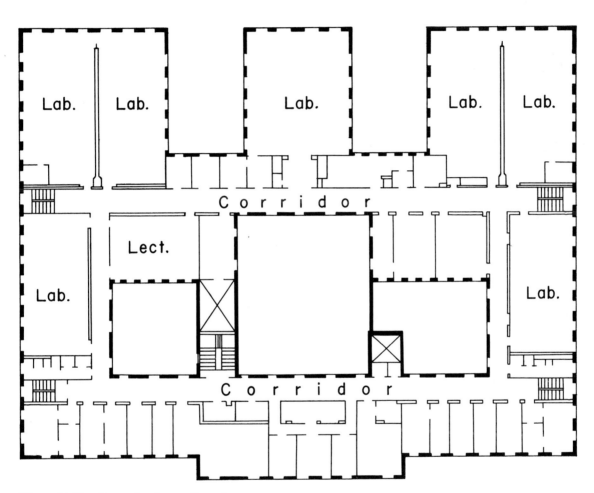

Figure 11.32   Open- closed-court floor plan.

CHAPTER XII

Planning for Science Teaching in the Small College

HARRY F. LEWIS

The Institute of Paper Chemistry
Appleton, Wisconsin

Laboratory planning for the small liberal arts college is generally somewhat different from its counterpart on the university campus. Instead of a building to meet the needs of a single department or a group of closely related departments (Life Science, for example), the college science building is generally built to house all the natural sciences, mathematics frequently being included. It may accommodate botany, zoology and microbiology, geology, home economics, astronomy and mathematics, as well as physics and chemistry and such specific pre-engineering subjects as engineering graphics. Commonly facilities must be provided for botany and zoology, physics and chemistry; thus chemistry finds itself neighbor to a greenhouse and sometimes to an animal room, as well as to the regular laboratory facilities required for biology and physics. Careful planning is necessary to be sure that the odors of chemistry, biology and the animal room do not permeate the halls of the building, and that chemistry's occasional floods do not seep through unexpected floor openings, with consequent damage to the electronic equipment of the physicist.

The heterogeneous nature of the several disciplines housed in the college science building has advantages as well as a few minor disadvantages. The beginning chemistry student cannot help picking up some appreciation of the scope and content of the other sciences, particularly those using their hall space for instructive displays of flora and fauna, interesting minerals and "push button" electronic experiments. Not only that, but the several departments can profit by shared facilities, such as a common shop manned by a competent instrument maker; a common receiving and shipping room run by a permanent stockroom man; special equipment important to biology or physics but occasionally needed by chemistry and vice versa; an attractively furnished seminar room; a science reference library for use by staff and advanced students; a well planned large auditorium; and a divisional secretary.

Since this book is directed particularly toward the laboratory needs of the chemist and the chemical engineer, no attempt will be made to consider the detailed requirements of either biology or physics[1] other than to indicate possible locations of these departments in a common science building and to stress the importance of having representatives of all departments to be housed in the projected building on the planning committee. It would seem, however, that what is said in the following pages with reference to the importance of flexible planning and interchangeable facilities to meet curriculum changes, relates just as much to biology and to physics as it does to chemistry.

PROBLEMS AND TRENDS TO BE CONSIDERED IN PLANNING FOR THE FUTURE

It is not easy to plan science facilities now for use in the years 1990-2000; yet this is what is required of the planning group. This is due in part to the difficulty in determining what proportion, if any, of the coming tide of students the particular college wants, will take or is planning for. This is a decision which will have to be made by the administrative officer of the institution and is subject to revision in any change of administration. Furthermore, the publicity now being given to opportunities for scientists, together with improved interest and teaching in science in high schools and colleges, might well result in an increase in the relative number of entering students who are planning a science major.

Still another factor which makes planning for chemistry somewhat of a gamble is the fact that the college chemistry curriculum is in a state of flux. This is due in part to the expected impact of improved science teaching in the high schools (thousands of high school science teachers have participated in summer and school year institutes—new modern high school texts are already being used on an experimental basis). Not only are teaching and course content in high schools being improved, but the course sequence and content of undergraduate chemistry are being examined critically.

For years the chemistry course has followed the familiar pattern of general chemistry $\longrightarrow$ qualitative and quantitative analysis $\longrightarrow$ organic chemistry $\longrightarrow$ physical chemistry. The relative numbers in these courses have dictated the number of laboratories per course in the same way that the level of laboratory work done in each course has dictated the equipment in these laboratories. But now the content and sequence of the courses are being questioned, and college chemistry is faced with the prospect of starting where high-school chemistry leaves off. A number of new first-year courses are being tested and are meeting with a degree of success. The Division of Chemical Education in June of 1960[2] held a conference at Bucknell University to review the status of undergraduate training of chemistry majors. Some colleges reported starting the freshman year with organic chemistry; others favored an integrated course in physics and chemistry. Many are considering giving some physical chemistry at an earlier stage in the curriculum, at the same time moving analytical chemistry to the junior or senior year, closing with work in instrumental analysis. Likewise, inorganic chemistry, with its new tools for investigating the structures and mechanisms of inorganic compounds and reactions, must find its place in the curriculum.

At this time it is too early to estimate what the curriculum picture will look like after the dust settles. It seems quite evident that the new will be different from the old, if only in course content. In contrast to past practice in laboratory design, these new first-year courses will require as much laboratory space per student as any of the more advanced courses. This is particularly true if the first year course is organic chemistry. Likewise, facilities for instrumental analysis differ from those required for the conventional laboratory course in analytical chemistry.

Fully as important to recognize in planning for chemistry is the trend in the colleges toward both faculty and undergraduate research.[3] Facilities for such research are missing from many of the current college chemistry buildings and will have to be provided. Since money is now available to support significant college research for both faculty and students in the summer period, the expansion of certain campus services to a full year basis is indicated. Finally, the introduction of research and independent study makes necessary the inclusion of space in the science building for a science library to house essential reference works and periodicals.

Still another factor which is bound to influence college science building design is the trend in the direction of small laboratories of a size to handle 24 students. Many teachers believe that this is about as large a group as can be handled effectively in the laboratory by one college teacher. Undergraduate laboratory assistants are useful, but they cannot replace a good teacher. By careful design it is possible to plan these smaller laboratories without adding greatly either to overall space requirements or to cost. In addition, if such facilities are designed with flexibility and multiple use in mind, they can be used for other chemistry courses as a changing curriculum requires.

Actually, the new buildings are being planned by teachers of this generation for use by teachers and students of future generations at a time when advancement in science is proceeding at a constantly increasing rate. Planning for the future under these conditions poses a tremendous challenge. One thing is certain—curriculum study is today an important phase of laboratory planning for the small college.

A START IN THE PLANNING—
THE IMPLEMENTATION OF THE
DECISION TO BUILD

Let us assume that the college trustees have decided to construct a new science building to house the departments of chemistry, physics and biology, and have indicated an amount of money for the purpose. What are the steps necessary to implement that decision? One should be to select a small building-planning committee made up in part of representatives of each department to be housed in the building. The selection of the committee and its chairman must be made by the administration. The most capable men in the departments, as far as the functions of the committee are concerned, should be selected regardless of rank. The chairman should be relieved of some of his teaching load and should serve the project until the completion of the building and its dedication. The chairman is often a member of the chemistry department staff, since the facilities required for that department are more complex than for either physics or biology. The committee will need to know the maximum size of the student body as projected by the adminis-

tration some years in the future before it can begin its work.

Another step is the selection of the architect. An earlier chapter suggests an approach to this. Needless to say, this is one of the important decisions, for an architect with little or no experience in the design of a science building can handicap the teaching and research carried out in the building as long as it stands, even though the building committee is on the alert and is aware of some of the hazards. Inexperience can be overcome to some degree by insisting that the architect employ an experienced consulting architect and consulting engineer.

Finally there is the selection of the site. If possible, this decision should be based on the recommendation of the architect and planning committee. If for some reason another site is selected, the recommendations of the architect and planning committee as to the placement of the building on the site should be given most serious consideration.

The Administration (representing the Owner) and the Building Planning Committee (representing the User) together with the Architect and, after the contract has been let, the Builder form a team in which each member has an important part to play, and in which each is dependent on the other. Decisions made by any one member of the team should be passed on to all the others automatically. The goal is a science building that will serve the needs of faculty and students efficiently and effectively for years to come. The perfect science building is probably yet to be built, but each one erected should have perfection as an objective. Poor planning by the planning committee or the architect makes this objective impossible; unwise decisions by the administration make it difficult.

QUESTIONS TO BE CONSIDERED
BY THE PLANNING COMMITTEE

The first member of the team to begin work following the decision to build and the selection of architect and site is of necessity the planning committee. It is the duty of the planning committee to review the space and functional needs of the departments being housed in the new building in the light of present practice and possible changes in the curriculum of the various departments, and to provide a quantitative picture of the functional requirements. This should be done in such a way as to prevent unnecessary duplication in facilities and to ensure their maximum use.

While it is difficult to predict all the questions the architect will want answered, a written report should be made by the planning committee covering where possible the items in the following check list, and such other facilities as may seem desirable.

Lecture, Recitation and Seminar Rooms

(1) *Auditorium.* Will there be a multiple—use auditorium, what capacity, type of seating and arrangement, provision for left-handed students, lecture table (height, length and width, services, special features), windows or windowless (if windows, method for darkening the room), air-conditioning or other form of ventilation, acoustical treatment, arrangement of chalk boards, projector screen dimensions and location, floor gradient (low, medium or high), lighting requirements, free wall space for Periodic Table and other charts, lecture preparation rooms and their furniture, and any other points of importance to the users.

(2) *Classrooms:* number and capacity of each, departmental location, type of seating, lecture table, size and services and provision for projector use.

(3) *Seminar rooms:* number, dimensions and capacity. Special services required, type of furniture.

Offices

(4) *Faculty offices:* number and departmental locations, sizes, departmental office, preferred location with respect to research and teaching laboratories.

(5) *Secretary's office and workroom.*

(6) *Work room for student assistants*: number and departmental locations, capacities, facilities and sizes.

Laboratories and Auxiliary Rooms

(7) *Student laboratories listed by departments and*

courses: capacity at one time, number of sections, bench length per student, bench and bench top materials, arrangement of services on bench, hood length per student, dispensing services for chemical supplies and equipment, safety features, width of module (bench center to bench center), peninsula or island bench arrangement, services required on benches, number of chalk boards and locations, preferred arrangement of room and its facilities. Laboratories for physics and biology—arrangement, capacities, special features, services.

(8) *Balance rooms:* preferred location, number of balances.

(9) *Instrumentation rooms:* air-conditioning, special equipment to be used in these laboratories, furniture, services (electricity, water, steam, air vacuum), facilities for darkening.

(10) *Photographic dark room:* number, size, equipment, services, preferred design, etc.

(11) *Optical dark room:* number, size, equipment, services, preferred design, method of darkening, etc.

(12) *Staff research laboratories:* number by departments, preferred location with respect to the individual offices, sizes, facilities, arrangements and services.

(13) *Student research laboratories:* number of student stations by departments, dimensions, capacities, facilities, preferred arrangement, services, locations.

The Science Library

(14) *Science library:* linear feet of shelf space (average 8 books—4 to 5 volumes bound periodicals per foot), present number of volumes in each category, number of reading stations at tables, present number of current periodicals, preferred location, carrels, adjoining facilities such as seminar room, office of departmental secretary, microcard or microfilm reading and storage room.

Stockrooms

(15) *Stock and dispensing rooms:* type of stock storage and dispensing rooms (concentrated or dispersed), locations, sizes, dimensions, storage for solvents and hazardous chemicals, alcohol storage, receiving room, locations of these with respect to the elevator, office facilities for man in charge of stockroom and his files.

Special Rooms

(16) *Animal rooms:* kinds and capacities, location, special facilities for ventilation, equipment, related facilities such as operating and autopsy rooms.

(17) *Greenhouse:* size, type, facilities, preferred location, controlled temperatures and humidities, adjoining work rooms, size, functions, equipment and services.

(18) *Planetarium:* size, type, location, capacity.

(19) *Observatory:* size, type, location, special equipment and facilities.

(20) *Museum facilities:* special rooms and for what purpose, use of hall cases, type of equipment, curator's office and work room.

(21) *Shop:* sizes, locations, equipment to be installed for mechanical or electrical shopwork or for glass blowing, mechanic—full or part time.

(22) *Controlled temperature or humidity rooms:* type (low or high temperature, etc.), desired conditions, number, location.

Special Equipment

(23) *Safety facilities:* number and location of safety showers, fire extinguishers, fire blankets, eye fountains.

(24) *Refrigerators and ice machines:* number, size, explosion-proof.

It should be clear from reading the above check list that these various items refer particularly to what might be called the academic and technical functions of the building. In addition, there are a variety of nontechnical facilities to be considered. Some of these are related to circulation within the building, e.g., halls, stairs, and especially an elevator. The janitor will need a small room where his stock of supplies will be kept; on each floor there should be an ample closet containing a floor sink and hot and cold water and the necessary shelves and hooks for janitor's supplies needed on the floor. The entering service mains and lines are generally brought in at a central point, from which they are distributed. This calls for a room adequate in size to meet these requirements and equipped with facilities for plumber and electrician. The various toilets and rest rooms are also a part of the nonacademic facilities; they need careful location and planning. Finally, many new buildings include in a central location vending machines for coffee, soft drinks and candy—items which otherwise will ultimately usurp a part of the hall. The architect will normally be responsible for the planning of these nontechnical facilities. He will also have the ultimate responsibility with regard to planning the academic and technical facilities.

Another decision to be reached by the planning committee, the architect and the administration concerns the location of the departments in the building. These may be arranged in a number of ways. One is to build a multi-floor building in which the departments are separated vertically. In a modification of this, the departments are divided horizontally, each being assigned to a specific floor or section of a floor. The latter method is often preferred to the former, since it is more nearly possible to keep the specific services, odors, and hazards involved in the work of the department within the bounds of a given floor. This also provides a minimum of stair climbing on the part of faculty in carrying out their teaching duties. A third arrangement, of interest where there is ample campus space, is that based upon the grouping of single-floor buildings each assigned to a given subject field. These can be arranged in a variety of ways. One is a quadrangle of buildings connected by enclosed passages which can serve several purposes, such as exhibit space for items of current interest in the specific natural science disciplines; the inside court provides an attractive place for students to read and study outdoors when the weather permits. In another arrangement departmental buildings are grouped around the facilities which are common to all, such as the auditorium and classrooms, storerooms and the departmental library. By far the most common is the multi-floor building with departments separated horizontally.

In the latter case, where the building consists of two stories and a basement with the basement part above ground, physics is generally in the basement, biology on the first floor, and chemistry on the second. In the past, these decisions have been based upon the assumption that physics needs a location where vibration will be minimum; biology frequently has a greenhouse situated outside the building on the ground level;

Figure 12.1   Grinnell College science hall.

and chemistry is better served by the top floor where the vents from its hoods will have short runs through the roof (even though its service lines will have the longest runs from the basement). Such reasoning may no longer be as significant as it once appeared to be.

The science building at Grinnell College (Figure 12.1) has been built with both physics and biology on the first floor. The structure consists of a central two-story and basement core with physics on one floor, chemistry on the floor above and with a central stock room in the basement; jutting out from two sides of the core is a single floor structure without basement which houses both biology and earth science.

A further modification of these various arrangements places a large auditorium in a stub at the end or out from the side of the main building, connected to it but isolated structurally so that it can be used as a separate unit by other groups than those of the science departments themselves. This is made possible by providing one general entrance to the building at the point where auditorium and main building are joined. The auditorium in the Hamline University building is located at the rear of the building (Figure 12.2),

Figure 12.2   Drew science hall, Hamline University.

Figure 12.3a   Olin hall of science Lafayette College.

while the one at Lafayette is in a stub at the end of the structure (Figure 12.3a).

Placement of the building on the site is also a matter of some importance. Generally, undergraduate student laboratory work is done in the afternoon. Hence there is value in planning the building in such a way that its long sides face north and south; thus the principal student laboratories can be placed together on the north face, and offices, small research laboratories and classrooms along the south face. The west wall can then be solid to serve as a side or back wall for classrooms. If it is not possible to establish this orientation for the building, it is desirable in many sections of the country to provide outside louvers for laboratories facing south and west, particularly if a curtain wall is used with a high percentage of glass in the wall structure. Such walls result in very hot laboratories in spring, summer and early fall; for summer comfort both air-conditioning and louvers are a necessity.

PLANNING FOR
SPECIFIC FUNCTIONS

Since the facilities needed in the college science building are qualitatively the same as those in the university building, a detailed description of all of them would involve unnecessary duplication of the material in Chapter 11. For this reason, emphasis in the following is placed particularly on the various items which are unique to the colleges.

Lecture and Recitation Facilities

The Auditorium. As has been mentioned, many college science buildings currently in process of construction are being provided with a large auditorium for common use by the different science departments. This is located with respect to the rest of the building so as to permit its use either as a part of the latter or independently of it. In this way it serves both the science disciplines and other college organizations requiring a good meeting place for large groups. Since it will often be used at night, arrangements must be made to provide easy entrance and exit apart from the main building structure. In addition, the auditorium section should be provided with both lounge, rest room and coat room facilities. This auditorium will generally seat from 200 to 250 people. Unless carefully planned acoustically, it may need to be provided with a good public address system. The "speakers" for this can serve for sound movies as well.

While other sections of this volume speak in

some detail to the design and construction of large lecture rooms (Chapters 11 and 14, Part 7), the following refers particularly to some features of concern in the college science building auditorium.

In a room to handle an audience of 200–250, it is necessary to provide a sloping floor. This may be either a constant slope or one which increases gradually from front to rear. Likewise, the slope may be either small or large. It is important that each student be provided with an unobstructed view of the table top as well as of the material going on the chalk board or projection screen. The first two rows of seats in such a room may be on floor level, with a gradual rise from this point on. The actual position of each row should be determined by drawing a sight line from the eye of a hypothetical person on each row down to the center of the top of the lecture table. The gradient should increase in such a way that every eye commands a good view of the lecture table top and the lecturer. In general, the length of the lecture room should be slightly greater than the width. Aisles should normally be provided so that no seat is farther than ten seats from an aisle; in some recent installations where the rows of seats are separated to permit easy passing, the center aisle may be omitted.

As this room may be used both by classes and outside groups, most institutions feel that there is value in providing better than average seating, and so install fully upholstered auditorium-type chairs. These can be obtained in very attractive colors with or without tablet arms. The reader is referred to earlier discussions of lecture room seating for comments on the arrangement of the seats. Such seats can be obtained in several widths; one satisfactory installation has used seats 22 in. wide from the center of the arm and placed from back to back at a distance of 33 in. In other installations the seats were slightly narrower but the rows were somewhat farther apart. If pedestal seats are used, these should be adequately spaced for comfortable seating and easy passing. In an earlier chapter a reasonable spacing for easy moving has been set at 26 by 38 in; these dimensions are also subject to shortening by 2 in. in either direction.

Ordinarily the auditorium will be provided with a lecture table equipped for experimentation. The length of such a table need not be more than 12 to 16 ft. An additional section of this table can be wheeled in from the lecture preparation room, ready to be used for lecture demonstration. These and other details will be found elsewhere in this volume. A single fixed chalk board, 25 ft or so long, placed across the front of the room with the chalk rail even with the top of the lecture table (that is, 36 in. high and with the board about 42 in. wide) serves most of the needs of the college teacher. The projection screen is centered on the wall above the board, leaving ample space for charts and the Periodic Table on either side of the screen. Some teachers prefer several movable boards each about 10 ft long, mounted one behind the other so that they can be pushed up and located right behind the lecture table. A disadvantage is that they are covered in part by the projector screen when it is in position for use. One solution is to mount the screen to the left of the chalk boards or to have in addition fixed boards on either side of the screen. Appropriate lighting enables these fixed boards to be used during projection.

If the room is to be used for both science and nonscience meetings, consideration should be given to making it useful for both functions, but primary consideration should be given to the science function. Careful planning, however, may make it easily adaptable to the nonscience purpose as well.

An example is the new science building at Ripon College. (See Figures 12.3b and 12.3c). Here one of the uses for the auditorium is that of a concert hall. The conversion of a chemistry lecture hall into an adequate concert hall is handled simply. The lecture table is easily disconnected from its services and rolled back into a pocket under the chalk board. Following this, wood panels are rolled out from recesses from either side of the stage to provide a completely panelled stage backing set at floor level. The room is acoustically treated so as to fit either requirement. In addition, a room has been built off the stage to store a concert grand piano.

The auditorium will be used in the academic program principally for lectures given to large

Figure 12.3b   Ripon College science auditorium showing lecture table disconnected from services in floor box.

Figure 12.3c   Ripon College science auditorium in use as a concert hall.

beginning classes in science. In this capacity, facilities for lecture demonstrations and projection will be used; these include a preparation room designed for setting up lecture experiments. This room or group of rooms can be placed immediately behind the large chalk board in the front of the auditorium, and when the chalk board is raised the experimental material can be passed through. The auditorium will also serve as a place for examinations by large classes or mixed groups of classes.

A satisfactory system for darkening the auditorium for projection is essential. Many teachers favor a windowless room; in this case an effective ventilating system becomes all-important. Where windows are provided, these may be blocked out by shades, Venetian blinds or drapes. The latter may be lined to make them lightproof; if carefully selected for color and pattern, they contribute markedly to the appearance of the room.

Class or Recitation Rooms. In addition to the large auditorium, the chemistry department in the average small college will need one or two additional classrooms. One of these may be sized to handle up to 65 or 70 students, another to handle 25 or 30. These are generally equipped with lecture-demonstration facilities smaller in size than that specified for the auditorium. As these rooms are often used for projection, they should be designed for darkening. Ample chalk boards will be needed and any added features which make for better acoustics, lighting and informal seating will increase their value.

Seminar Rooms. A seminar room is useful in a college science building. Not only is it good for small advanced classes, but also as a meeting place for the science staff as well as for conferences of students and staff with visitors. Conferences between students and personnel men proceed better in an attractive seminar room equipped for the purpose than they do with the conferees perched on stools in a corner of a laboratory. If possible, the room should include a small kitchenette, a projector and screen, chalk board and center table and comfortable chairs. Projection equipment, chalk board and extra folding chairs may be located in panels in the walls. In small colleges, a room 12 x 15 or 12 x 20 feet would be adequate. Special consideration should

Figure 12.3d   Seminar room, Swarthmore College.

be given to the design of an attractive seminar room. Figure 12.3d shows the seminar room in the Pierre S. duPont Science Building at Swarthmore.

Staff Offices

Since the chairman of the college chemistry department will have some administrative work to do, along with student conferences, it is desirable to plan at least one faculty office with this in mind. Such an office need not exceed 200 square feet.

The department secretary is often located adjacent to the chairman's office; her office will need to have at least 150 square feet since here will be located departmental files, office supplies, a mimeograph machine, etc. If the secretary is also to be in charge of the departmental or division science library, it may be better to locate her near the library. In this event, care should be taken to provide acoustical treatment for her room so that the noise of her office machines will not annoy users of the library.

All senior members of the faculty should have their own offices. From 100 to 150 square feet will be adequate for these. In planning the details of building, the ideas of individual teachers regarding arrangement and furnishing of their particular offices should be considered. These need not be identical cells. His office is the teacher's study, conference room and headquarters; here he will keep his personal chemistry library, his file and his academic records; here he will write his papers, correct his examinations and confer with students and colleagues. An attractive office will do much for his morale. At the same time, there should be some control so that the next person assigned the office will not be too unhappy with it.

In some cases, the faculty man will want his office and personal research laboratory in one room. A good illustration of such an arrangement may be seen in the chemistry departments of either Hamline University or the College of Wooster. Such a room will occupy about 250 to 300 square feet with a width of 10 to 12 feet. Others prefer to have the laboratory adjoining the office; still others prefer a complete separation of the two facilities. Some modification of the second plan is probably the most common.

In some institutions two members of the junior staff may share the same office and likewise an adjoining laboratory. Since the junior staff is likely to change at frequent intervals, these offices may be somewhat more standardized as to furniture and arrangements. Such rooms may each be from 150 to 250 square feet in area, the laboratory being somewhat larger than the space alloted to the office.

A small office room is frequently provided for the student assistants to be used in connection with their academic duties; here they grade papers and correct notebooks. Such a room may be furnished with chalk board, work tables and chairs. An effective modification involves a series of carrels, each 6 feet wide by 5 feet deep, equipped with a shelf for books and a drawer for papers. The panels which separate the units are acoustically treated. A room of this type at The Institute of Paper Chemistry is shown in Figure 12.4.

Figure 12.4　Suggested office room for student assistants.

Student Laboratories

In the conventional chemistry department, student laboratories are required for the courses in general chemistry, analytical chemistry, organic chemistry and physical chemistry. To these many now add a laboratory for instrumental analysis, with an optical darkroom and a photographic darkroom adjacent or not too far away, together with space for undergraduate research (the size and form of this will depend upon the number of research students) and a laboratory and counting room for work with radioisotopes.

In view of the possible changes faced by the conventional undergraduate chemistry curriculum, the planner will be concerned with designing laboratories flexible enough to meet future as well as current requirements. As an illustration, if the new curriculum adopted by the chemistry department calls for organic chemistry as its first-year course, consideration will have to be given to some difference in laboratory requirements. Laboratory benches for general chemistry frequently provide only 3 linear feet or about 6 square feet of working space per student; for organic chemistry the space desired is 5 to 6 linear feet or 10 to 12 square feet per student. Conventional general chemistry laboratory benches will therefore handle about half as many as in organic chemistry. Organic benches require steam for steam cones and steam distillation. In addition, other requirements for general chemistry are somewhat simpler than for organic chemistry.

In the face of possible curriculum changes and uncertain student loads, it seems desirable to standardize most student laboratories to provide about the same facilities and same bench space in each. The exceptions will be the physical chemistry laboratory, the specialized laboratories in instrumental analysis with adjoining darkrooms, radiochemistry and possibly the student laboratory (or laboratories) for advanced class work and research.

These standard laboratories should be designed for only as many student as a teacher can handle effectively at one time. An average figure is 24 students per teacher. A good figure for linear feet per student bench space would be 5;

for hood space per student, 0.85 to 1.0. A laboratory of approximately 1200 square feet (30 x 40 ft.–32 x 38 ft.) will provide for these requirements and allow for some variation in auxiliary equipment. The total expected enrollment in the particular courses may be handled by designing the cabinet work for sectional use; the expected maximum enrollment divided by 24 will indicate the number of sections to be accommodated. Since the first-year class in chemistry may be five times or more as large as the advanced classes, it will usually be necessary to provide it with twice the number of standard laboratories as for the second- and third-year courses.

The following items and services might make up the standard laboratory; these are open to change in line with the individual preferences of the instructor.

Benches. Three double laboratory benches with 20 linear feet of working space per side. These will handle 8 students per bench, each with 5 linear feet of bench space. They should be provided with gas, air, water, steam (4–10 psi pressure) and 110-volt alternating current. Vacuum for filtering, etc. may be obtained with aspirators, or a vacuum line may be included on the bench services. A mixing valve for steam and cold water provides hot water at the sink. Direct current may be brought in from cells or generated by means of AC-DC converters.

Arrangement of the cabinet work in the benches has in the past been generally determined by the instructor and course. Where the benches are designed to handle several sections, one cabinet per working space is provided for the storage of common ironware (ring stands, tripods, sand baths, etc.). A modification here would be to fasten ring stands on the shelves of the pipe racks where these are available. If the laboratory is to be used immediately by three sections, three large drawers equipped with locks can be provided and space for a fourth drawer can be left clear in the cabinet design. In the event of the need for additional sections, "tote drawers" can be brought in from a "tote drawer" cabinet and in this way as many as several additional sections can be handled at any one time. The above would seem to be one practical arrangement for all standard laboratories. Light-weight drawer "separates" such as are used in office desks may be designed to meet specific requirements. Actually a 5-foot bench space can be easily designed for four sections, making the capacity of the laboratory 96 students. In the interest of flexibility, the drawers and cabinet should handle the laboratory equipment for the greater share of the experiments in any course. Large or rarely used pieces of equipment may be checked out of the stock or dispensing room for use as required.

There are several arrangements used to handle effluents. The commonest is to run a trough down the center of the bench to a large "washup" sink at the end. This can be constructed of stone or lead-covered wood. The trough carries condenser and aspirator water to the sink; unfortunately it sometimes leaks and it often becomes cluttered with debris (old stoppers, filter paper, etc.) Over the trough is a pipe rack carrying the service pipes. On top of the pipes is a reagent shelf (Figure 12.5). Many teachers prefer to separate bench units with ample sinks set in between the first and second, and third and fourth students, making a sink directly available to each student; this serves for both process water and as a wash-up sink. In this arrangement the services may be carried over the sinks and down the desks in a conventional pipe rack-shelf or in box curbs, or they may be carried below the desk and emerge in turrets on both sides of the sink. A modification of this provides sinks in the same general location but on either side of the bench, making four in all. (Figure 12.6.) In this way, there is a place between two sinks for a service turret with water outlets on the sink sides and outlets for air, gas and current at either end. Outlets in the sinks serving several students should preferably be 2 inches in diameter rather than the customary 1½ inches.

The benches may be made of either wood or steel. Wood is the preferred material for high-school or college laboratories where maintenance is intermittent. For information about the properties of the various tops check pages 68–69.

Hoods. An adequate hood arrangement for most uses will be obtained where 0.85 to 1.0 linear feet of hood per student is installed. A laboratory for 24 students would then have from 20 to 24 feet of hoods. If the laboratory is to be

Figure 12.5   Teaching laboratories, Drake University.

air-conditioned, hoods of the pressurized (air-conditioned) type should be specified. Hoods should be serviced with adequate lighting, electric outlets, gas, steam and water, together with a cup sink. Controls should be placed outside the hood. The conventional hood may also serve as a convenient location for a chalk board.

Dispensing Facilities within the Laboratory. Two dispensing centers are useful in the standard laboratory, although one may be satisfactory. A good dispensing unit might consist of a wall bench unit, possibly 4 to 5 feet in length, bench top high and 2 feet wide, equipped with corrosion-resistant top and with one full-width shelf 15 inches from the floor. Fastened to the wall over the bench top or supported by the top is a set of three shelves, 10 inches wide, with the bottom shelf 1 foot above the bench top, the next shelf 1 foot higher and the top one 10 inches above that. A unit of this type may be located at each end of the hood section or on each side wall. An alternative is to use as the dispensing unit a combination of a small fixed weighing table or shelf large enough for the balance and a dispensing table on wheels, so that the assistant (or stockroom man) can stock it as indicated in the stockroom. In another modification, the hoods are separated into two sections by a long dispensing table unit equipped as above and including a wash-up sink.

Shelving and Storage Facilities within the Laboratory. The normal facilities already mentioned for storing and dispensing of chemicals and equipment within the standard laboratory would seem to be adequate for the experimental needs of the students. Some instructors like to maintain an extra supply of common chemicals on a side shelf in the laboratory. For this purpose, a section or two of steel or wood reagent shelving, up to 3 feet in length and provided with six shelves 1 foot apart and 8 inches wide, may suffice. In some laboratories a wooden equipment storage case with glass or solid doors will be useful. This may be from 3 to 6 feet long and 7 feet high, with shelves variably spaced and 12 to 18 inches deep.

The planner is urged to keep such shelving to the amount actually needed. Too frequently every unused foot of wall space is filled either with shelving or storage cases; these quickly become repositories for solutions without labels and long since past their prime, or for equipment out of repair or no longer in use. In other words, the laboratory provides one more place for "dead storage." More shelving can always be added, but whether this is done will depend on the way in which stockrooms are planned. The place for the storage of large supplies of chemicals and equipment is in the main stockroom or in an auxiliary dispensing room located adjacent to and opening into the standard laboratory. The latter is the source of replacement for student breakage and for the replenishment of chemical supplies; here should be stored the equipment which has only occasional use. One item of shelving which does have a use is that for the storage of desiccators in the analytical laboratory. This same unit may be utilized in the organic laboratory for the various chemicals required in qualitative organic analysis.

Facilities for Equipment to be used in Common. Table or bench facilities and services must be made available in the standard laboratory for ovens and electronic equipment (pH meters, electrolytic analysers, etc.). A heavy table 37 inches high and 24 to 30 inches wide with some type of asbestos composition top will be satisfactory for this purpose. A distillation rack will be useful in either organic, physical or research laboratories.

Safety Features. Three types of safety facilities may be provided in the standard laboratory—safety showers, safety eye fountains and fire blankets. These relate to student or staff accidents caused by chemicals or fire.

A safety shower should be placed preferably at each laboratory exit at a convenient spot, either inside or just outside the door. This shower should be easy for the person in trouble to find and turn on; a large overhead ring connected to the valve is commonly used for this purpose. Recently a safety shower provided with a brightly marked pole connected with the valve and running from floor to ceiling has become popular. Some of these have several shower nozzles which spray water all around the individual who has had the accident. Safety showers may or may not be provided with floor drains. An objection to the floor drain is that a shower used only rarely will not keep the floor drain trap sealed.

Safety eye fountains are not as common as safety showers. This is partly because the time required for the injured student to get to the bubbler may be sufficient to cause great damage to the eye. Much better eye protection is obtained by requiring the use of safety glasses by all in the laboratory. These protect the eye itself from injuries due to major accidents. Where eye

Figure 12.6 Laboratory benches with services in turrets, Northwestern University.

fountains are installed, they are commonly placed over a laboratory sink or in a pedestal in a prominent position in the laboratory.

One way to keep fire blankets available is to wind them on rollers in brightly painted, clearly labelled, vertically mounted cases; these may be fastened in the corner of laboratories where hazardous experiments are common, or they may be placed at intervals in the hall. They come equipped with a loop through which the student can put his arm and quickly wrap the blanket around him.

Another type of safety against fires is that involved in the control of laboratory fires. While ordinary laboratories are not commonly provided with overhead sprinkler or carbon dioxide extinguishing systems, every laboratory should be protected by one or more fire extinguishers of the type approved by the Underwriters Laboratory for the hazards involved. In general these will be of the Class A and B type. These should be placed where they can be quickly reached.

Finally, not too far from every laboratory there should be an adequately stocked Red Cross Cabinet located in a conspicuous position.

While a safety code does not come under the head of planning the laboratory building, every science department should have one. Workers in industrial laboratories and plants are "safety-conscious." College and university faculty and students often fail to be. This should be an important part of the training of the scientist, but it is not given the attention it should. A well-planned building will have the best in safety planning and in the application of safety principles in its operation.

Auxiliary Rooms. Since the standard laboratory may be used for quantitative studies in the various fields of chemistry, an adjoining balance room will be desired. A room of 100 square feet will provide room for 8 to 10 conventional balances, which will be adequate for 24 students. If Mettler-type balances are used, the space is more than adequate. Where the balance room is located between two first year chemistry laboratories, it may be desirable to double the area (20 x 10 ft) and make its 16 to 20 balances available to the students in both laboratories.

A second auxiliary room which may be located adjacent to the laboratory is a stock and dispensing room. Since this is largely used to provide the current needs of the students in the adjoining laboratory or laboratories, a room of 400 sq. ft. (20 x 20 ft) may suffice.

Arrangement of the Standard Laboratories. The facilities considered essential in the standard laboratory have been listed in the preceding pages of this section. The rest of the section is devoted to putting the facilities together in an effective manner. This is a good place to emphasize the importance of careful planning and a meeting of minds among planner, architect and laboratory furniture engineer in arranging the various required components of a standard laboratory. In one recent science building the laboratories were designed as island laboratories. A space of 3 feet was left between bench end and outer wall to provide a safety aisle along the outside wall in the case of fire. In the detailed further planning of the laboratory, this safety aisle seemed to some member of the planning team like an ideal place for additional shelving, storage cabinets and even for hinged shelves on the end of the benches for extra bench top space. Thus the original purpose of the island desks was lost.

The general plan is based upon the assumption that the laboratory can be approximately 1200 sq. ft. in area and from 38 to 40 ft long by 32 to 30 ft wide. If possible the laboratories should be located where they will not receive the full force of the afternoon sun; otherwise the windows should be adequately louvered. The inner wall will open into the hall, the outer may be the outer wall of the building.

The wall between the hall and the laboratory may be a double wall to provide for the service pipes and ducts running from basement to roof. These chases will carry hood ducts and other ventilation, water pipes and drains, gas, air and steam pipes and electrical conduits. Where laboratories are also located on the opposite side of the hall, the services can be carried across the hall, concealed above the suspended hall ceiling, which also provides acoustical treatment and flush lighting in the hall.

As a suggestion for one plan, the laboratory may have the three double benches at right angles to the outer wall. If peninsular benches are used, the windows can be located at the end of the aisles, with the benches between the windows. The hoods may be centered on the inside service-bearing wall. On each end of the hoods there can be a dispensing table. Outside the dispensing tables are the hall doors, which can be either double doors, each being 2 feet wide, or single 3-foot doors. Safety showers are located in the exit areas.

As has been shown in earlier chapters, laboratory benches may have either an island or a peninsular arrangement. In the first case they are set out from the wall 2 feet (or more if required) to provide a safety aisle along the outside wall; in the second they run flush to the outside wall. If the type of bench described earlier is used as a peninsular bench (this with its sinks is at least 22 feet long), the 30-foot (short) dimension of the room will have 8 feet or more left for hoods and the aisle between desks and hoods. Of this, the hoods will use 31 inches, leaving a space of at least 5 feet 11 inches for the aisle. If the island arrangement is used, the room should be widened by 2 feet if the same total bench area is desired. This can be done without adding greatly to the size of the room by making the module 9½ instead of 10 ft; the room now is 38 x 32 ft or 1216 square feet.

One arrangement of the standard laboratory for use as an organic chemistry laboratory might be as follows: three peninsular benches, accommodating 8 students each with 5 linear feet of desk space per student. Cabinets would be planned for three sections; in this way the room would provide for 72 students. Services would be provided by a combination of sink and turret centered on the desk, by locating these in a box curb in the center of the desk, or by the conventional trough and pipe rack; these include water, gas, possibly air, steam, 110V, and vacuum either from aspirators or a vacuum line (see Figure 12.7). Each student would have a steam cone. One side wall might be utilized for a 16-foot distillation bench; the other would provide the location of a wash-up sink, a small glass-blowing table and a table for ovens, cork corers and other common equipment. Chalk boards could be placed on the side walls, hoods or reagent shelv-

Figure 12.7   Chalkboard and hood, College of Wooster.

ing. A dispensing room and balance room-organic instrument room combination might well separate this laboratory and the laboratory for analytical chemistry. The latter might differ from the organic laboratory by replacing the distillation bench with a titration table, a table for pH meters and other instrumentation of use in the course in quantitative analysis.

As laboratories are often used for recitation or discussion purposes, care should be taken to make sure that the chalk boards are visible from all parts of it. One common mistake is to have the chalk board on a side wall where it is hidden from general view by high pipe racks (sometimes these may have two or even three shelves). This can be avoided by the use of service turrets and low box curbs and sink combinations, or by providing sash grooves on the wall so the board may be raised. An alternate method is to place the

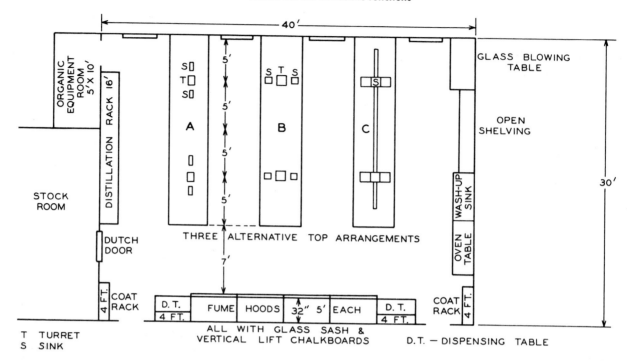

Figure 12.8   Suggested standard laboratory for organic chemistry.

chalk board in a separate sash groove on the hood or on the reagent shelf (Figure 11.15); in the first case (Figure 12.8) the glass sash of the hood will have its own groove. When the hood is in use, the chalk board will be run up out of the way. If four 5-foot hoods are used, all can be equipped with chalk boards if desired. In this arrangement, the instructor will speak from the area in front of the hoods. If desired, the benches can be equipped with pull-out seats and writing board approximately arranged as is shown in Figure 11.17.

LABORATORIES FOR PHYSICAL CHEMISTRY AND INSTRUMENTAL ANALYSIS

Laboratory work in physical chemistry can be carried on in a standard laboratory to which has been added a source of variable a.c.-d.c. While this makes for flexibility, the cabinet work of the standard benches is expensive and unnecessary. A simpler, equally effective arrangement is to provide a service rack (bench height and 18 inches wide) on the outside wall, the services coming out flush on the bench top. To this, tables can be pushed at appropriate intervals to take any required instruments. These can be stored on the other side wall in cabinets or in an assembly of parcel lockers such as are found in railroad stations. The service rack should be equipped with cup sinks and gooseneck taps fitted with hose connections. An alternate arrangement provides one or two regular wall benches such as are used in the standard laboratory. This makes available at least one good-sized sink. Combined with this might be appropriately arranged service islands, around which could be grouped heavy 30-inch or 36-inch free-standing tables. The tables should be solidly built to avoid vibration. Four 3 x 6 ft tables can be clustered around the services on one such island to provide ample room for 4 students. A demonstration table seems an unnecessary expense; equipment arrangements can be demonstrated on one of the 3 x 6 ft tables.

While the ordinary experiments in physical chemistry will not require the use of a hood, one 4-foot hood unit should be installed for special work.

Instrumental analysis will require about the same arrangement as physical chemistry, except that many instruments are now being supplied with their own bases; hence free floor space is indicated. Some instruments will be small and may be stored when not in use; others will need to be set up permanently. Adjoining the instrumental analysis laboratory there will be need for an optical darkroom and a small photographic darkroom. These rooms and the instrument laboratory should be provided with a controlled atmosphere.

The dimensions of the laboratories making up this group will depend in part on the size of the class and on the number of available instruments; in the average small college they might well be 30 x 30 ft each for the physical chemistry and instrumental analysis, 10 x 20 ft for the optical darkroom, and 10 x 10 ft for the photographic darkroom. The optical darkroom

should be provided with black walls, furnished with appropriate tables for instruments and serviced for gas, 110 V and with one gooseneck water outlet and a "Duriron" cup sink. The photographic darkroom is intended as a supplement to the optical darkroom not as a teaching laboratory for photography. Its principal equipment includes facilities for developing and printing and for the storage of photographic supplies.

Staff Research Laboratories

Many teachers prefer individual research laboratories. These may be from 150 to 300 square feet in area; the latter will be large enough for one or two students in addition to the teachers. Others prefer to share a laboratory with colleagues of like interest. Double the above laboratory for a two-man faculty laboratory. Still others want their office and laboratory to be combined in one room. Thus there is no fixed pattern for the faculty research laboratory. It should be equipped for almost any type of chemical research, with ample hood and bench space per man and with more service outlets

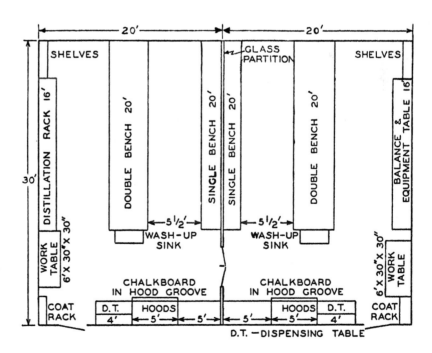

Figure 12.9 Division of a student laboratory into two student research laboratories.

than are used in the standard laboratory. Six feet of hood and 10 to 15 feet of bench provided with all the services used in the building ordinarily will suffice. A 3-foot writing unit in addition to the laboratory bench is useful unless the faculty office is in the same room.

Student Research Laboratories

Again there is no fixed pattern for an undergraduate research laboratory. The standard laboratory shown in Figure 12.7 will be generally satisfactory. This will handle up to 12 students when 2 students work on one side of the bench; if necessary, such a student research laboratory can be easily converted back into a class laboratory. Many teachers directing undergraduate research prefer no more than 6 students in a single research laboratory. Where this is the case, the standard laboratory of four modules can be easily changed into two two-module research laboratories by setting up a glass wall down the middle of the central bench, using the 4-sink bench at this location. If four hoods will have been installed in this laboratory, the two in the center can be separated by a few inches, making it possible to carry the glass wall between these hoods. A swinging door in the wall will

facilitate passage between the two laboratories (Figure 12.9).

A combination of two student laboratories, separated by a stockroom-balance room, is shown in Figure 12.10. While one laboratory has been set up for organic chemistry and the other for analytical, they can be easily modified for use in the first-year course. For purposes of illustration, one laboratory has been provided with island benches and the other with peninsular benches. Again, the organic laboratory departs from the standard laboratory by providing 6 linear feet of bench space per student, with working space for 21 students in a section. The analytical laboratory follows the suggested arrangement of a standard laboratory. Adjacent to the organic laboratory is one type of a faculty office-laboratory. Other arrangements are possible.

Science Library

In these times when undergraduate and faculty research programs are being developed in the college, a science reference library will be a welcome addition to the building. Unfortunately, one of the most controversial subjects in the planning of a modern science building is that of

Figure 12.10   Suggested combination of laboratories and auxiliary rooms.

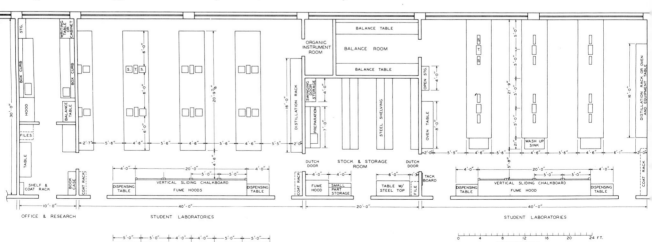

the science library. The desire of the scientists to have quickly available certain reference works to which they go frequently during the laboratory work in the advanced courses and in their research sometimes runs counter to the desire of the college librarian to keep under one roof all the books of the college. (See Figure 12.11).

This conflict has been aggravated by the action of some science teachers, who have insisted that the entire science library of the college (or any of its various components) be maintained in the science (chemistry, physics, biology) building. It has not been helped by those librarians who suggest that the presence of the science books in the college library provides the science students with at least a brief contact with the humanities. Part of the trouble is due to poor communication on the part of the scientists, part to a failure to cooperate with the librarian in his understandable desire to build up a strong science library in the main library. Possibly some science teachers fail to appreciate the importance of science as a liberalizing discipline, and because of this pay little attention to ordering such books and publications for the science section in the college library as give testimony to it. Likewise, the scientists who are in a sense science library "empire builders" might well review the purpose of their science libraries and check to see how well these have been carried out.

In the field of chemistry the material of prime importance to have in the science library includes first of all a group of reference works of the type of Beilstein's "Organischen Chemie," Mellor's "Comprehensive Treatise on Inorganic and Theoretical Chemistry," Heilbron's "Dictionary of Organic Compounds," "The International Critical Tables," together with recent monographs on special subjects. Then there are the abstract journals, particularly *Chemical Abstracts*. Finally, there should be the current numbers and bound volumes of the scientific publications of the professional societies represented in the building; for the chemists, these should include the various journals of the American Chemical Society, the *Journal of Chemical Physics* and the *Journal of Biological Chemistry*. Some colleges will have one or more foreign journals such as *Chemische Berichte, Annalen, Comptes Rendus, Jour-*

Figure 12.11   Science library, Swarthmore College.

nal of the London Chemical Society, and a few will have *Izvestiya.* In addition, both the main library and the science library might well carry a set of the *Journal of Chemical Education,* together with copies of books dealing with new approaches to the teaching of chemistry. It is not suggested that these are the only volumes of chemical material to go in the science library, but they are representative of the types which are most useful.

If books in the science disciplines are to be in the science building, they should be in one place; their dispersal by disciplines within the building is indefensible. The latter is particularly true when they are divided not only by discipline but by professor. A science library in one place is subject to supervision. Frequently there are students majoring in science who are interested in becoming science librarians. One of these might well be added to the staff of the librarian, be given some training in library science, and be made the science librarian. Still another way to provide supervision is to place the departmental secretary's office adjacent to the library with a glass wall and check-out counter separating the two.

The first step in planning for the science library would be for the science faculty to prepare a realistic estimate of the literature they feel should be included in the library. This should then be cleared with the librarian. Such an estimate will give the planning committee an idea of the shelf space necessary, figuring an average of four volumes of bound periodicals and eight volumes of books per linear foot of shelf space. A 3-foot shelf section with 6 shelves provides 18 linear feet, with 7 shelves, 21 linear feet. Dividing either of these into the total number of feet required for the entire library will give the current space needs.

In addition to the shelving, there will need to be cases for current periodicals, reading tables and several carrels. The number of tables will depend on the size of the institution and its activity in science and the nature of the books in its science library. In the event that microfilms make up a rather significant fraction of the library, special facilities for storage and reading should be considered. Miroflim should not be stored in a hot and dry location; under these conditions it may become embrittled. Microcards can be maintained in card files (but should not be packed in tightly). The new microcard readers may be used in an ordinary room. Books, microfilm and microcards alike will benefit from being maintained at a controlled humidity of about 50%, and in an atmosphere from which acid gases have been removed. If the library rooms are air-conditioned these requirements will be met.

From the information gathered together in the check list under the heading of science library, it will be possible for the architect and planning committee to lay out an adequate library for the present. How much extra space will be needed for natural growth, say for twenty years, is problematical. If the shelves are rigorously combed from time to time to eliminate books which no longer meet the objectives of the library, the rate of expansion may be kept down.

If the shelf space were to be so planned that the books currently available at the building dedication would fit on the 2nd, 3rd, 4th and 5th shelves of a six shelf section, 33% of the shelf space would be available for expansion. Fifty per cent would be about right for book expansion; for periodical expansion, 100% would be more likely. In the event that the sections are planned for 7 shelves, the 1st and the 7th might be left empty. Steel shelving is preferred for the stacks; it takes up less space and is readily adapted to the height of the volumes.

Stock and Dispensing Rooms

The average college science building will require a common receiving room opening on an unloading platform having access to a public highway. Such a room will be used to unpack shipments received and to pack up any outgoing shipments. In place of a separate room, space can be reserved for the purpose in a central stockroom, but this is not advisable.

The adjoining central stockroom should be large enough to store several years' inventory of chemicals, specimens and equipment. In addition, hazardous chemicals should be stored in a special well-ventilated room situated and opening outside the building. Alcohol must be kept in a locked vault which meets the requirements of the Internal Revenue Department. The central stockroom will also be the storage place for rarely used equipment; dead storage should be junked when the new building is occupied.

The central store room should be ventilated and kept dry. Dampness will encourage corrosion of equipment, spoilage of chemicals and loss of labels from containers.

An elevator running from the central stockroom to all the floors and to the attic is desirable. This item should be one of the first put in the plans and the last taken out in case costs are too high. Unfortunately the reverse is often the case. The elevator serves for both freight and passengers, but the latter use should be restricted to those among faculty or students who are unable to use the stairs.

The dispensing rooms on the various floors serve to maintain supplies which are to be used within a given time, say a semester. They are also for the storage of constantly used equipment not available in sufficient amount to issue to all students or for occasionally used equipment which is too large to store in the laboratory bench. They are the source of replacements for breakage. As dispensing rooms, they are used to make up solutions for student use in the laboratory and for the preparation of student unknowns. And finally at the end of the term they are the receiving stations for the checking in of student equipment. In one plan, dispensing rooms are located between student laboratories. One modification of the above plan for a central stockroom and a number of dispensing rooms is to have a central stockroom in the basement connected by elevator with small centrally located stock and dispensing rooms immediately above each other. A third modification is that in operation in chemistry at Grinnell College (see Figure 12.12). Here the stock and dispensing room for chemistry is surrounded on three sides by student laboratories so that a single stockroom man can serve all laboratory classes from his central location. Immediately below is the physics stockroom and below that the central stock and receiving room. An elevator services all three rooms. An arrangement of this kind is efficient and handy.

SPECIAL FACILITIES

Shops

The college science building should be provided with shop facilities for the construction and repair of experimental equipment of one kind or another. This will run all the way from a room provided with a bench and conventional hand tools for use by the professor and students to a group of specialized shops equipped with machine tools and an expert operator.

The space and services required will differ with the institution. The shop will preferably be located in the basement where noise and vibration may be kept down. This holds particularly for a carpenter shop. The space provided will run up from 100 to 200 square feet to whatever size is needed to handle the equipment. It should be dry, well ventilated and adequately lighted.

Some prefer to have a small electronics shop

in close proximity to the instrumental laboratories. Likewise, the organic chemists favor locating a glass-blowing shop near the organic laboratories. If this is done, attention might well be paid either to sound proofing the facility or to the purchase of quiet blast lamps.

Greenhouse

Virtually all college science buildings of recent construction have included one or more greenhouses in the space assigned the biology departments. The size and arrangements of these facilities have depended on the interests of the botany teachers. These will run from greenhouses of 400 square feet with work rooms inside the building to greenhouses and work rooms together of 1200 to 1500 square feet or more.

The planning committee will probably seek the assistance of manufacturers of these facilities before developing any specific ideas of their needs. The architect may be tempted to make the greenhouse a special feature of the building, locating it in front where it will be always in view. Unless the college is prepared to keep it in shape for this purpose, the architect should be restrained.

The greenhouse should be located in relation to the general building plan where it will get the best light. Many biology departments prefer putting it (and the department) at ground level with the greenhouse jutting out from the building, preferably on the south side. If the department is above ground level, stairs (or the elevator) leading between the two should be planned. Several buildings have the greenhouse and biology department on the second floor. At Hamline, where this is the case, the greenhouse is on top of the auditorium. Others have located the greenhouse on top of the science building handy to the elevator.

Animal Rooms

Another facility desired by most biology departments is a room or rooms for the housing of experimental animals. Here again the type and nature of these rooms will depend on the experimental program being carried on. The earlier discussion of this topic (p. 230–9) refers to the design and maintenance of animal quarters used

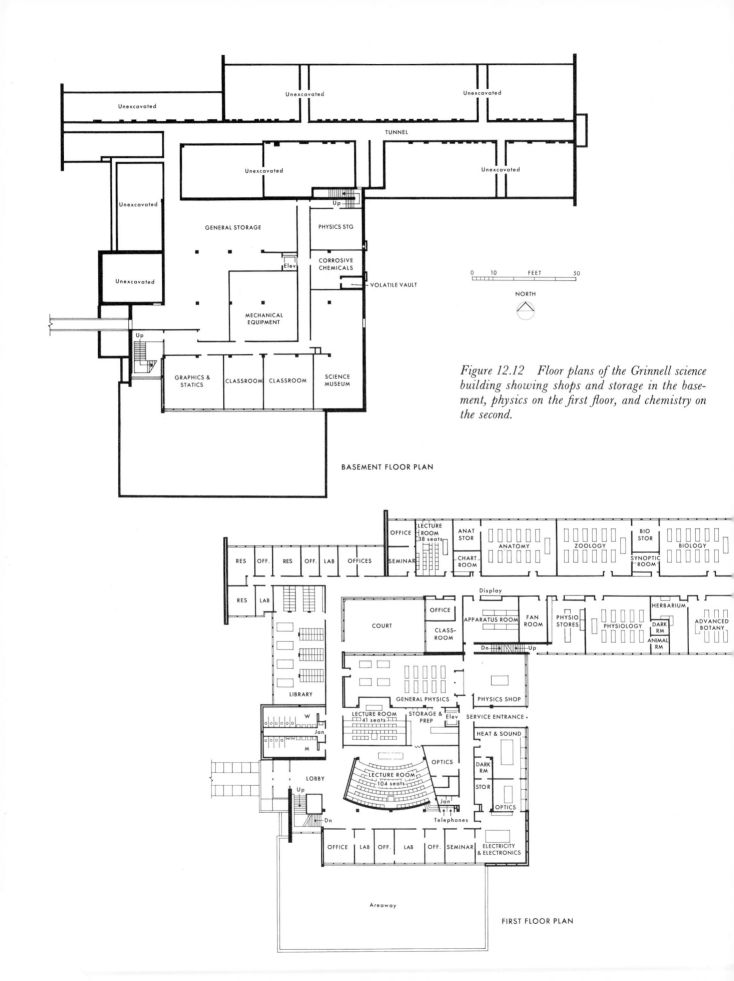

BASEMENT FLOOR PLAN

Figure 12.12   Floor plans of the Grinnell science building showing shops and storage in the basement, physics on the first floor, and chemistry on the second.

FIRST FLOOR PLAN

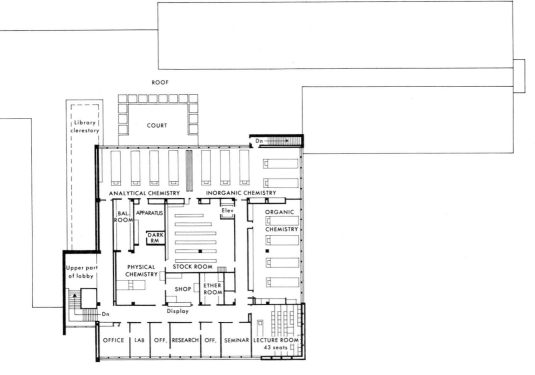

SECOND FLOOR PLAN

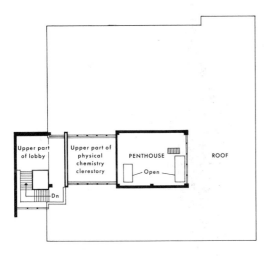

PENTHOUSE AND ROOF PLAN

in a sophisticated program. The information will be helpful in planning on a much simpler scale.

In general, animal rooms should be located in the college science building where there will be a minimum of noise and confusion. They should be designed with adequate ventilation to keep animal odors out of the halls and other rooms in the building. This should be done in such a way as to keep the animals out of drafts. Animal rooms and equipment should be built so as to be easily cleaned and sterilized. The representative of the planning committee most closely related to the use of the animal rooms may wish to visit satisfactory installations if he is inexperienced in their design.

Museum and Exhibit Cases

Since the science teachers of an earlier day were naturalists interested in the systematic study of all natural objects whether of animal, vegetable or mineral origin, it is not surprising that they were great collectors of such objects. These collections formed the basis for the college museums found in the older science buildings. This situation no longer exists. Science teachers tend to specialize to a greater degree and teach subjects which fall within the scope of their specialization. Only a few might be termed naturalists, and the collections which were common in the earlier days of college science teaching now are gathered together in the public and private institutions found in the large cities or special centers. As a result, the new science buildings either have no museum space at all, or have smaller rooms designed to illustrate the natural history of the region or some feature of local interest.

More common is the inclusion of exhibit cases in the walls of the new buildings. These make possible timely exhibits in the different science areas and thus give a broadening experience to students who use the building. Such exhibits are worthwhile when they are planned, well labelled, and changed at frequent intervals. "Live" exhibits interest people; "dead" ones are worse than none at all. If a museum is included in the planning, responsibility for the maintenance of the exhibits should be assigned to specific members of the various departments. If no one in the department or science division has the qualities and characteristics of a museum curator, it would be far better to omit museum or exhibit facilities in the halls. One exception is a well-lighted case

Figure 12.13   Lobby of Harold R. Stark Hall, Wilkes College science building.

in the hall outside of the science library where new books from either main library or science library may be shown.

Lobby

Frequently the projected science building is to be the gift of a foundation, or a science-minded alumnus, or is given as a memorial. Where this is the case, appropriate reference should be made to this in a place designed for the purpose, generally in the lobby or in an alcove off the lobby. Consideration should be given to designing an attractive lobby and location for the memorial tablet. Since the lobby in essence is the main entrance and front door combined, it sets the stage for the first impression of those entering the building, hence the need for careful and imaginative planning. A good illustration is the lobby in the Harold R. Stark Science Building at Wilkes College (Figure 12.13).

Somewhere in the vicinity of the front entrance an attractive directory should be placed, listing the names and room numbers of all the members of the faculty located in the building. Since the names will change to some degree annually, the unit should be planned with this in mind.

BIBLIOGRAPHY

1. Planners of physics laboratories are urged to consult Palmer, R. Ronald and Rice, W. M., "Modern Physics Buildings," New York, Reinhold Publishing Corporation, 1961.
2. For a review of new undergraduate chemistry curricula, see Willeford, B. R., Jr. and Clapp, L. B., "The Undergraduate Training of Chemistry Majors, A Report of the Bucknell Conference," J. Chem. Ed., 38, 251 (1961) and
Garrett, A. B., Cook, W. B. and Lippincott, W. T., "The College Chemistry Course for Non-Science Majors, A Report of the Montana State Conference," J. Chem. Ed., 38, 253 (1961).
3. The extent to which research is carried on in the small Liberal Arts College will be found in Lewis, H. F. and Reinheimer, J. D., "Research and Teaching in the Liberal Arts College, A Report of the Wooster Conference," Appleton, Wis., The Institute of Paper Chemistry, 1959.

RECENT COLLEGE SCIENCE BUILDINGS

Illustrated on the following four pages are twelve typical examples of recent college science buildings.

RECENT
COLLEGE
SCIENCE
BUILDINGS

Little Rock University
Little Rock, Arkansas
GINOCCHIO, CROMWELL, CARTER, DEES & NEYLAN

Wake Forest College
Winston Salem, North Carolina
LARSON AND LARSON

Wilkes College
Wilkes-Barre, Pennsylvania
LACY, ATHERTON & DAVIS

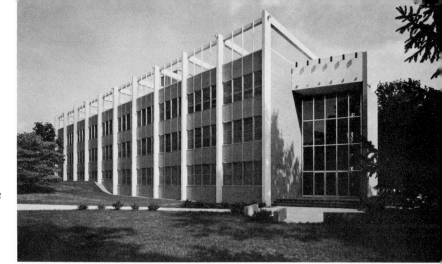

Lenoir Rhyne College
Hickory, North Carolina
CLEMMER & HORTON

Hamline University
St. Paul, Minnesota
HOLABIRD, ROOT, BURGEE AND ASSOCIATES

Manchester College
North Manchester, Indiana
MCQUIRE & SHOOK, COMPTON, RICHEY

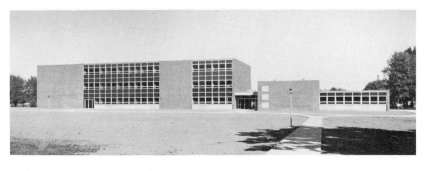

Florida Southern College
Lakeland, Florida
FRANK LLOYD WRIGHT

Pomona College
Claremont, California
SMITH, POWELL & MORGRIDGE

RECENT
COLLEGE
SCIENCE
BUILDINGS

Worcester Polytechnic Institute
Worcester, Massachusetts
ROGERS AND BUTLER

Indiana State Teachers College
Terre Haute, Indiana
MILLER, VRYDAGH & MILLER

Luther College
Decorah, Iowa
ATTFILLISCH & ASSOCIATES

Lake Forest College
Lake Forest, Illinois
PERKINS AND WILL

CHAPTER XIII

Planning the Chemical Engineering Building

JOSEPH H. KOFFOLT
and
ALDRICH SYVERSON

The Ohio State University
Columbus, Ohio

This chapter provides an excellent illustration of pro-grammed planning. Those involved included members of the administration of Ohio State University, staff members of the Department of Chemical Engineering, as well as members of Chemical Engineering Departments in other universities. Industries contributed with information and advice, and by permitting inspection of their facilities. Others who contributed time and experience included those from the office of the University Architect and alumni of the Chemical Engineering Department who worked hard on fund raising campaigns for equipment of the new building. Finally there were those who cooperated with the preparation of publicity of one type or another. Altogther some sixty individuals may be said to have participated in the planning of the Ohio State University Chemical Engineering Building. The principal author has said that the building represented 100% team work, with everyone carrying out his task to perfection. Space will not permit acknowledgements to all who worked on the team. This is the way to plan and build science buildings. If more institutions did the same, there would be fewer "monuments" built on the campuses of our colleges and universities.

THE EDITOR

This chapter gives the details relating to the new $2,400,000 Chemical Engineering Building at The Ohio State University. It now houses all chemical and petroleum engineering and some of metallurgical engineering. The second phase, which will cost another $2,000,000, will complete the facilities for all the branches of the chemical phase of engineering, including metallurgical and mining engineering, ceramic engineering and minerology. It is integrated in both the Engineering and Chemical Center of the University. In the next few years $7,700,000 is contemplated for the college's ten-year building program which began in 1954 and which eventually will include all other departments of the college either by new buildings or remodeling of present buildings.

PRELIMINARY PLANNING

The department of chemical engineering was assigned to "temporary" space in the new Mc-Pherson Chemical Laboratory in 1925 with the hope that in the very near future it would have a building of its own. Late in 1955 it finally appeared that the new building would be a reality. It was thought best to obtain first-hand information and visit as many university and industrial laboratories as possible. At least twenty industrial laboratories and about the same number of recent chemical engineering university buildings were visited and studied. Everyone was cooperative in giving information, furnishing blueprints and complete descriptions of their laboratories. In addition to this, the book "Laboratory Design" * gave much useful information. With this background of information the actual planning of the building was started.

ACTUAL PLANNING OF THE BUILDING

In anticipation that the new building would at last be a reality, the actual planning of the building was begun November 18, 1955. This was done as a joint and cooperative effort of the staff of the department. Each staff member was given a specific assignment and the responsibility of a specific phase of the building. Their ideas were integrated at meetings held nightly, each lasting four or five hours, covering a period of at least one month. An appraisal was made of the good and poor features of the present space as well as a critical analysis of the ideas gathered from visits, correspondence, and blueprints of other chemical engineering industrial and university laboratories. A list was made of the number and types of laboratories and offices needed, which totaled 88. Some of the special laboratories were: Precision Standards, Thermodynamics or Physical Measurements, Optical, Kinetics, Mass Transfer, Nuclear, Design, Unit Operations, etc. Detailed specifications, including sketches of the laboratory furniture, utilities, space, safety provisions were written for each laboratory. The total space, exclusive of hallways, storage and utility service space, totaled 82,000 square feet.

Early in 1956 the architectural firm of Small, Smith, Reeb, and Draz of Cleveland was commissioned to make the final plans, the detailed specifications, and the finished blueprints of the building. Eighty-six thousand dollars was allocated for this purpose. It soon appeared that the $2,400,000 which was allocated would not be

* Reinhold Publishing Corp., New York, 1951.

adequate for the 88 laboratories and offices. It was therefore necessary to revise the original plan. The next step was to integrate the work of the staff to give the architect information for preliminary planning and layout work. This resulted in a 132-page report which provided a basis for all future planning and decisions.

The first preliminary plans for the building were submitted by the architects November, 1956. These did not meet the specifications and layout desired. Many other meetings were held subsequently in which the preliminary layouts were revised. Finally, in June, 1957, the overall building plans were crystallized. During this period also final details, such as power and utility requirements, floor loads, telephones, safety features, air-conditioning, location of equipment in the Unit Operations Laboratory and the type and over-all dimensions of built-in laboratory furnishings such as tables, racks and hoods were specified quantitatively.

The first detailed semi-official blueprints of the building were received July, 1957. Once again these were checked and rechecked by members of the staff. Their comments were integrated in detailed reports. The final revised plans together with 200 pages of detailed specifications were approved by the Board of Trustees of the University in early September, 1957. Bids were then requested for the building proper. The firm of Baker and Combs Company, Morgantown, West Virginia, was awarded the general contract. Demolition of the temporary laboratories on the proposed site began December 1, 1957. Ground was broken January 16, 1958. The target date for the completion of the building was February 1, 1959, but due to strikes and other factors the building itself was not completed until June 1, 1959.

With the building under way September, 1957, detailed work was started again on the built-in equipment. A laboratory equipment company was contacted concerning the detailed specifications of built-in laboratory furniture.

Once again each staff member was given the responsibility for certain laboratories. This took one entire week. It resulted in 43 pages of specifications of single-spaced typing. The original estimate was $390,000. It went out for bids in October, 1958. Ten companies submitted bids ranging from a little over $200,000 to a little less than $290,000. The Metalab Company, Hicksville, New York was awarded the contract on November, 28, 1958. Once again, there was a series of meetings with the staff and the Metalab Company on the details of the blueprints submitted by them. This also resulted in voluminous reports concerning these details. The target date was August, 1959, but due to many delays caused by strikes and other factors, all the laboratory equipment was not completed till April, 1960. However, some of the laboratories were finished in late 1959. The Board of Trustees accepted the building for the University on May 5, 1960.

A complete and detailed photographic history of the building was made. This included the temporary buildings on the site, demolition of these buildings, the excavation, pouring of the concrete floor by floor, the steel structure for the Unit Operations Laboratory, the many miles of piping before it was covered with "Transite" or acoustic ceiling, and every finished laboratory.

GENERAL DESIGN OF THE BUILDING

The general design of the building is illustrated in Figure 13.2. It is L-shaped. Figure 13.1

Figure 13.1 Architect's rendering of the chemical engineering and mineral industries building, Ohio State University.

illustrates the architect's concept of the completed building which will be E-shaped. The back-up consists of concrete block of the lightweight type, which is not cinder block. The columns are on 20-ft centers and are poured concrete with reinforcing steel. This is also true of the floors. The Unit Operations Laboratory is of structural steel, the floors of which are of three types: reinforced steel and concrete, steel plate, and steel grating. The hallway walls are of glazed tile with matching vinyl tile flooring. The flooring in most of the laboratories is asphalt tile. The spandrel panels are Virginia Greenstone. The limestone block is variegated, hard select buff of the Indiana type.

The floor plans of the six floors of the building, which include the basement and penthouse, are illustrated in Figures 13.3 through 13.8. Table 13.1 gives a summary of space allocation for each floor. Table 13.2 is a summary of the space for laboratories offices, class-rooms and storage space.

SPECIAL FUNCTIONAL AREAS
Nuclear Engineering Laboratories (Rooms 29, 33, and 35)

(Figures 13.9, 13.10, and 13.11.) Nuclear laboratories are installed in the basement of the new Chemical Engineering Building so that chemical engineering students will be provided with modern facilities to carry out class laboratory experiments and research work using radioactive isotopes and radiation.

The laboratory consists of four rooms with connecting doors. The dressing room contains a shower and monitoring facilities; from this a low-level radiochemistry laboratory is accessible. Here work is done on chemical engineering problems, using tracers at the microcurie level. Conventional isotope laboratory benches and hoods of the bench type and walk-in style are available. The high-level laboratory is adjacent to the low-level laboratory and contains the same facilities. Work involving higher-level activity experiments in the multicurie range is confined to this laboratory. A counting room separately connected to the entrance and dressing room is available for precise counting work.

The walls of the entire laboratory are con-

Figure 13.2   The chemical engineering building, Ohio State University.

crete block covered with special "Amercoat" paints to provide an impervious undercoating and a peelable outer layer. The floors are covered with asphalt tile, since a continuous linoleum covering could not be laid at the basement level. Room ventilation is designed to produce the highest negative suction pressure in the high-level laboratory so that the net air movement is in the direction of highest activity.

These facilities are available for some of the laboratory requirements for the course Ch.E. 766, the second of a two-course sequence in Nuclear Chemical Engineering. The purpose of the laboratory portion of Ch.E. 766 is to survey a few of the more important phases of instrumentation methodology, and equipment design and operation which chemical engineers will encounter in the nuclear industry.

Floor plans of the chemical engineering building, Ohio State University.

Figure 13.3   Basement plan.

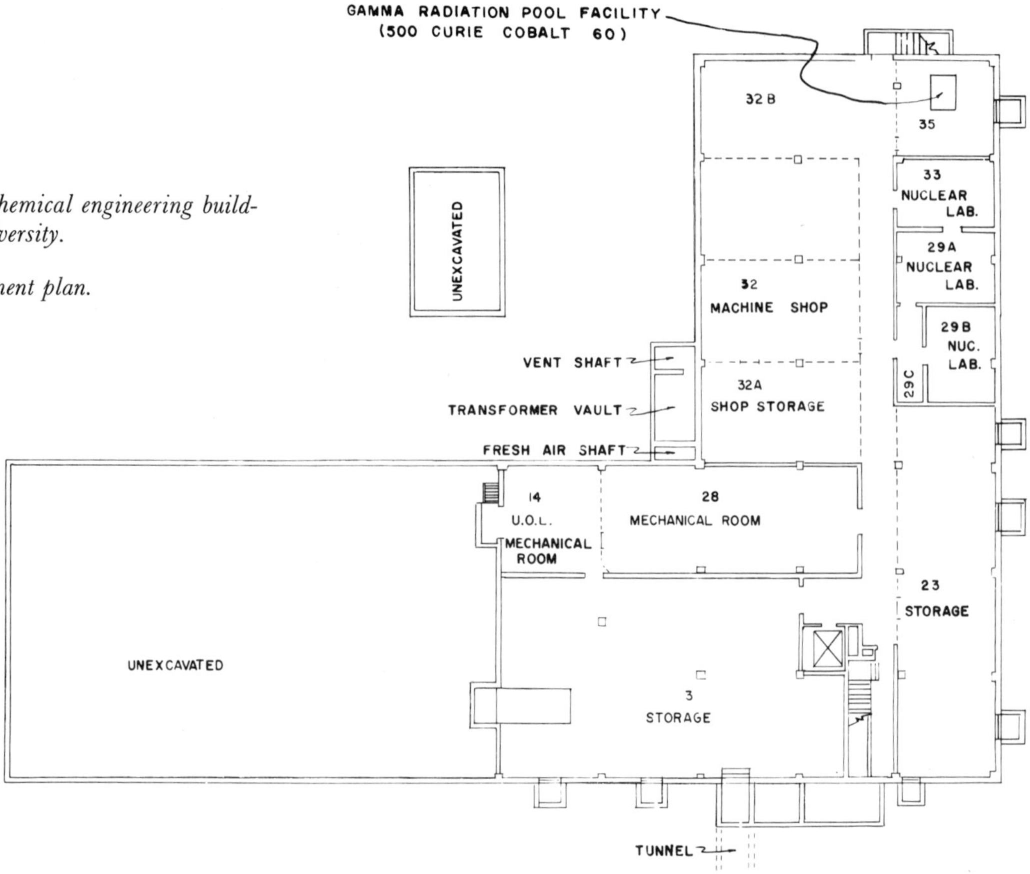

GAMMA RADIATION POOL FACILITY
(500 CURIE COBALT 60)

32 B

35

33
NUCLEAR
LAB.

29A
NUCLEAR
LAB.

29B
NUC.
LAB.

UNEXCAVATED

32
MACHINE SHOP

29C

VENT SHAFT

TRANSFORMER VAULT

FRESH AIR SHAFT

32A
SHOP STORAGE

14
U.O.L.
MECHANICAL
ROOM

28
MECHANICAL ROOM

23
STORAGE

UNEXCAVATED

3
STORAGE

TUNNEL

Figure 13.4   First floor plan.

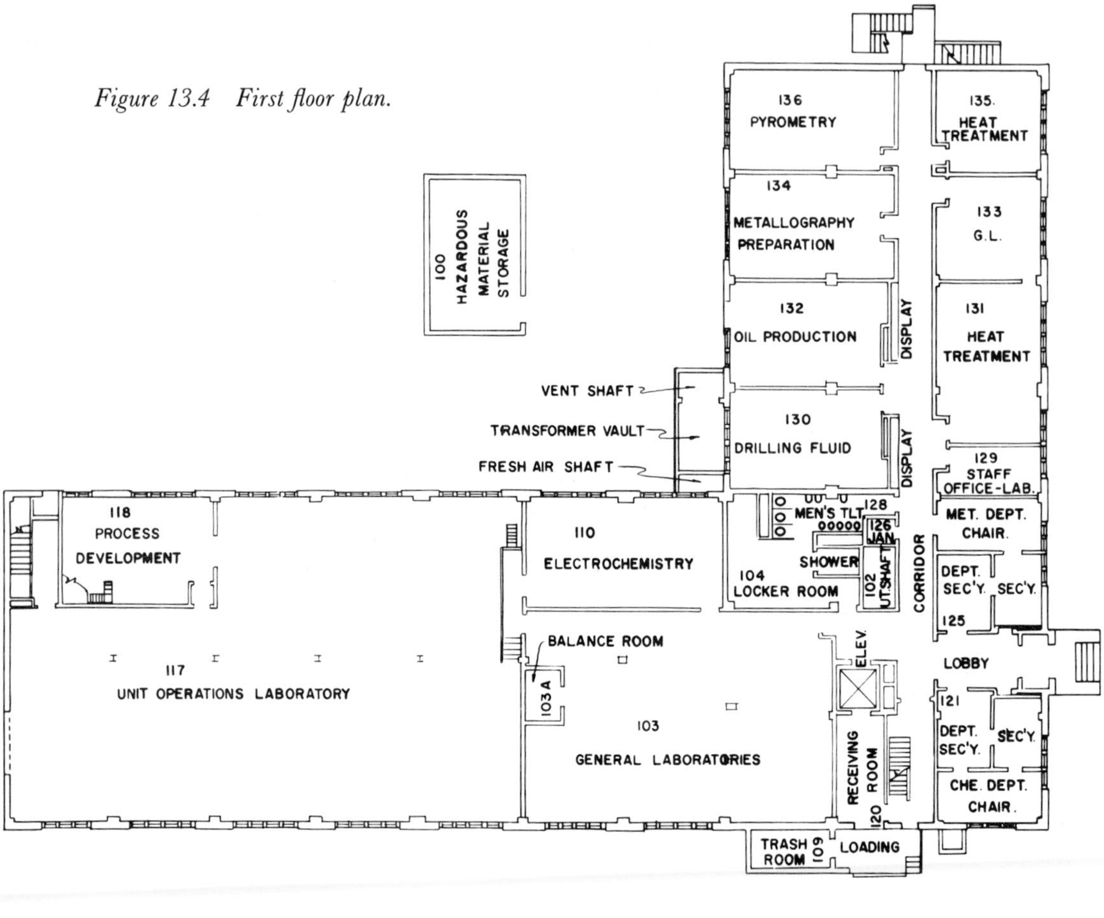

100
HAZARDOUS
MATERIAL
STORAGE

136
PYROMETRY

135.
HEAT
TREATMENT

134
METALLOGRAPHY
PREPARATION

133
G.L.

132
OIL PRODUCTION

131
HEAT
TREATMENT

DISPLAY

VENT SHAFT

TRANSFORMER VAULT

FRESH AIR SHAFT

130
DRILLING FLUID

DISPLAY

129
STAFF
OFFICE-LAB.

118
PROCESS
DEVELOPMENT

110
ELECTROCHEMISTRY

128
MEN'S TLT

126
JAN.

MET. DEPT.
CHAIR.

104
LOCKER ROOM

102
UT.SHAFT

SHOWER

CORRIDOR

DEPT.
SEC'Y. SEC'Y.

125

BALANCE ROOM

103A

ELEV

LOBBY

121

DEPT.
SEC'Y.

SEC'Y

117
UNIT OPERATIONS LABORATORY

103
GENERAL LABORATORIES

RECEIVING

120
ROOM

CHE. DEPT.
CHAIR.

TRASH
ROOM

109

LOADING

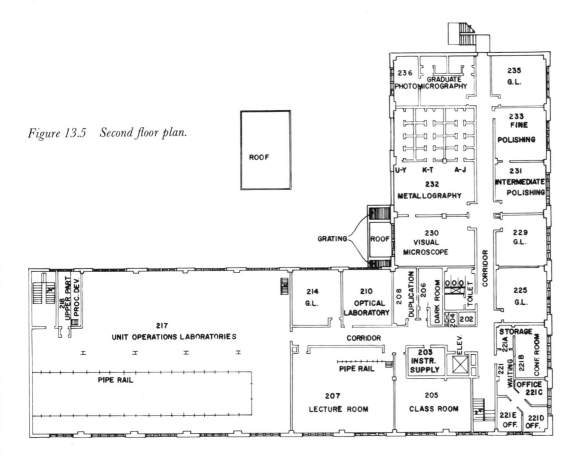

Figure 13.5   Second floor plan.

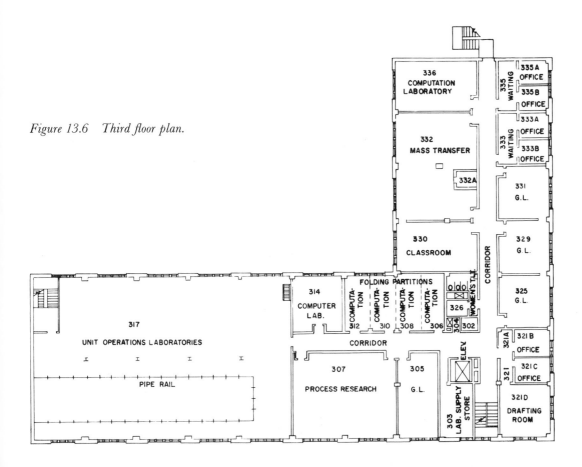

Figure 13.6   Third floor plan.

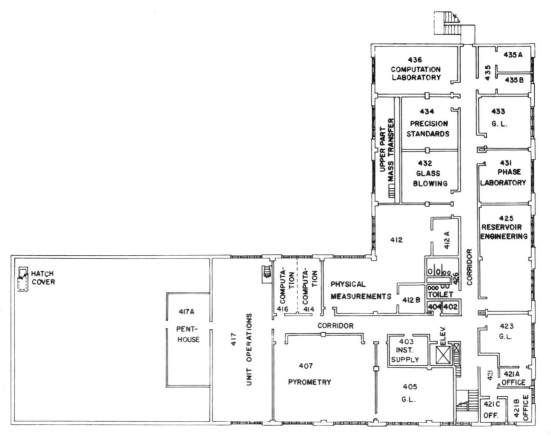

Figure 13.7   Fourth floor plan.

Figure 13.8   Penthouse and roof plan.

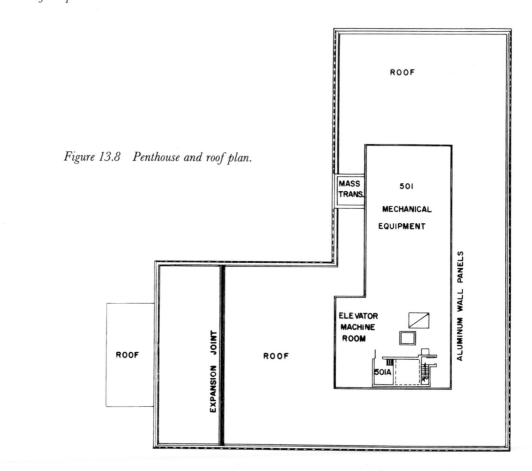

TABLE 13.1

CHEMICAL ENGINEERING BUILDING

Summary of Space Allocation by Floors

	ROOM NO.	NET SQ. FT.		ROOM NO.	NET SQ. FT.
A. BASEMENT			3. Graduate labs. (4)	325, 329, 331, 305	1,570
1. Mechanical service equipment rooms	14, 28	2,040	4. Group computation—conference labs. (4)	306, 308, 310, 312	880
2. Storage rooms and lab supply rooms	3, 23, 32B 29, 33, 35	4,780	5. Class computation lab.	336	600
3. Nuclear labs.	32	1,420	6. Computer lab.	314	410
4. Machine shop	32A	1,360	7. Classroom	330	590
5. Shop storage		700	8. Mass transfer	332	1,260
			9. Drafting and process design lab.	321D	420
Total basement		10,300	10. Offices and waiting rooms (6)	321B, 321C, 333A, 333B, 335A, 335B	1,300
Gross square feet		11,510			
			11. Laboratory supply storage	303	270
B. FIRST FLOOR					
			Total third floor		13,370
1. Unit operations	117	5,650	Gross square feet		16,375
2. Process development	118	635			
3. Electrochemistry	110	830	E. FOURTH FLOOR		
4. General laboratories	103	2,510			
5. Drilling fluid	130	610	1. Unit operations	417	1,360
6. Production lab.	132	640	2. Group computation— conference labs. (2)	414, 416	410
7. Graduate lab.	133	420	3. Class computation lab.	436	590
8. Chem. Engrg. Dept. Offices	121	500	4. Furnace, pyrometry room	407	1,240
9. Metallurgical Engrg. Dept. Offices	125, 129	725	5. Graduate labs. (3)	405, 423, 433	1,470
10. Pyrometry (Met. Eng.)	136	600	6. Thermodynamics and physical measurement labs.	412	1,480
11. Metallography (Met. Eng.)	134	605	7. Glass blowing lab.	432	420
12. Heat treatment (Met. Eng.)	131, 135	1,100	8. Precision standards lab.	434	420
13. Hazardous materials storage	100	490	9. Mass transfer lab.	403	400
14. Outside laboratory Cement floor platform		1,200	10. Phase lab.	431	420
			11. Petroleum reservoir Eng. Lab.	425	860
Total first floor net		16,515	12. Offices (5)	421A, 421B, 421C, 435A, 435B	840
Gross square feet		19,338			
			13. Instrument supply		150
C. SECOND FLOOR			14. Mechanical room	417A	595
1. Unit operations	217	4,600	Total fourth floor		10,655
2. Process development	218	200	Gross square feet		13,376
3. Lecture room	207	1,255			
4. Classroom	205	625	F. PENTHOUSE		
5. Instrument supply	203	180			
6. Graduate labs	214, 225, 229, 235	1,680	1. Mass transfer	532	100
			2. Mechanical service equipment room	501	4,350
7. Optical laboratory	210	420			
8. Duplicating room	208	205	Total penthouse—net and gross		4,450
9. Darkroom	206	220			
10. Conference room	221B	270			
11. Offices (3)	221A, 221C, 221D	500			
12. Visual microscope room (Met. Eng.)	230	590		NET SQ. FT.	GROSS SQ. FT.
13. Graduate photo-micrograph room (Met. Eng.)	236	620	G. SUMMARY		
14. Polishing rooms (2) (Met. Eng.)	231, 233	840	1. Basement	10,300	11,510
15. Metallography (Met. Eng.)	232	1,300	2. First floor	16,515	19,338
			3. Second floor	13,505	16,375
Total second floor		13,505	4. Third floor	13,370	16,375
Gross square feet		16,375	5. Fourth floor	10,655	13,376
			6. Penthouse	4,450	4,450
D. THIRD FLOOR					
1. Unit operations	317	4,800	Total	68,795	81,424
2. Process research and kinetics	307	1,270			

TABLE 13.2

CHEMICAL ENGINEERING BUILDING

Summary of Laboratory, Offices, Classrooms and Services

I. *Chemical Engineering Division*

		HEAD ROOM FEET	FLOOR SPACE SQ. FT.
A. LABORATORIES			
1.	Unit operations laboratories	40–52	16,410
2.	Mechanical service equipment room	12	430
3.	Process development laboratories	16–28	835
4.	Process research and kinetics	12	1,270
5.	Nuclear laboratories	12	1,420
6.	Electro-chemistry	12	830
7.	General laboratories	12	2,510
8.	Mass transfer	12–36	1,760
9.	Thermodynamics and physical measurements	12	1,480
10.	High temperature and pyrometry Lab.	12	1,240
11.	Optical laboratory	12	420
12.	Glass Blowing laboratory	12	420
13.	Precision standards	12	420
14.	Graduate laboratories (12)	12	5,140
15.	Computation laboratories (8)	12	2,480
16.	Phase laboratory	12	420
17.	Computer laboratory	12	410
18.	Petroleum production engineering— drilling fluids laboratory	12	610
19.	Petroleum production engineering— production laboratory	12	640
20.	Petroleum production engineering— reservoir engineering laboratory	12	860
21.	Process design drafting laboratory	12	420
	Total		40,895

B. OFFICES AND CLASSROOMS			
1.	Offices (17)	10	3,140
2.	Lecture room	9–10	1,255
3.	Classrooms (2)	10	1,215
4.	Conference room and graduate examination	10	270
	Total		5,880

C. SERVICES, STORAGE AND MISCELLANEOUS			
1.	Duplicating and darkrooms	10	425
2.	Shop	10	1,360
3.	Storage rooms, instrument supply	10	6,080
4.	Outside hazardous storage building	12	490
5.	Outside laboratory cement floor platform	—	1,200
	Total		9,555

II. *Metallurgical Engineering Department*

1.	Offices (4)*	10	725
2.	Heat treatment laboratories (2)	12	1,100
3.	Metallography preparation	12	605
4.	Visual microscopic laboratory	12	590
5.	Metallography laboratory	9–10	1,300
6.	Polishing laboratory	12	420
7.	Intermediate polishing laboratory	12	420
8.	Graduate photomicroscopic laboratory	12	620
9.	Pyrometric laboratory	12	600
	Total		6,380

III. *Hallways, Restrooms, Janitor's Closets, Elevator, etc.* — 12,629

IV. *Mechanical Equipment*

1.	Mechanical Equipment Room— Basement		1,610
2.	Mechanical Equipment Room— Penthouse		4,350
3.	Mechanical Equipment Room— Fourth Floor		595
	Total		6,555

V. *Overall Summary*

1.	Total Net		68,795
2.	Grand Gross Total		81,424

*To be assigned to Chemical Engineering when other two phases of the building are completed.

Gamma Radiation Pool Facilities (500 curie Cobalt-60). A small pool facility measuring 3 by 6 ft by 10½ ft deep is located in a fenced off section in the southeast corner of the chemical engineering building. The 500-curie source is divided into 12 pencil-type capsules measuring ⅝ in. diameter by 8 in. in length. This is located at the bottom of the pool in a holder designed so that various radiation configurations are possible. There is a 10-ft water shield above the surface of the pool. The gamma detector is located just above the pool as a warning device. Radia-tion experiments at various pressures and temperatures can be conducted by extension pipe and electric heating wire connected to the equipment which is to be radiated.

The experiments which will be carried out by the students in the Nuclear Laboratory are as follows:

1. Nuclear radiation detection
2. Isotope dilution assay methods
3. Pulse column extractor performance
4. Ion-exchange separation
5. Gamma radiation

Figure 13.9   Using carbon 14 in the radiotracer laboratory.

Figure 13.10   Walk-in hood in the nuclear laboratory.

Process Development Pilot Plant Laboratory (Rooms 118–218)

This laboratory is designed for carrying out small pilot plant scale studies in connection with Process Development courses. Micro-scale process studies will be carried out in other laboratories (Kinetics and Process Research Laboratory, General Laboratory, or Graduate Research Laboratories). This laboratory will be used primarily to confirm micro-scale results as well as to prepare larger quantities of special chemicals required for research and other course work.

The important equipment includes a 10-gal glass-lined reactor-distillation unit and a similar 30-gal stainless steel unit. The glass-lined unit is equipped with a 3-in. "Pyrex" Oldershaw sieve tray column which can be set up for 10 to 60 plates in multiples of ten. A 3-stage evactor is

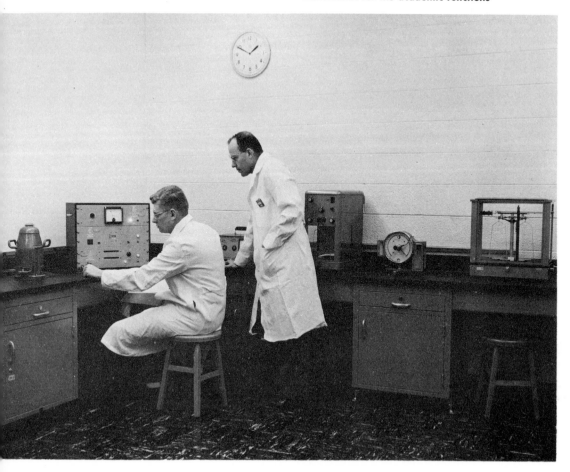

Figure 13.11   The counter room of the nuclear laboratory.

so arranged that it can be connected to either unit for vacuum operation.

All electrical equipment is of the Class I Group D type and the room is designed with air locks and suitable ventilation for handling combustible materials. To conserve space and still provide height for distillation columns, a 10-ft wide section of one end of the room is two floors high.

Micro Process Development and Kinetics Research Laboratory (Room 307)

This laboratory is used for research in the field of heterogeneous catalysis and related fields as well as for micro-scale process research. The laboratory has two 8-ft walk-in hoods for the operation of process units that require isolation. Apparatus is mounted on portable racks that can be moved into the hood. A distillation rack in the center of the room provides additional space for carrying out similar work that does not require isolation.

The Physical Measurements, Thermodynamic and Phase Laboratories (Rooms 412 and 431)

The Thermodynamics or Physical Measurements Laboratory has been planned and equipped specifically for the study of the P-V-T relations of pure compounds and mixtures.

(Figure 13.12.) Space is provided for 8 students to work on P-V-T properties covering a pressure range from atmospheric pressure to 150 atm and temperatures from 0° to 300°C. Each working space is provided with a connection to a high-precision dead-weight gage so that secondary pressure gages may be checked at any time. Thermocouples used in conjunction with high precision potentiometers are used for temperature measurement. A platinum resistance thermometer together with a high-precision bridge is available for calibration of the thermocouples.

As accessory facilities for the P-V-T work two racks, 14 ft long, have been provided upon which to mount distillation and high-vacuum equipment for the purification and the degassing of liquids and the preparation of mixtures of known composition. A walk-in ventilation hood is available for use when highly toxic materials

are to be studied. Two separate rooms in this Thermodynamics laboratory are provided for the storage of equipment and supplies.

The Phase Laboratory houses special equipment for the study of the phase behavior of mixtures at pressures up to 10,000 psi. This equipment is being used principally for graduate research.

Mass Transfer Laboratory (Rooms 332, 332A, and 332B)

This laboratory is used primarily for research in the mass-transfer operations of liquid-liquid extraction, absorption, diffusion from solids and diffusion from liquids (Figure 13.13). The laboratory is so constructed that in one end of the room equipment two stories high can be accommodated. Facilities for spot exhausting of fumes are included as are a table hood and a walk-in hood.

Figure 13.12   Purification of liquids for physical measurements in the chemical engineering thermodynamics laboratory.

Figure 13.13   Frequency response analysis in mass transfer in the mass transfer laboratory.

Figure 13.15   Student glass blowing laboratory.

Figure 13.14   The analog computer laboratory.

The laboratory will accommodate 8 to 10 graduate students working on separate research problems. At present, the following problems are being investigated:

1. Longitudinal diffusion in packed beds using frequency response techniques.

2. Diffusivity of high molecular weight solids in liquids.

3. Extraction of metal salts in aqueous solutions.

4. Heat and mass transfer in liquid-liquid systems.

Mass transfer work requiring low level radioisotopes is done in special graduate laboratories as Room 405 or in the Nuclear Laboratories.

The Computer Laboratory (Room 314)

This is designed to accommodate small computers with auxiliary equipment. The room is air-conditioned and is furnished with tables, stands, and cabinets suitable for each piece of equipment. (Figure 13.14.) At the present time, two Heathkit analog units along with auxiliary equipment such as oscilloscopes, function generators, x-y plotters, multipliers, etc. are used primarily for teaching purposes. The room will also accommodate a small digital unit or certain peripheral equipment for a larger unit.

Reservoir Engineering Laboratory (Room 427)

This laboratory is used for oil and gas production studies and investigations. It has facilities for phase behavior, and multiphase flow in porous media. The reservoir engineering lab is equipped to measure two general types of data: (1) those concerned with the physical nature of the complex porous reservoir media, and (2) those concerned with the reservoir fluid properties and phase behavior.

A virtually complete analysis can be made of a reservoir rock sample including sample preparation with diamond-cutting instruments and measurement of porosity, permeability, saturation, resistivity, capillary pressure, and displacement characteristics. The lab is equipped with a variable-volume pressure cell and temperature bath which permits placing the reservoir fluids in an environment which duplicates the natural reservoir pressure and temperature. The phase and viscosity variations with pressure and temperature can then be measured.

The laboratory is used for undergraduate and graduate instruction and research investigations.

Drilling Fluid Laboratory (Room 130)

This laboratory is used for undergraduate instruction and graduate research in the control of drilling fluid properties such as apparent viscosity, plastic viscosity, fluid loss, gel strength, weight, studies on the application of non-Newtonian theories, etc.

Optical Laboratory (Room 210)

This laboratory was designed for conducting instrumental analysis for research and instruction. The types of analytical instruments now in service include: infrared, ultraviolet, and ratio recording spectrophotometers, gas chromatograph, polariscope, microscope, etc. This laboratory is air-conditioned.

Precision Standards Laboratory (Room 434)

The Precision Standards Laboratory serves as a facility for primary standard of measurement.

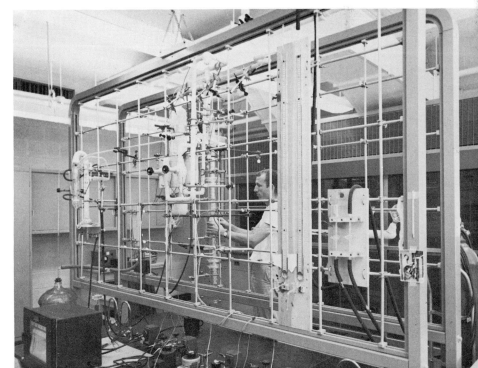

Figure 13.16   Kinetic sorption apparatus in the chemical engineering graduate laboratory.

It provides means for checking temperature, pressure, density, viscosity, volume and mass. Both room temperature and humidity are controlled to reduce environmental variables for standardization.

Glass Blowing Laboratory (Room 432)

(Figure 13.15.) This is a service laboratory for students and staff. The laboratory is equipped with glass-blowing facilities for construction and repair of glass apparatus for instruction and research.

Solvent Storage Building (Room 100)

It was deemed unsafe to store quantities of combustible solvents anywhere in the building. A separate building 20 by 30 ft was built in the "L" opening of the main building and at least 50 ft from it. The solvent storage building is of fireproof construction and is equipped with Class I Group D electrical fixtures, fans for high-level ventilation, safety showers, and floor drainage to permit rapid washing in the event of spillage or an accident. Containers up to 55-gal. drum size can be stored.

Graduate Research Laboratories

In addition to the above laboratories which are designed for specific areas of research and teaching, there are 18 general-purpose research laboratories. All these are about the same size and design, except for minor variations in arrangement and amount of apparatus assembly racks. (Figure 13.16.) Each room will accommodate 2 to 4 graduate students, depending upon the complexity of the apparatus. The principal laboratory equipment in each room includes a "walk-in" type hood, a bench type hood, laboratory benches, apparatus racks, cabinets and desks. The average size is 20 x 20 ft.

Versatility and safety were important considerations in the planning of these laboratories. Each room has an escape door to an adjacent room and a safety shower near the door leading to the hallway. At the present time, research in the fields of turbulence, fluidization, rheology, catalysis, mass transfer, and absorption is being carried out in these laboratories. It should also be pointed out that other laboratories such as

Unit Operations and Furnace and Pyrometry are also used for research as well as instruction.

Unit Operations Laboratory (Rooms 117, 217, 317, and 417)

(Figures 13.17 and 13.18.) These laboratories are used for undergraduate and graduate laboratory teaching in the unit operations, applied instrumentation, pilot plant work in the process development courses, and for research and theses problems which require head room and other special facilities available in these laboratories.

There are three balconies or mezzanines surrounding the central well served by an electrically operated 5-ton American Monorail "Monotrack" crane. The central well is 16 ft wide and 83 ft long. The three mezzanines are located at 16, 12, and 12 ft heights thereby giving four working floors off of a central well. The head room is 40 ft for three of the floors and 52 ft for the south mezzanine. The west mezzanine is 7 ft 6 in. wide and is 103 ft long. The floor is removable steel grating which permits installation of tall equipment. The east mezzanine is 38.5 ft wide and consists of three types of floors: (a) open steel grille floors, 7 ft 6 in. wide, on the cantilevered balcony, (b) steel plate floor, 9 ft 6 in. wide, and (c) poured reinforced concrete floor, 21 ft 6 in. wide so pitched to provide drainage to open trenches covered with steel grating. The south mezzanine is steel grating covering the open well end and runs the entire width of this laboratory.

UTILITIES AND SERVICES

Steam is generated at the University power house and is piped to the building. The total available quantity of steam is 13,300 lb per hour and at a pressure of 160 psi (g). This is reduced at the building to pressures of 5, 30 and 125 psi. Of this steam, 9,000 lb per hour is for heating and the remainder is for the various laboratories.

Water to the building is supplied from 6-in. feeder main at a pressure of 60 psi (g). This includes all cold water for all the laboratories, wash rooms, and fire hydrants. The fire hydrant water line branches off from the main to a 4-in.

Figure 13.17   Unit operations laboratory.

line, the valve of which is locked and cannot be closed except by the University fire marshall. There are also 1-in. and 2-in. hot-water lines for washrooms, showers and process work.

Distilled water is obtained from a Barnstead still Model No. SMG-20 (20 gpn capacity) located in the penthouse (sixth floor). Distilled water is supplied to the various laboratories by a ¾ in. aluminum line. Gas is supplied to the building through a 4-in. line and is at a pressure from 6 to 8 oz.

Air to all the laboratories with the exception of the Unit Operations lab is supplied from the University Power House through a 1½ in. line and at a pressure of 80 psi (g). This is further reduced to 30 and 5 psi (g) depending upon the type of air service required.

Figure 13.18   Unit operations laboratory, third floor.

The air supply to the Unit Operations Laboratory is independent of the University line. There are three compressors and/or blowers in the U.O.L mechanical room (Room 14). Data concerning these are:

PRESSURE	QUANTITY C.F.M.	TYPE OF EQUIPMENT
125 psi (g)	240	Ingersoll-Rand 10″ x 9″ Model ESH with a vertical 30″ x 7′-0″ vertical air receiver.
7 psi (g)	200	Roots-Connerville rotary positive displacement air blower.
25″ water	2200	American Blower 6-24 Type F fan with a Rockwell SA206 blast gate type damper on the outlet of the blower.

Electric Service

The primary supply to the building is 3-phase, 3 wire, 13,200 volts. The secondary voltage is 3-phase, 4-wire 120/208. The transformer vault (see basement plan) anticipates 3-500 KVA transformers, for power in the future. At the present time there are 3-333 KVA single phase, oil-immersed, and self-cooled.

Bus duct runs, both plug-in-type and feeder type are used in the Unit Operations Laboratory, furnance rooms and shop. Receptacles for all the other laboratories are three-prong polarized and grounded.

Exhaust Fans

There are a total of 65 exhaust fans manufactured by the American Blower Company for the various hoods and rooms which require fume exhaust. (Figure 13.19.) Each of these fans has its own individual motor and exhaust duct. All fans have aluminum wheels and the fan scrolls have neoprene protective coating. Most of the fans have spark-proof wheels and explosion-proof motors. All these are located in the penthouse of the building with the exception of two which are on the roof and are weather-proof. The capacities vary from 250 to 27,000 cfm.

Air Conditioning

All offices, class, lecture, conference, dark and duplicating rooms are air-conditioned, as are the computation, computer, precision standards, and optical laboratories. The conditioners are of the chilled water type. The chilled water generator is an Acme, "Flow-Therm" Packaged Liquid Chiller using "Freon-22" as a coolant. The cooling towers are also Acme, No. AT-30, with multi-fan section, spray chamber and water reservoir. With the exception of the lecture room (207) and the precision standards unit, all the units are of the Modine type, hung from the ceiling and provided with sound-absorbing bases.

Safety

Safety held the highest priority in the design of the building. All laboratories have a second escape door and an emergency shower actuated by a manual Logan rod. Each hood is connected to a separate exhaust fan located either on the roof or in the penthouse of the building. Each floor is equipped with wall hydrants, fire extinguishers of various types, cabinets for gas masks, fire blankets, stretchers, and first aid kits; fire alarm systems are located on each floor. A special sump is connected to the Unit Operations Laboratory floor drain system for diverting insoluble or hazardous organic liquids which might be accidentally spilled on the floor from the sewer system. Provisions are also made for venting all flammable vapors, waste process steam, entrained liquids, and non-condensible gases to the roof; appropriate containers on the roof of the fourth floor are provided.

Spot ventilation using movable canopy hoods is provided by ducts running the entire length of the Unit Operations laboratory, and also on all floors, and the Process Development Laboratory. The exhaust ducts are sized from 10 x 10 in. on the far side to 24 x 12 in. on the near side of the blower. Connection from the canopy hood to the duct is made by flexible hose to 6-in. nipples in the ducts. The exhaust fan for the unit operations lab is of the American Blower type (Size S222J.K.) with a capacity of 5300 cfm at 1¼ in. static pressure. The Process Development exhaust fan (Size S150F0) has a capacity of 5300 cfm at 1 in. static pressure. The wheel is spark-proof and the motor is explosion-proof. Both these fans are located on the roof of the building.

The fire alarm system is a complete, closed circuit, electrically supervised fire alarm system, continuous ringing, causing signal to sound all stations together. There are fire alarm pull stations of the break glass type on each floor. There is also a manual operating rod running through all floors. It is equipped with switch to initiate the closed circuit supervised system, and arranged to manually operate a 10 in. gong.

OTHER PERTINENT FEATURES OF THE BUILDING

Telephone Systems: All offices have telephones on independent numbers; however, there is also a signal in the departmental office when any one of the offices is called. If the call is not answered in a reasonable time the message is taken in the departmental office and the message is put in the post office box of the particular staff member.

Dictation: There are "Soundscriber" telephones in each office. Letters, reports and other communications are dictated through these telephones to the departmental office where they are typed.

Student Facilities: There are individual lockers for each student and also showers. In addition to the conference room (Room 221B) which is used for faculty, committee meetings, and oral examinations for Master's and Doctor's degrees; there is also Room 436 which is used for the Student Branch of the A.I.Ch.E. and also a computation and study room.

Paging System: Speakers are installed on each floor with the microphone located in the departmental office.

Vacuum Cleaning System: A "Vacuslot" floor type system is installed with outlets located in several places on each floor.

Lighting System: Lighting is such that in no room is it necessary to have auxilliary desk lamps. The recessed fluorescent lamps are rapid start, warm white.

The Elevator: An 8000 lb. capacity Otis elevator serves five of the six floors. The elevator is automatic with a 6 x 8 ft platform and operates at a speed of 100 ft/min.

TV Conduit System: Provisions are made anticipating closed circuit TV by the installation of an empty conduit system running from most of the laboratories to the lecture and class rooms.

Clocks of the synchronous type are installed in all hallways, lecture and class rooms and some of the larger laboratories. These clocks are either single or double spaced and are 12 in. in diameter.

Program Bells are 8 inch and 120 volt and arranged for control and supervision from the main campus control system.

Figure 13.19   Penthouse system, fume hood exhaust fan.

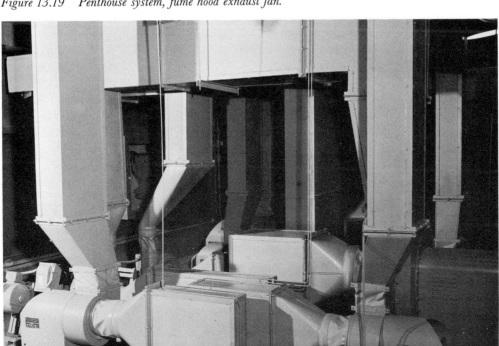

CHAPTER XIV

Specific

Laboratory

Planning

PART 1:

THE LABORATORY FOR GENERAL CHEMISTRY

TOBIAS H. DUNKELBERGER
University of Pittsburgh
Pittsburgh, Pennsylvania

There are few, if any, schools in which the number of students taking laboratory work in general chemistry is not greater than the number in all other laboratory courses combined. It is therefore most important to see that the laboratories are designed and equipped for convenient, efficient, economical operation. Primary attention must, of course, be given to the educational objectives, for unless the student has a useful educational experience in the laboratory there is little point to having one at all.

The discussion in this section applies to a single-purpose general chemistry laboratory. It will, however, accommodate work in qualitative analysis, since this is commonly included in the general chemistry course. Many of the features of laboratories intended to be used for several courses are the same as those described here, but the design of lockers and specifications of services will be different. Much of the description here is based on the laboratories in George Hubbard Clapp Hall (occupied in 1956) at the University of Pittsburgh. The photographs were taken in that building.

GENERAL ARRANGEMENT

The fundamental decision in the design of the laboratory is the size of class to be accommodated. This decision is closely related to the educational objectives and how one expects to realize them.

In George Hubbard Clapp Hall the laboratories are of such size that each laboratory assistant is in charge of no more than 24 students at a time. The building has five such laboratories on the same floor; thus one staff member can supervise the work of five laboratory assistants in the individual laboratories.

Each laboratory has at one end a classroom area equipped with a blackboard, a large demonstration slide rule, and a periodic chart of the elements (Figure 14.1). It is thus possible to seat the students for explanations of the work to be done, discussions, and quizzes. The students also have a place to sit while writing their reports and are therefore less reluctant than they otherwise would be to remain in the laboratory until this task is completed.

The classroom area takes the place of one laboratory table (8 students), but its value is such that this sacrifice of working space deserves serious consideration in designing a new laboratory. In particular, it eliminates the difficulty, which most instructors have experienced, of giving instructions to students who can scarcely see the blackboard or who have already busied themselves in setting up the experiment. Moreover, a number of schools are already giving certain laboratory instructions via closed-circuit television and this practice will undoubtedly become more common in the future. Provision of a classroom area provides the optimum physical situation for such instruction. Only a single viewing screen is required and it can be located where all the students can see it clearly. This arrangement eliminates the two major problems mentioned by teachers who have utilized television for instruction in ordinary laboratories,* namely (1) locating a limited number of screens in such a way as to give each sudent an unhindered view of one, and (2) getting the students to pay attention to the instructions and not attempt to carry out the operations until the instructions have been completed.

The laboratory layout is quite conventional:

* Symposium of the Division of Chemical Education, 135th Meeting, American Chemical Society, Boston, April 1959.

Figure 14.1   Laboratory classroom.

each laboratory contains three 13-foot tables (four working spaces on each side), 60 in. wide, with an aisle width of 6 feet between tables. The tables are flush with the outside wall; the passage between tables and shelving on the hall side is 4½ ft wide (Figure 14.2). A centrally located stock-room serves all five laboratories.

High student loads are handled by having each working space used over and over each week, as many as 13 times. The difficulty is, of course, that only a limited number of lockers—6 in George Hubbard Clapp Hall—can be placed beneath each working space. If, therefore, each student is to have a locker used solely by himself (and this is extremely desirable), provision must be made to locate some of the lockers elsewhere. Utilizing all possible space beneath reagent shelves, balance shelves, and blank areas of the walls provides an additional 136 lockers in each laboratory, an alcove banked 8-high with lockers (Figure 14.3)

provides 272 more, bringing to 334 the number of lockers (i.e., the possible weekly student capacity) available for each laboratory. This number is sufficient to exhaust all available scheduling times during the week.

The student whose locker is located elsewhere is at some disadvantage with respect to one whose locker happens to be immediately beneath his assigned working space. To minimize this inconvenience, one of the lockers beneath each working space is a dummy, provided with a false front and no drawer (Figure 14.1). A student can then bring the drawer from its location elsewhere, slip it into the empty space, and work without the inconvenience of having the drawer on top of the table.

Some schools have designed and built special lockers for the efficient storage of the particular collection of equipment used in their courses. Aside from the additional expense, this procedure

Figure 14.2   Laboratory in general chemistry.

Figure 14.3   General Chemistry locker area.

is of questionable value because the locker may not accommodate the different collection of equipment necessitated by a future change in the experiments performed. If large, seldom-used, or very fragile items are provided for separately, a simple box drawer serves most purposes as well as possible. Ringstands, rings, and tripods, for example, can be communal property, left on top of the table or stored in a separate cabinet; burettes and graduated flasks can be borrowed from the stockroom the day they are to be used.

The drawers are preferably designed for padlocks rather than for cabinet locks. The latter too soon become corroded and difficult to open, and attempts to remove them usually result in damage to the drawers. On the other hand, a stuck padlock can be removed, as a last resort, with a bolt-clipper. The padlocks may be either key or combination type, but, in any case, they should be master-keyed for ease of opening in case a student abandons his locker. With key-type locks and with large numbers of lockers it is desirable to have several key schedules in order to reduce to a minimum the probability that one

student's key will open another student's lock.

The table tops must be made of some chemical-resistant material. The demands are, however, not extreme and a number of materials will be quite satisfactory, making the selection in large part one of economics. Most laboratory workers think nothing is superior to soapstone (e.g., "Alberene") in durability and appearance. Impregnated sandstone (e.g., "Kem-Rock") and pressed, impregnated asbestos (e.g., "Kem-Stone") have an attractive, jet-black color and adequate corrosion resistance and are giving satisfactory service in many laboratories. Wood treated with acid-resistant paint should be avoided unless the installation is admittedly a temorary one.

LABORATORY SERVICES

Experiments in general chemistry usually do not require elaborate services. Gas and cold water are, of course, the rudimentary requirements; there should be at least two outlets for each service at each working space. Each student needs easy access to a sink. The sinks are preferably placed between each pair of working spaces (i.e., two sinks per table). If space is at a real premium sinks may be placed only at the ends of the tables, with a trough down the center of the table. This arrangement, however, is essentially incompatible with a down-draft ventilation system.

One outlet per student for 110-volt a.c. current should be considered well-nigh indispensable. It is, of course, quite indispensable if, e.g., electrically driven centrifuges are used in qualitative analysis. Direct current, supplied by a remote motor generator set or batteries, is very convenient but not essential. In general, no wide selection of d.c. voltages is demanded; few experiments require anything other than 6 volts, which can be supplied by four dry cells if a d.c. outlet is not available.

A supply of hot water is convenient but by no means indispensable, and, in any case, it is not necessary for each table; one outlet in each laboratory should be adequate. Steam is unnecessary.

Distilled water should be available, but it should not be piped to each table. *Experience shows that in the interest of economy it is advantageous to have the student go to a little trouble to obtain distilled water.* The outlets in George Hubbard Clapp Hall are therefore located in the halls, over the drinking fountains. The drain for the fountain then serves as the drain for any wastage. Distilled-water taps should be spring-closing, to protect the supply against carelessness. It is sometimes also desirable to restrict the flow to a small stream to make it inconvenient for the student to take excessive amounts.

General questions of ventilation are considered elsewhere in this volume. For general chemistry the problem is of limited severity since most of the experiments are designed to minimize ventilation problems and hazards. A satisfactory arrangement is to have small, high velocity down-draft hoods located on each table, one for each working space. These are better than larger hoods around the outside of the room or overhead hoods which, among other disadvantages, greatly obstruct the instructor's view of the laboratory. The table-top hoods conserve space inside the laboratory and also prevent fumes from a local source from spreading throughout the room. If balances or similar delicate instruments must be kept in

the laboratory, it is most important that the general atmosphere be kept free from contamination to minimize corrosion.

"House vacuum" systems are so troublesome, so difficult to maintain, and of such infrequent use in general chemistry that vacuum lines may well be kept out of the laboratory. Instead, provided the water pressure is adequate, an aspirator permanently attached to one of the water outlets provides a satisfactory and trouble-free solution to the vacuum problem.

Sulfide precipitation is still used in most work in qualitative analysis. There has been, however, a distinct shift from the use of gaseous hydrogen sulfide as a precipitating agent to reagents such as thioacetamide. The corrosiveness and poisonousness of gaseous hydrogen sulfide are so great that installation of pressure reducers or gasholders for handling the gas from high-pressure cylinders cannot be recommended. If one of the newer reagents is not to be used, a small, individual generator in which a paraffin-sulfur mixture ("Aitch-Tu-Ess") is heated is probably the best way to supply hydrogen sulfide.

If possible, balances should be provided in the ratio of one for each two students; smaller ratios can be tolerated if the experiments are so scheduled that the students do not all appear at the balance at the same time. The balances are preferably kept in a separate room, but they can be kept in the laboratory without serious corrosion if the ventilation is adequate. For several reasons, one of which is protection from corrosion, it is highly desirable for all weights to be kept in the stockroom, to be checked out by the student on the days he uses the balances.

Most instructors prefer that students stand while weighing. The balances should therefore be placed at a convenient height (46 in.); this is just right for the location of four spare lockers under the balance tables.

In view of the strong trend toward the use of single-pan balances, designers of new laboratories may well consider the possibility of tooling-up for this instrument. A ratio of one balance to five students is probably a feasible one; this would reduce by about half the space necessary for balances.

The table tops need have provision for only a

few bottles of common reagents; the remaining bottles may be kept on side shelves. It is desirable to have storage space in the stockroom for reagents not actually in use and to keep in the laboratory only those needed for current experiments. A pouring shelf, preferably made of table-top material, or at least treated with chemical-resistant paint, should be placed beneath the reagent shelf; on this shelf can also be located a trip-scale for weighing dry chemicals. Wheeled carts for transferring bottles are almost indispensable.

Although the work in general chemistry involves few hazards, safety equipment should never be skimped. It is wise to locate fire extinguishers both inside the room and in the hall outside. The liquid carbon dioxide type is much preferable to the soda-acid type. A fire blanket should be located in or near each laboratory, but one first-aid cabinet and one stretcher, located conveniently in the hall, should be adequate for several laboratories. An intense-spray shower, operated by a wire loop, should be located in each room; local safety regulations usually require this. A shower is important not only for fires, but even more so for chemicals on the face or in the eyes. Unless sinks are located at the ends of the tables it is virtually impossible to give prompt first aid without a shower. For chemicals in the eyes an eyewash fountain is highly desirable and may be required by local safety codes.

PART 2: THE ORGANIC CHEMISTRY LABORATORY

G. ROSS ROBERTSON
University of California
Los Angeles, California

Although scarcely more than a decade has passed since the publication of the first version* of this chapter, four developments in particular have led to numerous proposals for change of design in the organic domain. These four are: (a) increasing popularity of the single-section undergraduate laboratory, directed by one instructor; (b) rapidly growing interest in research in physical-organic chemistry and the use of physical instruments in the organic chemistry laboratory; (c) economic problems intensified by the deplorable "post-Korea" inflation of building costs; and (d) the projected educational boom of the 1960's, calling for increased building capacity on limited terrain, and more laboratory sections per room.

Revisions in design thus require most of the space available for this chapter. There remain numerous suggestions from Hurd which are still valid, but are not repeated in this new version.

FEATURES OF GENERAL DESIGN

Frankly, the newer specifications will not meet unanimous reader approval. Nevertheless, certain controversial dimensions, choices of materials and architectural layouts already have the benefit of several years' successful trial. Where justifiable, a range of measurements or other factors is offered, with the hope that the optimum will lie between maximum and minimum as described.

Small Laboratories

First it will be assumed that the old-style mass-education laboratory room holding 60, 100 or 150 students at one time is educationally obsolete. In a central building block, and particularly in a hollow-block structure, the large laboratory is an administrative nuisance. Adoption of the single-section room in charge of one instructor, even in elementary chemistry, is now giving outstanding satisfaction both as to student morale and quiet academic efficiency. Accordingly, the principal discussion here centers about a plan (Figure 14.4) for a single-section undergraduate laboratory, in several modifications, and a plan

* Hurd, Chas. D., in "Laboratory Design," edited by H. S. Coleman, National Research Council; Reinhold Publishing Corp., 1951, pp. 105–108.

(Figure 14.5) for a single research laboratory adapted to candidates for Masters' and Doctors' degrees. These plans assume that the building is to follow the classic central-corridor design. If a wider structure, with central utility channel is preferred, see special discussion of this scheme later in this chapter.

Unquestionably a few readers will consider both figures as too skimpy in measurements. Others, perhaps the majority, including those who must face the budget, may judge that Figure 14.5 is skimpy, but already too costly!

Certain economies recommended herewith are not in agreement with current manufacturers' ready-made products, but they do afford gains in enrollment capacity. These somewhat radical changes have proved satisfactory, however. In the author's laboratory they are being re-adopted by architects for projected building additions.

Use of the single-section plan means that the building committee concerned with organic chemistry should at an early date pay unusual attention to the framing of a proposed new structure, in contrast with the old plan of letting an

Figure 14.4   Single section undergraduate laboratory.

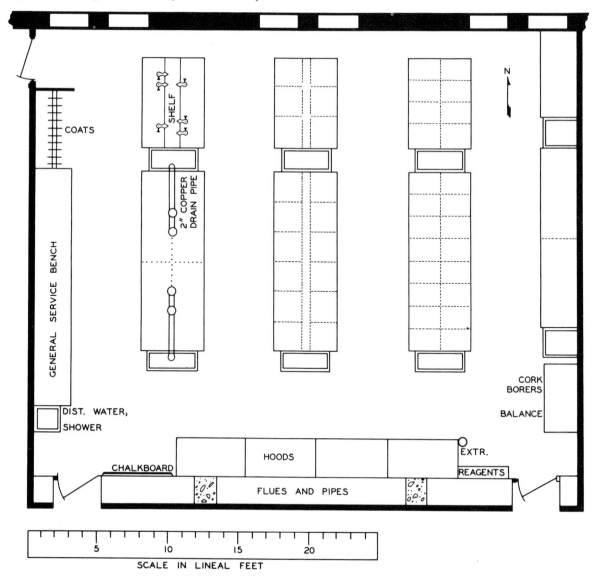

architect draw up a whole building, including fenestration and location of support pillars, before the committee has had a chance to relate design to function.

Above all things, there should be no post or pillar inside the working area of the single-unit laboratory. Normally this means that all pillars be integral with either corridor wall or outside wall. The clear span between a corridor post and outer wall should not exceed 30 ft, to avoid excessive size and cost of girders (note Figures 14.4 and 14.5). At the same time, the span or depth should not be much under 24 ft, in order (a) to avoid an excessively long laboratory, and (b) to preserve a high ratio of net useful area to gross area of building. Shallow rooms, such as 18 or 20 ft, are convenient for some purposes, but are wasteful of gross area in class laboratories.

As shown in the figures, principal doors are countersunk, or inset, from the corridor, thus occupying otherwise waste space; more important, they avoid a moving-door hazard from a corridor entered without warning by youthful, possibly impetuous people. In buildings with very

Figure 14.5   Plan for single research laboratory.

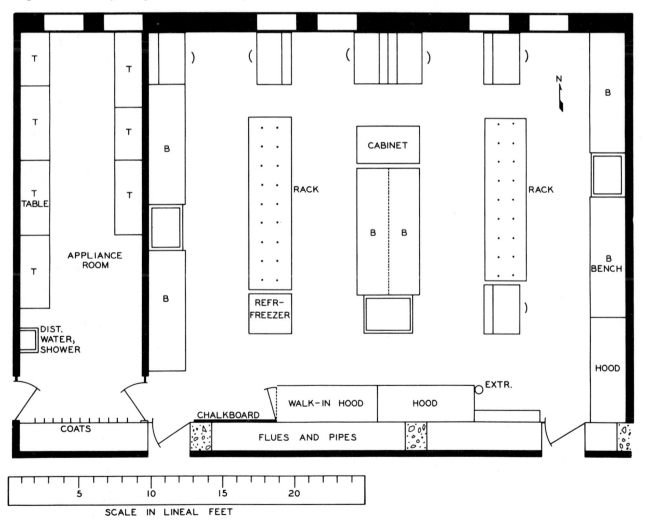

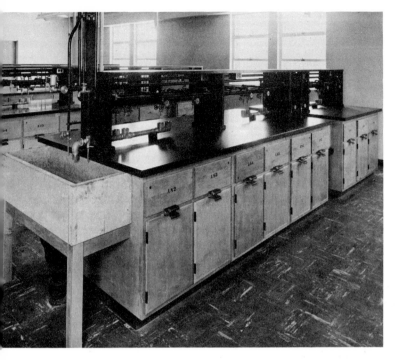

Figure 14.4a   Undergraduate organic chemistry laboratory.

Figure 14.4b   General chemistry laboratory.

busy corridor traffic, at least one foot may be deducted from allowance for corridor width in this way without incurring danger from face injuries caused by suddenly opened doors. It must be remembered that the fire warden is likely to require that all main laboratory doors open outward into corridors.

In face of the elaborate plumbing and ventilation requirements in organic chemistry, it is especially desirable that an easement of about two feet be allowed next to all corridor runs; this yields a channel from top floor to basement, and accommodates vertical pipe and flue risers serving successive floors.

Pipe "Exclusion." In the plan recommended here, all service pipes in the laboratories are out in the open. No water pipe, waste line, trough, cup sink, main sink, conduit nor any other passageway for a fluid should, in the present writer's opinion, be placed inside any laboratory bench. This sweeping statement (Figure 14.4a) will not please the artistic-minded member of the board of trustees, whose primary interest is in beautiful appearance on dedication day. Such insistence on elegant appearance puts both architect and furniture manufacturer "on the spot," and makes it difficult for the building committee to attain the space economies obviously possible by exclusion of pipes. The same committee will, however, get emphatic support from the superintendent of maintenance, and perhaps from the state board of public works or other efficiency agency.

Exclusion of pipes permits deep drawers and cupboards (Figure 14.4b) running through to the center of an island bench, or almost to the wall behind a wall bench. One may then use an 18-in. locker as a near equivalent of the shallow but wasteful standard commercial 24-in. locker, which has been considered the irreducible minimum in many organic laboratories. Since the laboratory bench top now needs no cuts or holes, it is highly resistant to leakage into drawers, with resultant increase in the probable life of the equipment.

For the organic worker, however, the uncut bench top sets the requirement of some kind of drain for condenser water on top of the bench. In Figure 14.4 (sketched in westerly island bench) the plan calls for appropriate lengths of

2-in. streamline copper tubing, now widely obtainable, with as many bullhead tees and elbows as may be needed to receive condenser water and steam condensate. Pipe services come from the ceiling to convenient positions under the reagent shelf (1.5 in. thick) set 16 in. above the bench top. The old-time troughs, prone to collect trash and to leak, are not recommended; actually many of these have been removed from old laboratories. The builder should not be allowed to cut the size of the copper drain below 2 in., to avoid risk of overflow in multiple use of valves.

A soapstone sink—not built into the bench—is adjacent to every laboratory worker. The waste line from this sink passes through a metal sleeve about 6 in. in diameter. The sleeve has been sealed into the concrete floor at time of pouring the floor slab. It is made of stout steel tubing, such as well casing, cut first and then dip-galvanized. As it stands on the floor form, and thus in its final position, it protrudes 1½ in. above final floor level, and thus will be able to prevent flooding of a room below. Ceramic sleeves are not recommended, since a leakproof replacement seems not to be possible after breakage. Furthermore, a leakproof cement curb around a simple drain hole at pouring time is apparently something which a contractor will not furnish. To install the curb afterward is not possible, since new cement does not adhere to old concrete. Although this sleeve recommendation may apply to any laboratory, it is especially significant in organic chemistry, where the hazard of flooding from broken condenser-water lines is the greatest.

Undergraduate Organic Laboratories

In Figure 14.4 may be seen a range from "generous allowance," or perhaps extravagance, to "economy design," optional features being sketched on successive benches. In any case, however, length of the student station, or personal work bench, is not reduced below 6 ft in organic chemistry, where flammable solvents are in use. Each student has one drawer and one cupboard in the station. Reduction of student station to 4 ft or less, with only two sections scheduled, as often done in the past, means an inexcusably crowded laboratory on four afternoons and idleness for most of the week.

Generous Allowance. In this option the locker design of the center island of Figure 14.4 is used. Here the standard commercial shallow drawer and cupboard, 2 ft wide, will suffice. Such liberal allowance is presumably suited to chemistry majors, at least for the second and third semester organic courses. Cork press and borers, rough balance, etc., are in the southeast corner; power-driven reduced-pressure outfits, a small distillation rack, a melting-point outfit and possibly an electric oven are on the west wall bench.

In this "generous" option the peninsular design, with benches running out to the windows, is arbitrarily rejected on account of fire hazard and inconvenience to the instructor. Extensive use of ether and other flammables in organic chemistry leads to this conclusion. The 2-ft north aisle is a satisfactory compromise between the island and peninsula proposals. It is ample for passage even of a fairly stout person, of course without necessity of passing another person. No fittings are placed on the north or window wall.

The efficiency of this plan is figured as follows: Three class sections of 21 students, total 63 students enrolled. Requirement in plan, in main room, 18.3 sq ft "net useful" area, not including flue space, per student enrolled. Incidentally expansion of the north aisle to 4 or 5 ft, as in old-time laboratories, with reduction in the number of lockers per row, would seem to be unjustifiable extravagance, raising the requirement to 20 sq ft or more per enrolled student.

Economy Designs. Even in the following space-saving options, the all-too-common restriction of a student locker in organic chemistry to a single drawer is not considered acceptable. Such skimpy allotment is not consistent with necessary storage of considerable amounts of liquids undergoing distillation and crystallization procedures in courses where a student should be taking pride in serious synthetic work, and with minimum risk of spillage. To be sure, one must admit the feasibility of the one-drawer outfit for test-tube organic chemistry and its handmaid, the "fill-in-the-blank" laboratory manual. In the face of current enthusiasm and excitement over better education in physical science, the writer holds that this is no time to issue skimpy freshman-type lockers to classes in organic chemistry.

Much more acceptable, in the "economy" range, is the layout using the easterly island design (Figure 14.4), with 18-in. lockers, for the three islands and east wall bench. Cork press, west distillation bench, etc. are retained. Efficiency, four sections of 21 students, total 84 students; 13.7 sq ft per student enrolled. To be sure, expansion of an organic laboratory function to cover four sections, or eight half-day sessions, often runs afoul of certain schedule makers, who would like to insist that Monday, Wednesday and Friday mornings be sacred to lecture programs. In the forthcoming educational rush such restriction will simply have to give way.

Further economies, presumably of interest in laboratories for large classes of premedical, agriculture and home economics students, are seen in the following alternate proposals:

(1) Use the 18-in. lockers, but cut off the most westerly 3½ ft of the Figure 14.4 laboratory, including the west bench; efficiency is now 12.5 sq ft per student enrolled.

(2) Leave the laboratory the same size as in Figure 14.4, but replace the westerly general-service bench with a duplicate of the easterly regular wall bench. Capacity is now 24 x 4 or 96 students; efficiency is 12.0 sq ft per student enrolled.

(3) Use the furniture specified in (2) above, but in a 28 ft room, with the north aisle eliminated and benches thus in peninsula layout. Only 11.2 sq ft are now required per student enrolled. Since the total area has been reduced, it is important to examine rating in square feet per student *in a given section* at one time. This is about 45 sq ft, and the room is still not seriously crowded.

Planners favoring the extreme economy of alternate (3) consider the accident hazard with peninsula design to be unimportant, provided no high superstructure is built on top of the island benches. With such precaution, there would then be no serious difficulty in pulling a partially disabled person over the bench in case he had been trapped by a solvent fire starting in the south end of his aisle. This situation should, however, be cleared with state and city fire wardens before a fundamental design is adopted.

Combined Laboratory and Quiz Room. The single-section room plan is especially well adapted to the scheme of conducting discussions and laboratory work in one room. Such an economical plan eliminates the troublesome search over a large campus for numerous special quiz rooms at odd hours. Apparently the first serious development of this plan started forty years ago at the University of California (Berkeley) and has now spread not only to other U.C. campuses, but also to Columbia, Kansas and elsewhere.

In organic chemistry the combination of laboratory and quiz may run somewhat in conflict with the "pipe-exclusion" scheme, since the extensive pipe assembly in such a laboratory tends to obstruct the view of students during a quiz session. An unusual design, with all laboratory workers facing in one direction during both laboratory and quiz sessions, has been developed at the State University of Iowa. (Figure 14.6.) All laboratory benches are of a type resembling wall benches, but are distributed throughout the room as long islands. The instructor stands on a slightly raised platform at the end of the laboratory for blackboard discussion sessions. The end position tends to minimize daylight glare from windows. The plan is particularly good for unannounced short sessions—perhaps lasting only one minute—when the instructor wishes to interject short admonitions without general class disturbance or interference with experiments in progress. Since the Iowa scheme calls for a relatively large amount of aisle space per student, no special economy of laboratory space results, that is, provided width of aisle is adequate to prevent a rear worker from causing injury to the person directly in front of him.

Advanced Undergraduate Laboratories

Modifications of Figure 14.4 for various grades of advancement in synthetic organic chemistry are simply arranged. If only qualitative organic analysis is to be handled, reduction in number of hoods is indicated, and addition of at least 10 linear feet of a bank of shallow reagent shelves for the large number of small specimen bottles needed on constant display. A side room for reference books and a few simple instruments is desirable; also strictly private assistants' quarters, with an extensive layout of rather shallow shelves,

Figure 14.6   Combination laboratory-classroom.

one bottle deep, for "unknown" samples. A small work bench and sink are included.

Ringstands. No space is wasted in cupboards for storage of ringstands. Two or three iron shelf clamps, perhaps of the style shown in Figure 14.7*, are permanently attached to the heavy shelf above each student station. A vertical rod 30 in. long is held in each clamp. Extended trial in the UCLA laboratory has shown that a cold-drawn ½ in. steel rod, cut and then dip-galvanized, is eminently satisfactory without service troubles. Two rods are mounted 13 in. apart at the left end of each student station in an organic laboratory; the third about 2½ ft from the nearer of the other two. With this spacing, 98% of the ordinary use of ringstands in undergraduate work is eliminated. Students usually prefer to elevate these rods slightly from the table level, leaving clearance below for good housekeeping. If the load on the stand is heavy, stability is attained by lowering of the rod to rest solidly on the table.

Fire Extinguishers. At least one 2-lb carbon dioxide extinguisher (EXTR, Figure 14.4) should be located near an exit door of the laboratory; one larger device (10 lb or more) at a convenient location within 100 ft of the laboratory. The

* See also the design shown by J. C. Bailar on page 95 of the first edition of this book.

2-lb extinguisher, close at hand, will account for nearly all fires of organic origin. Three spare 2-lb extinguishers are mounted in convenient reach just outside the organic storeroom dispensing window. Rule of the laboratory: If any part whatsoever of the contents of a 2-lb extinguisher is used, the device shall be surrendered promptly to the storekeeper for refilling, and one of the spares put in its place at the laboratory door. No embarrassing questions asked at the storeroom, and particularly no scolding of the student whose fire was probably the result of carelessness. Replacement is more important than moralizing!

Steam Service. Laboratory steam pipes should be thoroughly insulated with good lagging. A mounted steam bath, which collects dirt, is questionable and requires special plumbing. Recommendation: one of the excellent commercial portable aluminum-alloy steam baths, with rubber gas-burner tube from old stock for connection with steam valve over copper fitting. This aluminum device may well stand upon a wooden block, which elevates it to facilitate passage of condensate into the copper-tube drain.

Locks. The committee should be sure that no cabinet locks be used—either key or combination.

Figure 14.7   Ringstand clamped to reagent shelf.

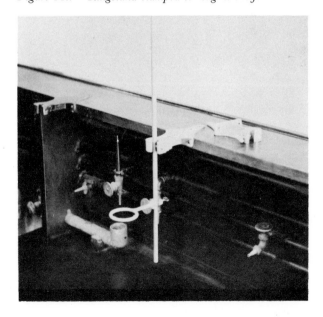

Combination padlocks, while not so elegant, are far superior in laboratory administration. At checking-in time (end of semester) the assistant merely exchanges locks, thus forestalling any later petty theft. No change of combination is required on any lock. Good records of makers' serial numbers and combinations are kept.

Ventilation. Presumably all air should enter near windows and pass through hoods. In undergraduate organic laboratories, where such extremely dangerous reagents as phosgene, hydrogen cyanide and hydrogen sulfide are unlikely to appear, effective general ventilation of the room is even more important than elaborate hood facilities. For example, if 20 students are engaged in experiments in which acetyl chloride and acetic anhydride are escaping in small amounts, the best protection is 12 to 18 changes of air per hour in the room. Widely different opinions on number of changes still prevail, with cost of heating or air conditioning closely related to the dispute.

Safety Shower. Although the conventional location of a shower mechanism is just inside a doorway, playful misuse of such a device has led to the modification arranged over a wall sink in the similitude of a domestic bathroom shower. A brightly painted lever arm, with excellent mechanical advantage on a positive-acting valve, gives quick and certain service. Incidentally, distilled water may be dispensed in routine at the same wall sink.

Wood vs. Steel Benches. In a sanitary, medical or dairy laboratory operated by responsible professional workers, steel furniture is recommended. For undergraduates using large amounts of strong acids and alkalies without skill or great care, hardwood is generally preferred. The battle against corrosion of steel benches in such a laboratory in future years would be serious. Steel furniture in a crowded laboratory is also somewhat noisy. Maple and birch are especially good, though medium-dark stained oak gives the promise of longest good external appearance. One should not forget that the rush to steel furniture after the war was closely related to the poor quality of unseasoned hardwood which characterized the period 1945-1950. Present-day maple, birch and oak are excellent and in good supply.

Bench-Top Material. No outstanding "best" table top seems to be recognized by impartial consumer authority. The building committee will simply have to weigh conflicting factors, including the following:

WOOD. Perhaps of lowest cost; involves minimum hazard of breakage of glassware; vulnerable to acids, caustic reagents and fire. If wood is specified, the committee should insist on a thickness ½ in. greater than the minimum normally acceptable in the laboratory from a structural standpoint. This allows for two power-sanding treatments in future years. With such specification, there should be no excessively deep slot or hole running upward from the bottom of the table top. Such slots are put in by manufacturers to accommodate bolt heads and nuts attached to internal cross rods. In any event, a wooden top offers opportunity in later years for some newly invented cover sheet of merit, perhaps stainless steel.

In the organic laboratory it is important that no *colored* coating, vulnerable to acetone or trichloroethylene, be used. Impregnation of the wood surface with polymeric material, such as polyfurfural or allied complex, is popular in America. A black finished surface results. In England and Holland, however, the black appearance is deplored by many. Instead it is the custom merely to stain the wood to reveal a natural warm-brown grain. Students are then required to apply a *colorless* wax treatment at regular intervals. Such table tops at least do not impart black smudges to flask and beaker bottoms. Although common paraffin has been used abroad, probably one of the high-class carnauba-beeswax preparations would be better.

SAWED NATIVE STONE. This material is extremely popular in eastern states, within range of reasonable freight rates. Resistance to reagents gives high rating. Principal disadvantages are hazard of breaking glassware, and in the cases of some type of stone, vulnerability to cracking with little or no chance for repair. Similar objections might be cited to ceramic tile, very popular in France. High wage scales in the tile-setting industry in America probably have excluded this option, even though repair would not be the problem.

SYNTHETIC STONE. This is strongly recommended by certain responsible manufacturers, but is subject to criticism from the standpoint of reagent attack. The material should have a tough, flexible asbestos fiber reinforcement, and in the organic laboratory, good polymeric impregnation.

GLASS FIBER-REINFORCED PLASTIC. This is a recent development which has not had a long period of trial. Such material should be of ample thickness, bringing to mind that no table-top material or coating for the surface should be thin.

STAINLESS STEEL. Although even stainless steel is vulnerable to attack by acids, surprisingly good results have been noted in undergraduate laboratories. Principal use is for radiochemistry applications; see pages 69, 160, 394.

Piped Services. Domestic water, gas, air, 110-120 volt alternating current service and steam are universally conceded to be necessary in the organic laboratory. Steam valves in the present plan would be mounted over openings in the copper-tube drain, just like condenser-water supply valves. Piped vacuum service is not unanimously approved, but is desirable if good traps are included in the system to receive unwelcome liquid masses which get in through carelessness in conducting filtration. It is the writer's opinion that wired-in direct current is an extravagance in an organic laboratory. It is more economical to bring a portable electronic rectifier to a bench for the exceptional case where d.c. is needed in an experiment in organic chemistry. Recent notable advances in electronics have made this practice more popular than in the old days.

Organic Research Laboratory

Figure 14.5 shows, perhaps to the extreme, the recent trend toward small quarters for the "home bench" of the individual graduate student. Even the 8-foot assignment of the figure might be slightly reduced, but the total area per graduate student in the whole system of connected organic research laboratories is greater than ever. This trend runs counter to the more classical needs of the researcher studying naturally occurring organic compounds. In laboratories where such interest predominates, one may still recommend Figure 14.5, but with the *temporary* use of a succession of portable tables, 3 feet wide, in place of half, three-fourths or even all of the more modernistic racks. Future alternation will then be simple as research problems may change. For the intermediate period only electric service and the floor drain need be provided. In any case, a full complement of costly 4½ ft standard benches is not needed in the positions now marked "racks."

In the organic field, the 6-man laboratory suggested by Hurd (*loc. cit.*) is a satisfactory compromise between the minimum of 4, bordering on unsafe from the accident-hazard standpoint, and 8, which begins to threaten research efficiency from too much distracting conversation.

The requirement per student in the main laboratory room is 145 sq ft net useful area. Slight additional economy could be achieved by addition of a second central bench to the plan of Figure 14.5, also an additional hood. The laboratory would of course be 9 ft longer, but would accommodate 8 students at 138 sq ft each.

Aisles between benches are reduced from the 5 ft value generally sanctioned as correct for undergraduate class traffic, to 4½ ft, the main aisle also being narrower. Workers who expect to introduce many gas cylinders or other obstructions resting on the floor may wish to hold to the 5 ft dimension, however. The student's personal laboratory bench, being now only 8 ft long, may well have deep drawers and cupboards, with pipe exclusion, as in the undergraduate plan already discussed. One very wide drawer may be provided for each student; perhaps also the long pigeonhole passageway for condensers and burets in island benches.

Hoods are always much longer in graduate laboratories for organic chemistry than those for class use. One is designated as a "walk-in" hood, a door on the west end (Figure 14.5) permitting removal of whatever bench or table may have been provided for the normal use of that unit. Space under normal table-top level in regular hoods may be devoted to storage of noxious materials, with care that vapors from such nuisances have free opportunity to escape into the hood flues. Controls for public utility services are outside hoods. Safety-glass windows are provided in such an arrangement so that it is impossible to cover the whole front of any one hood.

Racks consist of low tables, perhaps only 1 ft high, surmounted by vertical ½ in. rods held in a secure frame so that the whole assembly, facing east and west in the figure, may be operated as though it were a battery of ringstands 7 ft high. A floor drain under each rack serves both for rack apparatus and for general service protection against flooding.

A cabinet or portable table near the center bench takes care of solvent safety cans or miscellaneous equipment. The refrigerator-freezer is a conventional kitchen unit with capacity for a few pounds of frozen material. Special attention should be paid to spark-proofing in the electric connections of this device. Sinks (soapstone preferred) are much larger than in other research laboratories, especially the center sink, used for washing very large apparatus. For each research student a 42 in. single-post study desk, with two small drawers and one large file drawer, is surmounted with a simple pine bookcase.

A pair of such research laboratories open into the appliance-instrument room just west of the main room of Figure 14.5. According to the climate of the region, a variable outfit of coat hooks is designated. A combination distilled-water and oblique shower unit for domestic water is provided, as described in the undergraduate plan.

The marking T indicates an indefinite number of stout portable tables, 2 ft wide and perhaps in both 3½ ft and 5 ft lengths. Some of these might be in 37, 24 and 18 in. heights. These should be designated and drawn in the contract plans, but may be later moved around to suit researchers. One should not ordinarily specify built-in furniture in an appliance room.

The installation of special d.c. wiring is again questioned for an organic laboratory, in view of modern electronic rectifier service. Storage batteries serving such d.c. wiring would involve high cost for purchase and service. The necessary heavy wiring for distribution of central battery power is also very costly.

Auxiliary Research Laboratories

Special research rooms, once a minor part of organic chemistry, are of rapidly growing significance, and involve great and mounting cost. A few of these functions may be handled by the graduate students themselves without close supervision, and the smaller ones would be housed in the appliance and instrument room of Figure 14.5, for example, UV spectrophotometers, and even the new simplified infrared devices; also such items as thermostatic baths, low-pressure hydrogenators, ozonizer, microbalance and glass-working equipment.

A much more complex problem is offered by extensive instrumentation. The following list, with only very brief characterization, is just an illustration taken from recent plans of major universities in the face of the projected academic boom of the 1960's. Space allowances are subject to wide variation according to size of institution and prevailing research interests, and parts are of definite significance to small colleges as well as universities. Area is given in square feet net useful area, as usual:

Spectroscopy (spectrophotometry); laboratories in charge of trained, fulltime technicians, including ultraviolet and infrared instruments 1000

Mass spectrometry 500

Nuclear magnetic resonance 500
(Air conditioning essential, positions low in building may be desirable; sales engineers of the manufacturers should be consulted on details of this extremely valuable installation)

Polarimetry; precision instruments 200

Radiochemistry counting room or rooms; located at a considerable distance from possible "hot" laboratory and from radioactive materials storage; see p. 159 400

Chromatography; column, paper and gas 400

Microanalysis for carbon, hydrogen, nitrogen, etc., with air conditioning and vibration-free location for microbalances; fulltime technicians 700

Sealed-tube furnace room, with minimum of combustible matter in the vicinity; under supervision of the microanalyst 100

Ozonization laboratory—established as a separate room in view of explosion hazard; excellent ventilation required 200

Cold laboratory, for conduct of reactions by persons actually working in refrig-

erated atmosphere; storage of products and intermediates involved; range of working temperature, 0° to 5°C.	125
Cold storage, ordinary	75
Combined "deep-freeze" and "cold" room; interior room −20° to 0°C, exterior 0° to +5°C.	200
Grinding, chopping and extraction room, especially needed by workers with naturally-occurring compounds; coffee grinder, Wiley mill, percolators	400
Large-scale preparations—especially significant if no assistance of a chemical engineering division is available	250
Special hazards room, with high-velocity walk-in hood and high-speed stirring facilities mounted on walls. (In laboratories where students are not allowed to conduct research at night, this room may be expanded into a night-operations room with special fire protection, as in certain European buildings.	200
High-pressure laboratories autoclave division, perhaps shared with a biochemistry group	150
high-pressure hydrogenation; rooms with armorplate protective walls, controls in safe positions, and open louvers for escape of gas in explosion	200
Dead storage—for apparatus temporarily out of use, or waiting for dissembly	500

In addition to features cited above, building committees may well consider the following check list, taken largely from the recommendations of Hurd (*loc. cit.*):

Asphalt tile flooring (often criticized but actually giving wide satisfaction at low cost); location of balance rooms; adequate number of shut-off valves in laboratories; small shelves in student-locker cupboards; crushed ice dispensing service, now obtainable in much improved form from equipment not obtainable at the time of the Hurd record; use of squeegee devices; steam-heated cabinets for drying glassware; steel slots in walls for large-scale operations, and tall shaft to accommodate long fractionating columns.

More Building Per Acre of Campus

The projected expansion of college attendance poses the problem of wider, more capacious laboratory buildings on limited plots. Original builders of chemistry laboratories have rarely foreseen the desirability of earmarking adequate space for extension of facilities as now contemplated.

In such a predicament the committee of the 1960's is likely to consider the relegation of the whole "old" chemistry building to undergraduate instruction, and the construction of an annex, or extension, on the end of the old block, largely for advanced study. Unfortunately, there is usually not enough land to take care of a long extension on classical lines with central corridor. This calls for the more compact central-utility-channel design, known to chemical industry but relatively new to colleges.

Figure 14.8 is an extremely simplified sketch of the central-channel or "core" plan applied to a wide extension of an old-time narrow (70′) building. This extension, in the example chosen, is supposed to be particularly for organic research.

The outer rows of rooms (OFC), with daylight illumination, are used for offices and other rooms not requiring hoods or pipe lines. The inner, larger rooms (LAB) are laboratories with convenient access to the central channel. The whole structure is virtually an assembly of duplicate buildings, back to back, the service channel 7 to 8 ft wide separating the two "fire walls" that are the inner boundaries of the laboratories. The 7-ft zone is extremely cheap space, figured before pipe installation, with only stamped-metal catwalks as floors. One may thus provide ample space for plumbers and maintenance personnel.

Three objections at once arise. First, many faculty members prefer their private laboratories and offices to be contiguous. Secondly, it is improbable that any normal department of chemistry could use so much space without mechanical equipment as shown in Figure 14.8. This objection is met by planning a hybrid of the common scheme and the central-channel design. A short sample section from the center of such a structure is shown in Figure 14.9 which introduces one conventional flue-and-pipe easement in the southerly rooms. Offices appear on the north side only. Tolerances of dimensions of net useful areas might be approximately the following:

Offices, 13 to 15 ft deep.

Corridors, 6 to 6½ ft wide.

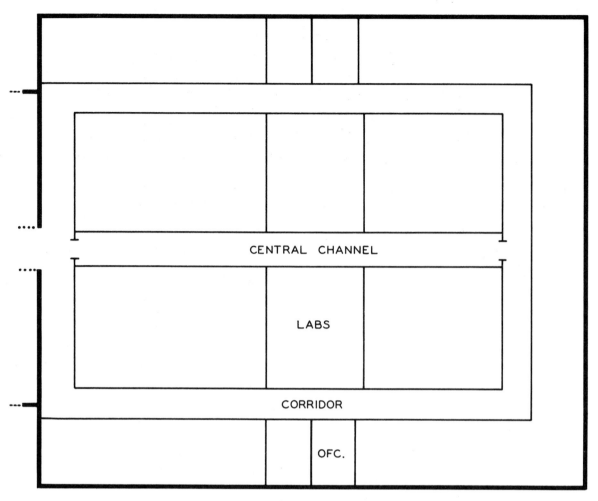

Figure 14.8 Central channel plan adapted to a narrow building.

Figure 14.9 Hybrid plan involving a combination of common scheme and central channel design.

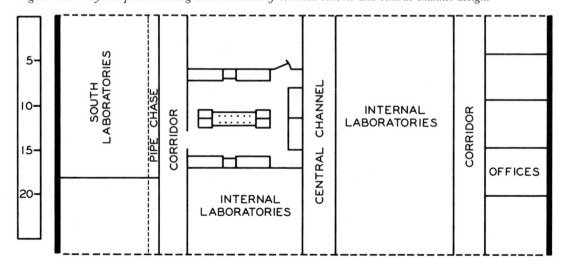

Interior laboratories, 25 to 27 ft deep; e.g., the organic research laboratory near the center of the figure.

Central channel, 7 to 8 ft wide.

South laboratories, 19 to 21 ft deep, exclusive of easement.

The third objection comes from workers who dislike windowless laboratories. Such workers have a rather weak case in view of their almost invariable present-day habit of turning on fluorescent lights, summer or winter. But they must have adequate forced ventilation in the central-channel plan.

Since the necessity of two corridors is an essential part of the central-channel plan, no particular increase of net useful building area efficiency results, in comparison with old patterns. Accordingly, the core plan is not recommended where land is plentiful.

On the credit side of the argument, especially in organic chemistry, is the displacement of hoods and their fire hazards to the back of a laboratory, next to the channel. This appears in Figure 14.9, showing a laboratory for 4 graduate students in "modern" organic chemistry.

More Students Per Laboratory

The most obvious answer to the cry of the 1960's to handle more students is to divide the bench space into more and smaller lockers. Usually this means the elimination of cupboards, a remedy already deplored in this chapter as far as organic chemistry is concerned.

A more reasonable answer has come from the University of California (Berkeley) by use of built-in supplementary locker blocks set just back of the students. Figure 14.10, another simplified sketch, shows the main principle by which the black strips (lockers without plumbing) are in alternate positions between the main work benches. It is not a complete diagram, to scale, of the Berkeley layout.

Actually a "pilot" laboratory has been installed on the Berkeley campus, and this room already has had several terms' trial with regular classes. In this trial laboratory not only is the feature idea of Figure 14.10 used, but there are also several changes in bench design and arrangement. Subject to some corrections in dimensions, an exten-

sive installation of organic laboratories on the new plan is now about to be finished. In any given room so arranged, seven or more class sections can be accommodated, some working from lockers in the principal benches (with piping) directly in front of the student, the others from lockers without plumbing directly behind. The supplementary locker cabinet presents drawer fronts and cupboard doors to workers on both sides of that unit.

Although the Berkeley plan requires much more space between main (piped) benches, the net result is a substantial reduction in total constructional cost per student below values for Figure 14.4 of this chapter. This is due in part to the low cost of cabinet work without piping. Unfortunately the rest of the Berkeley economy comes from reduction in length of student station, bench width and accessibility of sinks—revisions which do not meet unanimous academic approval outside. Nevertheless, designers of instructional laboratories for heavy student load should investigate the forthcoming Berkeley laboratories.

The California plan raises the question of how one can pack seven or eight sections of *organic* chemistry, with adequate time allowance, into a

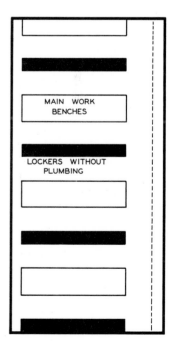

MAIN WORK BENCHES

LOCKERS WITHOUT PLUMBING

Figure 14.10 Experimental laboratory with locker blocks between work benches.

single week's schedule. The following solutions are offered; perhaps two or more of these might be useful simultaneously:

(1) Organize more "short-course," one-period schedules, especially for patrons from such fields as home economics and veterinary science.

(2) Use night schedules, sometimes popular if many dormitories are nearby.

(3) Schedule a "two-period" laboratory assignment, normally given at such a time as TuTh 1–4 p.m., at 12:30 p.m. to 6 p.m. on a single day. This plan may not suit local educational policy. At Berkeley, where it has been run experimentally, many students claim that they can get more real organic synthesis done in an uninterrupted 5½-hour period than in two 3-hour sessions. The teaching assistants are enthusiastic about the scheme, for rather obvious research reasons.

Part 3: PLANNING A QUANTITATIVE ANALYSIS LABORATORY

WARD B. SCHAAP AND LYNNE L. MERRITT, Jr.

Indiana University
Bloomington, Indiana

The laboratory for instruction in undergraduate quantitative analysis should be planned with the following considerations in mind.

(1) The size of the laboratory should allow efficient and convenient supervision.

(2) The appearance of the laboratory should be conducive to neat, careful work. The materials used should be attractive, but impervious to the chemicals used. Sufficient and convenient utility outlets must be available.

(3) The lighting must be adequate, so that frequent, careful measurements and readings can be made by the students with a minimum of eyestrain.

(4) Storage space (lockers) for student equipment should be convenient and adequate.

(5) Special-purpose areas are needed in the laboratory for storing and dispensing chemicals, for drying and igniting crucibles and samples, and for careful heating of solutions.

(6) Several adjacent rooms are needed for balances, miscellaneous instruments, storage and preparation of samples, solutions, and student records, for storage of glassware and miscellaneous student supplies.

The above considerations will be discussed individually in some detail. The article by G. G. Marvin* can be consulted for some additional or alternative suggestions.

* G. G. Marvin, "The Analytical Laboratory," *J. Chem. Ed.*, **24**, 329 (1947).

Size

We estimate from personal experience that the optimum number of students in a laboratory section that can be supervised efficiently and adequately by a single instructor is about 20 to 30. Too many students and too crowded conditions cause disturbance, noise and confusion, and decrease student working efficiency. Each student should have at least 5 or 6 ft of bench top space while he is working. Thus, only 3 students should be working at one time on one side of a 15–18-ft bench, and four such benches would be needed in a laboratory with a capacity of 24 students per section. Because the actual desk storage space available for each student in quantitative analysis should be about 16 to 20 in. wide, a laboratory unit containing four 18-ft benches would probably have a total capacity of 96 students working in four separately scheduled sections. Four 24-ft benches would give a capacity of 32 per section and a correspondingly larger total capacity. The width of the bench top should be from 48 to 54 in. The height of the benches should be about 36 in. and the aisles between benches should be from 50 to 60 in. across.

We believe that larger laboratory capacity should be attained by multiplying the number of basic optimum-sized laboratory units rather than by increasing the size over the optimum described above. (We have also found by experience that

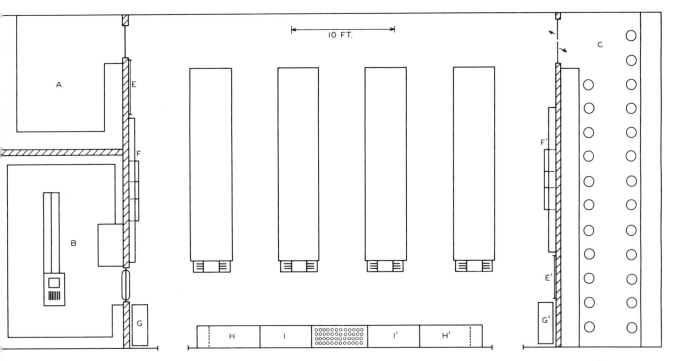

Figure 14.11   Quantitative analysis laboratory unit (for 24 students) showing adjacent rooms.

LEGEND

A: Instrument and calculation room, showing benches along walls.

B: Combination storeroom, office and solutions room, showing laboratory bench (with sink) and shelves at center, showing shelves, bins and desk along walls and dispensing door.

C: Balance room, illustrating possible position of balance tables, stools and entrance-exit doors.

E,E': Blackboards

F,F': Reagent dispensing areas, including laboratory bench and sink with shelving on both sides and above.

G,G': Hat and coat racks.

H,H': Hoods for drying ovens, open at front and on one side where table top is extended.

I,I': Hoods for muffle furnaces or racks of ignition burners.

J: Hood for steam bath (or possibly large, low (controlled)-temperature hot plates) for evaporation.

two 4-hour laboratory sections per week accomplish more than three 3-hour sections because of the time wasted in starting and cleaning up during each period.) Figure 14.11 shows an arrangement suggested for a quantitative analysis laboratory unit with a capacity of 24 students. If needed, a second similar laboratory and balance room could be placed on the other side of the office-storeroom and instrument room and connected by doors to them. In this case, the widths of the service rooms, which would then serve both laboratory units, should be increased somewhat, perhaps to about 18 ft.

Appearance, Materials and Utilities

The general appearance and atmosphere of a quantitative analysis laboratory should inspire careful work. Elimination of utility pipes, racks, faucets and outlets above bench top height, insofar as possible, gives the laboratory a modern, low, clean-swept appearance. This can be achieved by use of cup sinks, gooseneck water faucets, and pedestal-type electrical outlets and gas stopcocks. The utility pipes are then concealed under the bench. A large end-sink is needed for washing larger equipment. Sets of bottles for the commonly used reagents can be kept in polyethylene trays on each bench top. Larger reagent bottles and other chemicals can be kept in the reagent dispensing area where they can be poured, weighed and any spillage easily cleaned up (see below). A bench with this approximate layout is shown in Figure 14.12.

Hard stone (e.g., "Alberene") is the proven bench-top material. Wood tops that require frequent repainting or other treatments are undesirable because warm objects tend to stick and to pick up weighable deposits. White Carrara glass has been recommended by Marvin.[1] "Formica" is very attractive, available in colors, heat-resistant and impervious to almost all chemicals. (It is etched very slowly by concentrated sulfuric acid and is stained by solutions of silver salts. These stains, however, can be removed with nitric acid solutions. A medium to dark gray color would probably be the most practical.)

Each laboratory bench should have about 12 gas stopcock outlets distributed along its length and about 8 to 12 electrical outlets (110 V, a.c., perhaps as three pedestals with four receptacles each). If available, a vacuum line with 8 to 12 stopcocks is desirable. Alternately, 6 to 8 water faucets fitted with aspirators are needed on each bench to allow filtration by suction. (The position of the faucets relative to the sinks and the

design of the sinks should be such that splashing is minimized when aspirators are used.) One distilled water tap located at the sink at one end of the bench is sufficient. Traps and drain pipes made of "Pyrex" or polyethylene are to be preferred over metal pipes because of the resistance of these materials to acids and to mercury.

Lighting

Quantitative Analysis students make many careful, and exact readings and measurements. In order to minimize eye strain, the laboratory lighting should be of high intensity, but diffuse and as indirect as possible. Networks of fins below direct flourescent light fixtures help diffuse the light. Light-colored walls and white ceilings are desirable. Natural finish wood or light-colored, painted metal laboratory furniture is helpful.

Student Lockers

The student locker space should be more than enough to store all permanent equipment. Quantitative Analysis experiments often are not completed in one laboratory period, so samples and solutions frequently must be carefully stored from one period to the next without spillage or contamination. The lockers should be at least 16 in. wide. Usually the locker consists of a drawer (about 6 in. deep) and a cabinet below (with a half-shelf) capable of storing bottles up to about 14 in. tall. There should be a separate, protected box-like tube long enough to store glass burets. (About 33 in. is adequate length for buret storage, but the back ends will extend into the utilities area and must be planned for.) It is most convenient to have the lockers fixed so that a single padlock will serve both the drawer and the cabinet.

Special-purpose Areas Within Laboratory

An important aid to keeping the laboratory clean and safe from hazardous chemicals is to have one or two well-planned areas for storing and dispensing miscellaneous solid chemicals and reagent stock solutions. Such a dispensing area should have adequate storage shelves, a sink with wide drain boards and with tap and distilled water faucets. There should be sufficient space for at least two trip scales and this space should

Figure 14.12   Quantitative analysis laboratory bench.

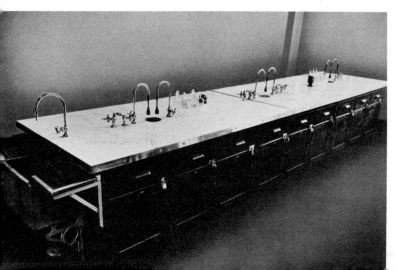

be easy to wash off in case anything is spilled.

One or two overhead safety showers should be strategically located in each laboratory for the protection of students whose clothing catches fire or who spill acid or caustic on themselves. The showers should be well marked, preferably with a painted circle on the floor. Other safety equipment, such as eye-washing fountains, first aid cabinets and fire extinguishers, must be conveniently located.

A laboratory serving 20 to 30 students should have three or four 18 x 18 x 12 in. drying ovens (110 or 220 V) or their equivalent for drying student equipment and samples. It is desirable to have these arranged so that the heat and fumes given off are exhausted.

The laboratory should also have several high-temperature muffle furnaces (200 V) for ignition of precipitates or, alternatively, a rack of about 24 to 36 high-temperature burners (with remote control of gas flow). The muffle furnaces or burner racks should be placed under a hood and exhaust fan so that the large amounts of heat, smoke and fumes given off do not escape into the laboratory.

For careful heating of sample solutions, when boiling is to be avoided, a steam bath is highly desirable. This should also be located under a hood and should be of adequate size. About 45 to 60 holes of 3 to 4 in. diameter and fitted with rings would be desirable for the size laboratory unit recommended earlier. Large, carefully controlled hot plates may perform the same function, but are less foolproof.

Adjacent Rooms for Balances, Instruments and Samples

Several service rooms adjacent to the quantitative analysis laboratory are required. One possible arrangement of these rooms in relation to the main laboratory is shown in Figure 14.11.

One of these rooms is for student balances. These are delicate, sensitive instruments and should be protected from laboratory fumes and drafts. It is desirable to have a balance for each student in a section. It is definitely undesirable to have more than two students in the same section assigned to one balance. Thus, the balance room should be planned to be of adequate size

to contain as many balances as students in a section.* Balances should not be too close together because each student must have room enough for his desiccator, several beakers and a laboratory notebook, in addition to manipulating the balance controls. We estimate a minimum distance of one balance every 27 to 30 in. Balances should not be placed close to radiators, windows or rapidly swinging doors, as all these are sources of drafts which adversely affect operation of the unprotected balance. Stools fastened to the floor at appropriate distances are much better than movable chairs. (Some laboratories have balance tables at a standing height to minimize loafing and "horseplay" in the balance room.) Balance tables should be securely fastened to bearing walls or, preferably, each balance can be set on a vibration-damping platform of some type (cantilever or floating). The balance tables should be about 36 in. high and about 20 to 24 in. deep. The entrance and exit door should have a wide window at eye height to eliminate collisions. (Separate entrance and exit doors might be preferable. Also, a foot-actuated mechanism to open the balance-room doors has been used successfully.) Aisles leading to the balance room should be wide and not subject to congestion by those working at benches and the balance room traffic.

A room for instruments, protected from laboratory fumes, is also desirable in the modern quantitative analysis laboratory. This room is needed to house electrodeposition apparatus, colorimeters, pH meters used in following acid-base, oxidation-reduction and precipitation titrations, etc. An area somewhat smaller than that for the balance room is adequate. If mercury is used, a hood and/or exhaust fan must be installed to remove the poisonous mercury vapor. Also, large stainless steel trays on the bench tops help keep mercury from spilling on the floor. Polyethylene or "Pyrex" drain traps are to be recommended where mercury is used near sinks.

The room for keeping and preparing student samples ("unknowns") usually doubles as an office for the laboratory instructor. Here he keeps

---

* Use of single pan, automatic balances would allow 4 to 6 students to be assigned to one balance and greatly decrease the space needed for balances.

the many different solid unknown samples, standard stock solutions and all records. If the room is well planned, a large amount of floor space is not needed. Most of the wall area from floor to ceiling can be covered with shelving of different heights (2 ft to 8 in.). Some of the shelving should be about 12 in. deep and 24 in. high and strongly supported in order to hold a number of 10 gal bottles of stock solutions. It would be convenient to have a sink with tap and distilled water in this room and to have a two-piece dispensing door opening into the laboratory. An office-type desk and locking filing cabinet and card file are desirable.

The student supply stockroom should be convenient to both the laboratory and the main stockroom. An elevator or dumbwaiter connecting with the main stockroom is highly desirable. Again, shelves from floor to ceiling, some bins for large or round items and sets of drawers for small items and hardware are required, in addition to a dispensing window or door(s).

In schools where it is planned to place the responsibility for the storerooms, for issuing "unknowns" and for solution preparation under a single (permanent) staff member, the corresponding areas described above can be combined into one larger room. The required shelving and furniture remain the same. Such a set-up is shown in Figure 14.11.

PART 4: PLANNING INSTRUMENTAL ANALYSIS LABORATORIES

LYNNE L. MERRITT, JR. AND WARD B. SCHAAP
Indiana University
Bloomington, Indiana

Since courses in Instrumental Methods of Analysis are becoming quite general in the college and university curriculum, attention must be paid to the proper planning of space for such laboratories. The needs of such a course are quite different from the ordinary quantitative analysis laboratory, but rather resemble those of a physical chemistry laboratory in many respects. Besides laboratory space for instruction in instrumental methods, there is usually needed similar space for housing of instruments used in research. This discussion will be concerned primarily with instructional space, but many of the same principles will apply to the design of rooms for research instruments.

The instructional space should preferably be divided into several separate, but contiguous rooms since several special needs must be met. It is best to keep most instruments away from the ordinary fumes of a chemical laboratory, especially acid fumes. Thus there should be one distinct area or room with provision for ordinary chemical benches in which the students will keep their laboratory equipment and on which they will prepare their materials, solutions and unknowns for use with the instruments. This space must have good ventilation, adequate hoods and should be supplied with the ordinary utilities such as hot and cold water, distilled water, gas, electricity and drains. In this area, the desks should be of standard laboratory height, 36 in., and the desk tops should be of a durable material, such as stone. Side shelves for chemicals should be provided in this area and also space for rough and for accurate weighings. In general only one analytical balance is necessary for a laboratory section of up to 10 or 12 students.

Many of the small and medium-sized instruments can be placed in one large, general instrument room. These instruments include colorimeters, spectrophotometers (both ultraviolet and infrared), refractometers, pH meters, titrimeters, fluorescence meters, gas chromatography apparatus, etc. Such apparatus generally requires only ordinary utilities, but especially electricity. The laboratory space should preferably be completely air-conditioned but, most important of all, the relative humidity should be kept below about 40 to 50%. This will increase the life of the instruments and will permit one to work with materials such as NaCl or KBr cells which are needed in the infrared region.

The amount of desk space needed can be estimated by adding up the lengths of the various pieces of equipment and allowing from 3 to 4 ft between each instrument for the placement of solutions and notebooks and for working space when the instruments need repair. Each working space should be provided with a cup sink and a cold water outlet, a gas outlet, an air outlet, and several 110-volt a.c. outlets. An ideal arrangement, if finances permit, would be to have all 110-volt a.c. outlets in the instrumental laboratory operate from a regulated source. If this is not possible, perhaps one outlet at each space might come from a regulated source. Several independently fused circuits should be provided in this room.

Desks for a general instrumental laboratory are conveniently 33 in. high, so that the instrument can be easily controlled by a seated operator and so that dials on the top of the instrument can be clearly read and operated. Space below the desk top should be open to allow for knee space. The desk tops can be made of synthetic materials such as "Formica" or of stone, but should not be of metal since many electrical instruments will be placed on them.

It is most convenient to have a special bench or area set aside for the repair of electrical equipment with provision for an oscilloscope; test equipment such as ohmmeters, voltmeters, ammeters, signal generators, tube checkers, etc.; soldering guns; and sufficient storage for electronic supplies (tubes, resistors, capacitors, switches, dials, transistors, screws and bolts, wire, connectors, fuses and the like). In the general instrumental laboratory, there should also be sufficient storage space for spare parts for each class of instruments. We have found that five locked cabinets, each 7 ft x 32 in. x 24 in., is about right.

Some instruments, either because of their size, special utility requirements, or unusual hazards in their operation, should be isolated in smaller rooms or areas, for example, the instruments using mercury, such as polarographs, some electrodeposition set-ups, amperometric titration equipment, etc. Such locations should have adequate ventilation. (Air removed should be vented outside, not returned to the air-conditioning equipment.) Stainless steel desk tops with raised edges are especially suitable in this area. The tops should slope toward one region where a mercury collection bottle can be placed. The drain traps in this area should also be made of plastic or of glass. In addition, the standard utilities are needed. A place in this room where a mercury purification unit can be placed should be included.

Spectrographic equipment, because of its large size, high cost and need for special services such as 220 V a.c., darkroom facilities and special ventilation over the source units, is usually isolated in separate rooms. Suggestions for design of spectrographic laboratories are available from the manufacturers of equipment. There are several small units available, designed especially for beginning instructional use. If such equipment is contemplated, then provision for a small hood over the source unit and a 220 V a.c. outlet and d.c. (if available) should be made in the area selected. Also the area should not be far from darkroom facilities.

X-ray diffraction units involve some likelihood of radiation exposure if ports are carelessly left open. They also require 220 V a.c. sources and a supply of cold water at 20-50 psi pressure, depending on the equipment selected. Thus X-ray equipment should be installed in a separate room or enclosed area with attention paid to the provision of necessary plumbing and electrical supply. The area should also be close to darkroom facilities.

Closely allied to X-ray equipment is radioactivity-measuring apparatus. If experiments in radioactivity are contemplated, then a separate area should be considered. Here, stainless steel desk tops are especially desirable, since they can be easily cleaned. A good hood, vented separately to the outside, should be provided for anything above the lowest level of radioactivity (above the microcurie range). The scalers should be removed from the area where preparations are made. It would probably be unwise to place the X-ray and radioactivity areas close to each other because of the mutual interaction of the radiations on the measuring equipment.

Flame photometers may discharge undesirable material, such as metallic vapors into the atmosphere, and therefore provision should be made for venting this area. Also flame photometers require space for tanks of gases such as acetylene, oxygen, etc. and an outlet for compressed air.

One darkroom area, properly situated close to the X-ray and spectrographic equipment, will probably serve for an instrumental analysis laboratory. The room may have more than one door, but if so, the lights should be arranged with signalling devices so that someone outside will not turn them on inside when the room is in use. Another idea is to enter the darkroom through light traps, a sort of maze which prevents light from entering the room from outside. Desks in a darkroom should be easily cleaned and, of course, a plentiful supply of cold water—preferably also

chilled water—and distilled water should be provided. Good ventilation and humidity and temperature control are desirable, especially in hot, humid climates. Instead of electrical or mechanical timers, the authors have found it better to install electric clocks with sweep-second hands and to illuminate the clocks with darkroom safelights.

Some instrumental analysis classes include instruction in microscopy. If this is intended, then there must be provided an area for storage of the microscopes and low benches at which the microscopes can be used. The benches should have a plentiful supply of electrical outlets for illuminating sources and also adequate artificial illumination overhead should be provided. It is desirable to arrange a northern exposure if natural illumination is to be used at all.

PART 5: A LABORATORY FOR INORGANIC SYNTHESIS

EDWIN M. LARSEN

The University of Wisconsin
Madison, Wisconsin

A laboratory of advanced inorganic chemistry should be planned and equipped for synthesis, analysis and the study of the physical properties of the compounds synthesized. This type of laboratory is not usually encountered in the United States because of the traditional division of courses between analytical, physical and inorganic chemistry. However, a laboratory course in which the three disciplines are merged certainly would make for a more stimulating experience than most of our inorganic preparation courses now present. In planning such a laboratory one must recognize that the synthetic work should not be solely limited to preparations made under existing room conditions of temperature, pressure and atmosphere, but that equipment should be available for producing wide variations in temperature, pressure, and atmospheres.

Conventional laboratory desks with both drawer and cupboard space should be available with about 6 linear feet of desk top per student. Here the simple manipulations, electrolyses, and ana-

lytical work may be carried out. In addition, the laboratory should contain several racks upon which vacuum lines may be constructed, and other apparatus supported. The vacuum lines are indispensable in the synthesis of compounds which are sensitive to moisture and oxygen of the air. On a vacuum line, volatile reagents may be distilled into a reaction ampule, or removed from the reaction system. Each vacuum line is usually designed with a specific purpose in mind, so no details will be given here. There are several valuable sources of information which may be consulted.[1,2] Each rack however, should be six feet long and just high enough to work on conveniently. It may be mounted on the floor or on a platform. The racks should be placed so as to permit work from either side, and be equipped with all the utilities. Since much of the vacuum line is built in place it would be well to have oxygen for the hand torch also piped to the location. It would be desirable to have a rack installed within a walk-in hood which had vertical lift safety glass doors, and equipped with a high velocity fan. This would make a rack available for work on volatile and toxic compounds such as the boron hydrides and other compounds of this type. For each two students there should be one conventional type hood, four feet in width and three feet in depth with vertical lift safety-glass doors, in which ordinary evaporations and ignitions may be carried out. There should be one hood, perhaps smaller, for use with perchloric acid evaporations only. A special hood is set aside for this purpose since the condensation of perchloric acid vapors on other condensates acting as reducing agents may lead to fires or explosions in the hoods. (See pages 76, 77, 90.)

In addition there should be glove boxes in which reagents can be dispensed or transferred to reaction vessels preparatory to attaching to the vacuum line, or in which a reaction itself may be carried out. Several glove boxes will be required because one is not generally suitable for all occasions. One may be concerned with the exclusion of moisture in one case, or the exclusion of moisture, oxygen and nitrogen in another. Yet in another circumstance, one might desire to operate in a partial vacuum, while in another one may be only interested in confining radioactive material within the box. The box may be placed on a desk against a wall, or two boxes of approximately the same size may be placed back to back on a table in the room. The kind of utilities fed to each box will be determined by the use to which it is to be put. A wide variety of glove boxes are now available commercially, although satisfactory ones may be constructed in the shop of a university.[3]

Many inorganic syntheses are carried out at temperatures other than room temperatures. Low temperatures are usually achieved by using a low boiling liquid or liquid mixtures. Lists of such low temperature systems are given in a variety of sources.[1, 4] At temperatures in the 25–400° range it is sometimes desirable to use constant temperature baths as a means of controlled heating. For this purpose one can use liquids progressing from water to higher boiling organic liquids, and finally fused salt and salt mixtures.

The high temperatures cover a variety of ranges and the nature of the reaction vessels to be heated may require a variety of shapes and sizes of furnaces. Tube furnaces of a variety of diameters and lengths with or without a hinged top are most frequently used. The use of resistance furnaces is common, but present difficulties at the high temperatures where the resistance unit requires a protective atmosphere. In addition, resistance units are relatively slow in heating and cooling. Some of these problems are overcome by using an induction furnace.[5] Information concerning the problems of high temperature chemistry can be found in a variety of sources.[6, 7, 8]

Hand in hand with heating equipment goes the temperature control and recording equipment. One could plan these so that the controlling and recording devices are all on one panel in the room, although it is convenient to have at least one such unit portable so that it can be moved from place to place as it is needed. Details of the type of equipment to be used will be found in the references already cited[4–8] and from manufacturer's bulletins.

Equipment for producing low as well as high pressures should be provided in the laboratory. The equipment for low pressures will range from the simple water aspirator on the laboratory bench to mechanical pumps, and mercury and oil diffusion pumps for use on the vacuum line. It is useful to have one mechanical pump placed on a dolly so that it may be easily transported from one site to another in the laboratory.

For reactions which are carried out at high pressure a special laboratory chamber should be constructed. For the purposes of this laboratory an area of 6 x 4 feet should be adequate. This area should be on the ground level at an outside wall. It should be constructed so that observations[9] and adjustments of equipment can be made outside of the room. Probably a rack upon which apparatus[9] can be supported will be the only "furniture" in the chamber. In addition to the utilities, the room should be well ventilated, and provided with automatic fire fighting equipment. The details of construction can best be obtained from specific papers on the subject.

An additional rack for mounting ion exchange columns should be provided. This rack should extend to the ceiling of the room for the columns are often quite long. Provision should be made for supporting columns which might vary in diameter from one-half inch to six inches and from one foot to twelve feet in length. A floor drain will be necessary to permit easy discharge of wastes. Some thought should be given to platforms to support the eluting agent containers, particularly when large volumes are involved, and similarly for the easy handling of large volumes of collected eluant. These columns[10, 11] may be used for experiments on the separation of ions, for analytical purposes, and for syntheses, especially in the exchange of anions, and the separation of geometrical isomers.

Preparations involving oxidation-reduction are often best carried out by electrolysis. In addition to a supply of various electrodes, and diaphragm materials, the most important item is a source of direct current. For most purposes a portable rectifier will meet most of the demand of aqueous electrochemistry. A rectifier, and voltage regulator along with an ammeter and voltmeter and the necessary connections can all be neatly packaged to give a portable unit which serves the purpose for most laboratory preparations. It does not seem necessary to have the laboratory wired for direct current. Examples of preparatory work done in electrochemistry are given in several laboratory books.[12, 13]

It is possible that syntheses involving radioactive isotopes will be encountered. It must be emphasized that the laboratory facilities must be designed with the nature of the radiation hazard in mind. In any event a separate hood in addition to a glove box should be available for this work. It should be designed so that the utilities can be connected and adjusted from the front or the side, and should be constructed of materials which can be easily cleaned. Hoods with these qualifications are available from many different manufacturers. Provisions must be included for the storage and disposal of radioactive materials. Again the nature and intensity of the radiation to be handled will determine the construction and location of such an installation. Provisions must also be made for the location of counting equipment for the quantitative determination of the radioactive species.[14,15] It would be good to have one such set of equipment easily portable so that it may be moved from the hood area, to glove box, to vacuum rack or ion exchange column when necessary.

In addition to the equipment for synthetic work, equipment and laboratory space should be available for analytical work and the study of the properties of the compounds prepared. If the chemistry building is to have an instrumental laboratory, then the students in this course should have access to that equipment and it would not be necessary to have a special instrument room associated with this laboratory. These instruments would include all forms of absorption spectroscopy, X-ray sources and cameras, apparatus for measuring magnetic properties, and polarimeter. This might also include equipment for calorimetry.

Additional examples of experimental equipment encountered in inorganic preparations will be found in books already cited[4, 12, 13] as well as other indispensable volumes.[16-23]

BIBLIOGRAPHY

1. Sanderson, R. T., "Vacuum Manipulation of Volatile Compounds," John Wiley and Sons, Ltd., New York, New York, 1948.
2. Farkas, A. and Melville, H. W., "Experimental Methods in Gas Reactions," MacMillan and Co., Ltd., London, England, 1939.
3. Tyree, S. Y., Jr. *J. Chem. Ed.* **31,** 603 (1954).
4. Dodd, R. E., and Robinson, P. L., "Experimental Inorganic Chemistry," Elsevier Publishing Co., Amsterdam, Netherlands, 1954.
5. Cable, J. W., "Induction and Dielectric Heating," Reinhold Publishing Corp., New York, New York, 1954.
6. American Institute of Physics, Vol. II, "Temperature, Its Measurement and Control in Science and Industry," Reinhold, New York, New York, 1941 (1955).
7. Campbell, Ivor E., "High Temperature Technology," John Wiley and Sons, Ltd., New York, New York (1956).
8. Bockrun, J. O'M., Mackenzie, J. D., and White, L. L., Butterworth Publications, Ltd., London, England (1959).
9. Williams, Roger, Jr., Vol. II, p. 87–114, "Encyclopedia of Chemical Technology," The Interscience Encyclopedia, Inc., New York, New York (1953).

10. Kunin, Robert, "Ion Exchange Resins," 2nd Ed., John Wiley and Sons, Inc., New York, New York (1958).

11. Nachod, F. C., and Schubert, Jack, "Ion Exchange Technology," Academic Press, Inc., New York, New York (1956).

12. Walton, H. F., "Inorganic Preparations," p. 167–81, Prentice Hall, Inc., New York, New York (1948).

13. Brauer, George, "Handbuch der Praparativen Anorganischen Chemie," Ferdinand Enke, Stuttgart (1954), Vols. I, II, and III.

14. Price, W. J., "Nuclear Radiation Detection," McGraw-Hill Co., Inc., New York, New York (1958).

15. Korff, S. A., "Electron and Nuclear Counters, Theory and Use," 2nd Ed., Van Nostrand, New York, New York (1955).

16. Biltz, H., Biltz, W., Hall, W. T., and Blanchard A. A., "Laboratory Methods of Inorganic Chemistry," John Wiley and Sons, New York, New York (1928).

17. King, A., "Inorganic Preparations," D. Van Nostrand Co., Inc., New York, New York (1936).

18. Booth, H. S., Ed., "Inorganic Syntheses," I. McGraw-Hill Book Co., Inc., New York, New York (1939).

19. Fernelius, W. C., Ed., "Inorganic Syntheses," II. McGraw-Hill Book Co., Inc., New York, New York (1946).

20. Audrieth, L. F., Ed., "Inorganic Syntheses," III. McGraw-Hill Book Co., Inc., New York, New York (1950).

21. Bailar, J. C., Ed., "Inorganic Syntheses," IV. McGraw-Hill Book Co., Inc., New York, New York (1953).

22. Moeller, Therald, Ed., "Inorganic Syntheses," V. McGraw-Hill Book Co., Inc., New York, New York (1957).

PART 6: LABORATORY DESIGN FOR THE UNDERGRADUATE PHYSICAL CHEMISTRY LABORATORY COURSE

PAUL BENDER

University of Wisconsin
Madison, Wisconsin

While the basic features of a good physical chemistry laboratory course are independent of student enrollment, the laboratory arrangements through which they are provided certainly are not. Some of the recommendations in the following discussion apply primarily when large enrollments must be accommodated; supplementary suggestions are made subsequently for the case in which the student load is small. The facilities required in the instructional laboratory are here divided for consideration into five groups: (1) laboratory desks and services, (2) stockrooms, (3) standard laboratory equipment, (4) special apparatus installations, and (5) offices.

LABORATORY DESKS AND SERVICES

A tested unit for laboratory planning is the 4-man desk, which provides 5 to 6 linear feet of working space for each of two men on either side. While larger units are feasible, this size provides ready access with minimum local congestion, facilitating the establishment of the good traffic pattern that the extensive use of special equipment installations in the physical chemistry laboratory requires.

The conventional laboratory desk with central reagent shelf, trough, and end sink has served effectively in many teaching laboratories. The specific needs of physical chemistry suggest, however, that significant advantages may be gained by modification of this standard design. Elimination of the reagent shelf and trough can permit a decrease of about 8 in. in width at each desk while actually increasing the useful working area of the desk top. This result can be obtained by dividing the desk into two sections and placing the sinks between them with a water tap and a good aspirator installed adjacent to each of the

4 working spaces. An additional advantage is a reduction of the plumbing required.

Gas lines have also been a standard laboratory desk feature. Although gas certainly is required at such particular locations as the hood, vacuum rack, etc., consideration of both the experiments commonly scheduled in the modern physical chemistry course and the current trends in the evolution of this course clearly shows that gas is *very* seldom required at the laboratory desk. Because of the possibility of substituting electric heating in some cases, combined with the availability of gas at the hood, etc. even complete elimination of gas from the laboratory desks could be considered. Alternatively, with the peninsula type desk, gas outlets at the wall end of the desk only should be more than sufficient. The aim in general should be to restrict the services supplied to those actually required by the laboratory course.

Four electric outlets should be provided at each work place. Since electric power requirements for physical chemical work are continually increasing, the desk lines installed should be heavy enough to provide adequate reserve capacity for future needs. A 220-volt 3-wire distribution system is recommended; for safety the outlets should be so connected that both hot wires are not accessible at a given work place. Direct current lines are made unnecessary by modern portable rectifier supplies. A good electric ground should be provided at each desk; water pipes or the electric conduit are most often used for this purpose with results adequate in many applications. The water system is usually appreciably inductive, however, and a separate grounding system is preferable.

Compressed air outlets should be provided at intervals throughout the laboratory, but not necessarily at each desk. An efficient filter should be installed in the air line where it enters the laboratory. Line pressure should not exceed 30 pounds in this application; a low-pressure supply at about 6 pounds should be available at the reagent shelf for use in dispensing solutions.

The style of laboratory desk selected depends in part on personal preference and in part on the space available. The peninsula type desk, for example, permits particularly efficient use of space by elimination of one aisle, which in turn reduces traffic in the vicinity of the working areas. The improved isolation of the student is conducive to efficient, individual work. While the use of steel laboratory furniture in research laboratories is increasing, wooden desks still can be highly recommended for student use. The number of desks in a laboratory is ordinarily determined by the size of section considered appropriate for supervision by a single senior staff member. To provide for the inevitable increase in enrollment, the number of equipment lockers per desk should be made as large as possible.

Determination of the optimum locker size requires careful study. Most physical chemistry laboratory experiments now utilize primarily specialized equipment which is either installed around the laboratory or issued from the stockroom. Correspondingly the amount of chemical glassware, etc., required for the individual student's use has decreased. The student locker should be large enough to accommodate the equipment for the experiments regularly in use, as shown by a current survey, with a reasonable allowance for future contingencies. A reduction of the locker inventory not only reduces the initial capital investment, but continues to contribute to efficient laboratory operation by minimizing breakage. Such auxiliary equipment as ringstands, rings, clamps, burette holders, etc., can be eliminated from the individual lockers by making it available from a central supply which ordinarily can utilize what would otherwise be waste space.

Experience shows that desk tops will be subjected to heat, organic solvents, alkali, acids, and dichromate cleaning solution. Soapstone desk tops, while inert to many reagents, are attacked by concentrated acids, are expensive and difficult to replace when broken, and increase glassware breakage because of their rigidity. The improved finishes now available permit wooden tops to satisfy nearly all requirements. An approach which merits careful consideration is the use of a stainless steel (or Monel) protective cover for a wooden top. Of the reagents pertinent here, stainless steel is highly resistant to all except hydrochloric acid, and for the concentrations and temperatures involved little difficulty should arise from this source, even with indifferent house-keeping. While a dull finish should be used, the relatively light background so provided for experimental work has many advantages, among which is the improved student outlook which an attractive laboratory can produce. Such a metal cover should be grounded, but there is no reason why this would increase shock hazards encountered with laboratory equipment.

Sinks for laboratory benches have most commonly been made of soapstone. Here again for the physical chemistry laboratory stainless steel should be considered. Such construction can facilitate variation of sink dimensions and provide sinks whose contours ensure good drainage. Each sink trap should have a drain plug. The drain material should be carefully selected, and "Duriron" or its equivalent in corrosion resistance is suggested. The higher initial cost compared to cast iron should be considered in the light of the total installation cost and the savings obtained by reduced maintenance. Exposed cold water pipes and drains should be insulated to prevent condensation problems in humid weather. Finally, it should be noted that the plumbing installations for the floor above are also of real concern to the physical chemistry laboratory planner.

Proper lighting is essential. Fluorescent lamp fixtures are now almost standard; it is important, however, to make sure that the planning of the lighting installation take into account the decline in intensity regularly encountered due to aging of the lamps and fouling of the associated reflector surface.

STOCKROOMS

The apparatus stockroom should be compact to expedite the handling of apparatus at the beginning and end of laboratory periods. Even when no increase in section size is anticipated, however, reserve storage space must be provided because the changes now taking place in the laboratory course tend to increase the amount of equipment carried by the stockroom.

Open shelves are most satisfactory for storage of items in regular use. Wood construction permits space to be filled in solidly, but in any case adjustable shelves are essential; the highest shelf should be approximately at eye level. A closed cabinet, preferably with glass panel doors, should be provided for storage of special apparatus issued only at intervals. The space above these cases can be used for close cupboards for the storage of reserve stocks and items which are seldom required. Such storage space is sometimes omitted because access to it is relatively difficult, but it can be very useful and is most easily provided in the initial installation. A set of drawers and small bins installed beneath the stockroom window counter will give convenient access to small items.

Storage of chemicals should be relegated to an adjacent prep room. The reagents stocked here should be restricted to those required by the teaching functions of the laboratory. The room should have forced ventilation, working space for preparation of solutions, etc., a sink with hot and cold water and a distilled water outlet, and a workbench for the repair of electronic equipment and other apparatus. A fractionating column suitable for purification of liquids in quantity may be included here if not conveniently available elsewhere.

Suitable storage facilities, in terms of modern radiochemical practices, must be provided for radioactive materials such as the radium-beryllium neutron source. It should be noted that such requirements are less stringent with a plutonium-beryllium neutron source.

A bulletin board should be provided near the stockroom for posting semester experiment assignments, notices of changes in procedures, etc.

STANDARD LABORATORY EQUIPMENT
Balance Room

The balance room should be well-ventilated and well-lighted. Because it appears impractical to assume that the techniques of balance use taught in the quantitative analysis course will automatically be used elsewhere, it is recommended that, if possible, glass panel walls be used for the balance room to facilitate observation of the work done there.

For a given section size the number of analytical balances required depends in part on the nature of the experiments most frequently assigned, and in part on the type of balance provided, since "Chainomatic" or other improved balances can greatly expedite student work. In any case, enough balances should be supplied so that any student may expect to find one almost immediately available when the need arises. One or more Westphal balances should also be provided. Care should be taken to allow enough space at each balance station for proper accommodation of both materials to be weighed and data pad or notebook.

Some experiments, such as study of the dissociation of nitrogen tetroxide by gas density measurements, require weighings of corrosive materials under conditions which involve considerable risk to the balance. A separate balance installation, well removed from the main balance room, should be provided for such cases.

In many laboratories each student locker is supplied with a set of weights. It is preferable to keep the weights at the stockroom, where they may be obtained on request by the student or issued routinely as part of the equipment provided for the particular experiment. In this way the capital investment in weights can be greatly reduced, while the student is assured of better weights through the routine inspection possible at the stockrooms. Experience with this system has shown no difficulties to offset its real advantages. Modern semi-automatic balances eliminate this weight problem.

Reagent Racks

Solid and liquid reagents to which students are to have free access should be kept in separate racks with trip-balance weighing stations located nearby; a shelf width of 3 ft should be entirely adequate. Standard solutions are best stored in large "Pyrex" bottles, with delivery forced by compressed air rather than a siphon arrangement. The air line pressure should be controlled at not more than 6 pounds. Since spillage or splashing of these solutions is unavoidable, a protective coating or cover is desirable for the table used.

Thermostats

Thermostats regulated at 25°C and 35°C are basic laboratory equipment. Beside giving adequate control of temperature, they must provide efficient use of space and simple but reliable means of inserting and removing equipment. A very satisfactory design is described in detail elsewhere.* Construction from stainless steel and plate glass is preferable. A typical thermostat size is 48 x 16 x 16 in.; for sections ranging up to 30 or more students two or three at 25°C and one at 35°C should suffice. Such a thermostat centered on a table 42 in. wide leaves adequate space at each side for auxiliary equipment and data pad; tables holding two thermostats are recommended. Duplex electric outlets should be provided at 2-ft intervals along each side of the table. Ample space must be allowed at each side to minimize disturbances due to laboratory traffic; adjacent working areas should be far enough away to guarantee at least a 4-ft traffic corridor.

A smaller thermostat held at 45°C is also recommended; the top of the frame should slope inward and be fitted with a cover to return condensate to the bath when it is not in use. It is desirable to provide for special experiment work, a thermostat the temperature level of which can be changed easily.

Thermostated water must be circulated to such instruments as refractometers and polarimeters. A small centrifugal pump can provide a flow rate adequate to minimize temperature change in the lines while eliminating undue pressure build-up in case the line becomes blocked. While the water may be drawn from one of the large thermostats, greater flexibility is obtained by providing a small thermostat for each group of instruments.

Hoods

Proper cleaning of glassware for some purposes requires the use of hot dichromatic-sulfuric acid cleaning solution. This material should be confined to an efficient hood which should have an independent exhaust system, and should not be tied in with the ventilation of any other area. Stainless steel has definite advantages as a working surface; a sink with water aspirator should be included. The Cornell-type open-front hood is recommended; a length of 8 to 10 feet is neces-

* "Experimental Physical Chemistry," Daniels *et al.,* 4th edition, McGraw-Hill Book Company, Inc., New York City, 1949.

sary to provide additional space for handling N_2O_4, etc. A closed cupboard under the hood and connected to the exhaust duct will be found very useful for the storage of concentrated acids, etc., the fumes from which should not be allowed to diffuse into the laboratory.

Miscellaneous

Safety showers and First Aid cabinets should be furnished in accordance with accepted standards.

Blackboards are very useful in the laboratory. For installation between successive peninsula-type desks a 3 x 4 ft size will suffice.

Provision must be made for student coats. While some recent laboratory designs have included a separate coatroom, the space devoted to this should be restricted to a minimum which can most easily be provided by a rack for coat hangers rather than by coat hooks.

The fenestration of the laboratory involves the integrated building design. Modern ventilation systems normally require that windows be kept closed, and artificial lighting must be used throughout the year. Windows facing a summer sun contribute to laboratory discomfort, and all windows produce drafts in cold weather. Windows usually take up wall space which could otherwise be put to practical use. It is hence recommended that careful consideration be given to the size and location of window areas in relation to the optimum use of space to be devoted to the physical chemistry laboratory, particularly if it is to have a ground-floor location for which the architectural treatment can differ from that of the upper floors. When the laboratory has a ground floor or basement location, care should be taken to prevent undue heating of the floor by underlying steam line tunnels.

SPECIAL INSTALLATIONS
Optical Equipment

Refractive index measurements are now used primarily in analytical procedures, as more satisfactory methods for correlating physical properties and molecular constitution have become available. Adequate working space for samples and record book, and proper illumination must be provided for each Abbe refractometer used.

If a centralized installation is used for fractional distillation work, a refractometer should be included. Instruments for general use should be located in the main laboratory.

Equipment for polarimetry, spectrography and Raman spectrography should be placed in an area which can be darkened conveniently. The use of a partition to close off one end of a special apparatus room should be considered here. The Raman spectrum excitation unit normally requires water cooling; a sink can be provided at this location, or water and drain lines run from an adjacent area such as the associated darkroom.

Darkrooms

While it is possible to use a single darkroom, even for a large section, it is preferable to provide two: a small one for spectrographic and x-ray work, and a larger one for general photographic work. A small refrigerator for storage of spectrographic plates, etc., a print dryer and film dryer should be provided in addition to the more routine darkroom equipment. Each darkroom entrance should have a light lock; a sliding outer door can help conserve space.

The darkrooms can be quite compact, and need not exceed 8 by 7 ft in inside dimensions. The spectrographic darkroom requires only a developing area and sink. The photographic darkroom should have a developing area or "wet side" and a "dry side" for handling photographic paper, etc. For the wet side the working surface should preferably take the form of a stainless steel tray which slopes slightly to drain into a stainless steel sink. For the dry side a "Formica" or "Micarta" surface is very effective.

Appropriate safe lights should be provided for the photographic materials used, and an external warning light to show when the darkroom is in use. Since student darkroom work provides a continual test of the resistance of darkroom timers to photographic solutions, the conventional darkroom timer can profitably be replaced for most purposes by a wall clock with luminescent face and sweep second hand. A cylindrical shield around the clock will minimize any effect on light-sensitive materials. It does not appear necessary to run a distilled water line or air line to the darkrooms.

Vacuum Rack

A vacuum rack for student use can be fitted into about 8 linear feet of wall space. Since such an installation must serve for an indefinite period, it should be constructed as far as possible from corrosion-resistant materials. Because of the variety of pumps, heaters and gauges which will be used there, 6 or 8 electric outlets must be provided, and adjacent gas outlet is essential also. An oxygen tank installation may be appropriate as well, depending on the amount of glass blowing included in the work there.

Glass-blowing Bench

Even the brief introduction to the art of glass blowing afforded by a few laboratory periods of supervised practice is found quite valuable by many students. Adequate coverage of a section can be provided by an 8-ft glass-blowing bench at which two students work at a time. The torches provided should be of good quality. For such a permanent installation copper tubing gas and oxygen lines can be connected to the burner by valves placed at the under side of the bench. Alternatively, *reinforced* rubber tubing can be used between the valves and the burner. The oxygen tank should be clamped in place, and instructions on the proper use of reducing valves posted conspicuously beside it.

Gas and oxygen outlets should also be provided for use with hand torches. A large metal scrap container, a hand brush and a dust pan are necessary. Glass-blowing tools such as carbon rods, plates, etc., should be issued from the stockroom rather than being kept at the bench.

Conductance Water

Ordinary laboratory distilled water is rarely pure enough for use in conductance measurements. Sufficient improvement will sometimes be obtained by redistilling the laboratory supply in an ordinary still of suitable capacity, but a regular conductance water still is preferable. (The use of such a still both for teaching and research purposes is not recommended, however, as it is desirable to restrict access to the teaching laboratory to periods when the supervisory staff is present.) Steam or electric heating for the still is advised. The conductance water supply must be protected from contamination. The use of a large polyethylene bottle, with spigot, can facilitate control of the atmosphere to which the water is exposed.

Special Apparatus Rooms

Experimental apparatus which cannot be issued routinely from the stockroom should be installed in special apparatus rooms rather than being left out in the main laboratory. The design of such rooms must anticipate the introduction of new experiments into the course and provide space for special experiment work. It is desirable to restrict the size of the individual room or to subdivide a larger area by means of partitions to facilitate individual student work. Here again large window areas in walls and partitions will increase the effectiveness of the teaching staff.

Miscellaneous

A nitrogen manifold should be provided, with several outlets fed through a reducing valve. The delivery valve should be of the toggle-valve type to avoid the rapid deterioration of needle valves in student hands. A chest for solid carbon dioxide with a conventional ice crusher, and an ice chest for commercial crushed ice are further recommended accessories.

A reference desk for student use is also very useful. The reference works supplied should be kept in a bookcase which can be locked when the laboratory is not in use. An electric calculating machine here can make feasible assignment of experiments for which the calculations would otherwise be too time-consuming.

OFFICES

As central as possible a location should be provided for the laboratory office. Glass window walls again should be used where possible. If the total student load is so large that two sections must be operated simultaneously, the desirability of having one office which can be partitioned into two units will outweigh other considerations.

The storage space required for records and reports depends on the general policy adopted for evaluation of student work. To make as satisfactory assignment of semester grades as possible, it may be considered desirable to have the full set of student reports available for inspection. The graded reports must be issued to the students for inspection and discussion, then returned to the office for filing. Multi-shelf glass-door cabinets are preferable for this purpose; a section of such a cabinet can be used as an easily inspected distribution file for reports to be graded.

An office table should be provided for use in consultation and oral quiz work with students. It should be large enough, however, to permit several people to work at once, as in cross-checking grades against filed reports, etc.

A coat locker, blackboard and a small bulletin board are essential. Provision should also be made, although not necessarily at the laboratory office itself, for reception of student reports at times when the laboratory is not open.

GENERAL COMMENTS

A central location for the stockrooms and special apparatus rooms will permit them to be used most effectively when large enrollments require the operation of two sections at the same time. Care must be taken in planning such a large installation to prevent it from being used as a traffic corridor.

Proceeding to the other extreme, the physical chemistry laboratory properly remains a specialized facility for a small class also, since it is the course content that actually fixes the features required. The advantages of a separate apparatus stockroom make it essential even with the smallest

groups. This stockroom can also be used as the laboratory office, where effectively private consultation and oral quiz conferences can be held in close proximity to the student working area. Joint use of a balance room by adjacent physical chemistry and quantitative analysis laboratories can be advantageous to both. If analytical balances are placed in the laboratory proper, protective cases should be provided for them.

With small classes much special apparatus, such as radiochemical counting equipment, etc., will be in use short periods only, rather than continuously throughout the school year. In this case a special desk in the laboratory can accommodate equipment in current use, with cupboards under the desk top supplementing the apparatus stockroom for instrument storage. A single darkroom should suffice; an auxiliary room for spectrographic equipment, etc., remains appropriate.

To obtain higher efficiency in the use of space, it may be considered necessary to give other course work in the laboratory used for physical chemistry. Instrumental analysis work appears entirely compatible with that of the physical chemistry laboratory course, but introductory quantitative analysis does not. The latter is commonly a service course for other departments to a greater extent than is true of physical chemistry, which leads to a difference in enrollments. Different hood and general ventilation arrangements and different student desk locker designs are appropriate in the two cases. On the other hand, a combined physical chemistry-quantitative analysis chemical stockroom and preparation room could be very practical.

PART 7: THE CHEMISTRY LECTURE ROOM

G. ROSS ROBERTSON
University of California
Los Angeles, California

If an entirely new chemistry building is to be constructed, and a large lecture hall (250 to 400 auditors) included, the relation of floor levels to ground level, and the closely related problem of slope gradient of the auditorium floor should be among the first considerations. These items should not wait until general building dimensions are independently fixed. The gradient, or difference in level, back to front, may vary from about 7 ft as minimum to one full story, 11 to 13 ft, or if

European amphitheater style is favored, as much as 16 or 20 ft. Since values below 7 and above 13 are likely to be unpopular, a brief summary of arguments for 7 and 13, respectively, may suffice. Perhaps a compromise might be best.

Low gradient is ideal optically in picture projection, since a lantern at convenient rear position sends a horizontal beam, without appreciable trapezoidal distortion, to center of screen. Low gradient is favored by instructors wishing to discourage students who look over shoulders in front during written examinations. It is very convenient when the architect wishes to place the basement about one half story below ground level, as suggested in the example discussed later.

Steep gradient makes it easier to see lecture demonstrations and gives slightly better acoustics, since sound waves traveling toward the rear are less disturbed by presence of auditors in front. It is convenient in cases where the architect wishes to place entrances and exits just one story apart, each in phase with a regular floor, without special stairway costs.

ENTRANCES AND EXITS

The entrance, or closely adjacent entrances, should be in the rear of the lecture room only. It is highly undesirable to allow public entry in front where distraction of attention by latecomers would be a persistent nuisance. A special entrance in front for lecturer and lecture-demonstration assistant should of course be provided. Exits in front are of course appropriate and in larger halls are probably required by law. Such front exits may be equipped with "panic bar" latches which forbid entry, but allow easy and certain exit under both routine and emergency conditions.

In view of the narrow corridors which are now the fashion, for economy reasons, traffic to and from the large lecture room should be kept outside the building as far as possible. The lecture hall, and thus its entrance, could be at the extreme end of a building block or of a stub wing protruding from the side of the main block. If the local winter climate is severe, entry should be through a sheltered lobby. Special interior access to this lobby should probably be provided by the architect in consideration of very cold weather. In California, however, a rain-sheltered porch will do.

ESTABLISHMENT OF FLOOR LEVELS

As a desirable option at this point in planning, assume the choice of low gradient, 7 ft from lecture-table floor level to rear floor level. The entrance is now set about a foot above ground level, offering easy ramp access for wheelchairs, but without hazard of flood from external sources. This sets the basement floor at the desirable level of 6 ft below ground. With light wells in front of basement windows, another 3 ft of floor depression might be tolerable, yielding a gradient as much as $7 + 3$, or 10 ft from lecturer to rear auditor. If still higher gradient is demanded, the entrance should be raised and the wheelchair problem solved at some other point in the building.

Adherence to the above specifications permits the floor at lecturer's position to be in phase with a main building floor. It is then convenient to move gas cylinders and other awkward demonstration equipment between storeroom or elevator and lecture desk.

The above independent treatment of the lecture hall is of special merit in the problem often met in small institutions, where two departments, not connected in function or administration, have been assigned a single building project for joint tenancy. Even in the case of UCLA, by no means a small institution, a "chemistry-geology" building was insisted on. This problem was handled in effective style by architect Gordon Kaufmann, with acoustic advice of V. O. Knudsen and L. P. Delsasso; working drawings by Stanton and Stockwell, successors to the late Mr. Kaufmann; and general supervision by the Office of Architects and Engineers of the University. Illustrations are presented here in view of the outstanding satisfaction which the unique group of three lecture rooms has given.

The group of rooms (Figure 14.13) with a porch and tiled court to the west, constitute a bridge between the geology and chemistry plants. In a colder climate the porch, slightly above ground level, would presumably have been enclosed. Geology and chemistry libraries were placed over the lecture halls because they require no water or sewer service. Storerooms and shops were admissible below, since the terrain slopes sharply toward the east. These lecture rooms are in great demand for scientific meetings of convention type, which can use the porch and court for most of the year for a general lobby, registration service, refreshments, etc.

GENERAL ROOM DESIGN

With an eye to Figure 14.13, a number of suggestions in design are promising. A lecture room should be without windows. This frees the architect in choice of positions regardless of obstruction of daylight, and affords protection from aircraft noise.

The breadth of the room should be only slightly less than the length, for acoustic reasons. As shown in Figure 14.13, the two front corners which would appear in a simple rectangular classroom are trimmed off obliquely, and the resulting polygonal wall front serves as means of reflecting the sound of the lecturer's voice. This form favors observation by the spectators of a long sequence of chalk boards (A, B, C) during partial occupancy—which means most of the time. Care is taken not to have a long stretch of curved rear wall, to prevent focusing of sound and reflection back into the central auditor area.

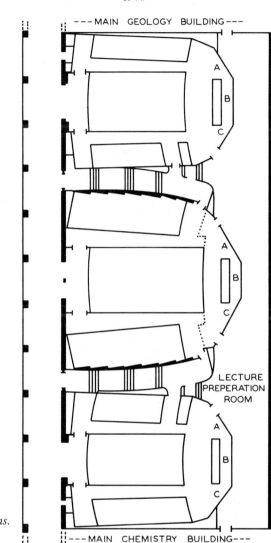

Figure 14.13   Lecture rooms.

Figure 14.14   Longitudinal vertical section of a large lecture hall.

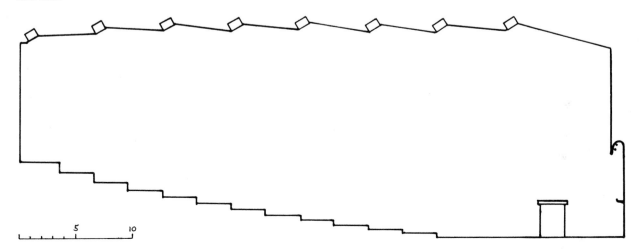

In Figure 14.14 (longitudinal section) the zigzag ceiling design, with appropriate angles figured by the acoustic engineer, permits reinforcement of sound waves without significant time lag—preferably without more than $\frac{1}{50}$ second difference in time between the arrival of the direct sound wave from the speaker and that of the detoured impulse which strikes a ceiling segment en route. Slight modifications of the original Knudsen-Delsasso specifications are indicated here to permit proper display of screen and charts, as discussed later.

Side walls are either slanted or broken into zigzag sections like the ceiling. Either procedure stops "flutter echo," a provoking nuisance caused by repeated reflections from side to side from smooth parallel walls.

Acoustic Surface Treatment

If the hall were only a small classroom, capacity 30 to 100, simple installation of perforated acoustic tile on the ceiling would be adequate. Reinforcement of sound would be of minor consequence. In the large rooms, however, there should be no sound absorbent placed on the ceiling, except possibly a few square yards in the extreme rear. About 40% coverage by absorptive tile may well go on the side walls, and 100% coverage, maximum acoustic efficiency, on the rear wall to prevent return of any sound which has already gone the length of the room. Tile with holes bored in random pattern is chosen for artistic reasons. In lecture halls designed on more elegant standards, lacquered ornamental plywood panels, perforated and mounted over glass-wool batts, are recommended. These were used on the UCLA job.

In any case one should never depend upon the now obsolete "acoustic plaster," or upon porous cinder blocks. These materials are initially satisfactory from the acoustic standpoint, but cannot be refinished (as with brush or spray) without choking the minute holes that are essential to the acoustic effect. Coarsely perforated acoustic tile, however, may be sprayed without destruction of acoustic value if the job is skillfully done.

The modern requirement of frequent air changes in an auditorium means powerful motors and fans, and resultant noise. Flues leading from such noisy machines to the lecture room should have interior lining of sound-absorbent material. Even though the machines themselves are not noisy, the incoming air, traveling at much higher speed than in older buildings, is prone to cause wind noise, thus drawing attention again to the lining problem.

Illumination

The illumination of a lecture room has improved during the past century to an astonishing degree—from about 1 foot-candle on the students' notebook (in favorable cases) to 50 in current recommendations. Perhaps 100 foot-candles may shortly be official. Building advisers, fearful that 75 or 100 foot-candles may be injurious to eyesight, should note that elimination of glare is considered more important just at present than restriction of foot-candle intensity to 50 or lower value.

Glare means the direct passage, or reflection, of light from an intense source into the eye in such a manner that false images are set up on the retina of the observer in a pattern superimposed on other and more legitimate images. With powerful fluorescent lamps as the main sources to consider in a new building, glare means in general the wrong position of a fluorescent tube with respect to the eyes of the occupant of the room.

In a lecture hall the "wrong" position may be one where an unshielded lamp sends out light laterally at angles less than 30° from the horizontal. Literally "glaring" examples of this fault were common many years ago, when bare unfrosted incandescent lamps were hung low in a room, with unpleasant, nearly horizontal radiating light rays. In an office the glare is more likely to involve reflected light, specifically, where the direct rays strike glossy paper from a position on the ceiling to the right of, and in front of the person attempting to write at a desk.

Abatement of glare in the lecture room may be effected by several methods, of which the following are important:

(1) Use of louvers, known colloquially as "egg crates."

(2) The Fresnel technique, in which light from an intense source passes through windows

of fluted or ribbed glass which refract the rays away from the offending angles.

(3) Use of translucent glass or plastic "diffuser" windows.

(4) Completely indirect illumination, in which the direct rays first strike white surfaces of ceiling and walls.

Methods (1) and (3) have the advantage of low initial cost. Proponents of (2) claim substantial savings on light bills as compensation for higher capital investment. Everyone is compelled to admit that (4) gives superb results, but the power bill may run high. In the face of rapid engineering research progress in this field, a single flat recommendation is scarcely appropriate. A building committee should only specify the technical results required, and let the architectural engineer come up with the proper up-to-date implements.

As far as an academic chemistry department is concerned, there seems to be no need for multiple controls on the main auditorium lights. A single remote-control solenoid-operated switch turns all main lights on and off. There should, however, be several locations where the single remote-control circuit may be operated, including front and rear doors, lecture desk, projector table or booth, and a position near the center of the auditorium where either an opaque-projection outfit or a small 35-mm lantern might be needed.

Simultaneous Projection and Writing

Simultaneous use of projection screen and chalk board is, for the physical scientist, an essential combination of services not considered by the conventionally "audio-visual" specialist. A lecturer should be able to write uninterruptedly on the chalk board as his slides are being shown, without cells for lights off and on. This is easily arranged by shielded illumination of the entire chalk board by two rows of fluorescent lamps which run the whole length of the three-section board. A double row is used so that failure of one tube will not leave an unsightly gap in the line. This feature is well shown in the recent addition to the Purdue University chemistry building. The fact that the shielded lamps are close to the chalk board level makes no trouble.

With lantern and shielded chalk board lamps

in operation, it is now necessary only to provide a well-shielded desk lamp for the lecturer, and a few Mazda down lights in well scattered ceiling positions, to give the students the chance to take a few notes. These special ceiling lights should be on a single remote control like the main light system. In the down-light circuit is interposed a special solenoid switch connected so that the down lights will be automatically *extinguished* during all times that the main auditorium lights are in operation, that is, during long periods when they are of no real use and merely run up service and power bills. The down lights need not be large; a total of 1 or 2 foot-candles on the tablet arms will suffice to permit a few incidental notes to be taken. Like the main lights, they should be controlled from the five or more standard locations.

The planners should avoid the common error of mounting chalk board lights 2 or 3 ft out in front of the chalk board. Such forward position would throw intolerable stray light on the screen, and ruin the simultaneous chalk board-screen possibilities, which are so valuable to lecturers who combine discussion of graphs with mathematics, or structual formulas.

In the UCLA lecture room the projection lantern is displaced to a convenient position next to the north aisle. This puts the projected picture at a slight angle (at C) instead of center. Such a position is much more convenient for the lecturer, who with hardly an extra step can view his notes, observe his slide, pick up a pointer, or write on the chalk board. Only in the case of dark 35-mm color slides is it necessary to turn off chalk board or ceiling down lights.

Projection Equipment

Planners should be careful not to purchase objectives and screens of the exact sizes required for commercial, properly masked slides, which have projection images of not more than 75-mm width. Many visiting scholars, with home-made slides, fail to use masks, and show slides with picture section as wide as 90 mm. Such pictures overrun the screen of supposedly correct width. The following example of a calculation is approximately in agreement with accepted standards of visual education:

Distance from screen to rear seat, 45 ft.

Distance from screen to lantern, 46 ft.

Normal acceptable width of projected picture, by standard audio-visual formula, $\frac{1}{6} \times 45 = 7.5$ ft.

Maximum width of slide image encountered in a properly-made commercial slide, 75 mm.

Objective required in this hall, 18-inch focal length: preferably not less than 4-inch aperture.

Resulting picture, 7.45 ft wide.

Oversize slide image provided by visitor, 90 mm wide.

Resulting projected picture, 8.9 ft wide.

Minimum commercial screen size required, 9-ft.

A final precaution may be added: Specify 3 ft extra vertical length of screen to serve as guard against impetuous persons who pull the screen down rapidly and may tear it from roller.

With projection screen at position C, panel B over the center chalk board may well display one of the presently popular wide periodic charts, with representation of actinides and lanthanides. At A it is convenient to mount an oxidation-reduction potential chart.

Additional details of lecture-room design are given by Knudsen and Harris*, and Robertson†.

* Knudsen, V. O., and Harris, C. M., "Acoustical Designing in Architecture," John Wiley and Sons, New York, 1950.
† Robertson, G. R., J. Chem. Education *36*, 197, (1959.).

Recent

Laboratory

Construction

CHAPTER XV

Description of Recent Laboratory Construction

Descriptions of new laboratories in the area covered by "Laboratory Planning for Chemistry and Chemical Engineering" have been included in this section. The ones shown are industrial research centers, laboratories designed to serve somewhat more specific objectives, university chemistry buildings and college science centers.

Selection of the particular buildings has not been easy. During the time which has elapsed since the publication of "Laboratory Design" in 1951, better than four hundred industrial companies and research institutes have built either new research and development facilities or have added to facilities already in use. One corporation alone has added at least twenty-five new facilities of this type. In the same time, at least two hundred college science centers and university chemistry and chemical engineering buildings have been opened; of these some 120 were built by small colleges. A list of this new construction will be found in the Appendix. These numbers are certainly minimum; included are buildings which have been announced in the technical or professional literature or which have been sent in (in the case of the colleges) in answer to a questionnaire submitted at the time of the Wooster Conference on Research and Teaching in the Liberal Arts College (1959). Without doubt many others could be added to the list.

The various presentations illustrate in part how planners approach the problem of site selection and the fitting together of buildings and site. This is particularly true in the case of the research centers. No attempt has been made to provide complete floor plans for the industrial spreads. In some cases the plan of a single floor is included as an illustration of circulation arrangements or building design. Where warranted, the detail of a group of laboratories will show how services are handled.

In the case of the academic buildings, floor plans are generally included. With college science centers, the location of the different disciplines are indicated.

It is our hope that these pages will help planning committees carry out the preliminary stages of their own planning somewhat more effectively. It should be said that the same applies to the buildings and laboratories which have received more detailed consideration elsewhere in the text.

Descriptions of the following buildings have been included in this section:

INDUSTRIAL RESEARCH CENTERS

Research Center, Koppers Company, Inc., Somervell Park, Monroeville, Pennsylvania; Voorhees, Walker, Smith, Smith & Haines, New York, New York

IBM Thomas J. Watson Research Center, International Business Machines Corporation, Yorktown, New York; Eero Saarinen and Associates, Birmingham, Michigan

Research Center, Diamond Alkali Company, Concord Township, Ohio; Giffels and Rossetti, Detroit, Michigan

Union Oil Research Center, Union Oil Company of California, Brea, California; Austin, Field and Fry, Los Angeles, California

Research Center, U.S. Rubber Company, Wayne Township, New Jersey; Shreve, Lamb and Harmon, New York, New York

Texus Research Center, Texas—U. S. Chemical Company, Parsippany, New Jersey; Wyatt C. Hedrick, Fort Worth, Texas

Homer Research Laboratories, Bethlehem Steel Company, Bethlehem, Pennsylvania; Voorhees, Walker, Smith, Smith & Haines, New York, New York

Central Research Laboratory, Minnesota Mining and Manufacturing Company, St. Paul, Minnesota; Giffels and Rossetti, Detroit, Michigan

Research Center, Monsanto Chemical Company, St. Louis, Missouri; Holabird and Root, Chicago, Illinois

SPECIALIZED RESEARCH LABORATORIES

Industrial Reactor Laboratories, Inc., Owned jointly by ten major U. S. companies, Plainsboro, New Jersey; Skidmore, Owings and Merrill, New York, New York

The Research and Development Division Building, Corning Glass Works, Corning, New York; Harrison, Abramovitz and Abbe, New York, New York

Armed Forces Institute of Pathology, Walter Reed Army Medical Center, Washington, D. C.; Faulkner, Kingsbury & Steinhouse, Washington, D. C.

Shell Oil Company Agricultural Research Laboratory, Shell Development Company, Modesto, California; Austin, Field and Fry, Los Angeles, California

Research and Development Tower, S. C. Johnson & Sons, Inc., Racine, Wisconsin; Frank Lloyd Wright, Taliesen, Spring Green, Wisconsin

UNIVERSITY BUILDINGS

Robert Bendridge Wetherill Laboratory of Chemistry, Purdue University, West Lafayette, Indiana; Walter Scholer & Associates, Lafayette, Indiana

Geology-Biology Laboratories, William Marsh Rice University, Houston, Texas; George Pierce—Abel B. Pierce, Houston, Texas

Acheson Hall of Chemistry, University of Buffalo, Buffalo, New York; Duane Lyman and Associates, Buffalo, New York

COLLEGE SCIENCE BUILDINGS

Pierre S. duPont Science Building, Swarthmore College, Swarthmore, Pennsylvania; Vincent G. Kling, Philadelphia, Pennsylvania

Science and Classroom Building, California State Polytechnic College, San Luis Obispo, California; Allison and Rible, Los Angeles, California

Farr Hall of Science, Ripon College, Ripon, Wisconsin; Frank C. Shattuck, M. F. Siewert and Associates, Neenah, Wisconsin

KOPPERS COMPANY, INC.

Research Center—Somervell Park

Monroeville, Pennsylvania,

Voorhees Walker Smith Smith & Haines, Architects

The new Koppers Research Center is located in the Borough of Monroeville about 25 minutes driving time from downtown Pittsburgh. Construction now complete consists of the main Laboratory and Office Building and auxilliary buildings such as the Boiler House, Switchgear Building and Gas Meter House. The Laboratory and Office Building is a multi-wing structure with each wing connected by glass enclosed passages. The Administration Building at the east end of the complex houses the executive offices, a 225-seat auditorium, an extensive research library, and cafeteria. The laboratories are housed in three interconnecting wings stepping down a gentle slope to the west. There are two service cores, incorporating toilets and elevators. One is located in the Administration Building and the other is centrally located in the middle laboratory wing to serve all three. Provision is made for expansion of the laboratory wings to south.

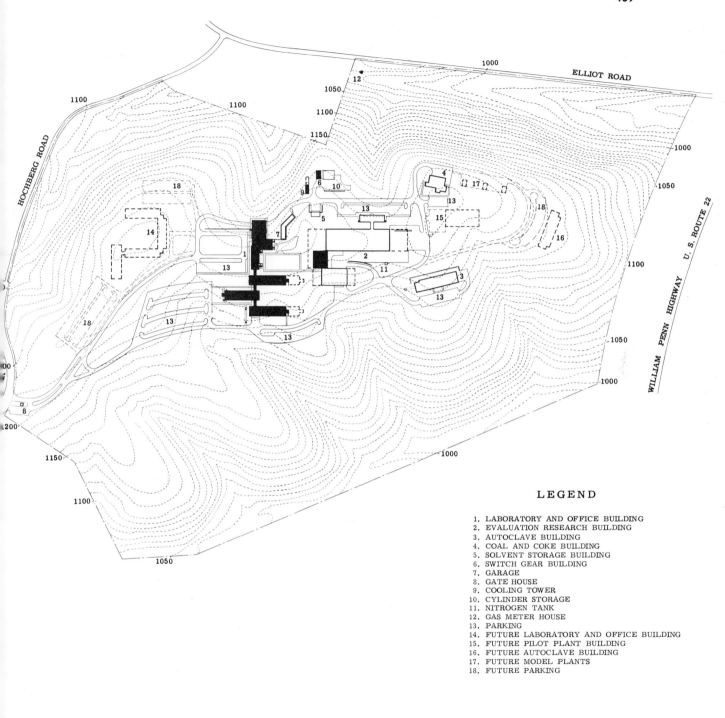

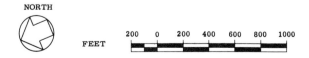

LEGEND

1. LABORATORY AND OFFICE BUILDING
2. EVALUATION RESEARCH BUILDING
3. AUTOCLAVE BUILDING
4. COAL AND COKE BUILDING
5. SOLVENT STORAGE BUILDING
6. SWITCH GEAR BUILDING
7. GARAGE
8. GATE HOUSE
9. COOLING TOWER
10. CYLINDER STORAGE
11. NITROGEN TANK
12. GAS METER HOUSE
13. PARKING
14. FUTURE LABORATORY AND OFFICE BUILDING
15. FUTURE PILOT PLANT BUILDING
16. FUTURE AUTOCLAVE BUILDING
17. FUTURE MODEL PLANTS
18. FUTURE PARKING

NORTH

FEET

| 200 | 0 | 200 | 400 | 600 | 800 | 1000 |

INTERNATIONAL BUSINESS MACHINES CORPORATION

Thomas J. Watson Research Center
Yorktown, New York

Eero Saarinen and Associates, Architects

The architectural challenge in designing this research center seemed to be that of reconciling two apparently contradictory requirements. On the one hand, we wanted to make the laboratories and research offices the most efficient and the most flexible of twentieth-century research centers. On the other, we wanted to find an expression for the building that would be appropriate to the personality of the users and the site and environment.

The Plan

First, the laboratories. An investigation of what had been happening in laboratory and office planning showed that there were several new factors that had to be recognized. One new fact of significance was the increasing demand for concentration, for a compact building with short communication lines and utmost privacy for groups of scientists. The expanding needs of research and its yet unknown frontiers made flexibility of space and arrangements more important than ever before.

Of primary significance was the fact that laboratories and offices today depend on air-conditioning and efficient fluorescent lighting rather than on windows for their ventilation and lighting.

Applying all these considerations to this problem of a research center for our time, we arrived at a new plan.

All laboratories and offices are located on inside about 120-foot-long cross corridors. The laboratories are placed back to back, with the laboratory utility core between them. And the offices are placed back to back, the wall between containing a specially-designed modular storage system for files, supplies, coats, etc.

These cross corridors are joined by two trunk corridors which run uninterruptedly along each side of the 1,090 foot-long building, the one on the north side a wall totally of glass, the one on the south side of glass and stone.

The advantages of this plan, both human and economic, are many. It allows the concentration and the flexibility which are required. It supplies desired privacy. Instead of thousands of feet of dreary corridors, the short trunk corridors give easy communication lines. The plan saves laboratory utility costs. By incorporating structural columns in the laboratory core and office storage walls, there are no free-standing columns except in the lobby. The reduction of outside wall reduces overall costs. The elimination of windows in the offices, and the substitution of the storage walls, greatly increases the possible arrangements for individual offices. Each individual can work in the best controlled environment with the most efficient use of air-conditioning and modern lighting.

Instead of small windows in offices and laboratories, covered with Venetian blinds or other sun-screening devices which obscure a view, the floor-to-ceiling windows on the outer main corridors can be uncovered, presenting an unobstructed view of the very beautiful landscape and providing an encounter with nature at the moments of relaxation when one has left office or laboratory and can enjoy it.

The Character

Now, to the other problem—the character of the building and its relation to its site. It has always seemed to me that many scientists in the research field are like university professors—tweedy, pipe-smoking men. In contrast to the efficient laboratories, we wanted to provide them with a more relaxed, "tweedy," out-doors sort of environment. In this aim, we were encouraged by

A typical segment of the laboratory-office plan showing utility cores between laboratories and the cross corridors between laboratories and offices.

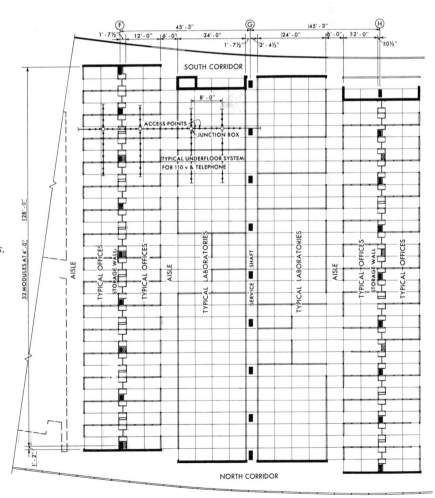

TYPICAL SEGMENT OF PLAN

The North corridor.

IBM

the beautifully hilly site and the landscape with its characteristic field-stone walls. We were also aware that IBM was anxious to provide a center which would not be in any way architecturally obnoxious to its Westchester neighbors.

All these considerations led us to the use of local stone, field-stone, much of which actually came from the site, to be used on end walls as well as the inner side of the peripheral corridors, and on lobby, auditorium and cafeteria walls.

The building was curved in a crescent, following the configuration of the hill. It is planned so that this curve can embrace the hill even further by extending the crescent in its future expansion.

The building is three-storied, but it appears variously as a one, or a two, or a three story building, depending on the point from which it is viewed. From the main access drive, sweeping across the main, or north front, the building appears as a three-story structure. If one approaches it from the parking lot, at the back, on the south side, one walks on a bridge, over a Japanese garden, sees the building as a one-story structure and enters on the third floor. If one comes in from the garden below, one sees a two-story building and enters on the second floor.

EERO SAARINEN

Site plan.

DIAMOND ALKALI COMPANY

Research Center

Concord Township, Ohio

Giffels and Rossetti, Architect-Engineer

Diamond Alkali Company's Research Center in Concord Township is located on an 800-acre, wooded site just outside of Painesville, Ohio. The units, now occupied, include a Research and Administration Building, a Process Development Building, High Pressure Laboratory and auxiliary structures for solvent storage, gas metering and sewage treatment. At the time of publication, additional units were in the programing stage.

The 75,000 sq. ft. Research Laboratory is the largest unit in the initially constructed group. Of reinforced concrete construction, the three-story structure contains 61 lab modules, 12' x 24'. The building is 100% air-conditioned with separate systems for the laboratories and the offices. The office system is zone controlled while the laboratories are individually controlled and are provided with a minimum of twelve air changes per

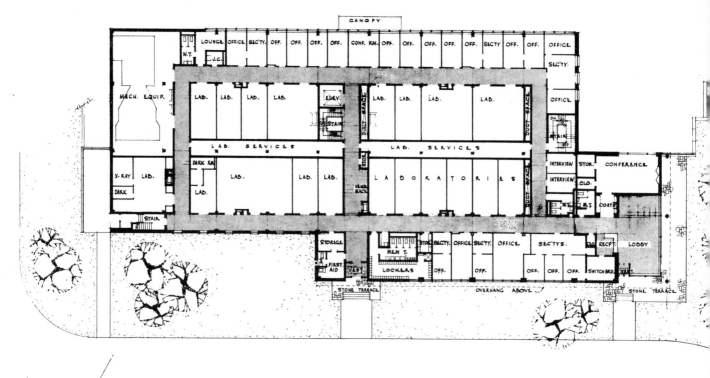

FIRST FLOOR PLAN

GRAPHIC SCALE   0 8 16 24

hour. Any number of the hoods, which run at a face velocity of 75 feet per minute, may be used at one time and the system automatically adjusts to the changing load. The refrigeration unit for the air conditioning system is gas absorption type of over 400 tons capacity.

The laboratories are located back-to-back with a common service corridor in between through which the normal services, compressed air, hot, cold and distilled water, natural gas, low pressure steam, vacuum and electricity are provided. Exhaust ducts and sewer lines are also located in this corridor. Wet and dry ice are provided at central stations. Cylinder gas is provided in each Lab as required. Supporting facilities in the structure include office space totalling approximately 9,000 sq. ft., technical library, a cafeteria adaptable for seminar use and other employe quarters to serve all the Center's personnel.

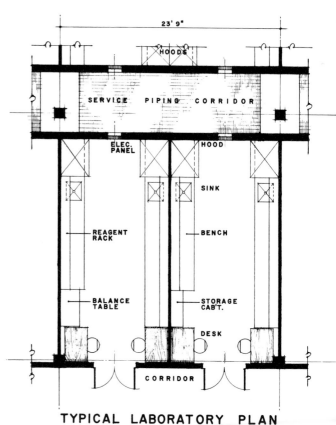

TYPICAL LABORATORY PLAN

Preliminary manufacturing operations are conducted on a small scale in one of the two 40-foot high multi-level process pilot areas.

DIAMOND ALKALI COMPANY

The Process Development Building, also three-story, is of steel frame construction with a total area of 34,000 sq. ft. Provided are six lab modules 12′ x 24′ and five other labs ranging in size from 24′ x 30′ to 54′ x 50′ for pilot work, crushing testing and special assignments. The offices and laboratories are air conditioned by two units with refrigeration supplied by a reciprocating type compressor of 65 tons capacity. The cooling tower is located on the roof over the Pilot area. Ventilation of 12 air changes per hour is provided for the Pilot Labs. Flexible duct exhaust connections are located at each working level of the Pilot Labs and the Rough Lab. The same services are provided in each lab and at each level of the Pilot Labs and Rough Lab as are provided in the Research and Administration Building. Space is also provided for lobby, employe facilities, shops, storage, and approximately 2,800 sq. ft. of office space.

Six high pressure lab cells, 6′ x 9′, a general lab or 12′ x 21′, shop, storage and office space are provided in the 32,500 sq. ft. High Pressure Laboratory. Construction of the single-story building is masonry with a steel framing supporting roof.

The high pressure lab area is of reinforced concrete construction. Heating and ventilation is provided by a package type vertical unit. Services and ventilation are provided to the high pressure cells through small protected openings. Blow out is provided from the cells by special sash. A heavy woven cable mat is suspended outside the windows to help confine any possible explosion.

UNION OIL COMPANY OF CALIFORNIA

Research Center
Brea, California
Austin, Field & Fry, Architects

This is one of the first campus-type plant projects for the petroleum industry wherein each facility can be enlarged as needed without affecting the relationship of the various departments. Two more typical laboratory structures are planned for the future to match the three now built.

Apart from the delightful visual attractiveness of the project, which is due in no small part to the landscaping, the outstanding features of the entire project are the underground tunnels which connect all buildings and which in turn house all the utility lines, which can be repaired, serviced, or replaced at any time without immobilizing any laboratory. Small trucks can move in and out these tunnels and cut down cost of maintenance tremendously.

Laboratories are designed on 10'4" x 26'0" modules, which is for a single 1-person laboratory. Each single laboratory has an office directly opposite. Double laboratories for two people are 20'8" and with all partitions between laboratories removable. Any combination of units to satisfy space demands for special research and experiments can be achieved in a matter of hours.

All partitions between offices and all the buildings are Hauserman and can be removed or relocated to meet the ever-changing needs of this project.

The laboratories facing to the north enabled the Architects to treat them as large studios with tremendous amounts of glass for excellent daylighting. In turn the offices on the south needed protection from bright sunlight and the lower ceilings with large overhangings give this protection. Hence the design of the pitched roof for each of the laboratory buildings was evolved and proved highly satisfactory in every respect.

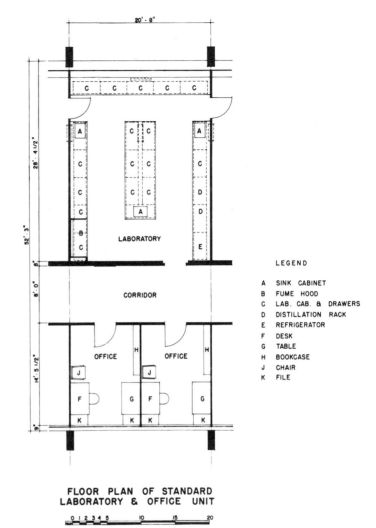

LEGEND

A   SINK CABINET
B   FUME HOOD
C   LAB. CAB. & DRAWERS
D   DISTILLATION RACK
E   REFRIGERATOR
F   DESK
G   TABLE
H   BOOKCASE
J   CHAIR
K   FILE

FLOOR PLAN OF STANDARD LABORATORY & OFFICE UNIT

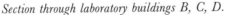

Section through laboratory buildings B, C, D.

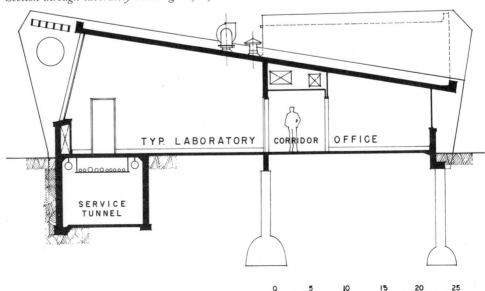

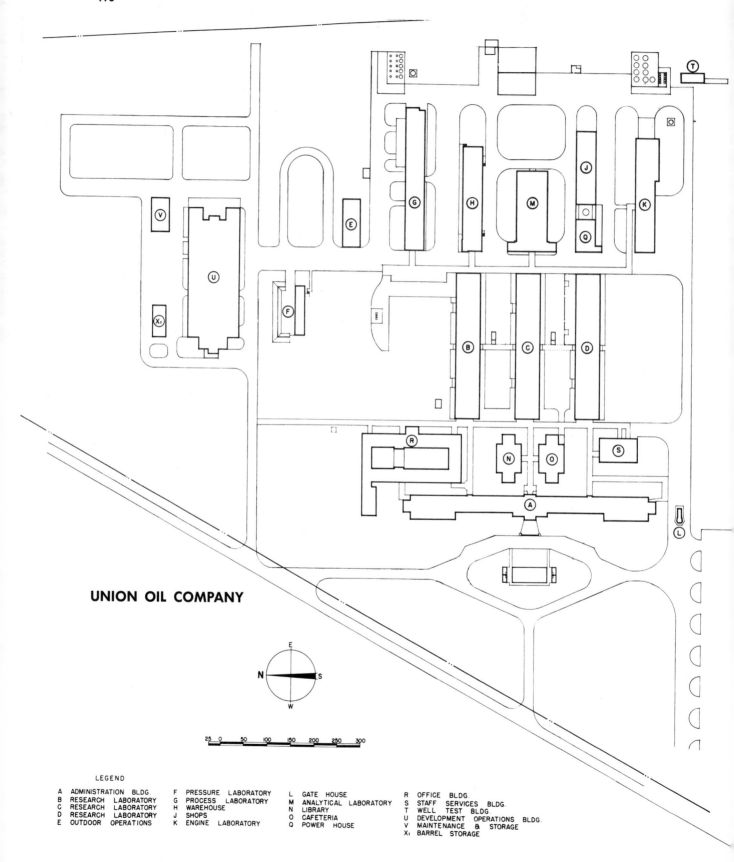

UNION OIL COMPANY

E
N — S
W

25 0   50   100   150   200 250   300

LEGEND

A   ADMINISTRATION BLDG.   F   PRESSURE LABORATORY   L   GATE HOUSE   R   OFFICE BLDG.
B   RESEARCH   LABORATORY   G   PROCESS LABORATORY   M   ANALYTICAL LABORATORY   S   STAFF SERVICES BLDG.
C   RESEARCH   LABORATORY   H   WAREHOUSE   N   LIBRARY   T   WELL TEST BLDG.
D   RESEARCH   LABORATORY   J   SHOPS   O   CAFETERIA   U   DEVELOPMENT OPERATIONS BLDG.
E   OUTDOOR   OPERATIONS   K   ENGINE LABORATORY   Q   POWER HOUSE   V   MAINTENANCE & STORAGE
                                                                                           X₁ BARREL STORAGE

UNITED STATES RUBBER COMPANY

Research Center

Wayne Township, New Jersey

Shreve, Lamb and Harmon Associates, Architects

The United States Rubber Company Research Center in Wayne Township, New Jersey is set in a hilly and densely wooded location with a drop in level to the west that affords a fine view of the Packanack Lake valley and bay beyond. The topography influenced the informal arrangement of the buildings. The asymmetric form of the main laboratory building is designed to permit future expansion at the ends without destroying apparent balance. Ideal conditions are afforded the staff of scientists and technicians for research in fields of new rubbers, plastics, textiles and chemicals.

The three-story main research building is of brick construction with stone base course, providing a total area of 114,100 sq. ft. The building houses 48 unit laboratories as well as special laboratories devoted to analytical, optical, textile and photographic work. There are 17 offices, 3 conference rooms, cafeteria, first aid room, stock rooms, and a library in the building.

The engineering research building is a two-story structure of brick, with a total area of 45,240 sq. ft. It contains completely equipped maintenance

Entrance lobby.

U. S. RUBBER COMPANY

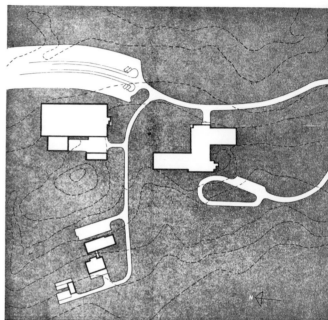

Site Plan.

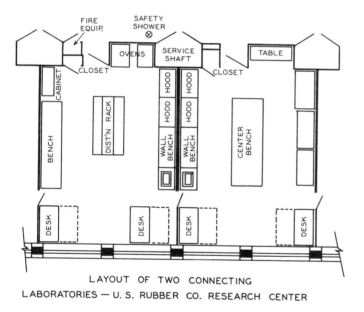

LAYOUT OF TWO CONNECTING
LABORATORIES — U. S. RUBBER CO. RESEARCH CENTER

shops, machine shop, carpentry shop, physical testing laboratory, mill room for rubber and plastics, mechanical engineering laboratory, and a radiation laboratory equipped with a 2,000,000-volt electron accelerator.

The chemical engineering building contains a total of 13,700 sq. ft. and is completely equipped with reactors ranging in size from five gallons to 100 gallons. It also contains vacuum, spray and rotary kiln driers, centrifuges and various filters.

TEXAS-U. S. CHEMICAL COMPANY

Texus Research Center

Parsippany, New Jersey

Wyatt C. Hedrick, Architect-Engineer

The Texas—U. S. Chemical Company Research Laboratory Plant consisting of a new research building, power plant building, and waste treatment plant is located on a 26 acre site outside the town of Parsippany, New Jersey. The site, once a large estate, has two lakes on the property and is also abundant with seventy feet high pines, maple, chestnut, and beech. The terrain is rolling in nature. The existing house dates back to the Eighteenth Century and at the present time is being used as an office and research building. This building will eventually be removed for a future laboratory expansion program.

The main laboratory building consists of three floors. The basement houses the mill room, press room, storage rooms, and mechanical facilities. The first floor consists of a reception area, business office, laboratories, and services. The second floor consists of laboratories, conference rooms, and the library. The power plant is adjacent to the main structure and connected by a tunnel and so designed for future expansion of the laboratory. The waste treatment plant is designed to handle both sanitary and chemical waste. The main laboratory is reinforced (pan joist) concrete construction and the power plant is steel frame.

The mechanical details include a complete self-contained facility (except the water service) consisting of the laboratory building, separate power plant, and waste disposal plant.

Unusual features of the laboratory building are the provision of seven services (hot water, cold

water, gas, vacuum, steam, compressed air, and acid drainage) for each laboratory table. The heating system is designed for 100% fresh air to accommodate the laboratory exhaust fans (two per laboratory) with provision for the addition of future cooling. Owner requirements were such that recirculating type hoods were not to be used and, in order to provide for diversity of hood operation, the main air supply fan is equipped with a variable speed fluid drive controlled from static pressure.

The acid waste and vent system within the laboratory building consists of approximately 1700 linear feet of "Pyrex" pipe and fittings.

A central dust collection system provides for the removal of carbon black from the various compounding rooms in the basement.

The physical testing laboratory and two special equipment rooms are air conditioned, to maintain 40% RH in the laboratory with an absorption system using the available steam required the year around for the laboratory building.

The power plant contains all of the service equipment for the various systems in the laboratory, consisting of H.P. boilers (oil fired), air compressor and dryer, vacuum pump, dust collector, circulating water system pump, and water heater. Service piping between the power house and the laboratory building is located in the walk-through tunnel.

The acid waste is entirely separated from sanitary waste until the final treatment (stripping volatiles at elevated temperature and aeration) has been completed. The sanitary and acid wastes are then combined, filtered, clarified, chlorinated, and discharged.

TEXUS RESEARCH CENTER

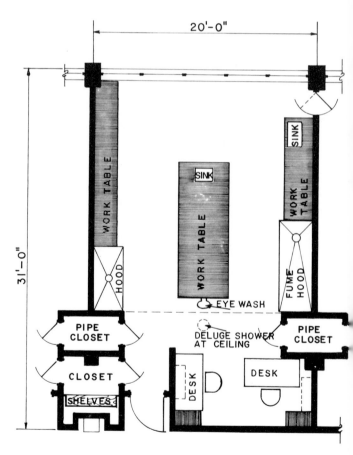

TYPICAL LABORATORY PLAN
SCALE ——————————————— 1/4" = 1'-0"

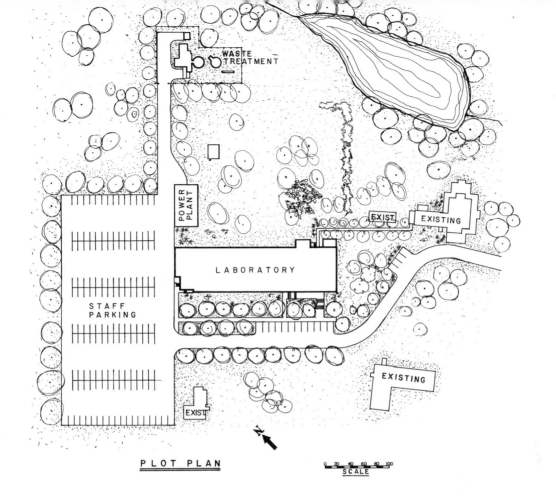

WASTE TREATMENT

POWER PLANT

LABORATORY

STAFF PARKING

EXIST

EXIST

EXISTING

EXISTING

N

PLOT PLAN

0 20 40 60 80 100
SCALE

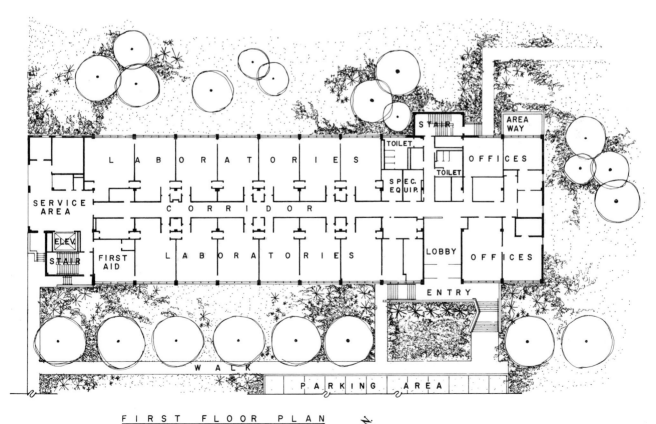

STAIR

AREA WAY

TOILET

LABORATORIES

OFFICES

SPEC. EQUIP.

TOILET

SERVICE AREA

CORRIDOR

ELEV.

STAIR

FIRST AID

LABORATORIES

LOBBY

OFFICES

ENTRY

WALK

PARKING AREA

N

FIRST FLOOR PLAN

0 5 10 15 20 25 30 35 40 45 50 55
SCALE

BETHLEHEM STEEL COMPANY

Homer Research Laboratories

Bethlehem, Pennsylvania

Voorhees Walker Smith Smith & Haines, Architects

The Bethlehem Steel Company's Homer Research Laboratories provide complete facilities for the Company's research program in steel and coal by-products technology. The general laboratories and offices building contains facilities for all bench-scale laboratory operations as well as most of the offices at the site. Also housed in the wings of this building are an electronic calculator, drafting services, meeting rooms, first aid, laboratory supplies, stockrooms and cafeteria. The tower contains a technical information center, library, mechanical equipment, and observation lounge. A two-story pilot plant, consisting of both low- and high-bay areas, is equipped to provide pilot-scale production of all experimental compositions. A mechanical engineering pilot plant, a chemical pilot plant and warehouse, shops, boiler plant and other utilities are also included in the research group.

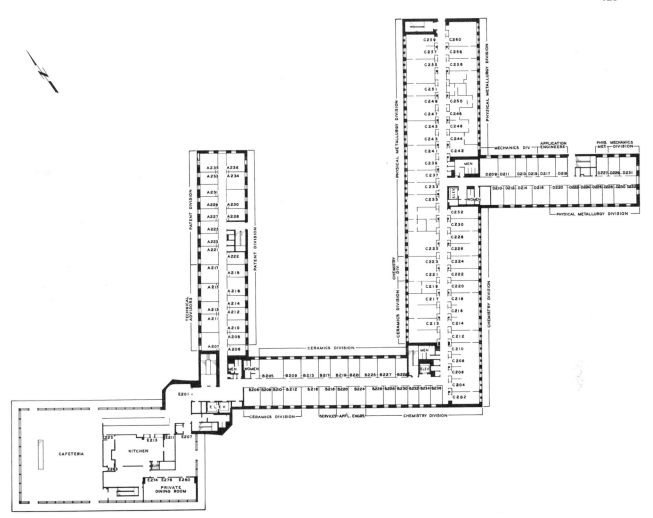

Second floor plan, administration and laboratory building.

The central research laboratory building.

MINNESOTA MINING AND MANUFACTURING COMPANY

Central Research Laboratory

St. Paul, Minnesota

Giffels and Rossetti, Architects-Engineers

In 1953, Minnesota Mining and Manufacturing Company started construction of a Central Research Laboratory Building on what was farm land adjacent to the city limits of St. Paul, Minnesota. Since that time, a continuous construction program for this growth company has resulted in nine major buildings and twelve auxiliary structures with others in various stages of planning and construction.

In 1962, the Company's corporate headquarters were moved into a new 14-story office building, which is the focal point of a campus-like research and development area.

Building services such as steam power, telephone and circulating chilled water for air conditioning are provided from a central area to all buildings located on 280 acres, architecturally planned for laboratory, pilot plant, and administrative functions.

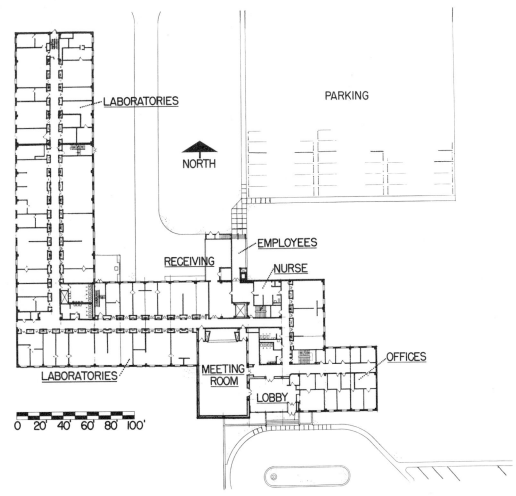

LABORATORIES

PARKING

NORTH

EMPLOYEES

RECEIVING

NURSE

LABORATORIES

OFFICES

MEETING
ROOM

LOBBY

0 20' 40' 60' 80' 100'

First floor plan, central research laboratory.

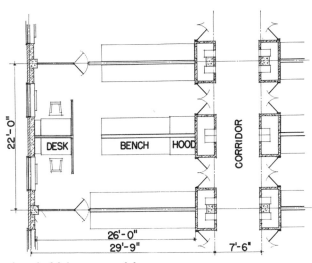

22'-0"

DESK

BENCH   HOOD

CORRIDOR

26'-0"

29'-9"

7'-6"

A typical laboratory module.

*A typical laboratory in the central
research building.*

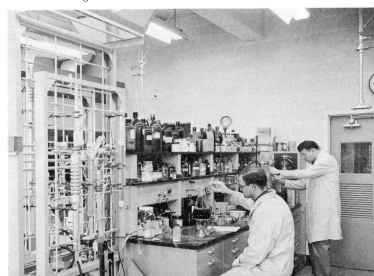

In this aerial photo the research center buildings are in the foreground. Buildings in the background are the general offices.

MONSANTO CHEMICAL COMPANY

Research Center

Creve Coeur, St. Louis, Missouri

Holabird and Root, Architect-Engineer
(with the architectural section of Monsanto's
Research and Engineering Division)

Monsanto Chemical Company's new Research Center in suburban St. Louis at Creve Coeur, Missouri, is one of the most modern and best equipped all purpose research laboratories in the country. The newly completed structures of the Center include two laboratory buildings; central services area; a special purpose laboratory and a warehouse—air conditioning building. In addition, the laboratories of the Inorganic Chemicals Division and the Agricultural Chemicals Division are considered part of the Center complex.

The new buildings of the Center with supporting facilities provide 463,000 square feet of en-

closed space, almost 11 acres. The previously constructed Inorganic and Agricultural Chemicals buildings include an additional 97,000 square feet. Each laboratory building contains 75 modular laboratory units (four man, 22' x 30'), eight larger laboratories and other facilities. The two central service buildings have a total of 15 conference rooms, a meeting room to seat 360, a library, two large analytical laboratories, receiving and shipping rooms and shops. The special purpose building provides the research staff with a number of individual laboratories separated from each other by heavy reinforced concrete walls and special pressure relief devices. Research personnel can control and observe experiments from remote vantage points.

Because the Center will house widely diversified groups of researchers, flexibility in laboratory design has been stressed. Used individually, the modular laboratories are adaptable to the com-

The instrumental analytical laboratory.

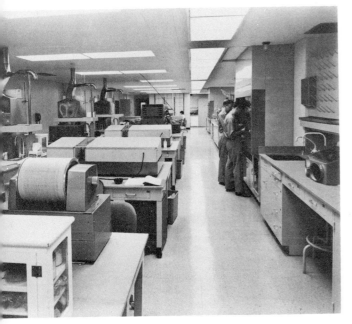

The information center is above the main entrance of the research center.

plete range of research requirements. All modular partitions are movable and utilities are brought in by overhead piping and dropped to bench elevation. Thus utilities are permanently installed even though walls and benches can be moved. The center section of the module accommodates four six-foot hoods plus two eight-foot distillation racks. However, the area can be completely open or made into walk-in type hoods. The hoods are a new concept, with three sliding glass doors and a continuous air slot around the periphery.

The major new buildings in the Center have four stories plus a ground floor level and a penthouse. Framework is of poured-in-place concrete. The exterior has brick end walls and other walls of porcelainized panels. In order to keep vibration in the laboratories at a minimum, the concrete floors are eight inches thick and the heavy machinery in the Center has been equipped with spring isolators and flexible connections.

Modular laboratory showing storage of liquid hydrocarbons, walk-in hood, distillation rack.

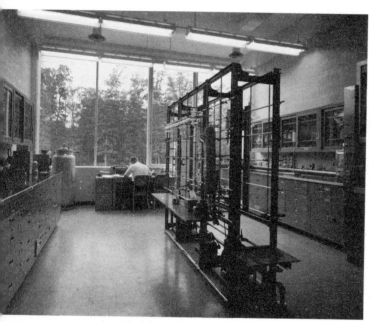

A typical laboratory.

Interior of the reactor building.

INDUSTRIAL REACTOR LABORATORIES, INC

Plainsboro, New Jersey

Skidmore, Owings & Merrill, Architects; Severud-Elstad-Krueger, Structural Engineers; Guy B. Panero, Mechanical Engineers; Turner Construction Company, General Contractor

Participating companies:
National Lead Company
American Tobacco Company
Continental Can Company
Corning Glass Works
Socony Mobil Oil Company
United States Rubber Company
American Machine & Foundry Company
Atlas Powder Company
Radio Corporation of America
National Distillers & Chemical Corporation

Ten major U. S. companies jointly own and share the nuclear facilities of the Industrial Reactor Laboratories, Inc., in Plainsboro, New Jersey. Each of the participating companies has its own laboratory facilities at the site, as does Columbia University which provides the technical staff for operation of the reactor. The reactor is of the "swimming pool" variety, designed by AMF Atomics Inc., to produce its chain reaction under 30 feet of demineralized water which serves as a moderator, cooler, and shield. The 5 megawatt reactor is housed in an SOM designed

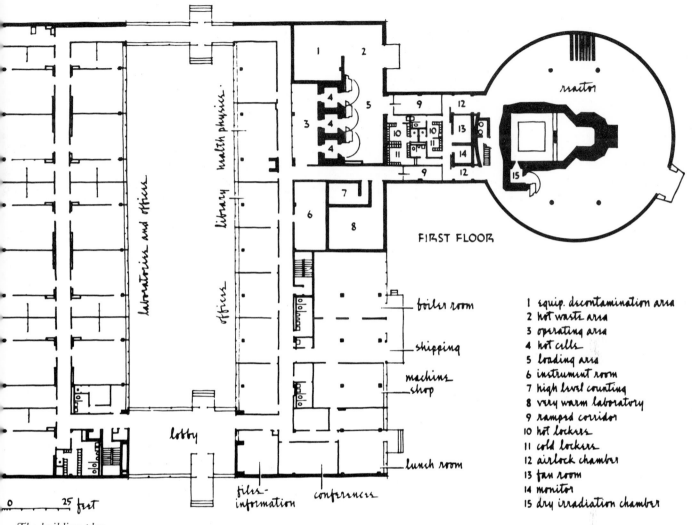

FIRST FLOOR

— boiler room
— shipping
— machine shop
— lunch room

film-information   conference

lobby

laboratories and offices   library   health physics   offices

reactor

1 equip. decontamination area
2 hot waste area
3 operating area
4 hot cells
5 loading area
6 instrument room
7 high level counting
8 very warm laboratory
9 ramped corridor
10 hot lockers
11 cold lockers
12 airlock chamber
13 fan room
14 monitor
15 dry irradiation chamber

0   25 feet

The building plan.

87-foot high beehive-shaped dome constructed of 3- to 12-inch thick concrete. The dome is sheathed in a specially designed aluminum skin.

The one-story lab building containing individual laboratories together with general offices, library, lunch room, conference room, shop and other facilities, surrounds a simple court. This allows maximum outside light for each of the laboratories. It is linked to the dome by a third building which provides facilities and lockers for personnel working in the hot-cell or reactor area.

Exclusive of the dome the installation contains 37,000 square feet. It is located on 300 acres

which have been set aside in the Walker-Gordon farms for the future development of a nuclear park. Thus any one of the participating companies may purchase part of the land to build its own laboratory and even reactor. The present installation is this country's largest nuclear research facility for industrial research which is entirely owned and operated by private industry.

AMF Atomics, a Division of American Machine and Foundry Co., both designed and fabricated the nuclear elements and served as agent for the operating group in the development of the project.

CORNING GLASS WORKS

Research and Development Division
Corning, New York

Harrison, Abramovitz & Abbe, Architects

Lobby of the administration building.

The Research and Development Division of the Corning Glass Works is quartered at Houghton Park, the company's research and administration center in Corning, New York. Here, a three-story research laboratory and a one-story development workshop provide more than 128,000 square feet of efficiently arranged floor space. Both buildings incorporate careful planning for future needs, and flexibility is the keynote of interior and exterior design.

Laboratory and office areas are air-conditioned, and each laboratory is provided with compressed air, gas, and oxygen as well as power outlets. Air-conditioning ducts and all service piping has been left exposed on the under side of the structural slab which is designed so that it may be punctured at any point regardless of the location of the workbench on the floor above.

Laboratories are located on one outside wall, the offices on the other with the corridor running between. Recessed doors from each lab provide easy exit without blocking the corridor. A completely flexible floor plan is provided by an exterior module of five feet (center-to-center window).

There are two conference rooms, a 100-seat auditorium in the basement, and a 14,000 volume

432

Laboratory detail.

The library.

technical library and reading room for the Corning scientists.

The three-story research laboratory (240 ft by 50 ft) is sheathed in polished, black, opaque glass set in a black anodized aluminum grid; the one-story development workshop (480 ft by 90 ft) is faced with glass block which has proved a fitting structural material for a glassworks. Windows in both buildings are glazed with heat-absorbing green-tinted glass.

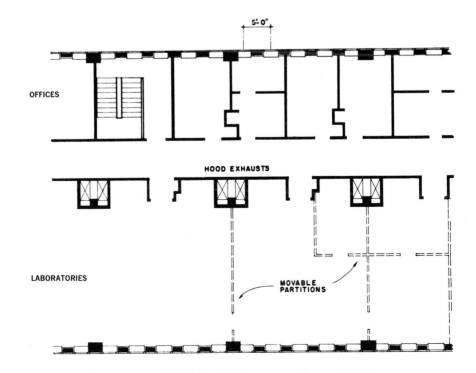

5'-0"

OFFICES

HOOD EXHAUSTS

LABORATORIES

MOVABLE PARTITIONS

The main facade showing the windowless, textured, monolithic concrete bomb-proof core.

UNITED STATES DEPARTMENT OF DEFENSE

Armed Forces Institute of Pathology

Walter Reed Medical Center

Washington, D. C.

Faulkner, Kingsbury & Stenhouse, Architect

The building for the Armed Forces Institute of Pathology includes many features but the most important is the design of the laboratories themselves. These are laid out on a modular basis and as the floor plan shows each one is backed up to a service core containing all the services which might be needed in any laboratory. The exhaust from each module is also run in this core. If a hood is needed in a laboratory it can be connected at any time to the exhaust duct for the module; otherwise the opening with a grille is merely left in the wall of the core.

The piping whether it is waste water, gas, air, etc., from the core to the needed position on the laboratory counter is not run in a partition but on a rack in the back of the casework. It was found, incidentally, by taking alternate prices that two sets of pipes could be racked on either side of a partition as cheaply as running one set in the partition. Keeping the pipes out of the partitions which are movable adds to the flexibility of the design. Another advantage is that in adding to or making changes in the services required in any laboratory it is not necessary to disturb those who are working in adjacent laboratories, or, since all pipes are run above the slab, those working in laboratories on the floor below.

Note—The system described above has been employed in two other laboratory buildings designed by this office, i.e., the Research Laboratory for the Children's Hospital and in the Second Army Medical Laboratory at Ft. Meade, Maryland, for which drawings are now being made.

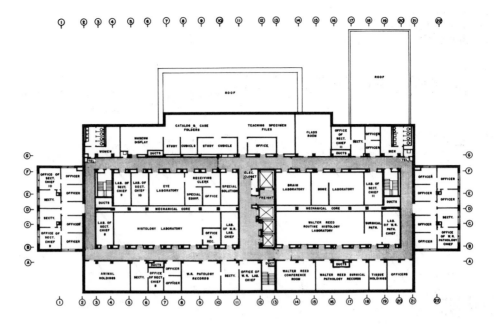

Typical floor plan showing various arrangements of laboratory modules adjacent to service core.

Plan of a typical laboratory.

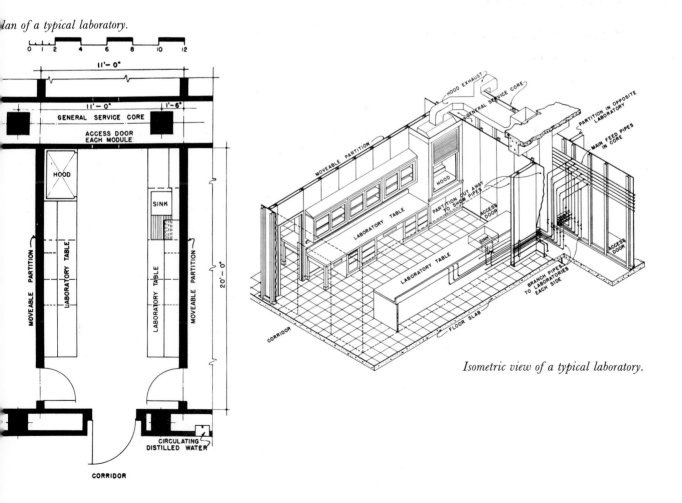

Isometric view of a typical laboratory.

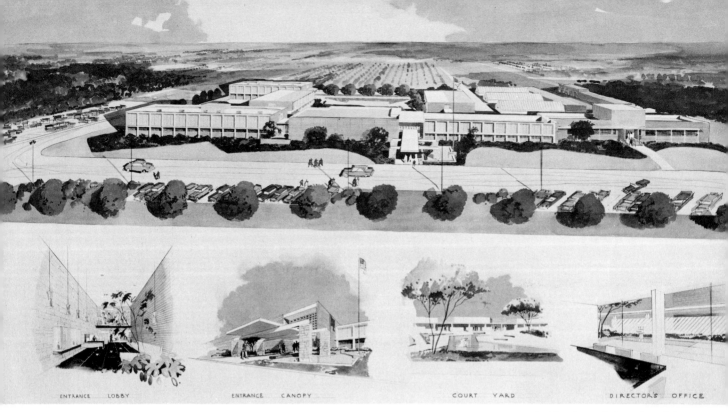

ENTRANCE LOBBY   ENTRANCE CANOPY   COURT YARD   DIRECTOR'S OFFICE

Architect's rendering of the laboratory.

SHELL OIL COMPANY

Agricultural Research Laboratory

Modesto, California

Austin, Field & Fry, Architects

These facilities have been built in a lush and beautiful area among the many ranches and orchards. The adequacy of this site proved no problem for the needed additions to the existing facilities since the topography and area available simplified the planning in relationship to the various buildings.

The plan of the new structures was to be of such a size as to accommodate not only the personnel working in the existing buildings and their enlargement, but also the employees and equipment that were operating in the Denver, Colorado, area. Shell Oil decided to close their operations in Colorado and concentrate the research on this campus.

The Architects and Engineers after considerable study decided upon designing the new buildings in precast concrete with a brick wainscot. The balance of the buildings was of precast concrete which included columns, girders, walls, and roof panels. These parts were cast by the Basalt Co. of Napa, California, which is approximately 100 miles to the north of Modesto. After the foundations and the floor slabs were in place, the trucks brought in the various construction elements which were assembled and erected practically over night. Time was of essence in the construction of this project and the savings made by this type of construction proved valuable by the end result of setting up their operations many months earlier than might have otherwise been possible.

Each individual laboratory follows the standard layout used by the Shell Oil Company all over the world with one unusual feature, the utility lines instead of being underground are overhead and drop down into pipe chases to each bench and hood. In turn each laboratory building is interconnected with the utility lines which are located on the top of all the covered walks. This provides easy access for replacements and repairs with a tremendous saving in time.

The campus-type layout is enhanced by beautiful landscaping and three decorative reflecting pools with one of the three being located at the main entrance to the Administration Building.

The operation of this laboratory consists in research and experimentation in the field of insecticides, fertilizers, and other types of products needed in the agricultural industry.

Among the other facilities of the laboratory is the Entomology Building wherein under perfect control of the air conditioning rooms, all types of insects are raised for experimental purposes.

Floor plan.

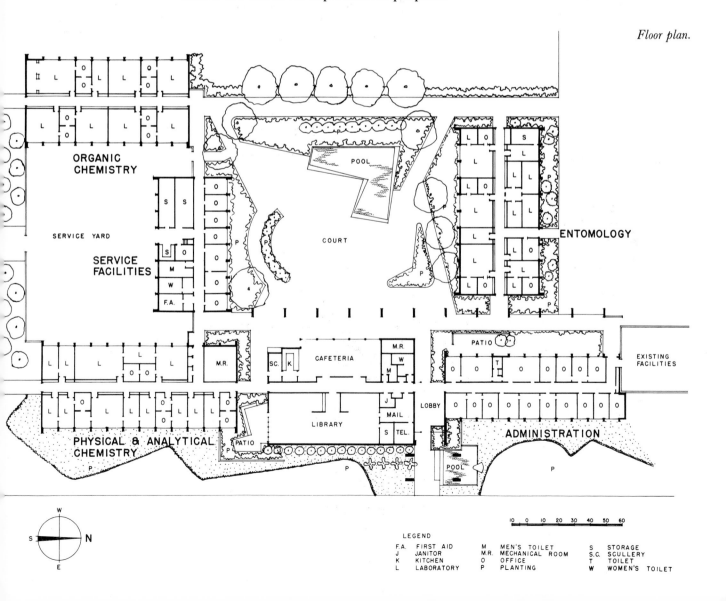

LEGEND

F.A.	FIRST AID	M	MEN'S TOILET	S	STORAGE
J	JANITOR	M.R.	MECHANICAL ROOM	S.C.	SCULLERY
K	KITCHEN	O	OFFICE	T	TOILET
L	LABORATORY	P	PLANTING	W	WOMEN'S TOILET

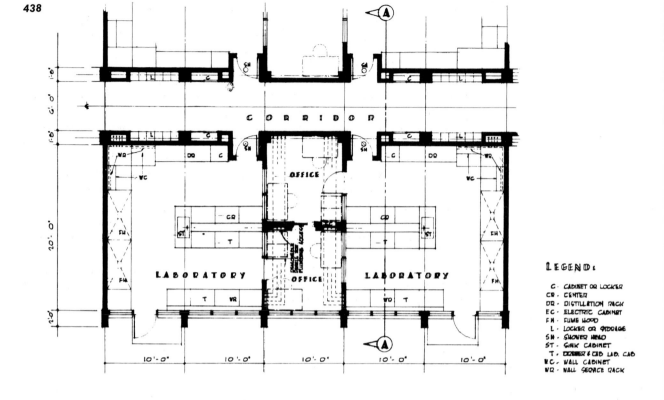

LEGEND:

- C · CABINET OR LOCKER
- CR · CENTER
- DR · DISTILLATION RACK
- EC · ELECTRIC CABINET
- FH · FUME HOOD
- L · LOCKER OR STORAGE
- SH · SHOWER HEAD
- ST · SINK CABINET
- T · DRAWER & CAB LAB. CAB
- WC · WALL CABINET
- WR · WALL SERVICE RACK

FLOOR PLAN OF STANDARD LABORATORY UNIT

SHELL OIL COMPANY

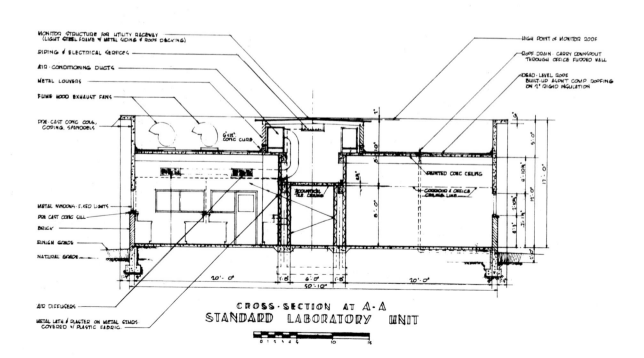

CROSS-SECTION AT A-A STANDARD LABORATORY UNIT

S. C. JOHNSON & SONS, INC.

Research and Development Tower
Racine, Wisconsin
Frank Lloyd Wright, Architect-Engineer

S. C. JOHNSON & SONS

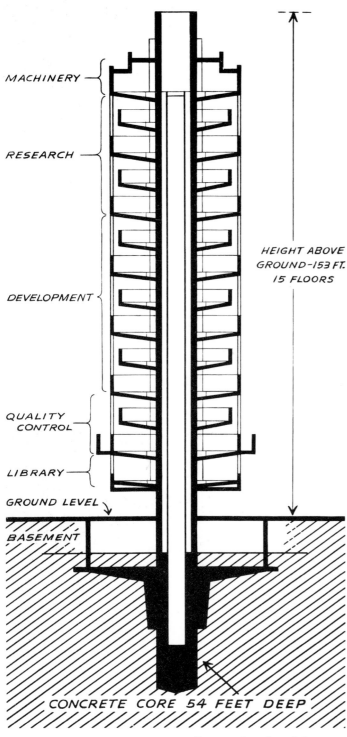

MACHINERY

RESEARCH

DEVELOPMENT

QUALITY
CONTROL

LIBRARY

GROUND LEVEL

BASEMENT

HEIGHT ABOVE
GROUND-153 FT.
15 FLOORS

CONCRETE CORE 54 FEET DEEP

Cross section plan of the tower.

The Research and Development Tower at the S. C. Johnson & Sons, Inc. plant at Racine, Wisconsin is the tallest building ever built without foundations directly under the side walls. Rising more than 150 feet in the air, the structure is 40 feet square, yet at ground level it is supported by a base only 13 feet across at the narrowest point.

Each of the 15 floors is cantilevered from the central core. This core rises 154 feet above the ground and is anchored to a concrete foundation which penetrates 54 feet into the earth and provides support for the tower in much the same manner as does the tap root of a tree.

Floors are in pairs, 40 feet square floors alternating with circular floors of slightly smaller diameter, an arrangement which permits the installation of tall laboratory equipment and facilitates communication. Each floor consists of an upper and a lower concrete slab, the lower slab tapering downward to the central core and forming the ceiling of the floor below. The resulting hollow space provides a plenum for the distribution of fresh air from the air-conditioning system.

The central core is a cluster of circular, reinforced concrete shafts. The center or main shaft is 13 feet in diameter and houses the air supply and exhaust chambers plus all the utility and building piping services. A circular elevator shaft cuts into this main shaft on one side, a semicircular stairway on the opposite side. The concrete walls of this "fibrous" stem vary in thickness from 7 to 10 inches and support the weight of the entire structure.

The walls are formed of 2 inch glass tubing laid horizontally and held in place by stainless steel wires binding them to aluminum supports on the inside. Between the rows of tubing are strips of synthetic rubber which serve as caulking. Behind the glass tubing is a wall of plate glass, separated from the tubing by a 3 inch air space. The square or main floor parapets are 5½ feet high and are faced with red tile brick. The exterior wall of the tower thus appears to consist of alternate faces of horizontally laid glass tubing and red tile brick.

In addition to the tower and administration building, other structures in the Administration and Research Center include a three story building housing the company's advertising center,

A laboratory unit.

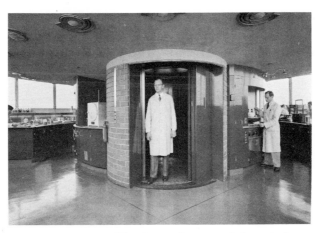

The elevator is a part of the central core.

the technical service department and a lounge, and a pilot plant adjoining the tower, two stories in height but with one below ground. The library floor of the tower is connected directly with the above three story building while at the third floor level, a glass enclosed runway leads to the administration building.

Four advantages cited for the tower design are: (1) Greater privacy is afforded chemists and laboratory technicians; (2) Corridors are eliminated making all space usable for work and service facilities; (3) The tower houses in natural relationship flowing downward Wax Research and Development, Control, Technical Service, Pilot Plant and out into the manufacturing area; and (4) The length of the various service feed lines is reduced.

The experimental engineering pilot plant where production methods are developed from laboratory bench processes.

PURDUE UNIVERSITY

Richard Bendridge Wetherill Laboratory of Chemistry
West Lafayette, Indiana

Walter Scholer and Associates, Architect-Engineer

The completion of the Richard Bendridge Wetherill Laboratory of Chemistry, culminating 27 years of planning and construction, provides Purdue University with one of the largest, most complete and most modern structures for teaching and research in Chemistry now in existence. Measuring 251 by 192 feet, there are four floors plus attic and basement, providing a total usable floor space of 160,000 sq. ft.

The building houses facilities for advanced teaching at the undergraduate and graduate levels together with research in all areas of chemistry. Facilities for the teaching of Freshman Chemistry are provided elsewhere.

The attached floor plans show the location of major facilities and general research and teaching areas. The basement includes most of the service facilities, including air conditioning and ventilation equipment, special electrical power sources and distribution system, oxygen distribution system, air-

FIRST FLOOR

PHYSICAL CHEMISTRY
TEACHING & RESEARCH

X-RAY DIFFRACTION

ELECTRON DIFFRACTION

INSTRUMENTAL ANALYSIS

RADIOCHEMICAL AREA

MACHINE SHOPS

SPECIAL INSTRUMENT SHOPS

SMALL LECTURE ROOMS AND
LECTURE-PREPARATION
ROOMS

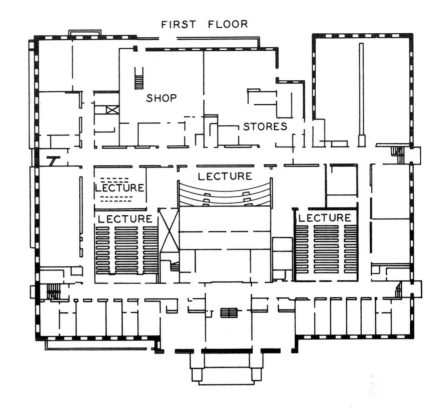

SECOND FLOOR

ADMINISTRATIVE OFFICES

INORGANIC CHEMISTRY
TEACHING & RESEARCH

SPECTROPHOTOMETER LAB-
ORATORY

INFRA-RED, RAMAN AND
MICROWAVE SPECTROSCOPY

EMISSION SPECTROSCOPY

STORE-ROOM OFFICES

MAIN LECTURE ROOM

MEMORIAL ROOM

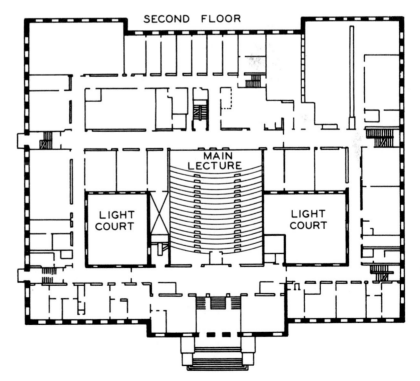

Plans of the first and second floors.

THIRD FLOOR

LIBRARY

ANALYTICAL CHEMISTRY
TEACHING & RESEARCH

BIOLOGICAL CHEMISTRY
TEACHING & RESEARCH

COLD ROOMS

WARM ROOM

ANALYTICAL BALANCE
ROOM

FIRST AID ROOM

BALCONY, MAIN LECTURE
ROOM

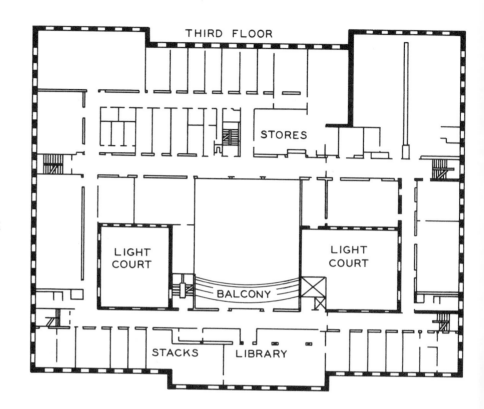

FOURTH FLOOR

ORGANIC CHEMISTRY
TEACHING & RESEARCH

ORGANIC OFFICES

DISTILLATION ROOM

COLD ROOM

GRADUATE STUDENT
ROOM

POLARIMETER ROOMS

PHOTOCHEMICAL DARK-
ROOMS

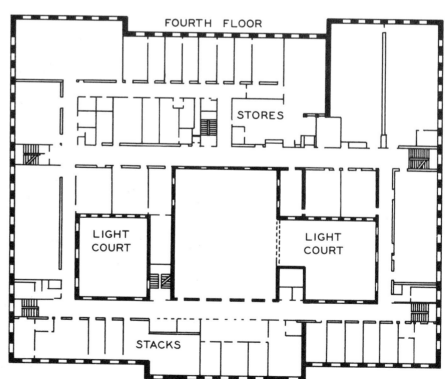

Plans of the third and fourth floors.

compressors, water softeners and a glass-blowing shop. In addition there are included armor-plated blow-out type cells for reactions involving high pressures or explosive materials. The attic provides storage area and specialized quarters for small animal experimentation.

Large store-room areas are provided on each floor with excellent facilities on the first floor for handling of in-coming shipments and dispersal to the various store-rooms.

Laboratories are provided with a complete range of electrical services, both a.c. and d.c. They also include ventilated hoods, steam, distilled water, compressed air and piped oxygen, in addition to the conventional facilities. All provide an emergency egress in addition to the main entrance. The radio-chemical area provides the most modern facilities for handling of materials of high activity with a minimum of risk to the research worker. Shower and locker rooms are provided for graduate students.

In addition to the main lecture hall, seating 463 persons, there are four smaller lecture rooms ranging in capacity from 80 to 170, and six recitation rooms. An air conditioned library provides space for 40,000 volumes.

Main lecture room.

PURDUE UNIVERSITY

Research laboratory for two students.

Chemistry library reading room.

The geology laboratory.

WILLIAM MARSH RICE UNIVERSITY

Keith-Wiess Geological Laboratories and
Anderson Biological Laboratories
Houston, Texas

George Pierce—Abel B. Pierce, Architects

This building complex represents a new kind of university laboratory building. For example, the numerous utilities are supplied through carefully spaced vertical cores to laboratories which, large or small, are grouped around them. Plenty of room has been left in the chases for bringing in any type of service in the future. Also, there are no interior corridors. Note that all toilet spaces, stairways and elevators have also been moved outside of the working space. In fact, the only permanent spaces in the actual main block of the building are the asbestos board paneled utility chases, thus giving complete FLEXIBILITY to the arrangement of laboratories as needs and programs of research change. These buildings will not be outmoded as soon as many others being built today for scientific research.

These new buildings were carefully located to fit easily and harmoniously into an existing campus containing some really fine examples of Italian Romanesque architecture. The architects also attempted to design buildings which would attain the highest standards of architectural design and character, that would be fine examples of contemporary architecture and would repeat and harmonize with the existing campus buildings but, at the same time, would express their own personality.

446

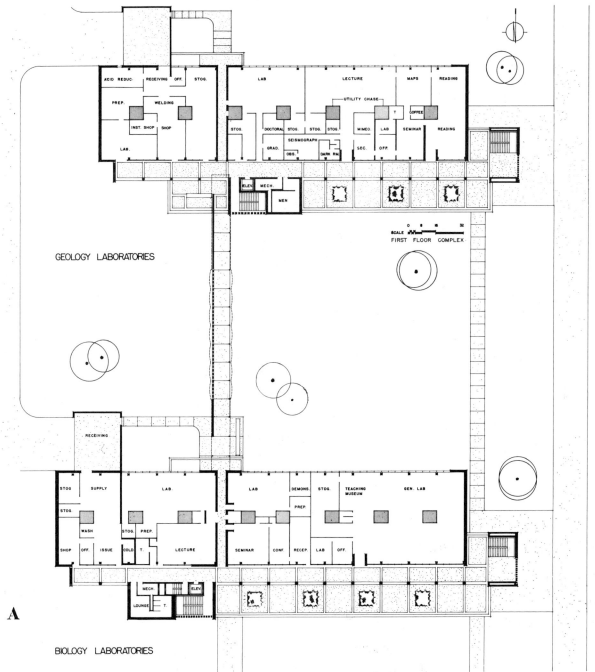

GEOLOGY LABORATORIES

ACID REDUC.	RECEIVING	OFF.	STOG.		LAB		LECTURE		MAPS	READING
PREP.	WELDING									
INST. SHOP	SHOP	STOG.	DOCTORAL	STOG.	STOG.	STOG.	MIMEO.	LAB	SEMINAR	READING
LAB.			GRAD.	SEISMOGRAPH		DARK RM.	SEC.	OFF.		
				OBS.						

UTILITY CHASE

COFFEE
T

ELEV MECH.
MEN

SCALE 0 8 16 32
FIRST FLOOR COMPLEX

BIOLOGY LABORATORIES

RECEIVING

STOG	SUPPLY		LAB.		LAB	DEMONS.	STOG.	TEACHING MUSEUM		GEN. LAB
STOG.	WASH		STOG. PREP.			PREP.				
SHOP	OFF.	ISSUE	COLD. T.	LECTURE	SEMINAR	CONF.	RECEP.	LAB	OFF.	

MECH. ELEV
LOUNGE T.

A

Floor plan of the geology and biology laboratories.

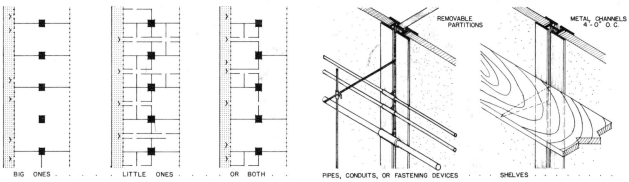

BIG ONES . . . . . LITTLE ONES . . . . . OR BOTH

REMOVABLE PARTITIONS

METAL CHANNELS 4'-0" O.C.

PIPES, CONDUITS, OR FASTENING DEVICES . . . SHELVES . . . . . .

B VARIATIONS IN LABORATORY ARRANGEMENTS   **C** ⌶ METAL CHANNEL DETAILS

North elevation.

UNIVERSITY OF BUFFALO

Acheson Hall of Chemistry
Buffalo, New York

Duane Lyman and Associates, Architect-Engineer

The Chemistry building known as Acheson Hall is a four story structure of approximately 83,000 square feet. The structural frame is reinforced concrete with flat slab type concrete floors. A large auditorium accommodating 400 people in stadium type seating is located at the south side accessible from the campus as well as from Acheson Hall.

The facade is modern in character, granite spandrels emphasizing horizontal treatment interrupted only by large stairways treated in Indiana limestone.

The laboratories are ventilated by a unique penthouse arrangement whereby some 60 exhaust fans supply positive ventilation to all fume hoods at all times.

Planned for undergraduate and graduate school education, the building is very well equipped. All laboratory piping is Duriron exposed for accessibility and much of the smaller piping at the laboratory tables is Owens-Corning Glass Company manufacture.

The finish of the building is relatively simple; plain painted concrete block walls, asphalt tile floors, and acoustically treated ceilings predominate.

An elevator was planned for easier distribution of chemical materials rather than for student convenience.

GROUND FLOOR

- 5 BASSETT AUDITORIUM
- 12 PHYSICAL CHEMISTRY LABORATORY
- 14 RESEARCH LABORATORY & OFFICE
- 17 INSTRUMENTS
- 18 STUDENT MACHINE SHOP
- 19 SUB-CRITICAL ASSEMBLY
- 20 GLASS BLOWING
- 22A GRADUATE RESEARCH
- 22 GRADUATE RESEARCH
- 23 GRADUATE RESEARCH
- 24 SENIOR RESEARCH PROBLEMS
- 24A HIGH PRESSURE ROOM
- 30 MECHANICAL EQUIPMENT
- 32 STUDENT LOUNGE
- 39 MAIN STOCKROOM
- 40 ADVANCED ORGANIC CHEMISTRY
- 42 SPECTROSCOPY LABORATORY
- 43 LECTURE PREPARATION ROOM

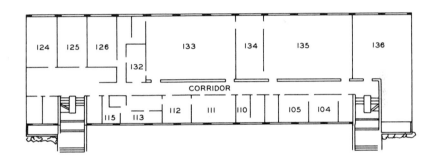

FIRST FLOOR

- 104 GRADUATE SCHOOL OFFICE
- 105 OFFICE, DEAN GRAD. SCHOOL
- 110 LABORATORY MANAGER
- 111 CHEMISTRY SEMINAR
- 112 OFFICE DEPARTMENT CHAIRMAN
- 113 CHEMISTRY DEPARTMENT OFFICE
- 115 EMPLOYMENT INTERVIEWS AND MIMEOGRAPH ROOMS
- 124 LECTURE ROOM
- 125 LECTURE ROOM
- 126 GRADUATE ASSISTANTS OFFICE
- 132 STOCK ROOM
- 133 QUANTITATIVE ANALYSIS LABORATORY
- 134 BALANCE ROOM
- 135 ELEMENTARY INORGANIC CHEMISTRY
- 136 CHEMISTRY LIBRARY

SECOND FLOOR

- 208 STOCK ROOM
- 211 GRADUATE RESEARCH
- 203, 204, 207, 212 OFFICE AND
- 202, 205, 206, 213 RESEARCH LABORATORY
- 214C FIRST AID
- 219 GRADUATE RESEARCH
- 220 LECTURE ROOM
- 224 LECTURE ROOM
- 231 GENERAL CHEMISTRY
- 233 GENERAL CHEMISTRY
- 235 GENERAL CHEMISTRY

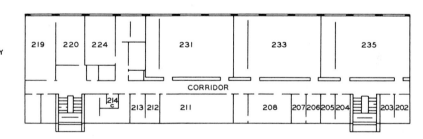

THIRD FLOOR

- 304 GRADUATE RESEARCH
- 305 STOCK ROOM
- 308 RADIOCHEMICAL INSTRUCTION
- 309 COUNTING ROOM
- 311 GRADUATE RESEARCH
- 317 FIRST AID
- 322 LECTURE ROOM
- 323 GRADUATE RESEARCH
- 332 ELEMENTARY ORGANIC LABORATORY
- 333 ELEMENTARY ORGANIC LABORATORY

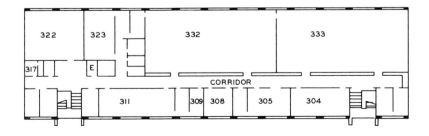

UNIVERSITY OF BUFFALO

Radiation research laboratory with air-foil fume hoods.

The unique arrangement of exhaust fans in the penthouse.

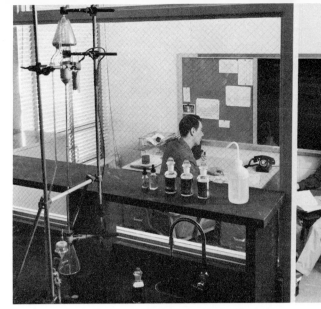

Student laboratory.

A faculty laboratory-office suite.

SWARTHMORE COLLEGE

Pierre S. duPont Science Building

Swarthmore, Pennsylvania

Vincent G. Kling, Architect

The Pierre S. duPont Science Building consists of four distinct wings organized around an open courtyard. The wings house physics classes, chemistry and math classes, a science library, and a 200-seat demonstration lecture hall. Independent research is encouraged by the provision of private laboratory spaces adjoining faculty offices, many of which are grouped around the courtyard.

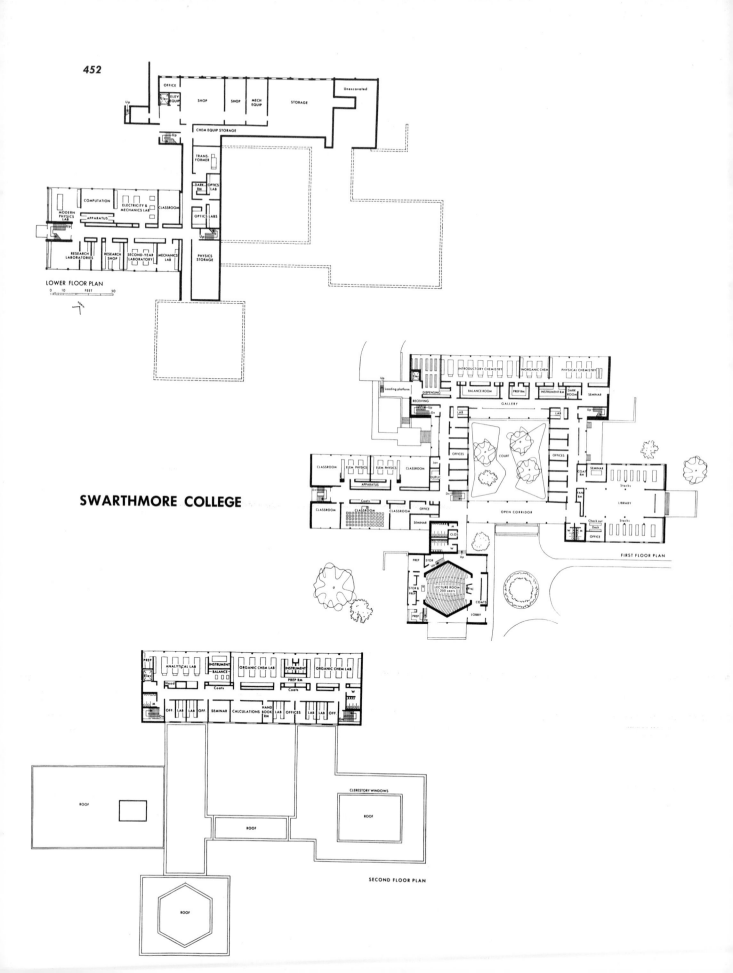

452

LOWER FLOOR PLAN

0 10 FEET 50

SWARTHMORE COLLEGE

FIRST FLOOR PLAN

SECOND FLOOR PLAN

Aerial view of the science and classroom building.

CALIFORNIA STATE POLYTECHNIC COLLEGE

Science and Classroom Building

San Luis Obispo, California

Allison and Rible, Architects

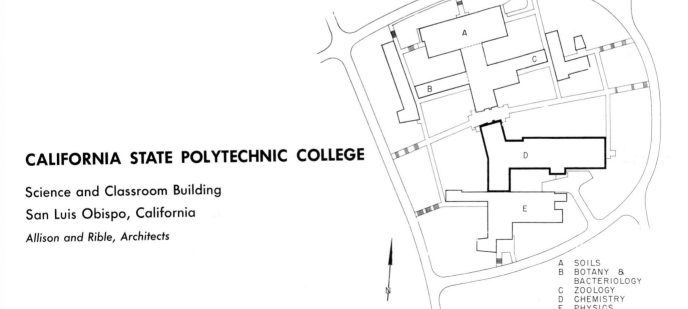

A SOILS
B BOTANY &
  BACTERIOLOGY
C ZOOLOGY
D CHEMISTRY
E PHYSICS

The building plan.

CALIFORNIA STATE POLYTECHNIC COLLEGE

The Science and Classroom Building, completed for the California State Polytechnic College, San Luis Obispo, California in 1955, consists of five separate building units with connecting covered passages.

The structure is a single story, with reinforced concrete floors and walls and composition roofing on wood sheathing over structural steel framing. It contains twenty-six laboratories, including eight for chemistry with adjoining equipment, storage and preparation rooms as well as balance rooms, a dark room, laboratories for extraction and Kjeldahl determinations and a cold room. The principal chemical laboratories are 42' x 25'.

Services in the chemical laboratories include hot and cold water, demineralized water, gas, compressed air, and oxygen. The preparation room for bacteriology and the animal autopsy room are provided with walk-in refrigerators.

Since the building accommodates many instructional programs which augment curricula pursued in adjacent buildings, the Science and Classroom Building has been located in the center of the campus. The rambling one-story structure is adapted to the rolling topography of this industrial-vocational college.

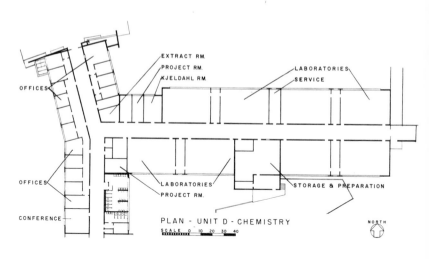

A chemistry laboratory.

RIPON COLLEGE

Farr Hall of Science
Ripon, Wisconsin

Frank C. Shattuck,
  M. F. Siewert & Associates, Architects

Farr Hall of Science of Ripon College, houses the departments of Biology, Chemistry and Physics. Certain economies were possible through the sharing of Lecture Rooms, Class Rooms, Storage and Reading Room.

The Chemistry facility is strictly an undergraduate operation, but capable of some advanced work. It is located on the top floor because two-thirds of the chemical fumes rise. Chases along the laboratory corridor walls rise from basement to penthouse for utility lines and ducts. The chase walls are demountable to give ready access to all services. Exhaust fans in the penthouse above the laboratories pull rather than push the fumes. Any leakage will be into rather than out of the ducts. Expensive fume duct runs are kept to minimum.

Small laboratories for research work are provided for each office, to make possible individual work on foundation grants. Faculty members can thus carry on work in their own fields with the aid of advanced students. The laboratory may also be used where setups should remain intact for long periods.

The building is based on the theory that a science laboratory need not be drab. Laboratory walls are white or off white for brightness, and are ideal where color of chemicals is critical to an experiment. Below table height, the cabinets are faced with plastic laminates in bright, clear color.

The Lecture Room is a multi-purpose facility. To change from a Science Auditorium to a recital hall for chamber music involves three steps. The first is to disconnect the utility connections which are snapped on to stubs in the desk and drop them into a pit in the floor, next the demonstration table, on wheels, is rolled back out of sight into a panelled recess, and finally wood panels are pulled out from either side of the chalk

Organic laboratory.

Principal student laboratories face North. The laboratory wing is 55 ft. wide. The building contains 47,321 square feet of which there are 21,187 sq. ft. in the basement, 17,046 on the First Floor and 9,088 on the Second Floor. Net assignable areas are: Chemistry, 7430 sq. ft.; Biology, 7800 sq. ft.; Physics, 4736 sq. ft.; shared area, 6534 sq. ft.

The building has a concrete frame, floors are cast-in-place concrete joists and filler block, the underside of which are painted for the laboratory ceilings, and in offices and some other spaces acoustic tile is cemented to the slab. The Lecture Hall is partially slab on grade, with steel joist roof. Exterior walls are brick with block backup. Interior partitions are block painted. Laboratory floors are concrete with Epoxy Resin sealer. Offices, corridors and classrooms have asphalt tile. Plastic fabric has been used on the walls of principal halls and lobbies.

The building is ventilated with cabinet heaters for the laboratories and offices, and a duct system for the Lecture Room and inside spaces. Hot water radiation uses steam from the college's central boiler plant with a converter in the building. A small gas fired boiler provides steam in the summer when the college plant is shut down.

board to cover the entire center front wall with its charts, etc. A grand piano which is stored on a dolly in a special room in the hall outside the lecture room is easily moved in for recitals or chamber music, or a portable podium may be brought in for lecture purposes. (See Page 326, Figures 12.3b and 12.3c).

The building is L-shaped stretching 143 ft. East and West and 197 ft. North and South.

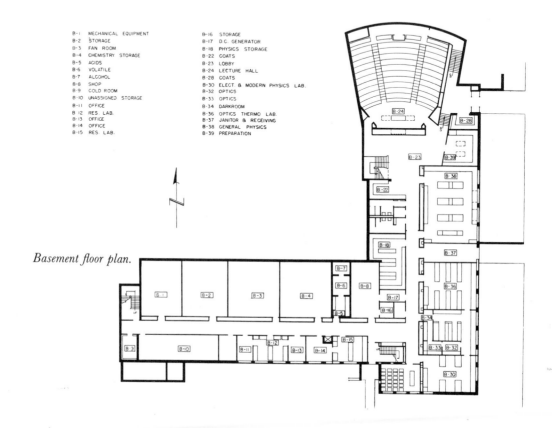

Basement floor plan.

B-1   MECHANICAL EQUIPMENT
B-2   STORAGE
B-3   FAN ROOM
B-4   CHEMISTRY STORAGE
B-5   ACIDS
B-6   VOLATILE
B-7   ALCOHOL
B-8   SHOP
B-9   COLD ROOM
B-10   UNASSIGNED STORAGE
B-11   OFFICE
B-12   RES. LAB.
B-13   OFFICE
B-14   OFFICE
B-15   RES. LAB.

B-16   STORAGE
B-17   D.C. GENERATOR
B-18   PHYSICS STORAGE
B-22   COATS
B-23   LOBBY
B-24   LECTURE HALL
B-28   COATS
B-30   ELECT. & MODERN PHYSICS LAB.
B-32   OPTICS
B-33   OPTICS
B-34   DARKROOM
B-36   OPTICS THERMO LAB.
B-37   JANITOR & RECEIVING
B-38   GENERAL PHYSICS
B-39   PREPARATION

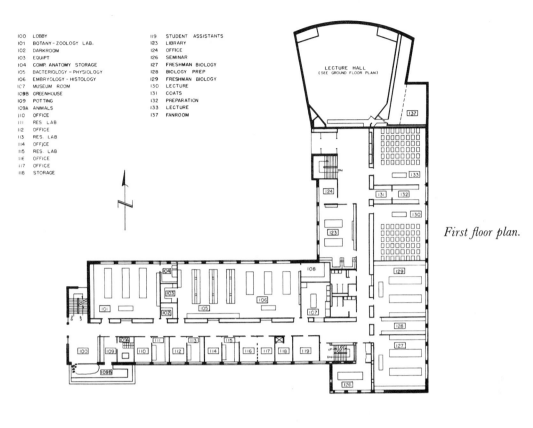

100 LOBBY
101 BOTANY - ZOOLOGY LAB.
102 DARKROOM
103 EQUIPT
104 COMP. ANATOMY STORAGE
105 BACTERIOLOGY - PHYSIOLOGY
106 EMBRYOLOGY - HISTOLOGY
107 MUSEUM ROOM
109B GREENHOUSE
109 POTTING
109A ANIMALS
110 OFFICE
111 RES. LAB
112 OFFICE
113 RES. LAB
114 OFFICE
115 RES. LAB
116 OFFICE
117 OFFICE
118 STORAGE

119 STUDENT ASSISTANTS
123 LIBRARY
124 OFFICE
126 SEMINAR
127 FRESHMAN BIOLOGY
128 BIOLOGY PREP
129 FRESHMAN BIOLOGY
130 LECTURE
131 COATS
132 PREPARATION
133 LECTURE
137 FANROOM

First floor plan.

RIPON COLLEGE

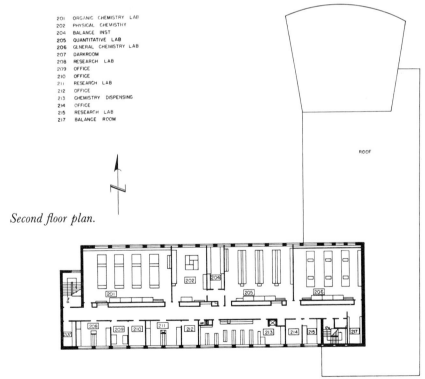

201 ORGANIC CHEMISTRY LAB
202 PHYSICAL CHEMISTRY
204 BALANCE INST
205 QUANTITATIVE LAB
206 GENERAL CHEMISTRY LAB
207 DARKROOM
208 RESEARCH LAB
209 OFFICE
210 OFFICE
211 RESEARCH LAB
212 OFFICE
213 CHEMISTRY DISPENSING
214 OFFICE
215 RESEARCH LAB
217 BALANCE ROOM

Second floor plan.

Appendixes

Index

Chemical

and Chemical

Engineering

Construction

1951–1961

Following is a list of chemical and chemical engineering laboratories built since the preparation of LABORATORY DESIGN which was published in 1951. The first section tells of new academic construction; this includes buildings specifically for chemistry or chemical engineering together with science centers for the smaller liberal arts colleges. In the second list, references are made to new chemical and chemical engineering laboratories designed for industrial or governmental use. Such new construction may take the form of additions to existing buildings, or new buildings added to an existing research center or it may represent entirely new research construction.

No claim is made for a complete listing in either section; to achieve this would be a large undertaking and the lists would be much longer. Nevertheless the information is sufficiently extensive so that planners in almost every section of the country should be able to pick out a few new buildings for study in their general region.

In most cases the source of the information is indicated. "CEN" is CHEMICAL AND ENGINEERING NEWS, a publication of the American Chemical Society, and the reference following tells where the story may be found by month, day, year and page. The many CEN references testify to the excellent coverage in this field of CHEMICAL AND ENGINEERING NEWS. Credit should go here to Robert F. Gould, Robert E. Henze, and Robert L. Silber of the staff of the American Chemical Society who checked thousands of pages of this publication in gathering the information. "HEW" refers to a listing of college and university science buildings provided by E. Eugene Higgins, Division of Higher Education, Office of Education of the Department of Health, Education and Welfare. "AC" together with reference indicates that the information came from ANALYTICAL CHEMISTRY, also a publication of the American Chemical Society. "Wooster" is a report of the Wooster Conference, 1959, on Research and Teaching in the Liberal Arts College. In this, information is given of new college science buildings together with costs, type of building and name of the architect. "MPB" refers to science buildings described in the recent book, MODERN PHYSICS BUILDINGS, by Palmer and Rice and published by the Reinhold Publishing Corporation in 1961. "BFR" references are taken from BUILDINGS FOR RESEARCH published in 1958 by the F. W. Dodge Corporation. In addition, a number of buildings are included without reference. These names have come to the editor from many sources.

The date in the fourth column in the academic list represents the year the building was completed. Dates have been omitted from the industrial list; in most cases the letters P, C and O are used to signify the planning stage (P), under construction (C), or in operation (O). These generally are found where several references are given for the same facility.

Following the listings of new construction is an index of these facilities by states.

ACADEMIC CONSTRUCTION

Agnes Scott College Decatur, Georgia	HEW	Campbell Science Hall	1951
Alabama, University of Medical Center University, Alabama		Basic science building	1951
Albany State College Albany, Georgia	HEW	Science building	1954
Alfred University Alfred, New York	CEN 10/27/58; 95	Myers Hall of Science	1958
Alma College Alma, Michigan		Science building	1959
Antioch College C. F. Kettering Foundation Yellow Springs, Ohio	CEN 12/8/52; 5166	Solar Energy Research Building	P
Aquinas College Grand Rapids, Michigan	Wooster	Science building	1959
Arkansas, University of Fayetteville, Arkansas	CEN 3/24/52; 1211	Chemical engineering wing	1952
Atlanta University Atlanta, Georgia	HEW	Chemistry building	1953
Atlantic Christian College Wilson, North Carolina	HEW Wooster	Science building	1954
Baldwin-Wallace College Berea, Ohio		Wilker Hall (chemistry & physics)	1960
Berea College Berea, Kentucky		Science addition	1959
Bethany College Lindsborg, Kansas	Wooster	Science building	1957
Birmingham-Southern College Birmingham, Alabama		Science building	1952
Blackburn College Carlinville, Illinois	HEW Wooster	F. W. Olin Science Building	1957

College/University	Source	Building	Year
Bluefield State College Bluefield, West Virginia	HEW	Technical science building	1954
Bowdoin College Brunswick, Maine	Wooster	Chemistry building	1952
Brandeis University Waltham, Massachusetts	CEN 1/3/55; 55 MPB 90–91 Wooster	Hayden Science Building	1955
Bridgewater College Bridgewater, Virginia	CEN 6/29/53; 2696 Wooster	Science building	1953
Bucknell University Lewisburg, Pennsylvania	CEN 2/8/54; 516 Wooster	F. W. Olin Science Building	1956
Buffalo, University of Buffalo, New York	AC 10/5/59; 84 CEN 10/12/59; 19	Acheson Hall of Chemistry Nuclear Research Laboratory	1959 1959

California Institute of Technology
Pasadena, California
	CEN 1/26/53; 351
	7/19/54; 2872
	3/12/56; 1200
		Norman W. Church Lab of
		  Chemical Biology
		Eudore Hull Spalding Laboratory
		  of Engineering
			
			1953
			
			P

California State Polytechnic College San Luis Obispo, California	Wooster	Science and classroom building	1955
California, University of Berkeley, California	CEN 3/10/52; 1006 8/11/52; 3320 10/27/52; 4492 10/20/52; 4396 5/16/53; 1102 BFR p. 59–61	Biochemistry & Virus Lab Cryogenics Laboratory Food technology building Heavy Ion Accelerator Building Radiation Laboratory	C 1952 1953 1953
Richmond, California Los Alamos, New Mexico Los Angeles, California Riverside, California Santa Barbara College Goleta, California	CEN 5/28/51; 2159 9/21/53; 3895 4/7/52; 1424 1/5/53; 72 9/22/52; 3956 12/7/53; 5092 CEN 10/13/52; 4276 7/5/54; 2704	Engineering Field Station Health Research Laboratory Medical Center Cancer research unit Chemistry Geology Building Physical Science Building Science building	P 1953 1954 1952 1953 1953 1954
White Mountain Research Station Mount Barcroft, California	CEN 8/11/52; 3318	Research laboratory	1952
Carroll College Helena, Montana	Wooster	Science building & library wing	1957
Case Institute of Technology Cleveland, Ohio	CEN 4/4/55; 1442 12/10/56; 6074	Addition to chemical engineering building	1956

Key to symbols: CEN-*Chemical and Engineering News;* HEW-Department of Health, Education and Welfare; AC-*Analytical Chemistry;* Wooster-report of the Wooster Conference; MPB-*Modern Physics Buildings;* BFR-Buildings for Research; P-in planning stage; C-under construction; O-in operation.

Castleton State Teachers College Castleton, Vermont	HEW	Science building	
Chicago, University of Chicago, Illinois	CEN 5/28/51; 2160 3/19/56; 1348 4/2/56; 1557 CEN 8/3/59; 69	Research Institute Low Temperature Laboratory Robert J. Flanagan Research Building La Rabida Sanitorium	1951 P P 1959
Citrus Junior College Azusa, California	HEW	Chemistry building	1953
College of the City of New York New York, New York	CEN 2/24/58; 101	Technology building	P
Claremont College Claremont, California	HEW	Baxter Science Laboratories	1953
Claremont Men's College Claremont, California		Pitzer Hall North (chemistry & physics)	1957
Clemson College Clemson, South Carolina	CEN 3/10/52; 1004 10/6/58; 134 1/11/60; 68	Chemistry building S. B. Earle Chemical Engineering Building	1952 1960
Coalinga Junior College Coalinga, California	HEW	Chemistry and physics	1957
Colorado School of Mines Golden, Colorado	CEN 9/3/51; 3630 7/30/54; 3428 9/1/52; 3636 6/1/53; 2306	Alderson Hall of Petroleum Engineering Coolbaugh Hall of Chemistry	1953 1953
Colorado, University of Boulder, Colorado	CEN 4/20/59; 105	Chemistry building	1959
Columbia University New York, New York	CEN 11/12/51; 4862 5/4/59; 78 11/15/54; 4578 AC 26, 35A, Nov. 54	Engineering center Geochemical lab (Palisades)	P 1954
Connecticut College New London, Connecticut	HEW	Hale Chemistry Laboratory	1954
Connecticut, University of Hartford, Connecticut Storrs, Connecticut	 Wooster	Science building Engineering building	1953 1959

Cornell University
Geneva, New York
Ithaca, New York
	
	CEN 4/12/54; 1490
	1/22/51; 297
	5/21/51; 2060
	9/10/51; 3717
	10/27/58; 95
	
	CEN 8/10/59; 126
		Food processing and chemical lab-
		  oratory building
		Materials processing and testing
		  laboratory
		William S. Geer Laboratory
		Sanitary Engineering & Radiation
		  Biology Laboratory
		Nuclear Technology Center
			P
			
			C
			1951
			
			C
			P

Delaware, University of Newark, Delaware	CEN 9/29/52; 4064	H. Fletcher Brown Laboratory of Chemistry	1952
Dillard University New Orleans, Louisiana	Wooster	Science building	1953
Drexel Institute of Technology Philadelphia, Pennsylvania	CEN 3/19/51; 1131	Alumni Scientific Laboratories	1951
Dubuque, University of Dubuque, Iowa	Wooster	Science building	1958
Earlham College Richmond, Indiana	Wooster	Science building	1952
Eastern Arizona Junior College Thatcher, Arizona	HEW	Science building	1955
Eastern Michigan College Ypsilanti, Michigan	HEW	Science building	1957
Eastern Nazarene College Wollaston, Massachusetts	Wooster	Science building	1959
El Camino College El Camino College, California	HEW MPB 96–97	Science quadrangle	1957–59
Emory and Henry College Emory, Virginia		Science building	1956
Emporia, College of Emporia, Kansas		Science hall	1957
Ferris Institute Big Rapids, Michigan	Wooster	Science building	1959
Florida Southern College Lakeland, Florida	Wooster	Science building	1953
Florida, University of Gainesville, Florida	CEN 4/16/51; 1546 2/3/58; 80	Engineering & industrial building Science & technology center	1951 P
Henry Ford Community College Dearborn, Michigan		Science building	1955
Fullerton Junior College Fullerton, California	HEW	Science building	1955
Furman College Greenville, South Carolina		Science building—center wing	1958

Key to symbols: CEN-*Chemical and Engineering News;* HEW-Department of Health, Education and Welfare; AC-*Analytical Chemistry;* Wooster-report of the Wooster Conference; MPB-Modern Physics Buildings; BFR-Buildings for Research; P-in planning stage; C-under construction; O-in operation.

Georgia Institute of Technology Atlanta, Georgia	CEN 6/11/51; 2391	Thomas P. Hinman Research Building	1951
	CEN 8/13/51; 3364	Price Gilbert Library	C
	12/28/53; 5380		1953
	4/14/58; 76	Radioisotopes & Bioengineering Laboratory	C
Georgia, University of Athens, Georgia	CEN 6/4/51; 2289	School of Pharmacy	1951
Goucher College Towson, Maryland	CEN 5/3/54; 1780	Hoffberger Science Building	1953
Graceland College Lamoni, Iowa	HEW	Science Hall	1954
Grinnell College Grinnell, Iowa	CEN 11/23/53; 4899 HEW MPB 98–99	Hall of Science	1952
Hahnemann Medical College and Hospital Philadelphia, Pennsylvania	CEN 2/12/51; 569 4/14/58; 42 2/22/60; 35	Isotope Laboratory Research Unit Clinical Research Building	1951 1958 C
Hamline University St. Paul, Minnesota	HEW	Drew Science Building	1951
Harvard University Cambridge, Massachusetts	CEN 4/9/51; 1414	Gordon McKay Applied Science Laboratory	1951
	CEN 11/2/59; 94	James Bryant Conant Chemical Laboratory	1959
Harvey Mudd College Claremont, California	Wooster	Science building	1959
Hawaii, University of Honolulu, Hawaii		Chemistry building	1953
College of the Holy Cross Worcester, Massachusetts	Wooster	Science building	1959
Hood College Frederick, Maryland	HEW	Chemistry and biology laboratory	1957
Humboldt State College Arcata, California		Science building	1953
Idaho, University of Moscow, Idaho	CEN 9/18/50; 3224	Radioisotopes laboratory	1951
Illinois Institute of Technology Chicago, Illinois Institute of Gas Technology Armour Research Foundation	CEN 8/6/51; 3174 9/10/51; 3716 1/7/52; 66 6/2/52; 2318	Research laboratory Freund Instrumentation Lab Research laboratories Rubber laboratory	P 1951 1952 1952

Illinois, University of Urbana, Illinois	CEN 1/22/51; 297 2/26/51; 764	East chemistry building	1951
Indiana University Bloomington, Indiana	CEN 2/22/51; 297	Atomic energy laboratory	C
Iowa State University of Science and Technology Ames, Iowa	CEN 10/1/51; 4095	Institute for Atomic Research	1951
Iowa Wesleyan College Mount Pleasant, Iowa		Science building	1961
Jacksonville Junior College Jacksonville, Florida	HEW	Science building	1956
John Brown University Siloam Springs, Arkansas	HEW	Science building	
Kalamazoo College Kalamazoo, Michigan	Wooster	Rebuilt physics and chemistry	1960
Kansas State Teachers College Emporia, Kansas	MPB 102–3	Science hall	1959
Kansas, University of Lawrence, Kansas	CEN 1/26/53; 350 4/26/54; 1693 MPB 104–5	Malott Hall—chemistry, pharmacy and physics	1954
King's College Wilkes-Barre, Pennsylvania	CEN 5/18/59; 106 Wooster	Science addition	1959
Knoxville College Knoxville, Tennessee	Wooster	Science building	1959
Lafayette College Easton, Pennsylvania	CEN 2/21/55; 730 2/11/57; 42 Wooster	Olin Hall of Science	1956
Lamar School of Technology Beaumont, Texas	CEN 11/5/51; 4690	Anthony F. Lucas Engineering Building	1951
Lenoir-Rhyne College Hickory, North Carolina		Minges Science building	1960
Little Rock University Little Rock, Arkansas		Science building	1959
Lock Haven State Teachers College Lock Haven, Pennsylvania	HEW	Ulmer Hall of Science	1952
Longwood College Farmville, Virginia		Science building	1951

Key to symbols: CEN-*Chemical and Engineering News;* HEW-Department of Health, Education and Welfare; AC-*Analytical Chemistry;* Wooster-report of the Wooster Conference; MPB-Modern Physics Buildings; BFR-Buildings for Research; P-in planning stage; C-under construction; O-in operation.

Louisiana State University New Orleans, Louisiana Branch	CEN 4/4/58; 54	Science building	1958
Louisville, University of Louisville, Kentucky	CEN 1/14/52; 172	Natural science building	P
Luther College Decorah, Iowa	Wooster	Valders Memorial Hall of Science	1961
Lycoming College Williamsport, Pennsylvania	HEW Wooster	Rebuilt science building	1957
Lynchburg College Lynchburg, Virginia	Wooster	Science building	1958
Manchester College North Manchester, Indiana	CEN 3/7/60; 58 Wooster	Hall of Science	1959
Manhattan College New York, New York	HEW	Hayden Science Hall	1953
The Marion Institute Marion, Alabama	HEW	Chemistry building	1953
Marshall College Huntington, West Virginia		Science building	1951
Maryland, University of College Park, Maryland	CEN 4/11/55; 1557 CEN 5/23/55; 2202	Glenn L. Martin Institute of Technology Headquarters and laboratories of Asphalt Institute	1951 O
Massachusetts Institute of Technology Cambridge, Massachusetts	CEN 5/5/52; 1876 11/15/54; 4583	Metals Processing Laboratory Karl F. Compton Lab of Nuclear Science & Electronics	P P
Massachusetts, University of Amherst, Massachusetts	CEN 11/16/59; 84	Chemistry laboratory (addition)	1959
McNeese State College Lake Charles, Louisana	HEW	Science building	1956
Miami, University of Coral, Florida	CEN 7/13/53; 2884	Chemistry of refrigeration	1953
Michigan, University of Ann Arbor, Michigan	CEN 4/25/55; 1776 11/24/58; 42	Phoenix Memorial Laboratory Germ-Free Laboratory	1955 1958
Millikin University Decatur, Illinois	Wooster	Science building	1954
Minnesota, University of Minneapolis, Minnesota	BRF 162–167	Chemical engineering laboratory	
Mississippi, University of University, Mississippi	CEN 1/22/51; 297	Physical chemistry laboratory	1951

Morehouse College Atlanta, Georgia	HEW Wooster	Chemistry building	1953
Mount Holyoke College South Hadley, Massachusetts	CEN 12/28/53; 5380	Chemistry building	1954
Mount Union College Alliance, Ohio	Wooster	Chemistry & physics	1958
Navario Junior College Corsicana, Texas	HEW	Science building	1952
Newark College of Engineering Newark, New Jersey	CEN 5/21/51; 2059	Arthur A. Mullaly Memorial Coatings Laboratory	1951
New Mexico State University University Park, New Mexico	CEN 3/23/59; 76	Chemistry building	1959
New Mexico, University of Albuquerque, New Mexico	CEN 9/17/51; 3872 HEW	John D. Clark Chemistry Building	1952
New York University New York, New York	CEN 12/3/51; 5154 CEN 6/9/58; 89 7/14/58; 68	Advanced Technology Center— Applied Science Building Engineering and Technology Building	P 1960
North Carolina State College Raleigh, North Carolina	CEN 6/4/51; 2288	Riddnick Engineering Laboratories	1951
North Carolina, University of Chapel Hill, North Carolina	CEN 10/12/53; 4216	Venable Hall of Chemistry (addition)	1953
North Dakota, University of Grand Forks, North Dakota	CEN 6/30/58; 86	Biochemistry Research Laboratory	C
North Texas State College Denton, Texas	CEN 6/16/52; 2516	Masters Hall of Chemistry and Biology	1952
Norwich University Northfield, Vermont	Wooster	James Jackson Cabot Hall of Science	1953
Notre Dame, University of South Bend, Indiana	CEN 11/9/53; 4696	Nieuwland Science Hall	1953
Occidental College Los Angeles, California	Wooster	Science building	1960
Oceanside-Carlsbad College Oceanside, California	HEW	Science building	1956
Ohio State University Columbus, Ohio	CEN 5/9/60; 44	Chemical engineering building Evans Laboratory of Chemistry	1960 1961

Key to symbols: CEN-*Chemical and Engineering News;* HEW-Department of Health, Education and Welfare; AC-*Analytical Chemistry;* Wooster-report of the Wooster Conference; MPB-Modern Physics Buildings; BFR-Buildings for Research; P-in planning stage; C-under construction; O-in operation.

Oklahoma Baptist University Shawnee, Oklahoma	Wooster	Science building	
Oklahoma State University Stillwater, Oklahoma	MPB 106–7	Chemistry-physics building	1958
Orange Coast College Costa Mesa, California	HEW	Science building	1957
Oregon State College Corvallis, Oregon	CEN 11/2/53; 4545 3/8/54; 940 HEW	Chemical engineering building	1954
Oregon, University of Eugene, Oregon	CEN 9/3/51; 3630 6/2/52; 2316	Science building (chemistry physics & biology)	1952
Ouachita Baptist College Arkadelphia, Arkansas	HEW Wooster	Science building	1951
Paine College Augusta, Georgia	HEW	Science building	
Pennsylvania State University State College, Pennsylvania	CEN 5/14/51; 1951 3/28/55; 1300 4/9/56; 1828 7/14/58; 68 10/31/60; 45	Chemistry building Nuclear reactor building Petroleum laboratory building Chemical engineering building	1952 1955 C 1960
Pennsylvania, University of Philadelphia, Pennsylvania	CEN 3/21/60; 44	Chemistry building	1960
Pensacola Junior College Pensacola, Florida	HEW	Science building	1957
Pfeiffer College Misenheimer, North Carolina	Wooster	Science hall	1958
Piedmont College Demorest, Georgia	Wooster	Science hall	1959
Polytechnic Institute of Brooklyn Brooklyn, New York	CEN 5/3/54; 1780 8/27/56; 4152 11/18/57; 88	New campus	1956
Princeton University Princeton, New Jersey	CEN 3/31/58; 106	Engineering quadrangle	P
Purdue University Lafayette, Indiana	CEN 12/31/51; 5532 6/27/55; 2716	Agricultural chemistry building Chemistry laboratory	1951
Redlands, University of Redlands, California	CEN 4/21/58; 92 Wooster	Chemistry & geology building	1956
Rennsselaer Polytechnic Institute Troy, New York	CEN 12/31/56; 6372	Swimming pool reactor	1956

Rhode Island, University of Kingston, Rhode Island	CEN 5/25/53; 2204 HEW	Pastore Chemical Laboratories	1953
Ripon College Ripon, Wisconsin		Farr Hall of Science	1961
Rochester, University of Rochester, New York	CEN 8/27/56; 4155	Nuclear emulsion laboratory	P
Rutgers University New Brunswick, New Jersey	CEN 4/28/52; 1753 5/24/54; 2125	Chemistry building Institute of Microbiology	1952 1954
Sacramento State College Sacramento, California	HEW	Chemistry building	1953
St. Anselm's College Manchester, New Hampshire	Wooster	Science building	1960
St. John's University Brooklyn, New York	CEN 5/23/55; 2220	Science-pharmacy building	P
St. Mary's College Notre Dame, Indiana	CEN 6/6/55; 2390	Science building	1955
St. Mary's College Winona, Minnesota	Wooster	Science building	1955
St. Mary's University San Antonio, Texas	CEN 6/9/52; 2414	Science building	1952
St. Petersburg Junior College St. Petersburg, Florida	HEW	Science building	1956
San Diego State College San Diego, California	CEN 6/27/60; 44	Chemistry-geology building	1960
San Francisco State College San Francisco, California	CEN 12/6/54; 4856	Science building	1954
Scranton, University of Scranton, Pennsylvania	Wooster	Science hall	1956
Seton Hall University South Orange, New Jersey	CEN 7/12/54; 2796	Science hall	1954
Simpson College Indianola, Iowa	HEW Wooster	Carver Science Hall	1956
South Dakota, State University of Vermillion, South Dakota	HEW	Medical and science building	1954
South Dakota School of Mines Rapid City, South Dakota	CEN 6/30/58; 86	Chemical and chemical engineering building	1958

Key to symbols: CEN-*Chemical and Engineering News;* HEW-Department of Health, Education and Welfare; AC-*Analytical Chemistry;* Wooster-report of the Wooster Conference; MPB-Modern Physics Buildings; BFR-Buildings for Research; P-in planning stage; C-under construction; O-in operation.

Southern California, University of Los Angeles, California	CEN 2/12/51; 569 4/28/52; 1752	Organic chemistry, graduate research laboratory	P 1952
Southwestern College Winfield, Kansas		Science hall	1951
Southwestern Louisiana Institute Lafayette, Louisiana	CEN 4/20/53; 1664	Chemistry building	1953
Southwestern University Georgetown, Texas	Wooster	Science building	
Spring Hill College Spring Hill, Alabama	HEW Wooster	Chemistry building	1957
Swarthmore College Swarthmore, Pennsylvania	CEN 5/2/60; 48 MPB 108–9	DuPont Science Building	1960
Syracuse University Syracuse, New York	CEN 4/2/56; 1568 CEN 5/20/57; 36	Chemical & metallurgical engineering laboratories Hugh P. Baker Forestry Lab- oratory	 1956 1957
Temple University Research Institute Philadelphia, Pennsylvania	CEN 5/30/55; 2296	Research laboratories	1955
Tennessee, University of Knoxville, Tennessee	CEN 6/23/52; 2623 5/10/54; 1913	Dabney Hall of Chemistry (addition)	 1954
Texas, University of Austin, Texas	CEN 12/24/51; 5451 2/22/60; 57	Experimental Sciences Building Science Research Institute	1951 C
Texas Technological College Lubbock, Texas	HEW	Science building	1951
Thiel College Greenville, Pennsylvania	Wooster	Rhodehouse Memorial Science Hall	 1959
Trinity University San Antonio, Texas	Wooster HEW	Science hall	1953
Tulsa, University of Tulsa, Oklahoma	CEN 2/5/51; 475	Petroleum Sciences Hall	1951
Tuskegee Institute Tuskegee Institute, Alabama	CEN 3/10/52; 1006	Carver Foundation Research Building	 1952
Union College Schenectady, New York	CEN 5/4/59; 78	Radiation laboratory	1959
United States Air Force Academy Colorado Springs, Colorado	CEN 12/2/57; 83	Thermodynamics laboratory	1957
Utah, University of Salt Lake City, Utah	CEN 8/2/54; 3038	Metals Research Center	1954

Ventura College Ventura, California	HEW	Chemistry building	1955
Wake Forest College Winston Salem, North Carolina	CEN 11/2/53; 4544 Wooster	Chemistry building	1954
Washington University St. Louis, Missouri	CEN 11/17/52; 4852 BFR 173–8	Louderman Hall of Chemistry Research Laboratories School of Medicine	1952

Wayne State University
Detroit, Michigan
	CEN 6/9/52; 2412
	  9/31/53; 3560
	  6/25/56; 3120
	  4/28/58; 65
		Parke-Davis Pharmacy Laboratory
		Kresge-Hooker Library
		Rubber Technology Laboratory
		Life Sciences Research Building
			1952
			1953
			1956
			P

Western Illinois University Macomb, Illinois	CEN 1/16/56; 238 HEW	Science building	1956
Western Michigan University Kalamazoo, Michigan	HEW	Paper technology	1957
Western Reserve University Cleveland, Ohio	CEN 8/29/60; 40	Science Center—chemistry to be ready first	1961
Westminster College New Wilmington, Pennsylvania	Wooster	Science building	
Wheaton College Wheaton, Illinois	CEN 12/5/55; 5270 Wooster	Breyer Chemistry Building	1955
Wilberforce State College Wilberforce, Ohio	CEN 1/15/51; 204	Benjamin Banneker Science Hall	1951
Wilkes College Wilkes-Barre, Pennsylvania	Wooster	Harold R. Stark Hall of Science	1957
Wilmington College Wilmington, Ohio	Wooster	Science building	1959

Wisconsin, University of
Madison, Wisconsin
	CEN 10/6/52; 4172
	  1/5/53; 72
	  9/24/56; 4635
		Chemical engineering building
		
		Biochemistry building, wing
			1952
			
			1956

Wooster, College of Wooster, Ohio		Rebuilt Severence Chemistry Laboratory	1960
Xavier University Cincinnati, Ohio	CEN 10/18/54; 4196	Thomas J. Logan Chemistry Building	1954
Yale University New Haven, Connecticut	CEN 1/24/55; 314	Biophysics laboratory	P

Key to symbols: CEN-*Chemical and Engineering News;* HEW-Department of Health, Education and Welfare; AC-*Analytical Chemistry;* Wooster-report of the Wooster Conference; MPB-Modern Physics Buildings; BFR-Buildings for Research; P-in planning stage; C-under construction; O-in operation.

INDUSTRIAL CONSTRUCTION

Abbot Laboratories			
Mundelin, Illinois	CEN 6/25/56; 3095	Agricultural & veterinary	P
	12/16/57; 26	research farm	C
North Chicago, Illinois	7/7/58; 28	Research center	C
	8/8/60; 26	Research & development laboratories	
Oak Ridge, Tennessee	4/21/52; 1637	Isotope production laboratory	
Aerojet-General Corporation			
Frederick, Maryland	CEN 11/23/59; 35	Automation, underwater acoustics	O
Airkem, Inc.			
New York, New York	AC 31, 63A, Aug. 59	Laboratory for the study of odors	
Air Products, Inc.			
Allentown, Pennsylvania	CEN 4/6/53; 1418	First of six research buildings	C
Air Reduction Company, Inc.			
Murray Hill, New Jersey	CEN 7/1/57; 23	Polymer development-paints	C
Piscataway Township, New Jersey	6/16/58; 35	Technical service & applications	P
Franklin Township, New Jersey	6/29/59; 25	Fuels & oxidizer research	C
Alco Products, Inc.			
Schenectady, New York	CEN 2/3/58; 29	Nuclear research laboratory	C
	5/26/58; 29	Research & development laboratory	O
Allegheny Ludlum Steel Corporation			
Brackenridge, Pennsylvania	CEN 4/29/57; 24	Research & development laboratory	P
Allied Chemical & Dye Corporation			
Barrett Division			
Edgewater, New Jersey	CEN 5/28/51; 2155	Addition to research laboratory	C
	7/21/52; 2996	Shadyside applications research	
		laboratory	O
General Chemical Division			
Morristown, New Jersey	CEN 3/2/53; 886	Research laboratory	
	AC 26, 37A, Sept. 54		
	CEN 9/20/54; 3720		O
	5/23/60; 28	Addition to laboratory space	P
Metropolis, Illinois	AC 32, 91A, Oct. 60	Control & development laboratories	
National Aniline Division			
Buffalo, New York	CEN 3/16/53; 1091	Research & engineering center	P
	5/23/55; 2192		O
Chesterfield, Virginia	7/15/57; 20	Fiber application laboratory	O
Nitrogen Division			
Hopewell, Virginia	10/13/52; 4268	Research & development facilities	P
	1/12/53; 152		C
	11/2/53; 4537	Organic research center	O
Alloy Rods Co.			
York, Pennsylvania	CEN 9/12/55; 3778	Research & development laboratory	O

Aluminum Company of America			
Mervin, Pennsylvania	CEN 9/14/59; 29	Research & development center	P
New Kensington, Pennsylvania	9/10/51; 3708	Expansion of research facilities	C
Ambric Testing and Engineering Associates, Inc.			
Philadelphia, Pennsylvania	CEN 6/22/59; 26	New testing laboratories	O
American Aniline Company			
Patterson, New Jersey	CEN 11/12/56; 5506	Sales office & dye testing laboratory	C
American Brass Co.			
Waterbury, Connecticut	CEN 1/18/60; 33	Research center	P
American Can Co.			
Barrington, Illinois	CEN 3/15/54; 1014	Research & development laboratory	C
	9/13/54; 3600		C
	6/13/55; 2480		O
American Cholesterol Products			
Edison, New Jersey	CEN 4/8/57; 22	New plant & laboratory	O
American Cyanamid Co.			
Bound Brook, New Jersey		New research center	
Chicago, Illinois	CEN 9/30/54; 3857	Paper chemicals application laboratory	O
Princeton, New Jersey	12/31/56; 6357	Agricultural center	P
Stamford, Connecticut	9/21/53; 3878	Agricultural chemicals research laboratory	O
	9/28/53; 4020		
	7/14/58; 26	Ionization & radiation center	P
Wallingford, Connecticut	2/3/58; 29	Product development laboratory	C
Winchester, Massachusetts	4/21/53; 1638	Maximum recovery laboratory (Atomic Energy Commission laboratory)	
American Enka Corp.			
Enka, North Carolina	CEN 6/28/54; 2574	Research building	C
	8/23/54; 3348		C
American Latex Products Corp.			
Hawthorne, California	CEN 4/28/58; 32	Research & development laboratory	O
American Machine & Foundry Co.			
Springdale, Connecticut	CEN 7/13/53; 2874	Chemical research & development laboratories	C
	2/21/55; 708	Research reactor (nuclear)	O
American Maize-Products Co.			
Hammond, Indiana	CEN 11/10/52; 4741	Enlargement of research department	
	6/29/59; 25	Research laboratory	P
American Marietta Co.			
Seattle, Washington	CEN 5/4/53; 187	Enlargement of laboratory and production facilities	P
	4/14/58; 31	Research center	C

Key to symbols: CEN-*Chemical and Engineering News;* HEW-Department of Health, Education and Welfare; AC-*Analytical Chemistry;* Wooster-report of the Wooster Conference; MPB-Modern Physics Buildings; BFR-Buildings for Research; P-in planning stage; C-under construction; O-in operation.

American Metal Products Co. Ann Arbor, Michigan	CEN 1/4/60; 27	Engineering science labs	O
American Potash & Chemical Corp. Los Angeles, California	CEN 7/14/52; 2896	Research laboratories for boron and lithium	P
Trona, California	10/4/54; 3974	Control laboratory	O
Whittier, California	6/22/53; 2606	Tilt-up research laboratory	
	9/12/55; 3845		O
	2/18/57; 24	Research laboratories	O
American Smelting & Refining Co. South Plainfield, New Jersey	CEN 1/20/58; 34	Wing to house asbestos research	C
	11/9/59; 28	Central research laboratories	O
Amoco Chemicals Corp. Chicago, Illinois	CEN 3/31/58; 40	Technical service laboratory	O
Applied Science Laboratories Inc. State College, Pennsylvania	CEN 9/29/52; 4060	Applied Science Laboratory	C
Arapahoe Chemicals, Inc. Boulder, Colorado	CEN 9/29/52; 4060	Addition—doubles laboratories and triples office space	
	2/15/60; 35	Addition—doubles research and office facilities	P
Archer-Daniels-Midland Co. Bloomington, Minnesota	CEN 12/5/60; 36	Research center	P
Minneapolis, Minnesota	5/28/51; 2150	Pilot plant	O
Peoria, Illinois	11/10/60; 30	Multi-million dollar chemical center	C
Argonne National Laboratory Chicago, Illinois	CEN 7/30/51; 3103	Cyclotron vault and chemistry building	C
Lemont, Illinois	3/10/58; 29	Fuels technical center (AEC)	P
	7/7/59; 28		C
Armco Steel Corporation Middletown, Ohio	CEN 10/26/59; 32	Doubles research facilities	P
Armour Industrial Chemical Co. McCook, Illinois	CEN 3/28/60; 35	Research laboratory and pilot	P
	7/4/60; 30	plant	C
Armour Research Foundation Chicago, Illinois	CEN 6/8/53; 2408	High temperature laboratory	O
	6/27/55; 2706	Research laboratory	C
	9/17/56; 4502	Addition to metals research building	
	12/10/56; 6059	Combustion laboratory	O
	7/21/58; 34	Chemistry building	P
	11/3/58; 70	Metals research building	O
	6/22/59; 26	Chemical engineering building	C
Armstrong Cork Co. Lancaster, Pennsylvania	CEN 7/21/52; 3012–13 BFR 93–97	Research and development center	C

Arner Co., Inc.
  Buffalo, New York   CEN 3/12/51; 1016   Experimental laboratory

Atlantic Research Corporation
  Alexandria, Virginia   CEN 12/3/56; 5980   Headquarters & laboratory building
                                  1/7/57; 66   Laboratory   P
                                  2/9/59; 36   Missile research center   O
  Gainesville, Virginia   8/18/52; 3436   Rocket fuel pilot plant

Atlas Powder Company
  Marshall, Texas   CEN 1/12/59; 30   Darco experimental laboratory   C
  Reynolds, Pennsylvania   12/12/55; 5362   Nitration process laboratory   O
  Wilmington, Delaware   12/3/56; 5980   Technical center
                                  2/4/57; 24   C
                                  6/2/58; 24

Atomic Energy Commission
  Ames, Iowa   CEN 2/8/60; 30   Metals Process Development Facility   C
  Boulder, Colorado   4/16/51; 1536   P
  Hanford Works, Richland,
    Washington   1/5/53; 58   Library   O
  Oak Ridge, Tennessee   12/14/59; 36   Radioisotope laboratories   O
                                  7/11/60; 27   High level radioactive laboratory   P
  Upton, Long Island, N.Y.   12/12/60; 35   Radiation engineering laboratory   C

Atomic Power Development
    Associates
  Detroit, Michigan   CEN 2/21/55; 714   Atomic fuel testing laboratory   P

AVCO Corporation
  Wilmington, Delaware   CEN 6/8/59; 28   Research & development center
                                                             for space missile technology   O

Babcock & Wilcox Co.
  Alliance, Ohio   CEN 3/18/57; 26   Expansion of research center
  Lynchburg, Virginia   3/17/58; 34   Expansion of critical experiment
                                                             laboratory   C

Baird-Atomic, Inc.
  Cambridge, Massachusetts   CEN 5/4/59; 30   Spectrochemical applications
                                                             laboratory   O

J. T. Baker Chemical Company
  Phillipsburg, New Jersey   CEN 10/11/54; 4062   Research laboratory building   P
                                  6/20/55; 2598   Warehouse for chemicals   O
                                  10/29/56; 5248   Research laboratories
                                  AC 28, 49A, Oct. 56

G. Barr & Co.
  Chicago, Illinois   CEN 8/22/55; 3476   Research & development laboratory   O
                                  7/14/58; 26   Expansion of research & develop-
                                                             ment facilities   C

Key to symbols: CEN-*Chemical and Engineering News;* HEW-Department of Health, Education and Welfare; AC-*Analytical Chemistry;* Wooster-report of the Wooster Conference; MPB-Modern Physics Buildings; BFR-Buildings for Research; P-in planning stage; C-under construction; O-in operation.

Battelle Memorial Institute Columbus, Ohio	CEN 7/16/51; 2918	5th new research building	
	8/18/52; 3448	6th major building started	C
	9/14/53; 3766	Chemical research laboratory	C
	10/25/54; 4284	Reactor development laboratory	
	1/17/55; 218	Chemical engineering, metallurgy and minerals processing	C
	10/3/55; 4182	Atomic energy research center	
	11/12/56; 5512		O
Battenfeld Grease & Oil Corp. Kansas City, Missouri	CEN 11/3/52; 4628	Laboratory & materials handling building	C
Don Baxter, Inc. Glendale, California	CEN 6/21/54; 2470	Research laboratory	O
Beaver & Black Chicago, Illinois	CEN 1/12/53; 150	Laboratories in biological science, physics, chemistry and physics-organic chemistry	C
Beckman Instruments, Inc. Fullerton, California	CEN 3/11/57; 18	Research & development building	P
Biofirm Corporation Wasco, California	AC 31, 73A, May 59	Research center	O
Bituminous Coal Research Inc. Columbus, Ohio	CEN 3/10/52; 990	Research center	P
	10/12/53; 4207		O
Bjorksten Research Laboratories Houston, Texas	CEN 9/16/57; 34	Research laboratory	O
Madison, Wisconsin	4/28/52; 1736	Mining and metallurgical division	O
	5/5/52; 1866	Radiochemicals division	O
Bordon Co. Bainbridge, New York	CEN 4/5/54; 1338	Sand laboratory	C
Chicago, Illinois Polyco Department	9/12/55; 3776	Service laboratory—water base paints	
Fayetteville, North Carolina	12/9/57; 38	Technical service laboratories	O
Philadelphia, Pennsylvania	12/17/51; 5361	Chemical research laboratories	C
	11/9/53; 4668	General research laboratory	O
Springfield, Oregon	5/9/60; 24	Product development laboratory and dry adhesive plant	P
Borg-Warner Corp. Des Plaines, Illinois	CEN 10/10/55; 4278	Research center	C
Bristol-Myers Co. Syracuse, New York	CEN 12/8/58; 31	Addition for cancer & pharmaceutical research	P

Brookhaven National Laboratory Upton, Long Island, N.Y.	CEN 12/26/55; 5578 8/6/56; 2754	Medical research center	P C
Bruning, Charles, Co., Inc. Mount Prospect, Illinois	CEN 10/26/59; 34	Research center	C
Buckeye Cellulose Corp. Memphis, Tennessee	CEN 8/18/52; 3440 5/31/54; 2187	Research building Cellulose & soy beans research laboratory	C O
Cabot, Godfrey L. Cambridge, Massachusetts	CEN 6/8/53; 2410	Research laboratories	O
California Ink Co. Berkeley, California	AC 31, 53A, Jan. 59	Research center	
California Research Corp. Richmond, California	CEN 12/13/54; 4928 5/30/55; 2292 3/18/57; 20 AC 32, 97A, Dec. 60	Expansion of laboratories Laboratory-administration building Research laboratories Analytical separations laboratories	P C O
California Spray-Chemical Corp. Richmond, California	CEN 11/14/55; 4910	Bio-screening laboratories	O
Camile Dreyfus Laboratory North Carolina Research Triangle, North Carolina	CEN 2/22/60; 34	Polymer chemistry research	P
Carborundum Company, The Niagara Falls, New York	CEN 4/28/58; 32	Product development laboratory	O
Cargill Co., The near Minneapolis, Minnesota	CEN 6/10/57; 20	Research laboratories	O
Carnation Co. Van Nuys, California	CEN 10/19/53; 4306	Research facilities	O
Carpenter Steel Co., The Reading, Pennsylvania	CEN 2/25/57; 26	Corrosion research laboratory	C
Carter Oil Co. Tulsa, Oklahoma	CEN 9/8/52; 3722	Expansion of research laboratory	P
Carter Products Co., Inc. Cranbury, New Jersey	CEN 3/28/60; 35	Research laboratory	O
Carwin Co., The North Haven, Connecticut	CEN 7/11/55; 2892	Expansion of laboratory & office facilities	 C
Catalin Corporation of America Fords, New Jersey	CEN 12/17/56; 6176 1/7/57; 66	Research laboratory Special chemical laboratory	P P

Key to symbols: CEN-*Chemical and Engineering News;* HEW-Department of Health, Education and Welfare; AC-*Analytical Chemistry;* Wooster-report of the Wooster Conference; MPB-Modern Physics Buildings; BFR-Buildings for Research; P-in planning stage; C-under construction; O-in operation.

Celanese Corporation of America			
Clarkwood, Texas	CEN 1/12/53; 152	Petrochemical research center	O
Charlotte, North Carolina	3/7/55; 950	Development laboratories	C
Summit, New Jersey	8/17/53; 3378	Application laboratory	C
Cenco Instruments Corporation			
Chicago, Illinois	CEN 9/8/52; 3720	Research & development laboratory	C
	3/15/54; 1009		O
Central Commercial Co.			
Northfield, Illinois	CEN 10/8/51; 4175	Research & development laboratories	O
Centrico, Inc.			
Englewood, New Jersey	CEN 1/6/58; 43	Technical service and testing laboratories	O
Chemical Construction Corp.			
New Brunswick, New Jersey	CEN 11/25/57; 32	Development laboratory	P
Chemstrand Corp.			
Durham, North Carolina	CEN 7/20/59; 26	Research center	P
Chrysler Corp.			
San Leandro, California	CEN 11/17/52; 4838	Metallurgical laboratory	P
CIBA Pharmaceutical Products Inc.			
Summit, New Jersey	CEN 8/6/51; 3172	Macrobiology laboratory	P
	12/9/57; 38	Pharmacy research & development laboratories	O
	11/16/59; 30	Quality control division	O
Cities Service Co.			
Cranbury, New Jersey	CEN 10/31/55; 4640	Product development center	P
	7/1/57; 24	Research laboratory	O
Clinton Corn Processing Co.			
Clinton, Iowa	CEN 7/8/57; 19	Research center	O
Colgate-Palmolive Co.			
Bloomfield, New Jersey	CEN 10/10/55; 4278	Central research laboratory	P
	5/14/56; 2366	Basic & applied research laboratory	P
New Brunswick, New Jersey	9/13/54; 3600	Radioisotopes laboratory	O
	10/5/59; 32	Basic & applied research laboratories	P
Piscataway Township, New Jersey	11/14/60; 36	Research center	C
Colorado Department of Agriculture			
Denver, Colorado	AC **26**, 28A, Jan. 54	Laboratory for the control of sales of feed, fertilizer, dairy products & insecticides	
Columbia Carbon Co.			
Monroe, Louisiana	CEN 5/14/56; 2368	Office and laboratory center	C
Princeton, New Jersey	6/29/59; 25	Research center	O

Columbia-Southern Chemical Corp.
  Barberton, Ohio   CEN 1/30/56; 456   Research building expansion   C
                                    5/12/58; 24   Research center
  Natrium, West Virginia   8/16/54; 3252   Two labs to house development and
                                                         pilot plant operations and for con-
                                                         trol and research work   C

Combustion Engineering, Inc.
  Windsor, Connecticut   CEN 12/26/55; 5572   Nuclear engineering and development
                                                         center   P

Commercial Solvents Corporation
  Thermatomic Carbon   CEN 9/19/55; 3904   Carbon black application laboratory C
  Sterlington, Louisiana

Connecticut Agricultural
    Experimental Station
  New Haven, Connecticut   CEN 2/9/59; 36   Research center   O

Consolidated Electrodynamics Corp.
  Pasadena, California   CEN 12/1/56; 5927   Engineering, research, and market-
                                                         ing center   O

Continental Can Co., Inc.
  Chicago, Illinois   CEN 6/25/56; 3094   Engineering-research laboratory   O

Continental-Diamond Fibre
    Corporation
  Newark, Delaware   CEN 2/16/59; 30   Research center   P
                                    11/9/59; 28   O

Continental Oil Co.
  Ponca City, Oklahoma   CEN 2/2/53; 440   Research laboratories
                                    9/13/54; 3602   Laboratory in oil tank   C
                                    3/28/55; 1288   Research laboratory in tank   C
                                    10/1/56; 4753   Radiation laboratory   P
                                    7/18/60; 39   Research & development laboratory   P

Copolymer Corp.
  Baton Rouge, Louisiana   CEN 10/13/58; 26   Research building   O

Corn Products Refining Co.
  Argo, Illinois   BFR 149–153   Research laboratory & pilot plant

Corning Glass Works
  Corning, New York   CEN 6/3/57; 24   Laboratories and administration
                                                         building   O
                                    10/10/60; 34   Research & engineering center   P

Courtaulds, Inc.
  Mobile, Alabama   CEN 2/8/54; 476   Research laboratory   C

Key to symbols: CEN-*Chemical and Engineering News;* HEW-Department of Health, Education and Welfare; AC-*Analytical Chemistry;* Wooster-report
of the Wooster Conference; MPB-Modern Physics Buildings; BFR-Buildings for Research; P-in planning stage; C-under construction; O-in operation.

Cowles Chemical Co. Skaneateles Falls, New York	CEN 7/11/55; 2892	Research laboratories	O
Crippen Laboratories, Inc. Baltimore, Maryland	CEN 7/23/51; 3013 2/8/54; 478	Research laboratory Petroleum research & testing laboratory	O O
Crobaugh, Frank L., Co. Cleveland, Ohio	CEN 12/9/57; 38	Research laboratories	O
Crossett Co. Crossett, Arkansas	CEN 1/20/58; 32	Research laboratories expansion	C
Crown Cork & Seal Company, Inc. Towson, Maryland	CEN 10/17/55; 4407	Research development & head- quarters building	
Crown Zellerbach Corp. Camas, Washington	CEN 6/30/52; 2714–5 6/7/54; 2266	Development laboratory Central research laboratory	O P
Cudahy Packing Co., The Omaha, Nebraska	CEN 5/4/53; 1870	Expands pharmaceutical research facilities	O
Cutter Laboratories, The Berkeley, California	CEN 8/5/57; 30	Research building	C
Cyclo Chemical Los Angeles, California	CEN 5/4/59; 30	Expand laboratory and production facilities	C
Despatch Oven Co. Minneapolis, Minnesota	CEN 4/18/55; 1662	Research & testing laboratory	O
Diamond Alkali Company Concord Township, Ohio Painesville, Ohio	CEN 5/11/59; 34 9/29/59; 38 4/27/59; 30	Research center Chemical research center Technical service and applications laboratory	P P C
Diamonite Products Manufacturing Canton, Ohio	CEN 5/20/47; 25	Research laboratory, product development, and pilot facilities	O
Ditto Incorporated Lincolnwood, Illinois	CEN 7/2/56; 3251	Research & development laboratory	O
Dodge & Olcott, Inc. New York City, New York	CEN 3/1/54; 808 6/10/57; 24	Organic research laboratory Cosmetic testing laboratory	O O

Dow Chemical Company			
Midland, Michigan	CEN 8/27/51; 3540	Organic, spectroscopy & special service laboratories & technical library building	P
	6/2/52; 2311	Library	O
	6/1/53; 2296	E. C. Britton Laboratory	O
	8/30/54; 3412	Biochemistry research laboratory	C
	9/6/54; 3496	Latex research laboratory	P
	3/19/56; 1334	Biochemical research laboratory	O
	7/13/59; 30	Agricultural research center	
	10/31/60; 26		
Freeport, Texas	8/27/51; 3540	Research center	P
	4/28/52; 1734		
	8/24/53; 3472		O
	10/26/53; 4438		
Ygnacio Valley, California	7/4/60; 27	Inorganic research laboratory	
Dowell, Inc.			
Tulsa, Oklahoma	CEN 1/16/56; 224	Research laboratory	
Subsidiary of Dow Chemical	1/16/56; 307		
	AC 28, 45A, May 56	Basic research and oil well services	
Dravo Corporation			
Pittsburgh, Pennsylvania	CEN 6/24/57; 20	Research and development laboratory	O
Du Pont, E. I., de Nemours & Co., Inc.			
Akron, Ohio	CEN 5/20/57; 25	District office and laboratory	P
Chestnut Run, Delaware	11/8/54; 4463	Textile research laboratory	
	1/31/55; 404	Rubber service laboratory	C
	11/14/55; 4906	Film laboratory (research and development)	
	3/25/57; 22	Sales service center	C
	4/30/56; 2129	Elastomers new product development and technical service laboratory	O
	7/8/57; 20	Polychemicals department—sales service laboratory	P
	8/22/60; 24	Industrial & biochemicals department—sales service laboratory	P
	3/14/55; 1070	Laboratory for freon research	C
Circleville, Ohio	9/7/59; 31	Laboratory and office facilities for polyester film technical section	C
Deepwater Point, New Jersey	8/6/51; 3172	Addition to rubber research lab	
Gibbstown, New Jersey	9/7/53; 3632	Explosives department—organic laboratory (research and development)	O
Kinston, North Carolina	12/29/52; 5447	Research & development laboratory for dacron polyester fiber	P
Martinsburg, West Virginia	12/20/54; 5032	Experimental and development laboratory	P

Key to symbols: CEN-*Chemical and Engineering News;* HEW-Department of Health, Education and Welfare; AC-*Analytical Chemistry;* Wooster-report of the Wooster Conference; MPB-Modern Physics Buildings; BFR-Buildings for Research; P-in planning stage; C-under construction; O-in operation.

Newark, Delaware	3/17/52; 1100	Haskell laboratory of industrial toxicology	P
	12/5/54; 5032	Pigments research laboratory	O
Newport, Delaware	8/2/54; 3044	Industrial products laboratory textile fibers department	
Niagara Falls, New York	CEN 7/1/57; 21	Research & development center	
	AC **30**, 63A, Dec. 58	Facilities for polymeric film studies	
	CEN 1/26/59; 35	Research center	O
Old Hickory, Tennessee	10/6/52; 4162	Cellophane research laboratory	C
Wilmington, Delaware	CEN 5/21/51; 2038	New research campus	
	1/18/54; 223	Polychemicals laboratory	P
	7/12/54; 2764	Film research laboratories	C
	8/23/54; 3352	Technical service laboratories for film department	P
	9/6/54; 3496	Electrochemicals & pigment departments—research laboratories	
	12/6/54; 4834	Organics & explosives laboratories	C
	2/27/56; 1028	Enlarged technical library	
	8/27/56; 4127	Radiation physics laboratory	C
	5/18/59; 32	Research laboratory for elastomer chemicals	C
	10/31/60; 28	Physical research laboratory	C
DX-Sunray Oil Co.			
West Tulsa, Oklahoma	CEN 5/28/56; 2636	Laboratory expansion	P
Dyna-Therma Chemical Corporation			
Culver City, California	CEN 7/18/60; 39	Research laboratory	O
Eastern Gas & Fuel Associates			
Everett, Massachusetts	CEN 6/30/58; 26	Research laboratory addition	C
Eastman Kodak Co.			
Rochester, New York	CEN 12/8/58; 31	Physics & chemistry laboratory	P
	4/13/59; 27	Physics research	P
	7/6/59; 28	High-pressure laboratory	O
Eimco Corp., The			
Palatine, Illinois	CEN 11/29/54; 4750	Research & development center	
Eli Lilly and Co.			
Greenfield, Indiana	CEN 5/7/56; 2238	Agricultural research center	P
	6/29/59; 21		
Indianapolis, Indiana	4/20/53; 1638	Development & control building	P
Emery Industries, Inc.			
Cincinnati, Ohio	CEN 1/18/54; 224	Research center	C
	8/8/55; 3238	Ernest Twitchell Memorial Laboratories	O
Engelhard Industries, Inc.			
Newark, New Jersey	CEN 6/15/59; 24	Research & development laboratory	O

Enjay Co., Inc. Linden, New Jersey	CEN 5/30/55; 2286	Technical service laboratory in petrochemicals	O
	10/8/56; 4875	Technical service laboratory in polymers	O
	10/29/56; 5251 11/17/58; 27	Plastics wing to customer-service research laboratories	P
Enthone, Inc. New Haven, Connecticut	CEN 1/26/59; 35	Research laboratory	O
Escambia Chemical Corp Wilton, Connecticut	CEN 12/31/56; 6357 4/29/57; 24 10/27/58; 26	Research & development laboratory Research center	P C O
Ethyl Corp. Baton Rouge, Louisiana Detroit, Michigan Houston, Texas	CEN 5/16/55; 2064 2/7/55; 492 12/19/55; 5476 12/6/54; 4838	Research laboratory Gasoline testing laboratory Expansion of oil research facilities	C P O P
Evans Research & Development Corp. New York, New York	CEN 9/21/59; 28	Radioisotope laboratory	O
Fabric Research Laboratories Dedham, Massachusetts	CEN 10/11/54; 4062 12/12/55; 5362 AC **30**, 45A, Jan. 58	Laboratory & office building	C O
Farnow, Inc. Long Island City, New York	CEN 8/27/56; 4141	Research and development laboratory	O
Ferro Corporation Cleveland, Ohio	AC **28**, 51A, June 56	Technical center	
Filtrol Corp. Vernon, California	CEN 11/26/51; 5057	Research center for cracking catalysts	P
Fine Organics, Inc. Lodi, New Jersey	CEN 2/4/52; 427	Enlarge buildings to house increased laboratory and production facilities	P
Food Machinery and Chemical Corporation Middleport, New York Princeton, New Jersey	CEN 5/30/60; 30 11/7/55; 4799 3/28/60; 35 AC 32, 81A, July 60	Research center for pesticides Central research laboratory	P P O O

Key to symbols: CEN-*Chemical and Engineering News;* HEW-Department of Health, Education and Welfare; AC-*Analytical Chemistry;* Wooster-report of the Wooster Conference; MPB-Modern Physics Buildings; BFR-Buildings for Research; P-in planning stage; C-under construction; O-in operation.

Foote Mineral Co. Exton, Pennsylvania	CEN 5/5/58; 29 8/31/59; 26	Technical center Research & engineering building	P C
Formica Corp. Evendale, Ohio	CEN 8/10/59; 30	Research & product development laboratory	C
Foster Grant Co., Inc. Leominster, Massachusetts	CEN 8/17/59; 28	Research center	C
Frontier Chemical Co. Wichita, Kansas (Division of Vulcan Materials Co.)	CEN 6/29/59; 25	Research & development building	P
Fullam, Ernest E. Inc. New York (near Albany- Schenectady)	CEN 12/9/57; 38	Research and development laboratory	C
Funk Foundation for Medical Research New York, New York	CEN 1/26/53; 342	Chemical research laboratories	O
Gallery Chemical Co. Los Angeles, California	CEN 7/18/60; 39	Research & development laboratory	
Geigy Chemical Corp. Ardsley, New York	CEN 3/3/58; 33	Research laboratories	C
General Dynamics Corp. San Diego, California (Corvair Division) (General Atomic Division)	CEN 7/18/60; 47 2/11/57; 22 7/13/59; 138	Research laboratory John Jay Hopkins Laboratory for Pure and Applied Science	P C O
General Electric Company Richland, Washington San Jose, California Palo Alto, California Schenectady, New York Tarrytown, New York	CEN 11/5/51; 4685 12/21/59; 30 9/6/54; 3500 10/29/56; 5229 11/5/56; 5394 1/18/54; 223 6/21/54; 2470 AC **28**, 69A, Feb. 56 CEN 8/22/55; 3467 2/20/56; 804 3/2/59; 60 8/12/57; 32 AC **30**, 43A, July 58	Aquatic biology laboratory Expansion to include new head- quarters building, new laboratory and administration building Electric tube laboratory Bearing & lubricant testing & engineering center Radiation laboratories Knolls Research Laboratory Analytical laboratory Metals & ceramic laboratory Applied research and development laboratory Radiation laboratory Research center	 P P C O P O O P
General Mills, Inc. Golden Valley, Minnesota	CEN 12/8/58; 31 9/4/59; 38	Research center	P C

General Motors Corp. Detroit, Michigan	CEN 11/8/54; 4469 5/28/56; 2640 AC 28, 52A, Sept. 56	Isotope laboratory Technical center	P
Glidden Company, The Baltimore, Maryland	CEN 2/9/59; 36 2/15/60; 33	Research & development center	P O
Chicago, Illinois	5/7/51; 1845	New laboratory at the Nubian Industrial Division	O
Cleveland, Ohio	6/15/59; 28	Central research laboratory	P
Goodrich, B. F. Company, The Cleveland, Ohio	CEN 3/19/51; 1096 5/28/51; 2155	Research center	O
Goodyear Tire & Rubber Co., Inc. Akron, Ohio	CEN 7/23/51; 3012 10/24/55; 4509	Paint development laboratory Research & development laboratory	
Litchfield Park, Arizona	12/17/56; 6182 10/24/55; 4509	Radiation laboratory Laboratory	
Gordon and Campbell Morristown, New Jersey	CEN 1/6/58; 40	Research & development laboratory	O
Grace, W. R., & Co. Clarksville, Maryland	CEN 11/3/58; 26 AC 31, 91A, Feb. 59	Washington Research Center	O
Clifton, New Jersey	CEN 5/14/56; 2365 3/18/57; 22	Polymer chemicals division—head- quarters and application laboratory	O
Grain Processing Corp. Muscatine, Iowa	CEN 8/20/56; 4034	Research laboratory	C
Gruen Industries, Inc. Cincinnati, Ohio	CEN 11/14/55; 4910	New company for engineering, development and production	P
Gulf Oil Corp. Harmarville, Pennsylvania	CEN 5/28/51; 2154 1/5/53; 59 9/26/55; 4060 6/17/57; 23	Chemistry research laboratory Nuclear science laboratory Research center	C O C
Philadelphia, Pennsylvania Port Arthur, Texas	6/14/54; 2374 11/21/55; 5019 AC 28, 41A, Jan. 56	Technical research laboratory Testing laboratory	O O
Gulton Industries, Inc. Metuchen, New Jersey	CEN 8/6/56; 3752	Engineering, research & testing laboratory	C
Hagan Chemicals & Controls Inc. Orrville, Ohio	CEN 4/14/52; 1538	Research & development laboratory	C

Key to symbols: CEN-*Chemical and Engineering News;* HEW-Department of Health, Education and Welfare; AC-*Analytical Chemistry;* Wooster-report of the Wooster Conference; MPB-Modern Physics Buildings; BFR-Buildings for Research; P-in planning stage; C-under construction; O-in operation.

Hanson-Van Winkle-Munning Co. Matawan, New Jersey	CEN 7/7/58; 28	Research & development laboratories	C
Harbison-Walker Refractories Co. Pittsburgh, Pennsylvania	CEN 1/19/59; 26 6/15/59; 25 AC **31**, 63A, July 59	Garber Research Center	O
Harlan Associates Los Angeles, California	CEN 6/20/55; 2600	Wilson Research Laboratory	O
Hart Products Corp. Jersey City, New Jersey	CEN 8/6/56; 3752	Research & development laboratories	O
Haveg Industries, Inc. Taunton, Massachusetts	CEN 7/11/60; 26	Research & development laboratory	O
Hazel-Atlas Glass Plainfield, Illinois (Division Continental Can)	CEN 1/11/60; 32	Research & development laboratory	P
Hazelton Laboratories Falls Church, Virginia	CEN 1/4/60; 27	Research laboratory	O
Hercules Powder Co. Wilmington, Delaware	CEN 4/19/54; 1557	Agricultural chemical laboratory	O
Herty Foundation Savannah, Georgia	CEN 11/10/58; 25	Research laboratory and pilot plant	O
Heyden Newport Corporation (Heyden Chemical Div.,) Garfield, New Jersey	CEN 8/20/51; 3464	Laboratories in chemical research division	O
High Voltage Engineering Corp. Burlington, Massachusetts	CEN 1/19/59; 26 2/8/60; 28	Research & development laboratory	P O
Hilton-Davis Chemical Co., The Cincinnati, Ohio Greenville, South Carolina	CEN 12/10/51; 5260 9/6/54; 3500	Textile dyestuff laboratory Service laboratory and distribution center	O O
Hodag Chemical Corp. Chicago, Illinois	CEN 8/24/59; 26	General laboratories	O
Hoffman-La Roche, Inc. Nutley, New Jersey	CEN 8/22/55; 3474 3/9/59; 28	Pharmaceutical laboratory Chemical laboratory	O C
Hogan Chemicals & Controls Pittsburgh, Pennsylvania	CEN 6/1/59; 30	Addition to research facilities	P

Hooker Chemical Corp. Grand Island, New York	CEN 10/1/56; 4754 11/11/57; 40 6/8/59; 22 AC 31, 95A, Nov. 59	Central research laboratory	P
Houdry Process Corp. Linwood, Pennsylvania	CEN 7/23/56; 3549	Addition to research & development laboratory	C
Houston Technical Laboratories Houston, Texas (Subsidiary Texas Instruments)	CEN 11/14/55; 4910	New plant for its geophysical instru- ment subsidiary (Texas Instruments)	C
Humble Oil & Refining Co. Houston, Texas	CEN 9/27/54; 3854 BFR 141–143 CEN 2/18/52; 671	Research center Research center for its exploration and production departments	O C
Baytown, Texas	6/25/56; 3188	Pilot plant building	O
Hysol Corporation Olean, New York	CEN 7/4/60; 30	Expanding general laboratory facilities	C
Ideal Cement Co. Boettcher, Colorado	CEN 7/27/53; 3064	Research center	O
Illinois State Water Survey Urbana, Illinois	CEN 10/29/51; 4602	Laboratory & office building	O
Industrial Bio-Test Laboratories Northbrook, Illinois	CEN 9/10/56; 4354 12/28/59; 27	Toxicological research laboratory	C
Industrial Nucleonics Corp. Columbus, Ohio	CEN 9/14/59; 38	Research, engineering, and manu- facturing plant	O
Industrial Reactor Laboratories, Inc. Plainsboro, New Jersey	CEN 10/1/56; 4739 10/8/56; 4972	Reactor facility	P
The Institute of Paper Chemistry Appleton, Wisconsin	CEN 6/15/53; 2502 1/13/58; 30 11/24/58; 42	General administration building 1st of three units completed Lou Calder Plant Biochemistry Laboratory	O O O
Interchemical Corp. Hawthorne, New Jersey	CEN 1/28/57; 21	Pilot plant	O
International Business Machines Corp. Yorktown, New York	CEN 6/2/58; 28	Research center	P

Key to symbols: CEN-*Chemical and Engineering News;* HEW-Department of Health, Education and Welfare; AC-*Analytical Chemistry;* Wooster-report of the Wooster Conference; MPB-Modern Physics Buildings; BFR-Buildings for Research; P-in planning stage; C-under construction; O-in operation.

International Latex Corp. Dover, Delaware	CEN 6/1/59; 31	Research laboratory	O
International Lubricant Corp. New Orleans, Louisiana	CEN 6/1/59; 31	Offices and laboratories	O
International Minerals & Chemical Corp. East Point, Georgia Noralyn, Florida Skokie, Illinois	CEN 10/25/54; 4278 AC **26,** 39A, April 54 CEN 1/29/51; 386	Control laboratories Analytical laboratory Central research laboratory	O P
International Shoe Co. Hartford, Illinois	CEN 11/17/52; 4838	Plastics laboratory	O
International Telephone and Telegraph Corporation Clifton, New Jersey	CEN 7/1/57; 86	Laboratory	O
Island Creek Coal Co. Holden, West Virginia	CEN 3/31/58; 40	Coal carbonization research laboratory	P
Jefferson Chemical Co., Inc. Austin, Texas	CEN 6/2/52; 2311 10/6/52; 4160 9/21/53; 3883	Addition to laboratory Research laboratory	P
Johns-Manville Manville, New Jersey	CEN 4/16/51; 1532	Addition to research center	
Jones & Laughlin Steel Corporation Pittsburgh, Pennsylvania	CEN 7/12/54; 2766 11/14/55; 4922	Research center	C O
Kaiser Aluminum & Chemical Corp. Chicago, Illinois Milpitas, California	CEN 8/10/59; 30 3/24/58; 26	Packaging research & development center expansion Research laboratories	C O
Kaiser Refractories & Chemical Corp. Mexico, Missouri	CEN 10/10/60; 34	Technical center	C
Kelco Co. San Diego, California	CEN 4/22/57; 40	Research laboratory	C
Kendall Co. Cambridge, Massachusetts	CEN 4/20/51; 1741	Theodore Clark Laboratory	O
Kennecott Copper Corp. Bedford, Ohio Salt Lake City, Utah	CEN 8/20/56; 4009 AC **26,** 29A, Aug. 54 CEN 6/20/55; 2598	Pilot plant for grandular zirconium Research laboratory Expansion of research laboratory	P P
Kidde, Walter & Company, Inc. Belleville, New Jersey	CEN 3/3/52; 892	Engineering & development building	C

Koppers Company, Inc.

Arroyo, Pennsylvania	CEN 7/9/56; 3390	Coal chemicals pilot plant	C
Kobuta, Pennsylvania	9/21/53; 3880		
	1/3/55; 33		
	4/11/55; 1536	Development laboratory for chemical division	P
	8/22/55; 3472		
Lock Haven, Pennsylvania	4/15/57; 22	Laboratory for development of new dyes and chemicals	P
Monroeville, Pennsylvania	6/5/56; 3095	Research center	P
	1/12/59; 19	Research center	C
Verona, Pennsylvania	9/28/53; 4016	Tar research laboratory	P

Kordite Co.

Macedon, New York (Subsidiary of National Distillers and Chemical Co.)	CEN 12/14/59; 36	Research & technical service center	P

Kraft Foods Co.

Glenview, Illinois	CEN 8/26/57; 24	Addition to research laboratories	C

Laberco Laboratories

Roselle Park, New Jersey	CEN 1/12/59; 30	Research laboratory	C

Leeds & Northrup Co.

North Wales, Pennsylvania	CEN 2/18/57; 24	Research & development building	P
	6/16/58; 35	Research center	C

Lever Bros. Co.

Edgewater, New Jersey	CEN 11/24/52; 4954 BFR 156–160	Research laboratory	

Libbey-Owens-Ford Glass Co.

Toledo, Ohio	CEN 3/31/58; 42	Technical center	P
Waterville, Maine	10/3/55; 4178	Research "nerve center"	C

Liggett & Meyers Tobacco Co.

Durham, North Carolina	CEN 10/10/60; 32	Enlarges research facilities	O

Lithium Corp. of America

Minneapolis, Minnesota	AC 27, 45A, Nov. 55	Analytical & control laboratory	

Little, Arthur D. Inc.

West Cambridge, Massachusetts	CEN 2/2/53; 430	Research laboratory	P
	11/30/53; 4970		
	8/29/55; 3564	Research & Development Building	O
	12/1/56; 5930	General purpose building	P

Lockheed Aircraft Corp.

Dawsonville, Georgia	CEN 8/27/56; 4142	Nuclear test center	P

Key to symbols: CEN-*Chemical and Engineering News;* HEW-Department of Health, Education and Welfare; AC-*Analytical Chemistry;* Wooster-report of the Wooster Conference; MPB-Modern Physics Buildings; BFR-Buildings for Research; P-in planning stage; C-under construction; O-in operation.

Lukens Steel Co. Philadelphia, Pennsylvania	CEN 3/18/57; 26	Physical testing laboratories	C
Lummus Co., The Newark, New Jersey	CEN 7/15/57; 20	Engineering development center	O
Magnet Cove Barium Corp. Houston, Texas	CEN 1/21/57; 22	Office and laboratory space	P
Mallinckrodt Chemical Works St. Louis, Missouri	CEN 1/25/54; 297 AC **26**, 29A, Feb. 54	Organic research laboratories	O
Mallory-Sharon Metals Corp. Niles, Ohio	CEN 7/13/53; 2874–6	Research & development laboratory for titanium research	O
Marbon Chemical Division Washington, West Virginia (Division of Borg-Warner Corp.)	CEN 8/25/58; 29	Research and sales center	O
Marion Laboratories Kansas City, Missouri	CEN 2/1/60; 25	House administration, packaging and shipping, and some temporary manufacturing and control facilities	O
Marron Laboratories Skokie, Illinois	CEN 11/26/56; 5818	Clinical laboratory	O
McCrone, Walter C., Assoc. Chicago, Illinois	CEN 3/14/60; 27	Instrumental analysis laboratory	O
McDanel Refractory Porcelain Co. Beaver Falls, Pennsylvania	CEN 3/23/53; 1198	Research laboratory	O
McDowell Company, Inc. Cleveland, Ohio (Dwight Lloyd Division)	CEN 7/30/56; 3702	Minerals processes laboratory	O
Mead Corp., The Chillicothe, Ohio	CEN 6/16/52; 2508 5/18/53; 2084 9/7/59; 30	Research & development laboratory Research center expansion	C O P
Merck & Co., Inc. Danville, Pennsylvania	CEN 1/13/58; 30	Technical service laboratory	P
Merck Institute for Therapeutic Research Rahway, New Jersey	CEN 11/12/51; 4854 5/18/53; 2080	Expanded research facilities	C O

Merrell, Wm. S., Co.			
Cincinnati, Ohio	CEN 12/3/51; 5164–5	Organic research laboratories	
(Division of Vick Chemical Co.)	6/16/52; 2508	Autoclave laboratory	C
	12/1/52; 5602	Research laboratory	C
	7/8/57; 20	Organic chemistry research laboratory	P
	10/7/57; 33	Research laboratory	C
	9/1/58; 34	Organic chemistry research laboratory	O
Plainfield, New Jersey	10/6/58; 38	Research laboratory for medicinal chemicals	
Metal Hydrides Incorporated			
Beverly, Massachusetts	CEN 5/5/52; 1868	Research & chemical hydride building	C
Metal & Thermit Corporation			
Rahway, New Jersey	CEN 8/8/55; 3236	Office, research, distribution center	C
	8/6/56; 3750		O
Metasap			
Harrison, New Jersey	CEN 2/7/55; 492	Testing and research laboratory	
(Subsidiary of Nopco Chemical Co.)			
Michigan Chrome & Chemical Co.			
Detroit, Michigan	CEN 11/11/57; 40	Laboratory addition	C
Midwest Research Institute			
Kansas City, Missouri	CEN 6/29/53; 2690	Science center	P
	12/21/53; 5284–6	Research laboratory	C
	AC 27, 29A, June 55	Research center	
	CEN 5/26/58; 36	Research laboratory	
Miles Laboratories, Inc.			
Elkhart, Indiana	CEN 4/16/51; 1534	Addition to research laboratory	
Millipore Filter Corp.			
Bedford, Massachusetts	CEN 1/19/59; 26	Plant & laboratory for manufacturing and research	
Minneapolis-Honeywell Regulator Co.			
Denver, Colorado	CEN 11/29/54; 4750	Research & product development center	O
Hopkins, Minnesota	AC 27, 51A, Oct. 55	Research center	
Minute Maid Corp.			
Plymouth, Florida	CEN 4/13/53; 1534	Research & development laboratory	O
Minnesota Mining & Manufacturing Co.			
St. Paul, Minnesota	CEN 5/15/55; 2058	Research laboratory	

Key to symbols: CEN-*Chemical and Engineering News;* HEW-Department of Health, Education and Welfare; AC-*Analytical Chemistry;* Wooster-report of the Wooster Conference; MPB-Modern Physics Buildings; BFR-Buildings for Research; P-in planning stage; C-under construction; O-in operation.

Monsanto Chemical Co. Creve Coeur, Missouri	CEN 8/18/52; 3436	Agricultural & biological research laboratory	O
	8/2/54; 3044	Inorganic chemical research center	
Everett, Massachusetts	9/14/59; 34	Research center	O
Miamisburg, Ohio	2/6/56; 555	Mound Laboratory (AEC) expansion	
Nitro, West Virginia	7/27/53; 3063	Engineering research laboratory	P
	2/28/55; 848		O
	2/20/56; 806	Pilot plant building	O
St. Louis, Missouri	9/14/53; 3770	Analytical laboratory	O
	1/17/55; 216	Paper chemicals laboratory	C
	1/16/56; 217	Headquarters and laboratories	
	4/29/57; 20	Inorganic research laboratory	O
	12/9/57; 38	Agricultural chemicals laboratory and greenhouse	C
	5/19/58; 76	Organic synthesis laboratory	O
	11/3/58; 26	Agricultural research center— organic division	O
Springfield, Massachusetts	8/22/55; 3469	Plastics laboratory	
	11/2/53; 4536		
Texas City, Texas	1/25/54; 298	Research laboratories (addition)	
	9/17/56; 4502	Addition to research building	P
Moorman Mfg. Co. Quincy, Illinois	CEN 9/10/51; 3711	Research laboratories	
Morningstar-Paisley, Inc. New York, New York	CEN 5/19/58; 20	Sales and laboratory facilities	
Morton Salt Co. Woodstock, Illinois	CEN 8/24/53; 3469 4/23/56; 2008 5/3/54; 1762	Research laboratory	
Muehlstein, H., & Co. Jersey City, New Jersey	CEN 4/5/54; 1336	Research laboratories	
Nalco Chemical Co. Chicago, Illinois	CEN 12/9/57; 38	Administrative & laboratory facilities	O
	8/1/60; 26	Laboratory, office and manufacturing chemicals expansion	C
Narmco Industries Inc. San Diego, California	CEN 8/12/57; 35	Research center	
National Canners Association Berkeley, California	CEN 9/10/51; 3711 10/29/51; 4600	Research laboratories	O
National Cash Register Co. Dayton, Ohio	CEN 8/13/56; 3872	Engineering research center	C
National Dairy Products Corp. Glenview, Illinois	CEN 5/11/59; 34	Research facilities	

National Institutes of Health Bethesda, Maryland	CEN 7/9/51; 2832 7/20/53; 2990	Clinical center	C
	7/11/60; 24	Biologic standards building	O
National Lead Co. Houston, Texas	CEN 6/9/52; 2400	Research laboratory for drilling muds	O
National Research Corp. Newton, Massachusetts	CEN 1/4/54; 50	Petrochemical laboratory	C
Natural Rubber Bureau Laboratory Rosslyn, Virginia	CEN 2/18/52; 671	Research laboratory	O
National Spectrographic Laboratories, Inc. Hialeah, Florida	CEN 4/13/59; 27	Spectrographic laboratory and sales office	C
	6/29/59; 25	Analytical laboratory	
National Starch & Chemical Corp. Plainfield, New Jersey	CEN 8/22/55; 3474	Addition to Alexander Research Laboratory	
	3/17/52; 1105	Research laboratory	C
Neville Chemical Co. Pittsburgh, Pennsylvania	CEN 2/4/57; 24	Research laboratory addition	P
Nopco Chemical Company Newark, New Jersey	CEN 8/29/60; 24	Research laboratories	
Norton Company Santa Clara, California	CEN 1/21/57; 24	Development laboratory	O
Norwich Pharmacal Co. Norwich, New York	CEN 10/19/53; 4306	Research laboratory	P
	2/28/55; 848	Research center	
Nuclear Development Corp. of America Pawling, New York	CEN 3/7/55; 950	Laboratory	
	4/23/56; 2009	Radiochemistry laboratory	C
Nutrilite Products, Inc. Buena Park, California	CEN 5/14/51; 1959	Research laboratory nutritional supplements	
Oakite Products, Inc. New York, New York	CEN 10/18/54; 4166	Research & product development laboratories	

Key to symbols: CEN-*Chemical and Engineering News;* HEW-Department of Health, Education and Welfare; AC-*Analytical Chemistry;* Wooster-report of the Wooster Conference; MPB-Modern Physics Buildings; BFR-Buildings for Research; P-in planning stage; C-under construction; O-in operation.

Oak Ridge National Laboratories Oak Ridge, Tennessee	CEN 10/11/54; 4065	Research laboratory, Solid State Division	P
Ohio Oil Co. Littleton, Colorado	CEN 2/21/55; 714 11/12/56; 5512 2/3/58; 29	Research laboratory	P
Olin Mathieson Chemical Corp. New Haven, Connecticut	CEN 11/24/58; 28	Metallurgical research center	C
Owens-Corning Fiberglas Corporation Granville, Ohio	CEN 5/11/59; 34	Basic & applied research and product testing laboratories	
Owens-Illinois Glass Co. Toledo, Ohio	CEN 7/6/53; 2780 10/3/55; 4178 AC **27**, 29A, Dec. 55	Technical center	
Pacific Testing Laboratories Seattle, Washington	CEN 12/13/54; 4929	Office and laboratory	P
Pacific Vegetable Oil Corp. Richmond, California	CEN 5/5/58; 29	Laboratory facilities and head- quarters building	O
Pacific Yeast Products Wasco, California	CEN 10/1/56; 4754 12/16/57; 24	Central research laboratory	C O
Pan-American Petroleum Corp. Tulsa, Oklahoma	MPB 116–7	Research center 1953	
Pan-American Refining Company Texas City, Texas	CEN 2/15/54; 576 2/21/55; 710	High pressure research laboratory	C O
Parke, Davis & Co. Ann Arbor, Michigan	CEN 12/10/56; 6044 4/15/57; 21	Medical research center	P C
Detroit, Michigan	1/14/52; 163 1/19/53; 250 4/25/60; 32	Research laboratory Virus research laboratory Research laboratory	O O
Rochester, Minnesota	3/21/60; 25	New & remodeled building at Parke- dale biological laboratories	P
Parker Pen Co. Janesville, Wisconsin	CEN 7/26/54; 2958	Remodeled laboratory for research and development	
Paul-Lewis Laboratories, Inc. Milwaukee, Wisconsin	CEN 11/9/59; 28	Research laboratories to be expanded	

Pennsalt Chemicals Corp. King of Prussia Park, Pennsylvania	CEN 1/4/60; 27	Technical center	P
Perkin-Elmer Corp., The Norwalk, Connecticut	CEN 7/23/52; 2620 AC **26**, 33A, June 54	Infra-red laboratory	
Peter Brent Brigham Hospital Cambridge, Massachusetts	CEN 6/21/54; 2475	Biophysics research laboratory	
Petrolite Corp. Webster Groves, Missouri	CEN 6/24/57; 22	Research laboratory	O
Pfaulder Co., Rochester, New York	CEN 5/19/53; 2083	Research building	
Pfizer, Chas., & Co. Inc. Groton, Connecticut	CEN 12/9/57; 38	Chemistry & biochemistry research building	P
	10/10/60; 31	Medical research laboratories	O
Maywood, New Jersey	11/10/52; 4741	Radiobiochemical laboratory	C
Philadelphia Quartz Co. Philadelphia, Pennsylvania	CEN 6/26/50; 2174	Research laboratory on soluble silicates	
Philip Morris, Inc. near Richmond, Virginia	CEN 7/13/59; 30	Research center	
Phillips Petroleum Co. near Bartlesville, Oklahoma	CEN 5/9/55; 1952	Chemical research laboratory	P
Picatinny Arsenal Dover, New Jersey	AC **26**, 33A, March 54	Radioisotope laboratory	
Pitman-Moore Co. Zionsville, Indiana	CEN 10/26/59; 34	Tissue culture laboratory	P
Pittsburgh Coke & Chemical Co. Neville Island, Pennsylvania	CEN 8/13/51; 3300	Central research laboratory	
Pittsburgh Plate Glass Co. Harmar, Pennsylvania Springdale, Pennsylvania	CEN 2/8/54; 476 7/20/53; 2984 1/3/55; 32 12/9/57; 38 7/4/60; 30	Basic & applied research facilities Paint division research laboratories Basic & applied research laboratories Development building for Paint and Brush Division Wing to Paint & Brush Division	P P O P
Polymer Industries, Inc. Springdale, Connecticut	CEN 4/6/59; 28 1/18/60; 33	Research laboratory and office facilities	

Key to symbols: CEN-*Chemical and Engineering News;* HEW-Department of Health, Education and Welfare; AC-*Analytical Chemistry;* Wooster-report of the Wooster Conference; MPB-Modern Physics Buildings; BFR-Buildings for Research; P-in planning stage; C-under construction; O-in operation.

Portland Cement Association			
Skokie, Illinois	CEN 7/9/56; 3346	Research center	
	12/3/56; 5930		
	9/29/58; 34	Structural laboratory	O
Powell, John, & Co., Inc.			
Port Jefferson, Long Island			
New York	CEN 2/12/51; 564	Pesticide research laboratory	
Procter & Gamble Company			
Cincinnati, Ohio	CEN 11/21/55; 5027	Basic research laboratory	
	8/19/57; 20	Technical center	
	6/22/59; 26	Winton Hill Technical Center	O
Miami Valley, Ohio	9/15/52; 3848	Research & development laboratories	O
	AC **28**, 53A, Dec. 56		
	CEN 3/15/54; 1010	Expansion of laboratories	
Quaker Oats Co.			
Barrington, Illinois	CEN 10/29/56; 5246	Research center	
Quintessence Laboratories			
New York 13, New York	CEN 12/10/56; 6048	Plant, office & laboratory	
Raybestos-Manhattan, Inc.			
Stratford, Connecticut	CEN 5/20/57; 24	Research laboratory	O
Raybo Chemical Company			
Huntington, West Virginia	CEN 4/14/52; 1542	Research & development laboratories	
Rayonier, Inc.			
Whippany, New Jersey	CEN 8/5/57; 23	Research center	O
Republic Aviation Corp.			
Farmingdale, Long Island			
New York	CEN 8/11/58; 33	Research & development center	
Redstone Arsenal			
Huntsville, Alabama	CEN 3/30/52; 1294	General Josiah Gorgas Laboratory for rocket research	
Reheis Company			
Berkeley Heights, New Jersey	CEN 2/22/60; 35	Control & research laboratory	
Reichhold Chemicals, Inc.			
Elizabeth, New Jersey	CEN 10/8/56; 4875	Technical service laboratory	O
South San Francisco, California			
	10/6/52; 4162	Office & laboratory quarters	
Summit, Illinois	5/19/52; 2100	Technical service laboratory	
Research Triangle Institute			
Research Center, North Carolina	CEN 11/2/59; 29	Research center, polymer chemistry	P
Resin Research Laboratories			
Newark, New Jersey	CEN 6/14/54; 2374	New facilities	O
	12/24/56; 6286	Resin research center	C

Rexall Drug and Chemical & El Paso Natural Gas Products Cos. Paramus, New Jersey	CEN 8/29/60; 24	Research laboratories	P
Reynolds Metals Company Richmond, Virginia	CEN 11/11/57; 40	Research & development laboratories expansion	P
Reynolds, R. J., Tobacco Co. Winston Salem, North Carolina	CEN 2/2/53; 430 2/23/53; 768	Research laboratory	O
	4/28/58; 32	Addition to research laboratory	O
Richardson Co., The Melrose Park, Illinois	CEN 1/20/58; 32	Pilot plant-laboratories	C
Richfield Oil Corp. Anaheim, California	CEN 1/31/55; 404 11/19/56; 5714	Research center	C O
Riker Laboratories, Inc. Los Angeles, California	CEN 2/24/58; 33	Research laboratories	O
Rinsheld-Mason Co. Detroit, Michigan	CEN 3/3/52; 898	Research laboratory	O
Rocketdyne Santa Susana Mountains, California	CEN 3/3/58; 33	Research center	O
Rockwell Manufacturing Co. Dubois, Pennsylvania	CEN 8/27/56; 4141	Gas meter research & development laboratory	O
Pittsburgh, Pennsylvania	11/14/60; 38	Enlarged and modernized chemical engineering laboratories	O
Rohm & Haas Co. Bristol, Pennsylvania	CEN 6/4/56; 2759	Research laboratories addition	
Rorer, Wm. H., Inc. Philadelphia, Pennsylvania (Fort Washington Industrial Park, Pennsylvania)	CEN 11/7/60; 38	Research laboratories	
St. Regis Paper Company Pensacola, Florida	CEN 12/17/56; 6176	Adhesives laboratory	P
Schering & Co. Union, New Jersey	AC **32**, 115A, Nov. 60	Quality control center	
Scientific Associates St. Louis, Missouri	CEN 7/11/55; 2894	Consulting laboratory	

Key to symbols: CEN-*Chemical and Engineering News;* HEW-Department of Health, Education and Welfare; AC-*Analytical Chemistry;* Wooster-report of the Wooster Conference; MPB-Modern Physics Buildings; BFR-Buildings for Research; P-in planning stage; C-under construction; O-in operation.

Scott Paper Company
    International Airport
        Philadelphia, Pennsylvania
		Research laboratory and office
		    building
			O

Searle, G. D., & Co.
    Chicago, Illinois
	CEN 10/24/55; 4510
	8/13/56; 3874
	1/23/56; 340
		Office & laboratory addition
		Radioactive tracer laboratory
		Basic paint research & development
		    laboratory
			
			O
			
			O

(Skokie, Illinois)	8/29/60; 24	Research & development laboratories	P
Seiberling Rubber Company Newcomerstown, Ohio	CEN 3/23/59; 26	General laboratory	

Shallway Corp.
    Connellsville, Pennsylvania
	CEN 4/23/56; 2009	Shell molding research & development
		    center
			O

Sharp & Dohme Co. West Point, Pennsylvania	CEN 5/19/52; 2098	Medicinal research laboratories	O

Shell Chemical Company
    Martinez, California
    Union, New Jersey
	CEN 11/11/57; 38
	9/12/55; 3844
	7/9/56; 3342
	8/27/56; 4142
		Market development unit
		Technical service laboratory
		Technical service laboratory addition
		Addition to customer service
		    laboratory
			P
			C
			C
			
			P

Shell Development Co.
    Emeryville, California
    Modesto, California
 	
    Houston, Texas
	CEN 12/30/57; 22
	11/26/56; 5818
	
	5/21/56; 2502
		Process development laboratory
		Expansion of agricultural research
		    center
		Office & laboratory building
			C
			
			P
			O

Shell Oil Co. Norco, Louisiana	CEN 1/6/58; 43	Control laboratory	P

Sherwin-Williams Co.
    Chicago, Illinois
    Garland, Texas
	CEN 11/28/60; 29
	4/22/57; 38
		Research center
		Research laboratories
			
			P

Siebel, J. E., Sons Co. Chicago, Illinois	CEN 10/15/51; 4274	Research laboratories	P

Signal Corps Engineering Laboratory
    Fort Monmouth, New Jersey
	CEN 2/27/56; 930	Research & development laboratory
		    (biggest research building in U.S.)	

Sinclair Research Laboratories, Inc. Harvey, Illinois	CEN 12/31/56; 6372	Nuclear radiation laboratory	C
Skeist Laboratories Newark, New Jersey	CEN 12/12/55; 5362	Research laboratory	O

Smith, A. O., Corp. Middletown, Wisconsin	CEN 10/10/60; 34	Research center, solid state physics	P
Smith, Kline, & French Laboratories Upper Merion, Pennsylvania	CEN 6/1/59; 31	2 wings for research and development	P
Snell, Foster D., Inc. Bainbridge, New Jersey (Supplee Laboratories Division)	CEN 7/7/52; 2818	Research laboratories	P
Socony Mobile Oil Co., Inc. Paulsboro, New Jersey	CEN 10/17/55; 4400 AC **29**, 47A, July 57 CEN 4/1/57; 18	Analytical laboratory Nuclear research center	C
Sonneborn, L., Sons, Inc. Petrolia, Pennsylvania	CEN 6/24/57; 27	Research laboratories	
Sonoco Products Co. Hartsville, South Carolina	CEN 11/28/60; 29	Research laboratory	O
Southwest Chemical & Plastics Co. Houston, Texas	CEN 6/13/60; 35	Laboratory and research facilities	P
Southwest Research Institute San Antonio, Texas Science City, Texas	CEN 12/13/54; 4942 6/4/51; 2289 4/23/56; 2010 7/30/56; 3645	Test laboratory Mechanical research laboratories Research centers, housing, recreation areas Nuclear laboratory	O O P P
Spectrochemical Laboratories Pittsburgh, Pennsylvania	CEN 7/7/58; 28	Analytical laboratory	O
Speer Carbon Co. Niagara Falls, New York	CEN 2/4/57; 24	Research & development laboratory	P
Spencer Chemical Co. Kansas City, Kansas	CEN 1/9/56; 120	Chemical research center	P
Spencer, Kellogg & Sons, Inc. Buffalo, New York	CEN 3/26/56; 1450	Research center	O
Squibb, E. R., & Sons New Brunswick, New Jersey	CEN 12/21/59; 29	Cancer research laboratory	O
Staley, A. E., Mfg. Co. Decatur, Illinois	CEN 2/9/59; 36	Research center	C
Standard Oil of Indiana Seymour, Indiana Sugar Creek, Missouri Whiting, Indiana	CEN 8/25/58; 28 1/4/54; 49 6/29/53; 2690 10/8/56; 4875 10/27/58; 26 AC **31**, 59A, March 59	Research & development laboratories Engineering & research laboratories Automotive fuels testing laboratory (addition) Pilot plant & addition to laboratories Technical service laboratory	C O O O

Standard Oil of Ohio Cleveland, Ohio	CEN 2/7/55; 490 6/23/58; 31	Engine research laboratory Research center dedicated	O
Standard Oil of New Jersey Baton Rouge, Louisiana	CEN 1/16/56; 228 10/20/58; 34	Addition to research laboratories Research laboratories	P O
Linden, New Jersey	5/24/54; 2093 10/18/54; 4170 12/6/54; 4830 7/11/55; 2890 8/15/55; 3385 AC **27,** 43A, Sept. 55	Sales & technical service laboratory Performance test center Radiation laboratory Radiation laboratory 16th laboratory-office building Enjay laboratories for customer service—in petrochemical field	P P P
	CEN 12/3/56; 5986	Pilot plant	O
Stanford Research Institute Menlo Park, California	CEN 7/8/57; 28 10/21/57; 34 10/13/58; 22 11/30/59; 35	Plastics laboratory Metallurgical laboratory Research laboratories Health research laboratories	P C O P
South Pasadena, California	7/16/56; 3446	Physical sciences, economics & engineering laboratories	
Stanolind Oil & Gas Co. Tulsa, Oklahoma	CEN 12/17/51; 5361	Research building	C
Stauffer Chemical Company Chauncey, New York	CEN 12/31/51; 5528 7/27/53; 3064 12/12/55; 5362 7/2/56; 3247	Laboratory Odor removal Addition to laboratory	P C O
Delaware City, Delaware Richmond, California	11/23/59; 34 8/23/54; 3350 6/9/58; 27	Research center Research center expansion Process development laboratory	P P
Strong, Cobb, Arner Inc. Murray Hill, New Jersey	CEN 6/6/60; 39	Laboratory	C
Strong-Scott Mfg. Co. Minneapolis, Minnesota	CEN 12/24/56; 6288	Customer service laboratory (AIA Award)	
Stuart Co. Pasadena, California	AC **31,** 69A, April 59	Pharmaceutical research laboratories	

Sullivan, Eugene C., Research
  Laboratories
Corning, New York
	AC **29,** 73A, Sept. 57	Research laboratories, administration
		  building and development building	

Sun Chemical Corp. Long Island City, New York	CEN 7/23/51; 3013	Suntone colors laboratory	

Key to symbols: CEN-*Chemical and Engineering News;* HEW-Department of Health, Education and Welfare; AC-*Analytical Chemistry;* Wooster-report of the Wooster Conference; MPB-Modern Physics Buildings; BFR-Buildings for Research; P-in planning stage; C-under construction; O-in operation.

Sun Oil Co.			
Marcus Hook, Pennsylvania	CEN 9/23/57; 31	Research laboratory	O
	AC **30,** 73A, Sept. 58		
Toledo, Ohio	CEN 5/7/56; 2238	Control & engineering laboratory	C
Swift & Company			
Chicago, Illinois	CEN 1/3/55; 34	Nutrition research facilities expanded	O
Sylvania-Corning Nuclear Corp.			
Andover, Massachusetts	CEN 12/24/56; 6286	Nuclear research center	P
Sylvania Electric Products Inc.			
Emporium, Pennsylvania	CEN 2/22/60; 36	Research & development center	
Towanda, Pennsylvania	2/18/57; 24	Engineering laboratory and pilot plant	C
	10/20/58; 28	Research & development laboratory	
Takamine Laboratory			
Clifton, New Jersey	CEN 8/26/57; 24	Research & office building	O
Technical Tape Corp.			
New York, New York	CEN 10/29/51; 4602	Research laboratory	O
Tennessee Eastman Company			
Kingsport, Tennessee	CEN 6/9/52; 2416–7	Sales & development laboratory	O
	2/9/59; 36	Tenite development laboratory	
Texaco, Inc.			
Beacon, New York	CEN 5/23/55; 2194	Research & testing laboratories	C
	6/11/56; 2868	Jet fuels laboratory	O
	5/20/57; 24	Research center	O
	6/17/57; 27	Nuclear radiation laboratory	C
	9/8/58; 34		O
Houston, Texas	4/21/52; 1637	New buildings for research division	
Port Arthur, Texas	5/6/57; 24	Product control laboratory	O
	6/27/60; 24	Research center	P
Texas-U. S. Chemical Co.			
Morristown, New Jersey	CEN 12/3/56; 5980	Research center	
Parsippany, New Jersey	11/16/59; 29	Research & development laboratory (expansion)	P
Textile Research Institute			
Princeton, New Jersey	CEN 3/26/51; 1223	Computing laboratory & shops	P
Thiokol Chemical Corporation			
Brigham City, Utah	CEN 2/2/59; 31	Development laboratory	P
Thompson Products Inc.			
Cleveland, Ohio	CEN 3/18/57; 26	Research & development center	C
Tracerlab Inc.			
Richmond, California	CEN 6/29/53; 2690	Research & office building, tilt wall	
	4/5/54; 1330	Western division laboratory & office	O

Key to symbols: CEN-*Chemical and Engineering News;* HEW-Department of Health, Education and Welfare; AC-*Analytical Chemistry;* Wooster-report of the Wooster Conference; MPB-Modern Physics Buildings; BFR-Buildings for Research; P-in planning stage; C-under construction; O-in operation.

Trane Co., The			
La Crosse, Wisconsin	CEN 11/17/52; 4838	Research & testing laboratory	C
Trubek Laboratories			
East Rutherford, New Jersey	CEN 3/24/58; 26	Research & development laboratories	O
Truesdail Laboratories			
Wilmington, California	CEN 8/18/58; 29	Service laboratory for the Long Beach-Los Angeles area	O
UBS Chemical Company			
Marlboro, Massachusetts	CEN 3/30/59; 26	Polymer development laboratory and pilot plant	C
Union Carbide Corporation			
Union Carbide Chemicals Co. Division			
Clayton, North Carolina	CEN 2/15/60; 35	Biological research laboratory	C
	7/7/58; 28	Technical service laboratory	
Eastview, New York	8/17/59; 28	Research institute	C
Greenburgh & Mount Pleasant, New York	7/9/56; 3340	Basic research and development laboratory	C
Raleigh, North Carolina	12/31/56; 6357	Experimental farm for agricultural chemical research	
South Charleston, West Virginia	10/29/56; 5248	Development laboratory	P
	12/10/56; 6046	Engineering building	P
	10/26/59; 24	Technical center	C
	10/10/60; 34	Olefins laboratory	P
Tarrytown, New York	5/16/60; 42	Technical service laboratory	O
Union Carbide Metals Co. Division			
Niagara Falls, New York	12/12/55; 5371	Chemical engineering research laboratory	O
	AC **30**, 67A, Oct. 58	Research and development analytical laboratory	
National Carbon Co. Division			
Cleveland, Ohio	CEN 4/25/55; 1772	Basic research laboratory	C
Parma, Ohio	9/17/56; 4501	Solid state laboratory	
	AC **28**, 67A, Nov. 56		
Nuclear Division			
Sterling Forest, New York	CEN 7/1/57; 23	Nuclear research center	O
	8/11/58; 33	Nuclear & ore laboratories	C
	8/3/59; 26	Research center	O
Union Oil Co. of California			
Brea, California	CEN 2/4/52; 426 BFR 136–139	Research center	O
United Carbon Company			
Houston, Texas	CEN 2/22/60; 49	Research & development center	C
United Lacquer Mfg. Corp.			
Linden, New Jersey	CEN 11/12/51; 4854	Research facilities tripled in size	

United States
  Department of Agriculture

Albany, California	CEN 11/16/59; 23	Wool processing laboratory	
Plum Island, Long Island			
New York	8/11/52; 3316	Animal research laboratory	P

Department of Commerce
  National Bureau of Standards

Boulder, Colorado	AC 27, 33A, Jan. 55	Cryogenic engineering laboratory	
	CEN 11/29/54; 4755	Boulder laboratories	O
Gaithersburg, Maryland	6/25/56; 3112	New laboratories	P
Washington, D. C.	4/30/51; 1749	Protective coatings laboratory	O
	6/14/54; 2376	Gamma ray laboratory	O

Department of Defense
Department of the Army
  Chemical Corps
    Camp Detrick

Frederick, Maryland	10/4/54; 3970	Biological laboratory	
Quartermaster Corps			
Natick, Massachusetts	10/25/54; 4284	Research & development center	O
	AC 26, 47A, Oct. 56		
Stockton, California	CEN 11/19/56; 5615	Ionizing radiation center	

Department of the Navy

San Francisco, California	10/31/55; 4716	Radiological defense laboratory	O
Woods Hole, Massachusetts	1/21/52; 251	Oceanographic laboratory	P
	2/16/53; 680		P
Naval Research Laboratory			
Washington, D. C.	3/14/55; 1080	Atomic-biological-chemical warfare laboratory	P
	8/17/59; 28	Radiation laboratory	P

Department of the Interior
  Bureau of Mines

Fort Snelling, Minnesota	7/7/58; 55	Research laboratories	P
Grant Forks, North Dakota	9/10/51; 3718	Charles R. Robertson Lignite Research Laboratory	
	11/5/51; 4732–3		
Morgantown, West Virginia	6/27/55; 2706	Petroleum, gas, and coal research center	O
	AC 29, 51A, Jan. 57		

U. S. Borax & Chemical Corporation

Anaheim, California	CEN 12/10/56; 6044	Research laboratory	P

U. S. Industries, Inc.

Pompano Beach, Florida	CEN 2/4/57; 24	Research & development center	P
	2/3/58; 29		O

United States Rubber Company

Betheny, Connecticut	CEN 3/11/57; 18	Laboratory and office space	
Emerson, New Jersey	3/16/53; 1091	Research center	P
Naugatuck, Connecticut	2/23/59; 30	Research laboratory	C
	3/14/60; 27	Product development & technical service	C
Preakness, New Jersey	8/23/54; 3352	Research center	P
Wayne Township, New Jersey	AC 29, 55A, Nov. 57	Research center	

United States Steel Corporation			
Clairton, Pennsylvania	CEN 12/8/58; 31	Chemical laboratory	O
Pittsburgh, Pennsylvania	8/10/53; 3278	Research center	C
	4/6/53; 1443		
U. S. Stoneware Co., The			
Stow, Ohio	CEN 10/5/59; 25	Research laboratory	O
Universal Oil Products Co.			
Des Plains, Illinois	CEN 4/26/54; 1665	Research laboratories	C
	12/19/55; 5482		O
Upjohn Co., The			
Kalamazoo, Michigan	CEN 7/20/53; 2978	Research tower	
Valchem Co.			
Langley, South Carolina	CEN 6/6/60; 39	Expansion of research & development facilities	C
Vanadium Corp.			
Cambridge, Ohio	CEN 2/1/54; 389	Research center	C
Veterans Administration Hospital			
Madison, Wisconsin	CEN 12/23/56; 6288	Radioisotope laboratory for bio-chemical & clinical research	
Victor Chemical Works			
Chicago Heights, Illinois	CEN 6/9/58; 27	Research laboratory	C
	6/22/59; 26		
Vitro Laboratories			
Silver Spring, Maryland	CEN 12/12/55; 5362	Laboratory	P
Volvair Corp.			
Akron, Ohio	CEN 9/9/57; 24	Product development laboratory	O
Walker Laboratories			
Mount Vernon, New York	CEN 11/19/51; 4968	Medical research, pharmaceutical products	
Wallace & Tiernan, Inc.			
Tonawanda, New York	CEN 9/12/60; 37	Research laboratories	P
Wallerstein Co.			
Mariner's Island			
Staten Island, New York	CEN 7/23/51; 3012	General laboratory	
Walter Kidde Nuclear Laboratories			
Garden City, Long Island,			
New York	CEN 10/20/52; 4384		C
Warner-Lambert Co.			
Morris Plains, New Jersey	CEN 4/4/55; 1422	Research laboratory	C
	5/30/60; 30	Research facilities doubled	
	7/25/60; 33		C

Key to symbols: CEN-*Chemical and Engineering News;* HEW-Department of Health, Education and Welfare; AC-*Analytical Chemistry;* Wooster-report of the Wooster Conference; MPB-Modern Physics Buildings; BFR-Buildings for Research; P-in planning stage; C-under construction; O-in operation.

Western Petrochemical Co. Chemical Industries Park Newark, New Jersey	CEN 1/4/60; 27	Research & development laboratory	O
Westinghouse Electric Corporation Churchill Borough, Pennsylvania	CEN 6/22/53; 2598 5/9/55; 1954 9/24/56; 4621 7/16/56; 3440 11/9/59; 28	Research center Addition to research laboratory Research & development center	C O O P P
Kansas City, Missouri near Pittsburgh, Pennsylvania Youngwood, Pennsylvania	1/3/55; 33 8/10/59; 29 AC 29, 51A, March 57	Jet engine research & development Astronuclear laboratory Analytical & instrumental laboratories	 O
	CEN 10/13/58; 36	Ceramic research laboratory	O
West Virginia Pulp & Paper Co. Williamsburg, Pennsylvania	CEN 12/17/56; 6182	Graphic arts research laboratory	
Wisconsin Alumni Research Foundation Madison, Wisconsin	CEN 2/10/58; 33	Laboratories for bacteriology and food technology	
Witco Chemical Co., Inc. Chicago, Illinois Los Angeles, California	CEN 3/30/59; 26 11/16/59; 30	General laboratory Laboratory & plant office	
Wyandotte Chemicals Corp. Wyandotte, Michigan	CEN 1/15/51; 200 6/8/53; 2402 7/14/58; 26	Research center Research laboratory Expansion of research facilities	P O O
Wyeth Laboratories, Inc. East Whiteland Township, Pennsylvania	CEN 10/31/60; 28	Office, manufacturing, laboratory and warehouse structures	C
Marietta, Pennsylvania	CEN 3/16/53; 1091	Applied virus research	C
Wyssmont Company, Inc. Long Island City, New York	CEN 2/4/57; 24	Laboratory & engineering facilities	
Yuba Consolidated Industries, Inc. Benicia, California	CEN 1/6/58; 38	Research & development center	O
Zep Manufacturing Corp. Atlanta, Georgia	CEN 7/23/56; 3549	Plant and technical laboratory	P

Key to symbols: CEN-*Chemical and Engineering News;* HEW-Department of Health, Education and Welfare; AC-*Analytical Chemistry;* Wooster-report of the Wooster Conference; MPB-Modern Physics Buildings; BFR-Buildings for Research; P-in planning stage; C-under construction; O-in operation.

INDEX OF CONSTRUCTION BY STATES

(Academic construction is indicated by *italic* page numbers.)

APPENDIX 2

Bibliography

Buildings for Research, an *Architectural Record Book,* F. W. Dodge Corporation, New York, 1958.

Burris-Meyer, Harold and Cole, Edward R., *Theatres and Auditoriums,* Reinhold Publishing Corporation, New York, 1949.

Burris-Meyer, Harold and Goodfriend, Lewis S., *Acoustics for the Architect,* Reinhold Publishing Corporation, New York, 1957.

Coleman, H. S. (ed), *Laboratory Design,* National Research Council Report, Reinhold Publishing Corporation, New York, 1951. (Out of print.)

The Design of Physics Research Laboratories, The Institute of Physics (London), Chapman & Hall, Limited, London and Reinhold Publishing Corporation, New York, 1957.

The Design of Research Laboratories, The Nuffield Foundation, Division of Architectural Studies, Oxford University Press, London, 1961.

Heating, Ventilating and Air Conditioning Guide, American Society of Heating and Air Conditioning Engineers, Inc., 62 Worth Street, New York 13, N. Y. (Issued annually.)

Illuminating Engineering Society Handbook, Illuminating Engineering Society, 1860 Broadway, New York 23, N. Y., 1959.

National Plumbing Code, American Society of Mechanical Engineers, 29 W. 39th Street, New York, 1955.

Noise Control in Buildings, Building Research Institute Conference Report, Building Research Institute, Washington, D. C., 1959.

Palmer, R. Ronald and Rice, William M., *Modern Physics Buildings: Design and Function,* Reinhold Publishing Corporation, New York, 1961.

Parkin, P. H., and Humphreys, H. R. *Acoustics, Noise and Buildings,* Frederick A. Praeger, New York, 1958.

Project on Design of Physics Buildings—Selected Reprints of Articles on Physics Buildings, American Institute of Physics, 335 E. 45th Street, New York, 1959. (See for bibliography of pertinent journal articles.)

Rappoport, Arthur E., *Manual for Laboratory Planning and Design,* The College of American Pathologists, Prudential Plaza, Chicago, Illinois, 1960.

Schramm, Werner, *Chemische und Biologische Laboratorien,* 2nd ed., Verlag Chemie—GMBH—Weinheim/Bergstr., Germany, 1960.

Time Saver Standards, An *Architectural Record Book,* F. W. Dodge Corp., New York, 1954.

Uniform Building Code, International Conference of Building Officials, 610 South Broadway, Los Angeles 14, California, 1958.

509

Index